PEARSON CUSTOM MATHEMATICS

Finite Mathematics (MTH 110)
Trenholm State Technical College

PEARSON

Senior Vice President, Editorial: Patrick F. Boles
Senior Acquisitions Editor: Debbie Coniglio
Development Editor: Christina Martin
Editorial Assistant: Jeanne Martin
Operations Manager: Eric M. Kenney
Production Manager: Jennifer Berry
Art Director: Renée Sartell
Cover Designer: Josh Read

This special edition published in cooperation with Pearson Learning Solutions.

Printed in the United States of America.

Please visit our website at *www.pearsonlearningsolutions.com*.

Attention bookstores: For permission to return any unsold stock, contact us at *pe-uscustomreturns@pearson.com*.

Pearson Learning Solutions, 501 Boylston Street, Suite 900, Boston, MA 02116
A Pearson Education Company
www.pearsoned.com

ISBN 10: 1-256-17893-4
ISBN 13: 978-1-256-17893-4

Contents

THE ART OF PROBLEM SOLVING

20th Century Fox Film Corp./Everett Collection

The 1995 movie *Die Hard: With a Vengeance* stars Bruce Willis as New York Detective John McClane. In this film, McClane is tormented by villain Simon Gruber (Jeremy Irons), who plants bombs around the city and poses riddles and puzzles for disarming them. In one situation, Simon gives McClane and store owner Zeus Carver (Samuel L. Jackson) the following riddle by telephone to solve in 5 minutes.

> *On the fountain there should be two jugs. Do you see them? A 5-gallon and a 3-gallon. Fill one of the jugs with exactly 4 gallons of water, and place it on the scale, and the timer will stop. You must be precise. One ounce more or less will result in detonation.*

McClane and Carver were able to solve the riddle and defuse the bomb. Can you solve it? The answer is on the next page.

1 SOLVING PROBLEMS BY INDUCTIVE REASONING

Characteristics of Inductive and Deductive Reasoning • Pitfalls of Inductive Reasoning

Solution to the Chapter Opener Problem This is one way to do it: With both jugs empty, fill the 3-gallon jug and pour its contents into the 5-gallon jug. Then fill the 3-gallon jug again, and pour it into the 5-gallon jug until the latter is filled. There is now $(3 + 3) - 5 = 1$ gallon in the 3-gallon jug. Empty the 5-gallon jug, and pour the 1 gallon of water from the 3-gallon jug into the 5-gallon jug. Finally, fill the 3-gallon jug and pour all of it into the 5-gallon jug, resulting in $1 + 3 = 4$ gallons in the 5-gallon jug.

(*Note*: There is another way to solve this problem. See if you can discover the alternative solution.)

Characteristics of Inductive and Deductive Reasoning

The development of mathematics can be traced to the Egyptian and Babylonian cultures (3000 B.C.–A.D. 260) as a necessity for problem solving. To solve a problem or perform an operation, a cookbook-like recipe was given, and it was performed repeatedly to solve similar problems.

By observing that a specific method worked for a certain type of problem, the Babylonians and the Egyptians concluded that the same method would work for any similar type of problem. Such a conclusion is called a *conjecture*. A **conjecture** is an educated guess based on repeated observations of a particular process or pattern. The method of reasoning we have just described is called *inductive reasoning*.

Inductive Reasoning

Inductive reasoning is characterized by drawing a general conclusion (making a conjecture) from repeated observations of specific examples. The conjecture may or may not be true.

In testing a conjecture obtained by inductive reasoning, it takes only one example that does not work to prove the conjecture false. Such an example is called a **counterexample.**

Inductive reasoning provides a powerful method of drawing conclusions, but there is no assurance that the observed conjecture will always be true. For this reason, mathematicians are reluctant to accept a conjecture as an absolute truth until it is formally proved using methods of *deductive reasoning*. Deductive reasoning characterized the development and approach of Greek mathematics, as seen in the works of Euclid, Pythagoras, Archimedes, and others. During the classical Greek period (600 B.C.–A.D. 450), general concepts were applied to specific problems, resulting in a structured, logical development of mathematics.

Deductive Reasoning

Deductive reasoning is characterized by applying general principles to specific examples.

We now look at examples of these two types of reasoning. In this chapter, we often refer to the **natural,** or **counting, numbers:**

$$1, 2, 3, \ldots$$ Natural (counting) numbers

↑ Ellipsis points

The three dots (*ellipsis points*) indicate that the numbers continue indefinitely in the pattern that has been established. The most probable rule for continuing this pattern is "add 1 to the previous number," and this is indeed the rule that we follow.

Now consider the following list of natural numbers:

$$2, 9, 16, 23, 30.$$

What is the next number of this list? What is the pattern? After studying the numbers, we might see that $2 + 7 = 9$, and $9 + 7 = 16$. Do we add 16 and 7 to get 23?

June

S	M	Tu	W	Th	F	S
1	2	3	4	5	6	7
8	9	10	11	12	13	14
15	16	17	18	19	20	21
22	23	24	25	26	27	28
29	30					

July

S	M	Tu	W	Th	F	S
		1	2	3	4	5
6	7	8	9	10	11	12
13	14	15	16	17	18	19
20	21	22	23	24	25	26
27	28	29	30	31		

Figure 1

Do we add 23 and 7 to get 30? Yes. It seems that any number in the given list can be found by adding 7 to the preceding number, so the next number in the list would be $30 + 7 = 37$.

We set out to find the "next number" by reasoning from observation of the numbers in the list. We may have jumped from these observations to the general statement that any number in the list is 7 more than the preceding number. This is an example of *inductive reasoning*.

By using inductive reasoning, we concluded that 37 was the next number. Suppose the person making up the list has another answer in mind. The list of numbers

$$2, 9, 16, 23, 30$$

actually gives the dates of Mondays in June if June 1 falls on a Sunday. The next Monday after June 30 is July 7. With this pattern, the list continues as

$$2, 9, 16, 23, 30, 7, 14, 21, 28, \ldots.$$

See the calendar in **Figure 1**. The correct answer would then be 7. The process used to obtain the rule "add 7" in the preceding list reveals a main flaw of inductive reasoning. ***We can never be sure that what is true in a specific case will be true in general. Inductive reasoning does not guarantee a true result, but it does provide a means of making a conjecture.***

We now review some basic notation. Throughout this book, we use *exponents* to represent repeated multiplication.

$$\text{Base} \rightarrow 4^3 = 4 \cdot 4 \cdot 4 = 64 \quad \text{4 is used as a factor 3 times.}$$

(↑ Exponent)

Exponential Expression

If a is a number and n is a counting number $(1, 2, 3, \ldots)$, then the exponential expression a^n is defined as follows.

$$a^n = \underbrace{a \cdot a \cdot a \cdot \ldots \cdot a}_{n \text{ factors of } a}$$

The number a is the **base** and n is the **exponent.**

With deductive reasoning, we use general statements and apply them to specific situations. For example, consider the **Pythagorean theorem:**

In any right triangle, the sum of the squares of the legs (shorter sides) is equal to the square of the hypotenuse (longest side).

Thus, if we know that the lengths of the shorter sides are 3 inches and 4 inches, we can find the length of the longest side. Let h represent the length of the longest side.

$$3^2 + 4^2 = h^2 \quad \text{Pythagorean theorem}$$
$$9 + 16 = h^2 \quad 3^2 = 3 \cdot 3 = 9;\ 4^2 = 4 \cdot 4 = 16$$
$$25 = h^2 \quad \text{Add.}$$
$$5 = h \quad \text{The positive square root of 25 is 5.}$$

Thus, the longest side measures 5 inches. We used the general rule (the Pythagorean theorem) and applied it to the specific situation.

Reasoning through a problem usually requires certain *premises*. A **premise** can be an assumption, law, rule, widely held idea, or observation. Then reason inductively or deductively from the premises to obtain a **conclusion.** The premises and conclusion make up a **logical argument.**

EXAMPLE 1 Identifying Premises and Conclusions

Identify each premise and the conclusion in each of the following arguments. Then tell whether each argument is an example of inductive or deductive reasoning.

(a) Our house is made of adobe. Both of my next-door neighbors have adobe houses. Therefore, all houses in our neighborhood are made of adobe.

(b) All keyboards have the symbol @. I have a keyboard. I can type the symbol @.

(c) Today is Tuesday. Tomorrow will be Wednesday.

SOLUTION

(a) The premises are "Our house is made of adobe" and "Both of my next-door neighbors have adobe houses." The conclusion is "Therefore, all houses in our neighborhood are made of adobe." Because the reasoning goes from specific examples to a general statement, the argument is an example of inductive reasoning (although it may very well have a false conclusion).

(b) Here, the premises are "All keyboards have the symbol @" and "I have a keyboard." The conclusion is "I can type the symbol @." This reasoning goes from general to specific, so deductive reasoning was used.

(c) There is only one premise here, "Today is Tuesday." The conclusion is "Tomorrow will be Wednesday." The fact that Wednesday immediately follows Tuesday is being used, even though this fact is not explicitly stated. Because the conclusion comes from general facts that apply to this special case, deductive reasoning was used. ■■■

The earlier calendar example illustrated how inductive reasoning may, at times, lead to false conclusions. However, in many cases, inductive reasoning does provide correct results if we look for the most *probable* answer.

EXAMPLE 2 Predicting the Next Number in a Sequence

Use inductive reasoning to determine the *probable* next number in each list below.

(a) 5, 9, 13, 17, 21, 25, 29 **(b)** 1, 1, 2, 3, 5, 8, 13, 21 **(c)** 2, 4, 8, 16, 32

SOLUTION

(a) Each number in the list is obtained by adding 4 to the previous number. The probable next number is $29 + 4 = 33$. (This is an example of an *arithmetic sequence.*)

(b) Beginning with the third number in the list, 2, each number is obtained by adding the two previous numbers in the list. That is,

$$1 + 1 = 2, \quad 1 + 2 = 3, \quad 2 + 3 = 5,$$

and so on. The probable next number in the list is $13 + 21 = 34$. (These are the first few terms of the famous *Fibonacci sequence.*)

(c) It appears here that to obtain each number after the first, we must double the previous number. Therefore, the most probable next number is $32 \times 2 = 64$. (This is an example of a *geometric sequence.*) ■■■

ABC/Everett Collection

In the 2003 movie *A Wrinkle in Time*, young Charles Wallace, played by David Dorfman, is challenged to identify a particular sequence of numbers. He correctly identifies it as the **Fibonacci sequence.**

Inductive reasoning often can be used to predict an answer in a list of similarly constructed computation exercises, as shown in the next example.

EXAMPLE 3 Predicting the Product of Two Numbers

Consider the list of equations. Predict the next multiplication fact in the list.

$$37 \times 3 = 111$$
$$37 \times 6 = 222$$
$$37 \times 9 = 333$$
$$37 \times 12 = 444$$

SOLUTION

The left side of each equation has two factors, the first 37 and the second a multiple of 3, beginning with 3. Each product (answer) consists of three digits, all the same, beginning with 111 for 37×3. Thus, the next multiplication fact would be

$$37 \times 15 = 555, \quad \text{which is indeed true.}$$

Table 1

Number of Points	Number of Regions
1	1
2	2
3	4
4	8
5	16

Pitfalls of Inductive Reasoning

There are pitfalls associated with inductive reasoning. A classic example involves the maximum number of regions formed when chords are constructed in a circle. When two points on a circle are joined with a line segment, a *chord* is formed.

Locate a single point on a circle. Because no chords are formed, a single interior region is formed. See **Figure 2(a)**. Locate two points and draw a chord. Two interior regions are formed, as shown in **Figure 2(b)**. Continue this pattern. Locate three points, and draw all possible chords. Four interior regions are formed, as shown in **Figure 2(c)**. Four points yield 8 regions and five points yield 16 regions. See **Figures 2(d) and 2(e)**.

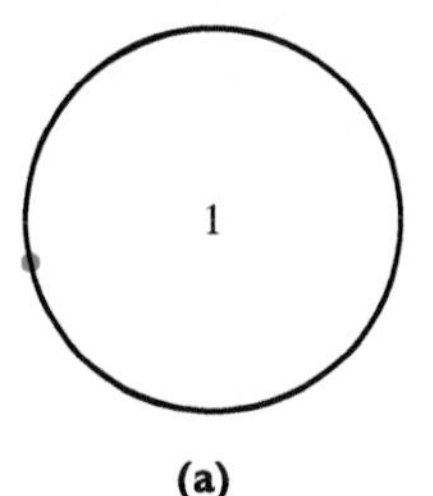

(a)

(b)

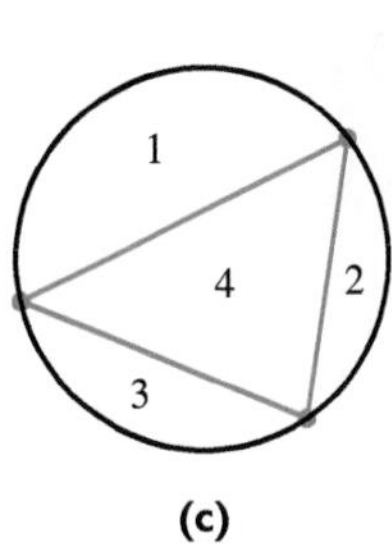

(c)

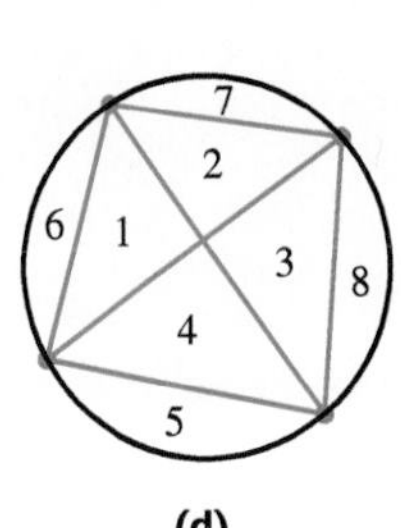

(d)

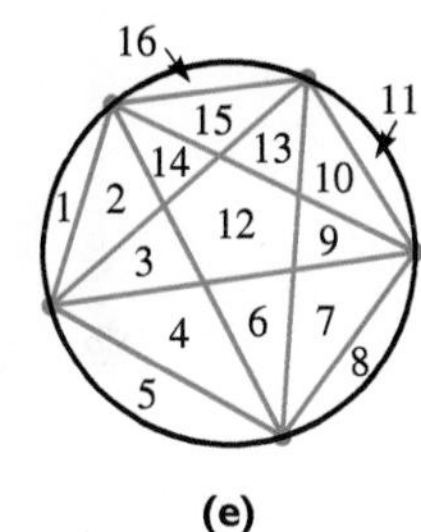

(e)

Figure 2

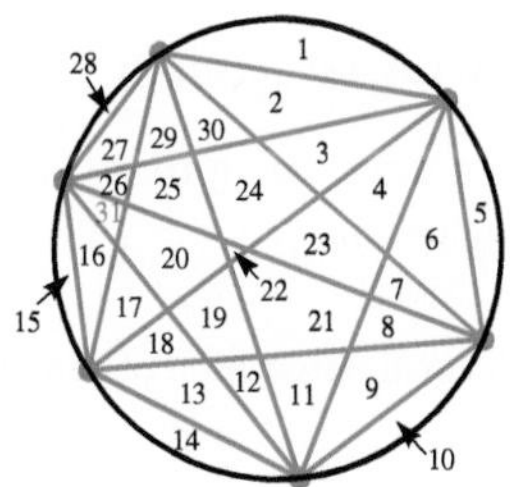

Figure 3

The results of the preceding observations are summarized in **Table 1** in the margin. The pattern formed in the column headed "Number of Regions" is the same one we saw in **Example 2(c)**, where we predicted that the next number would be 64. It seems here that for each additional point on the circle, the number of regions doubles. A reasonable inductive conjecture would be that for six points, 32 regions would be formed. But as **Figure 3** indicates, there are *only 31 regions*. The pattern of doubling ends when the sixth point is considered. Adding a seventh point would yield 57 regions. The numbers obtained here are

$$1, 2, 4, 8, 16, 31, 57.$$

For n points on the circle, the number of regions is given by the formula

$$\frac{n^4 - 6n^3 + 23n^2 - 18n + 24}{24}.\text{*}$$

*For more information on this and other similar patterns, see "Counting Pizza Pieces and Other Combinatorial Problems," by Eugene Maier, in the January 1988 issue of *Mathematics Teacher*, pp. 22–26.

We can use a graphing calculator to construct a table of values that indicates the number of regions for various numbers of points. Using X rather than n, we can define Y_1 using the expression given on the previous page. (see **Figure 4(a)**). Then, creating a table of values, as in **Figure 4(b)**, we see how many regions (indicated by Y_1) there are for any number of points (X).

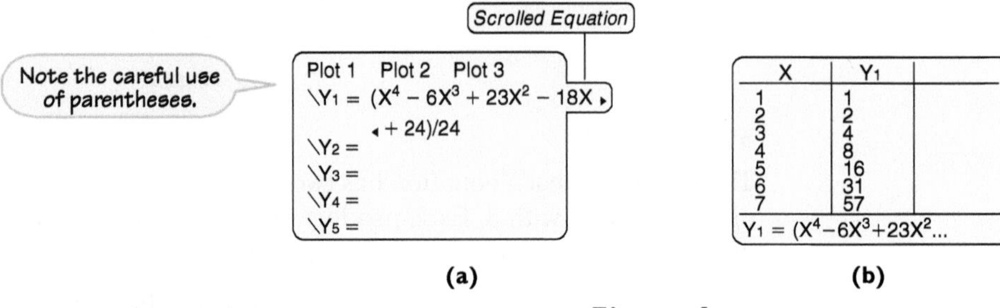

Figure 4

For Further Thought

Inductive Reasoning Anecdote

The following anecdote concerning inductive reasoning appears in the first volume of the *In Mathematical Circles* series by Howard Eves.

A scientist had two large jars before him on the laboratory table. The jar on his left contained 100 fleas; the jar on his right was empty. The scientist carefully lifted a flea from the jar on the left, placed the flea on the table between the two jars, stepped back, and in a loud voice said, "Jump." The flea jumped and was put in the jar on the right. A second flea was carefully lifted from the jar on the left and placed on the table between the two jars. Again the scientist stepped back and in a loud voice said, "Jump." The flea jumped and was put in the jar on the right. In the same manner, the scientist treated each of the 100 fleas in the jar on the left, and each flea jumped as ordered.

The two jars were then interchanged and the experiment continued with a slight difference. This time the scientist carefully lifted a flea from the jar on the left, yanked off its hind legs, placed the flea on the table between the jars, stepped back, and in a loud voice said, "Jump." The flea did not jump, and was put in the jar on the right. A second flea was carefully lifted from the jar on the left, its hind legs yanked off, and then placed on the table between the two jars. Again the scientist stepped back and in a loud voice said, "Jump." The flea did not jump, and was put in the jar on the right. In this manner, the scientist treated each of the 100 fleas in the jar on the left, and in no case did a flea jump when ordered. The scientist recorded the following induction:

"A flea, if its hind legs are yanked off, cannot hear."

For Group or Individual Investigation

Discuss or research examples from advertising that lead consumers to draw incorrect conclusions.

1 EXERCISES

In Exercises 1–12, determine whether the reasoning is an example of deductive or inductive reasoning.

1. If the mechanic says that it will take seven days to repair your car, then it will actually take ten days. The mechanic says, "I figure it'll take a week to fix it, ma'am." Then you can expect it to be ready ten days from now.

2. If you take your vitamins, you'll feel a lot better. You take your vitamins. Therefore, you'll feel a lot better.

3. It has rained every day for the past six days, and it is raining today as well. So it will also rain tomorrow.

4. Carrie's first three children were boys. If she has another baby, it will be a boy.

5. Finley had 85 baseball cards. His mom gave him 20 more for his birthday. Therefore, he now has 105 of them.

6. If the same number is subtracted from both sides of a true equation, the new equation is also true. I know that $9 + 18 = 27$. Therefore, $(9 + 18) - 13 = 27 - 13$.

7. If you build it, they will come. You build it. Therefore, they will come.

8. All men are mortal. Socrates is a man. Therefore, Socrates is mortal.

9. It is a fact that every student who ever attended Delgado University was accepted into graduate school. Because I am attending Delgado, I can expect to be accepted to graduate school, too.

10. For the past 97 years, a rare plant has bloomed in Columbia each summer, alternating between yellow and green flowers. Last summer, it bloomed with green flowers, so this summer it will bloom with yellow flowers.

11. In the sequence 5, 10, 15, 20, 25, . . . , the most probable next number is 30.

12. Lady Gaga's last four single releases have reached the Top Ten in the pop charts, so her current release will also reach the Top Ten.

David Livingston/Getty Images

13. Discuss the differences between inductive and deductive reasoning. Give an example of each.

14. Give an example of faulty inductive reasoning.

Determine the most probable next term in each of the following lists of numbers.

15. 6, 9, 12, 15, 18

16. 13, 18, 23, 28, 33

17. 3, 12, 48, 192, 768

18. 32, 16, 8, 4, 2

19. 3, 6, 9, 15, 24, 39

20. $\frac{1}{3}, \frac{3}{5}, \frac{5}{7}, \frac{7}{9}, \frac{9}{11}$

21. $\frac{1}{2}, \frac{3}{4}, \frac{5}{6}, \frac{7}{8}, \frac{9}{10}$

22. 1, 4, 9, 16, 25

23. 1, 8, 27, 64, 125

24. 2, 6, 12, 20, 30, 42

25. 4, 7, 12, 19, 28, 39

26. $-1, 2, -3, 4, -5, 6$

27. 5, 3, 5, 5, 3, 5, 5, 5, 3, 5, 5, 5, 5, 3, 5, 5, 5, 5

28. 8, 2, 8, 2, 2, 8, 2, 2, 2, 8, 2, 2, 2, 2, 8, 2, 2, 2, 2

29. Construct a list of numbers similar to those in **Exercise 15** such that the most probable next number in the list is 60.

30. Construct a list of numbers similar to those in **Exercise 26** such that the most probable next number in the list is 9.

Use the list of equations and inductive reasoning to predict the next equation, and then verify your conjecture.

31.
$$(9 \times 9) + 7 = 88$$
$$(98 \times 9) + 6 = 888$$
$$(987 \times 9) + 5 = 8888$$
$$(9876 \times 9) + 4 = 88{,}888$$

32.
$$(1 \times 9) + 2 = 11$$
$$(12 \times 9) + 3 = 111$$
$$(123 \times 9) + 4 = 1111$$
$$(1234 \times 9) + 5 = 11{,}111$$

33.
$$3367 \times 3 = 10{,}101$$
$$3367 \times 6 = 20{,}202$$
$$3367 \times 9 = 30{,}303$$
$$3367 \times 12 = 40{,}404$$

34.
$$15873 \times 7 = 111{,}111$$
$$15873 \times 14 = 222{,}222$$
$$15873 \times 21 = 333{,}333$$
$$15873 \times 28 = 444{,}444$$

35.
$$34 \times 34 = 1156$$
$$334 \times 334 = 111{,}556$$
$$3334 \times 3334 = 11{,}115{,}556$$

36.
$$11 \times 11 = 121$$
$$111 \times 111 = 12{,}321$$
$$1111 \times 1111 = 1{,}234{,}321$$

37.
$$3 = \frac{3(2)}{2}$$
$$3 + 6 = \frac{6(3)}{2}$$
$$3 + 6 + 9 = \frac{9(4)}{2}$$
$$3 + 6 + 9 + 12 = \frac{12(5)}{2}$$

38.
$$2 = 4 - 2$$
$$2 + 4 = 8 - 2$$
$$2 + 4 + 8 = 16 - 2$$
$$2 + 4 + 8 + 16 = 32 - 2$$

39.
$$5(6) = 6(6 - 1)$$
$$5(6) + 5(36) = 6(36 - 1)$$
$$5(6) + 5(36) + 5(216) = 6(216 - 1)$$
$$5(6) + 5(36) + 5(216) + 5(1296) = 6(1296 - 1)$$

40.
$$3 = \frac{3(3-1)}{2}$$
$$3 + 9 = \frac{3(9-1)}{2}$$
$$3 + 9 + 27 = \frac{3(27-1)}{2}$$
$$3 + 9 + 27 + 81 = \frac{3(81-1)}{2}$$

41.
$$\frac{1}{2} = 1 - \frac{1}{2}$$
$$\frac{1}{2} + \frac{1}{4} = 1 - \frac{1}{4}$$
$$\frac{1}{2} + \frac{1}{4} + \frac{1}{8} = 1 - \frac{1}{8}$$
$$\frac{1}{2} + \frac{1}{4} + \frac{1}{8} + \frac{1}{16} = 1 - \frac{1}{16}$$

42.
$$\frac{1}{1 \cdot 2} = \frac{1}{2}$$
$$\frac{1}{1 \cdot 2} + \frac{1}{2 \cdot 3} = \frac{2}{3}$$
$$\frac{1}{1 \cdot 2} + \frac{1}{2 \cdot 3} + \frac{1}{3 \cdot 4} = \frac{3}{4}$$
$$\frac{1}{1 \cdot 2} + \frac{1}{2 \cdot 3} + \frac{1}{3 \cdot 4} + \frac{1}{4 \cdot 5} = \frac{4}{5}$$

A story is often told about how the great mathematician Carl Friedrich Gauss (1777–1855) at a very young age was told by his teacher to find the sum of the first 100 *counting numbers. While his classmates toiled at the problem, Carl simply wrote down a single number and handed it in to his teacher. His answer was correct. When asked how he did it, the young Carl explained that he observed that there were* 50 *pairs of numbers that each added up to* 101. *(See below.) So the sum of all the numbers must be* $50 \times 101 = 5050$.

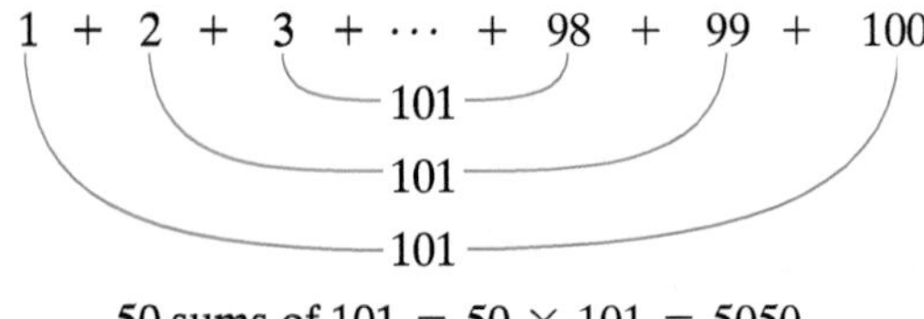

50 sums of 101 = 50 × 101 = 5050

Use the method of Gauss to find each sum.

43. $1 + 2 + 3 + \cdots + 200$

44. $1 + 2 + 3 + \cdots + 400$

45. $1 + 2 + 3 + \cdots + 800$

46. $1 + 2 + 3 + \cdots + 2000$

47. Modify the procedure of Gauss to find the sum $1 + 2 + 3 + \cdots + 175$.

48. Explain in your own words how the procedure of Gauss can be modified to find the sum $1 + 2 + 3 + \cdots + n$, where n is an odd natural number. (When an odd natural number is divided by 2, it leaves a remainder of 1.)

49. Modify the procedure of Gauss to find the sum $2 + 4 + 6 + \cdots + 100$.

50. Use the result of **Exercise 49** to find the sum $4 + 8 + 12 + \cdots + 200$.

51. What is the most probable next number in this list?

12, 1, 1, 1, 2, 1, 3

(*Hint:* Think about a clock with chimes.)

52. What is the next term in this list?

O, T, T, F, F, S, S, E, N, T

(*Hint:* Think about words and their relationship to numbers.)

53. **(a)** Choose any three-digit number with all different digits. Now reverse the digits, and subtract the smaller from the larger. Record your result. Choose another three-digit number and repeat this process. Do this as many times as it takes for you to see a pattern in the different results you obtain. (*Hint:* What is the middle digit? What is the sum of the first and third digits?)

(b) Write an explanation of this pattern.

54. Choose any number, and follow these steps.

(a) Multiply by 2.
(b) Add 6.
(c) Divide by 2.
(d) Subtract the number you started with.
(e) Record your result.

Repeat the process, except in Step (b), add 8. Record your final result. Repeat the process once more, except in Step (b), add 10. Record your final result.

(f) Observe what you have done. Then use inductive reasoning to explain how to predict the final result.

55. Complete the following.

142,857 × 1 = ______
142,857 × 2 = ______
142,857 × 3 = ______
142,857 × 4 = ______
142,857 × 5 = ______
142,857 × 6 = ______

What pattern exists in the successive answers? Now multiply 142,857 by 7 to obtain an interesting result.

56. Refer to **Figures 2(b)–(e)** and **Figure 3**. Instead of counting interior regions of the circle, count the chords formed. Use inductive reasoning to predict the number of chords that would be formed if seven points were used.

2 AN APPLICATION OF INDUCTIVE REASONING: NUMBER PATTERNS

Number Sequences • Successive Differences • Number Patterns and Sum Formulas • Figurate Numbers

Number Sequences

An ordered list of numbers such as

$$3, 9, 15, 21, 27, \ldots$$

is called a *sequence*. A **number sequence** is a list of numbers having a first number, a second number, a third number, and so on, called the **terms** of the sequence.

The sequence that begins

$$5, 9, 13, 17, 21, \ldots$$

is an *arithmetic sequence,* or *arithmetic progression.* In an **arithmetic sequence,** each term after the first is obtained by adding the same number, called the **common difference.** To find the common difference, choose any term after the first and subtract from it the preceding term. If we choose $9 - 5$ (the second term minus the first term), for example, we see that the common difference is 4. To find the term following 21, we add 4 to get $21 + 4 = 25$.

Similarly, the sequence that begins

$$2, 4, 8, 16, 32, \ldots$$

is a *geometric sequence*, or *geometric progression.* In a **geometric sequence,** each term after the first is obtained by multiplying by the same number, called the **common ratio.** To find the common ratio, choose any term after the first and divide it by the preceding term. If we choose $\frac{4}{2}$ (the second term divided by the first term), for example, we see that the common ratio is 2. To find the term following 32, we multiply by 2 to get $32 \cdot 2 = 64$.

EXAMPLE 1 Identifying Arithmetic and Geometric Sequences

For each sequence, determine if it is an *arithmetic sequence,* a *geometric sequence,* or *neither.* If it is either arithmetic or geometric, give the next term in the sequence.

(a) $5, 10, 15, 20, 25, \ldots$ **(b)** $3, 12, 48, 192, 768, \ldots$ **(c)** $1, 4, 9, 16, 25, \ldots$

SOLUTION

(a) If we choose *any* term after the first term, and subtract the preceding term, we find that the common difference is 5.

$$10 - 5 = 5 \quad 15 - 10 = 5 \quad 20 - 15 = 5 \quad 25 - 20 = 5$$

Therefore, this is an arithmetic sequence. The next term in the sequence is

$$25 + 5 = 30.$$

(b) If any term after the first is multiplied by 4, the following term is obtained.

$$\frac{12}{3} = 4 \quad \frac{48}{12} = 4 \quad \frac{192}{48} = 4 \quad \frac{768}{192} = 4$$

Therefore, this is a geometric sequence. The next term in the sequence is

$$768 \cdot 4 = 3072.$$

(c) While there is a pattern here (the terms are the squares of the first five counting numbers), there is neither a common difference nor a common ratio. (Verify this) This is neither an arithmetic nor a geometric sequence. ∎

Successive Differences

Some sequences may provide more difficulty in making a conjecture about the next term. Often the **method of successive differences** may be applied in such cases. Consider the sequence

$$2, 6, 22, 56, 114, \ldots.$$

Because the next term is not obvious, subtract the first term from the second term, the second from the third, the third from the fourth, and so on.

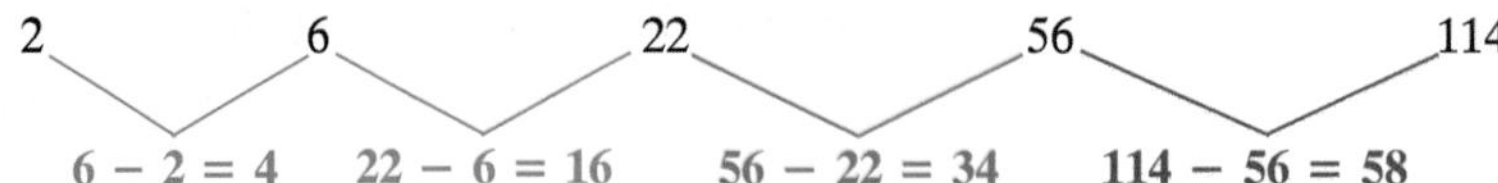

Now repeat the process with the sequence 4, 16, 34, 58 and continue repeating until the difference is a constant value, as shown in line (4).

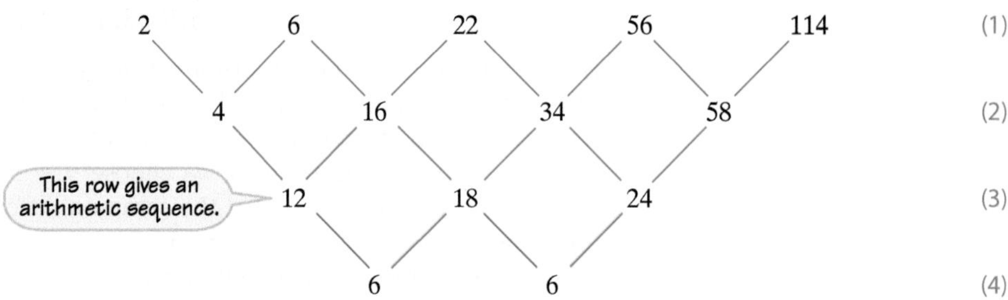

Once a line of constant values is obtained, simply work "backward" by adding until the desired term of the given sequence is obtained. Thus, for this pattern to continue, another 6 should appear in line (4), meaning that the next term in line (3) would have to be $24 + 6 = 30$. The next term in line (2) would be $58 + 30 = 88$. Finally, the next term in the given sequence would be $114 + 88 =$ **202.**

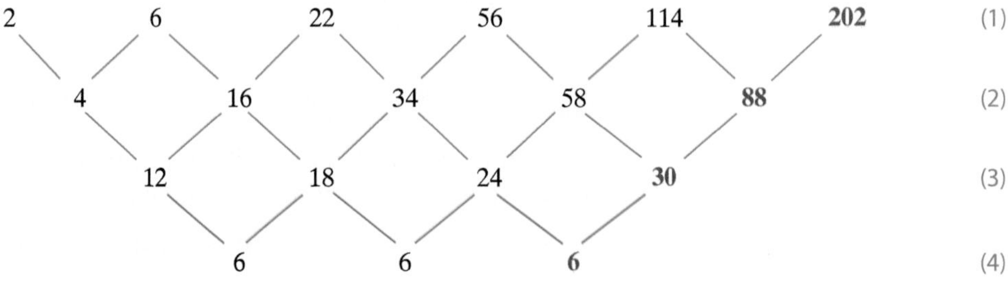

EXAMPLE 2 Using Successive Differences

Determine the next number in each sequence.

(a) 14, 22, 32, 44, ... **(b)** 5, 15, 37, 77, 141, ...

SOLUTION

(a) Use the method of successive differences to obtain the following.

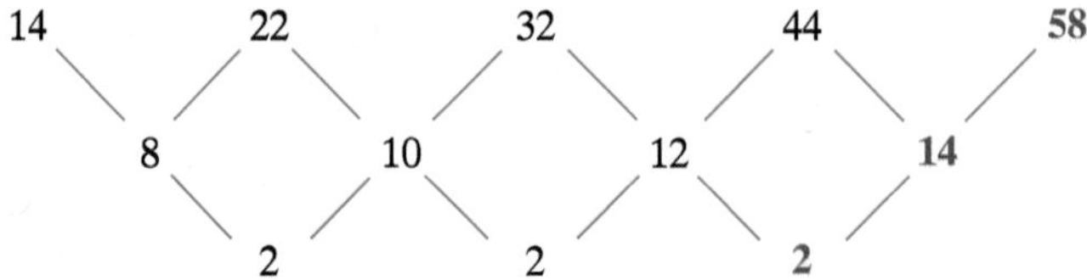

Once the row of 2s was obtained and extended, we were able to get $12 + 2 = 14$, and $44 + 14 = 58$, as shown above. The next number in the sequence is **58.**

(b) Proceeding as before, obtain the following diagram.

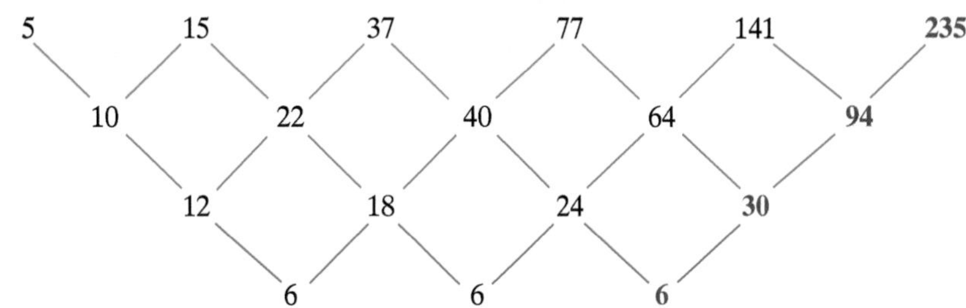

The numbers in the "diagonal" at the far right were obtained by adding: $24 + 6 = 30$, $64 + 30 = 94$, and $141 + 94 = 235$. The next number in the sequence is **235**. ∎∎∎

The method of successive differences will not always work. For example, try it on the Fibonacci sequence in **Example 2(b)** of **Section 1** and see what happens.

Number Patterns and Sum Formulas

Mathematics features a seemingly endless variety of number patterns. Observe the following pattern.

$$1 = 1^2$$
$$1 + 3 = 2^2$$
$$1 + 3 + 5 = 3^2$$
$$1 + 3 + 5 + 7 = 4^2$$
$$1 + 3 + 5 + 7 + 9 = 5^2$$

In each case, the left side of the equation is the indicated sum of consecutive odd counting numbers beginning with 1, and the right side is the square of the number of terms on the left side. Inductive reasoning would suggest that the next line in this pattern is as follows.

$$1 + 3 + 5 + 7 + 9 + 11 = 6^2$$

Evaluating each side shows that each side simplifies to 36.

We cannot conclude that this pattern will continue indefinitely, because observation of a finite number of examples does *not* guarantee that the pattern will continue. However, mathematicians have proved that this pattern does indeed continue indefinitely, using a method of proof called **mathematical induction.** (See any standard college algebra text.)

Any even counting number may be written in the form $2k$, where k is a counting number. It follows that the kth odd counting number is written $2k - 1$. For example, the **third** odd counting number, 5, can be written

$$2(3) - 1.$$

Using these ideas, we can write the result obtained above as follows.

Sum of the First n Odd Counting Numbers

If n is any counting number, then the following is true.

$$\mathbf{1 + 3 + 5 + \cdots + (2n - 1) = n^2}$$

EXAMPLE 3 Predicting the Next Equation in a List

In each of the following, several equations are given illustrating a suspected number pattern. Determine what the next equation would be, and verify that it is indeed a true statement.

(a)

$$1^2 = 1^3$$
$$(1 + 2)^2 = 1^3 + 2^3$$
$$(1 + 2 + 3)^2 = 1^3 + 2^3 + 3^3$$
$$(1 + 2 + 3 + 4)^2 = 1^3 + 2^3 + 3^3 + 4^3$$

(b)

$$1 = 1^3$$
$$3 + 5 = 2^3$$
$$7 + 9 + 11 = 3^3$$
$$13 + 15 + 17 + 19 = 4^3$$

(c)

$$1 = \frac{1 \cdot 2}{2}$$
$$1 + 2 = \frac{2 \cdot 3}{2}$$
$$1 + 2 + 3 = \frac{3 \cdot 4}{2}$$
$$1 + 2 + 3 + 4 = \frac{4 \cdot 5}{2}$$

(d)

$$12{,}345{,}679 \times 9 = 111{,}111{,}111$$
$$12{,}345{,}679 \times 18 = 222{,}222{,}222$$
$$12{,}345{,}679 \times 27 = 333{,}333{,}333$$
$$12{,}345{,}679 \times 36 = 444{,}444{,}444$$

SOLUTION

(a) The left side of each equation is the square of the sum of the first n counting numbers, while the right side is the sum of their cubes. The next equation in the pattern would be

$$(1 + 2 + 3 + 4 + 5)^2 = 1^3 + 2^3 + 3^3 + 4^3 + 5^3.$$

Each side simplifies to 225, so the pattern is true for this equation.

(b) The left sides of the equations contain the sum of odd counting numbers, starting with the first (1) in the first equation, the second and third (3 and 5) in the second equation, the fourth, fifth, and sixth (7, 9, and 11) in the third equation, and so on. The right side contains the cube (third power) of the number of terms on the left side in each case. Following this pattern, the next equation would be

$$21 + 23 + 25 + 27 + 29 = 5^3,$$

which can be verified by computation.

(c) The left side of each equation gives the indicated sum of the first n counting numbers, and the right side is always of the form

$$\frac{n(n + 1)}{2}.$$

For the pattern to continue, the next equation would be

$$1 + 2 + 3 + 4 + 5 = \frac{5 \cdot 6}{2}.$$

Because each side simplifies to 15, the pattern is true for this equation.

(d) In each case, the first factor on the left is 12,345,679 and the second factor is a multiple of 9 (that is, 9, 18, 27, 36). The right side consists of a nine-digit number, all digits of which are the same (that is, 1, 2, 3, 4). For the pattern to continue, the next equation would be as follows.

$$12{,}345{,}679 \times 45 = 555{,}555{,}555$$

Verify that this is a true statement. ■■■

The patterns established in **Examples 3(a) and 3(c)** can be written as follows.

Special Sum Formulas

For any counting number n, the following are true.

$$(1 + 2 + 3 + \cdots + n)^2 = 1^3 + 2^3 + 3^3 + \cdots + n^3$$

and $$1 + 2 + 3 + \cdots + n = \frac{n(n + 1)}{2}$$

We can provide a general deductive argument showing how the second equation is obtained.

Let S represent the sum $1 + 2 + 3 + \cdots + n$. This sum can also be written as $S = n + (n - 1) + (n - 2) + \cdots + 1$. Write these two equations as follows.

$$S = 1 + 2 + 3 + \cdots + n$$
$$S = n + (n - 1) + (n - 2) + \cdots + 1$$
$$2S = (n + 1) + (n + 1) + (n + 1) + \cdots + (n + 1)$$ Add the corresponding sides.
$$2S = n(n + 1)$$ There are n terms of $n + 1$.
$$S = \frac{n(n + 1)}{2}$$ Divide both sides by 2.

Figurate Numbers

Pythagoras and his Pythagorean brotherhood studied numbers of geometric arrangements of points, such as **triangular numbers, square numbers,** and **pentagonal numbers. Figure 5** illustrates the first few of each of these types of numbers.

The **figurate numbers** possess numerous interesting patterns. Every square number greater than 1 is the sum of two consecutive triangular numbers. (For example, $9 = 3 + 6$ and $25 = 10 + 15$.)

Disney Enterprises, Inc.

In the 1959 Disney animation *Donald in Mathmagic Land*, Donald Duck travels back in time to meet the Greek mathematician **Pythagoras** (c. 540 B.C.), who with his fellow mathematicians formed the Pythagorean brotherhood. The brotherhood devoted its time to the study of mathematics and music.

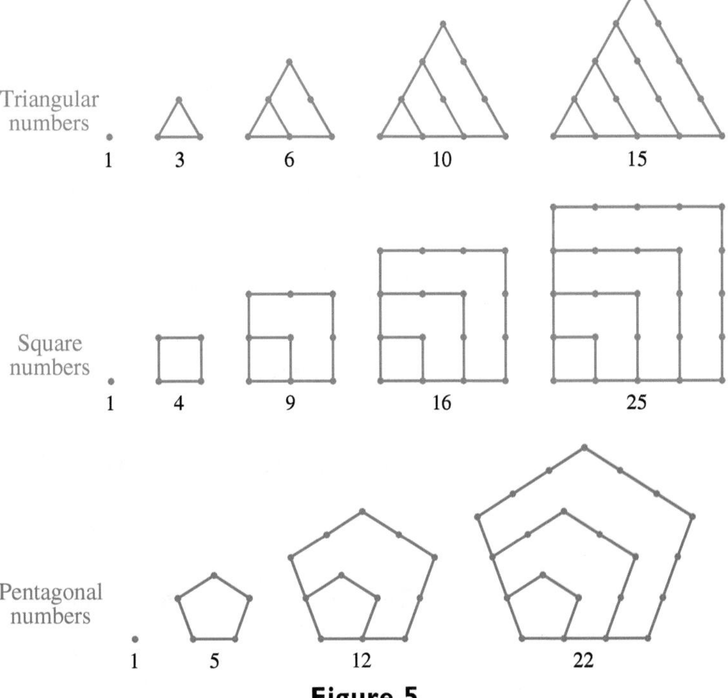

Figure 5

Every pentagonal number can be represented as the sum of a square number and a triangular number. (For example, $5 = 4 + 1$ and $12 = 9 + 3$.) Many other such relationships exist.

In the expression T_n, n is called a **subscript.** T_n is read **"T sub *n*,"** and it represents the triangular number in the nth position in the sequence. For example,

$$T_1 = 1, \quad T_2 = 3, \quad T_3 = 6, \quad \text{and} \quad T_4 = 10.$$

S_n and P_n represent the nth square and pentagonal numbers, respectively.

Formulas for Triangular, Square, and Pentagonal Numbers

For any natural number n, the following are true.

The nth triangular number is given by $\mathbf{T}_n = \dfrac{n(n+1)}{2}$.

The nth square number is given by $\mathbf{S}_n = n^2$.

The nth pentagonal number is given by $\mathbf{P}_n = \dfrac{n(3n-1)}{2}$.

EXAMPLE 4 Using the Formulas for Figurate Numbers

Use the formulas to find each of the following.

(a) seventh triangular number

(b) twelfth square number

(c) sixth pentagonal number

SOLUTION

(a) $T_7 = \dfrac{n(n+1)}{2} = \dfrac{7(7+1)}{2} = \dfrac{7(8)}{2} = \dfrac{56}{2} = 28$ Formula for a triangular number, $n = 7$

(b) $S_{12} = n^2 = 12^2 = 144$ Formula for a square number, $n = 12$

$12^2 = 12 \cdot 12$

Inside the brackets, multiply first and then subtract.

(c) $P_6 = \dfrac{n(3n-1)}{2} = \dfrac{6[3(6)-1]}{2} = \dfrac{6(18-1)}{2} = \dfrac{6(17)}{2} = 51$

EXAMPLE 5 Illustrating a Figurate Number Relationship

Show that the sixth pentagonal number is equal to the sum of 6 and 3 times the fifth triangular number.

SOLUTION

From **Example 4(c),** $P_6 = 51$. The fifth triangular number is 15. Thus,

$$51 = 6 + 3(15) = 6 + 45 = 51.$$

The general relationship examined in **Example 5** can be written as follows.

$$P_n = n + 3 \cdot T_{n-1} \quad (n \geq 2)$$

EXAMPLE 6 Predicting the Value of a Pentagonal Number

The first five pentagonal numbers are 1, 5, 12, 22, 35. Use the method of successive differences to predict the sixth pentagonal number.

SOLUTION

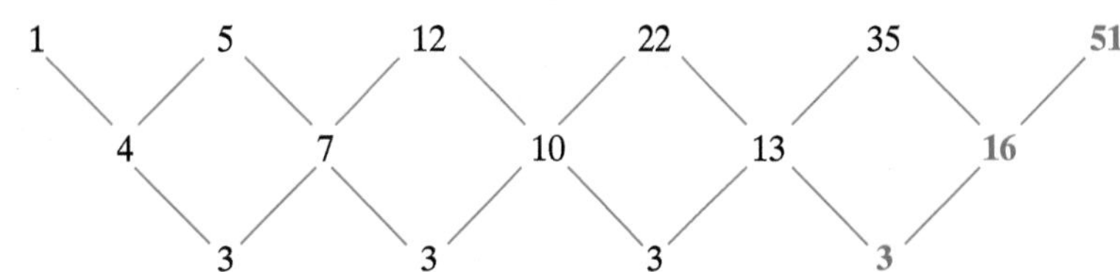

After the second line of successive differences, we work backward to find that the sixth pentagonal number is 51, which was also found in **Example 4(c).**

For Further Thought

Kaprekar Constants

Take any three-digit number whose digits are not all the same. Arrange the digits in decreasing order, and then arrange them in increasing order. Now subtract. Repeat the process, using a 0 if necessary in the event that the difference consists of only two digits. For example, suppose that we choose a number whose digits are 1, 4, and 8, such as 841.

$$\begin{array}{r} 841 \\ -148 \\ \hline 693 \end{array} \quad \begin{array}{r} 963 \\ -369 \\ \hline 594 \end{array} \quad \begin{array}{r} 954 \\ -459 \\ \hline 495 \end{array}$$

Notice that we have obtained the number 495, and the process will lead to 495 again.

The number 495 is called a **Kaprekar constant.** The number 495 will eventually always be generated if this process is applied to such a three-digit number.

For Group or Individual Investigation

1. Apply the process of Kaprekar to a two-digit number, in which the digits are not the same. (Interpret 9 as 09 if necessary.) Compare the results. What seems to be true?
2. Repeat the process for four digits, comparing results after several steps. What conjecture can be made for this situation?

2 EXERCISES

For each sequence, determine if it is an arithmetic *sequence, a* geometric *sequence, or* neither. *If it is either arithmetic or geometric, give the next term in the sequence.*

1. 6, 16, 26, 36, 46, . . .

2. 8, 16, 24, 32, 40, . . .

3. 5, 15, 45, 135, 405, . . .

4. 2, 12, 72, 432, 2592, . . .

5. 1, 8, 27, 81, 243, . . .

6. 2, 8, 18, 32, 50, . . .

7. 256, 128, 64, 32, 16, . . .

8. 4096, 1024, 256, 64, 16, . . .

9. 1, 3, 4, 7, 11, . . .

10. 0, 1, 1, 2, 3, . . .

11. 12, 14, 16, 18, 20, . . .

12. 10, 50, 90, 130, 170, . . .

Use the method of successive differences to determine the next number in each sequence.

13. 1, 4, 11, 22, 37, 56, . . .

14. 3, 14, 31, 54, 83, 118, . . .

15. 6, 20, 50, 102, 182, 296, . . .

16. 1, 11, 35, 79, 149, 251, . . .

17. 0, 12, 72, 240, 600, 1260, 2352, . . .

18. 2, 57, 220, 575, 1230, 2317, . . .

19. 5, 34, 243, 1022, 3121, 7770, 16799, . . .

20. 3, 19, 165, 771, 2503, 6483, 14409, . . .

21. Refer to **Figures 2 and 3** in **Section 1.** The method of successive differences can be applied to the sequence of interior regions,

$$1, 2, 4, 8, 16, 31,$$

to find the number of regions determined by seven points on the circle. What is the next term in this sequence? How many regions would be determined by eight points? Verify this using the formula given at the end of that section.

22. Suppose that the expression $n^2 + 3n + 1$ determines the nth term in a sequence. That is, to find the first term, let $n = 1$. To find the second term, let $n = 2$, and so on.

(a) Find the first four terms of the sequence.

(b) Use the method of successive differences to predict the fifth term of the sequence.

(c) Find the fifth term by letting $n = 5$ in the expression $n^2 + 3n + 1$. Does your result agree with the one you found in part (b)?

In Exercises 23–32, several equations are given illustrating a suspected number pattern. Determine what the next equation would be, and verify that it is indeed a true statement.

23. $(1 \times 9) - 1 = 8$
$(21 \times 9) - 1 = 188$
$(321 \times 9) - 1 = 2888$

24. $(1 \times 8) + 1 = 9$
$(12 \times 8) + 2 = 98$
$(123 \times 8) + 3 = 987$

25. $999{,}999 \times 2 = 1{,}999{,}998$
$999{,}999 \times 3 = 2{,}999{,}997$

26. $101 \times 101 = 10{,}201$
$10{,}101 \times 10{,}101 = 102{,}030{,}201$

27. $3^2 - 1^2 = 2^3$
$6^2 - 3^2 = 3^3$
$10^2 - 6^2 = 4^3$
$15^2 - 10^2 = 5^3$

28. $1 = 1^2$
$1 + 2 + 1 = 2^2$
$1 + 2 + 3 + 2 + 1 = 3^2$
$1 + 2 + 3 + 4 + 3 + 2 + 1 = 4^2$

29. $2^2 - 1^2 = 2 + 1$
$3^2 - 2^2 = 3 + 2$
$4^2 - 3^2 = 4 + 3$

30. $1^2 + 1 = 2^2 - 2$
$2^2 + 2 = 3^2 - 3$
$3^2 + 3 = 4^2 - 4$

31. $1 = 1 \times 1$
$1 + 5 = 2 \times 3$
$1 + 5 + 9 = 3 \times 5$

32. $1 + 2 = 3$
$4 + 5 + 6 = 7 + 8$
$9 + 10 + 11 + 12 = 13 + 14 + 15$

Use the formula $S = \frac{n(n+1)}{2}$ *to find each sum.*

33. $1 + 2 + 3 + \cdots + 300$

34. $1 + 2 + 3 + \cdots + 500$

35. $1 + 2 + 3 + \cdots + 675$

36. $1 + 2 + 3 + \cdots + 825$

Use the formula $S = n^2$ *to find each sum. (Hint: To find n, add 1 to the last term and divide by 2.)*

37. $1 + 3 + 5 + \cdots + 101$

38. $1 + 3 + 5 + \cdots + 49$

39. $1 + 3 + 5 + \cdots + 999$

40. $1 + 3 + 5 + \cdots + 301$

41. Use the formula for finding the sum

$$1 + 2 + 3 + \cdots + n$$

to discover a formula for finding the sum

$$2 + 4 + 6 + \cdots + 2n.$$

42. State in your own words the following formula discussed in this section.

$$(1 + 2 + 3 + \cdots + n)^2 = 1^3 + 2^3 + 3^3 + \cdots + n^3$$

43. Explain how the following diagram geometrically illustrates the formula $1 + 3 + 5 + 7 + 9 = 5^2$.

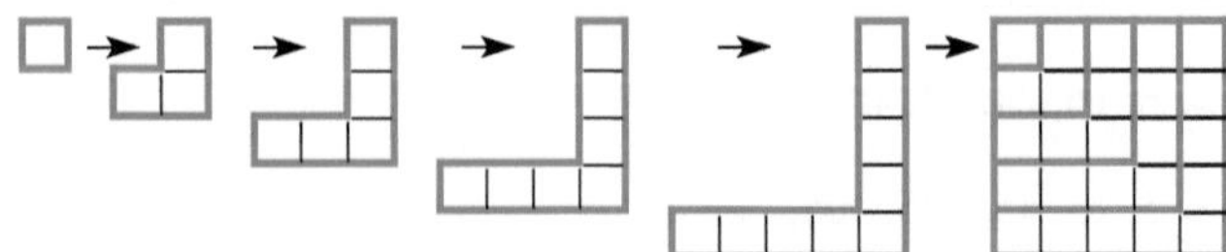

44. Explain how the following diagram geometrically illustrates the formula $1 + 2 + 3 + 4 = \frac{4 \times 5}{2}$.

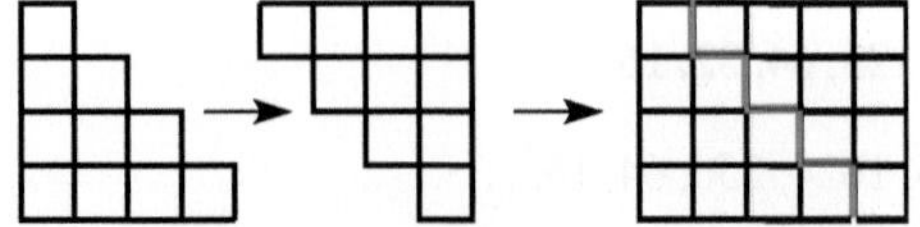

45. Use patterns to complete the table below.

Figurate Number	1st	2nd	3rd	4th	5th	6th	7th	8th
Triangular	1	3	6	10	15	21		
Square	1	4	9	16	25			
Pentagonal	1	5	12	22				
Hexagonal	1	6	15					
Heptagonal	1	7						
Octagonal	1							

46. The first five triangular, square, and pentagonal numbers may be obtained using sums of terms of sequences, as shown below.

Triangular	Square	Pentagonal
$1 = 1$	$1 = 1$	$1 = 1$
$3 = 1 + 2$	$4 = 1 + 3$	$5 = 1 + 4$
$6 = 1 + 2 + 3$	$9 = 1 + 3 + 5$	$12 = 1 + 4 + 7$
$10 = 1 + 2 + 3 + 4$	$16 = 1 + 3 + 5 + 7$	$22 = 1 + 4 + 7 + 10$
$15 = 1 + 2 + 3 + 4 + 5$	$25 = 1 + 3 + 5 + 7 + 9$	$35 = 1 + 4 + 7 + 10 + 13$

Notice the successive differences of the added terms on the right sides of the equations. The next type of figurate number is the **hexagonal** number. (A hexagon has six sides.) Use the patterns above to predict the first five hexagonal numbers.

47. Eight times any triangular number, plus 1, is a square number. Show that this is true for the first four triangular numbers.

48. Divide the first triangular number by 3 and record the remainder. Divide the second triangular number by 3 and record the remainder. Repeat this procedure several more times. Do you notice a pattern?

49. Repeat **Exercise 48,** but instead use square numbers and divide by 4. What pattern is determined?

50. **Exercises 48 and 49** are specific cases of the following: When the numbers in the sequence of n-agonal numbers are divided by n, the sequence of remainders obtained is a repeating sequence. Verify this for $n = 5$ and $n = 6$.

51. Every square number can be written as the sum of two triangular numbers. For example, $16 = 6 + 10$. This can be represented geometrically by dividing a square array of dots with a line as shown.

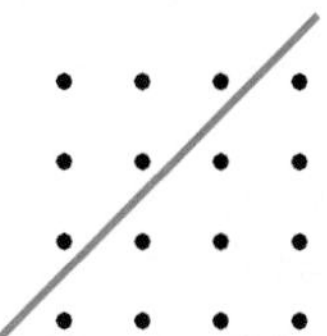

The triangular arrangement above the line represents 6, the one below the line represents 10, and the whole arrangement represents 16. Show how the square numbers 25 and 36 may likewise be geometrically represented as the sum of two triangular numbers.

52. A fraction is in **lowest terms** if the greatest common factor of its numerator and its denominator is 1. For example, $\frac{3}{8}$ is in lowest terms, but $\frac{4}{12}$ is not.

(a) For $n = 2$ to $n = 8$, form the fractions

$$\frac{n\text{th square number}}{(n + 1)\text{st square number}}.$$

(b) Repeat part (a) with triangular numbers.

(c) Use inductive reasoning to make a conjecture based on your results from parts (a) and (b), observing whether the fractions are in lowest terms.

*In addition to the formulas for T_n, S_n, and P_n, the following formulas are true for **hexagonal** numbers (H), **heptagonal** numbers (Hp), and **octagonal** numbers (O):*

$$\mathbf{H}_n = \frac{n(4n - 2)}{2}, \quad \mathbf{Hp}_n = \frac{n(5n - 3)}{2}, \quad \mathbf{O}_n = \frac{n(6n - 4)}{2}.$$

Use these formulas to find each of the following.

53. the sixteenth square number

54. the eleventh triangular number

55. the ninth pentagonal number

56. the seventh hexagonal number

57. the tenth heptagonal number

58. the twelfth octagonal number

59. Observe the formulas given for H_n, Hp_n, and O_n, and use patterns and inductive reasoning to predict the formula for N_n, the nth **nonagonal** number. (A nonagon has nine sides.) Then use the fact that the sixth nonagonal number is 111 to further confirm your conjecture.

60. Use the result of **Exercise 59** to find the tenth nonagonal number.

Use inductive reasoning to answer each question.

61. If you add two consecutive triangular numbers, what kind of figurate number do you get?

62. If you add the squares of two consecutive triangular numbers, what kind of figurate number do you get?

63. Square a triangular number. Square the next triangular number. Subtract the smaller result from the larger. What kind of number do you get?

64. Choose a value of n greater than or equal to 2. Find T_{n-1}, multiply it by 3, and add n. What kind of figurate number do you get?

In an arithmetic sequence, the nth term a_n *is given by the formula*

$$a_n = a_1 + (n - 1)d,$$

where a_1 *is the first term and d is the common difference. Similarly, in a geometric sequence, the nth term is given by*

$$a_n = a_1 \cdot r^{n-1}.$$

Here r is the common ratio. Use these formulas to determine the indicated term in the given sequence.

65. The eleventh term of 2, 6, 10, 14, . . .

66. The sixteenth term of 5, 15, 25, 35, . . .

67. The 21st term of 19, 39, 59, 79, . . .

68. The 36th term of 8, 38, 68, 98, . . .

69. The 101st term of $\frac{1}{2}, 1, \frac{3}{2}, 2, \ldots$

70. The 151st term of 0.75, 1.50, 2.25, 3.00, . . .

71. The eleventh term of 2, 4, 8, 16, . . .

72. The ninth term of 1, 4, 16, 64, . . .

73. The 12th term of $1, \frac{1}{2}, \frac{1}{4}, \frac{1}{8}, \ldots$

74. The 10th term of $1, \frac{1}{3}, \frac{1}{9}, \frac{1}{27}, \ldots$

75. The 8th term of $40, 10, \frac{5}{2}, \frac{5}{8}, \ldots$

76. The 9th term of $10, 2, \frac{2}{5}, \frac{2}{25}, \ldots$

3 STRATEGIES FOR PROBLEM SOLVING

A General Problem-Solving Method • Using a Table or Chart • Working Backward • Using Trial and Error • Guessing and Checking • Considering a Similar, Simpler Problem • Drawing a Sketch • Using Common Sense

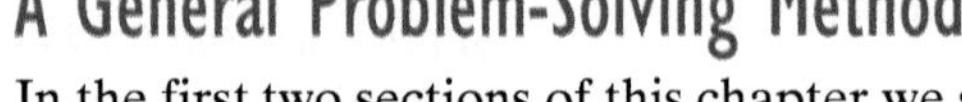

A General Problem-Solving Method

AP Images

George Polya, author of the classic *How to Solve It*, died at the age of 97 on September 7, 1985. A native of Budapest, Hungary, he was once asked why there were so many good mathematicians to come out of Hungary at the turn of the century. He theorized that it was because mathematics is the cheapest science. It does not require any expensive equipment, only pencil and paper. He authored or coauthored more than 250 papers in many languages, wrote a number of books, and was a brilliant lecturer and teacher. Yet, interestingly enough, he never learned to drive a car.

In the first two sections of this chapter we stressed the importance of pattern recognition and the use of inductive reasoning in solving problems. Probably the most famous study of problem-solving techniques was developed by George Polya (1888–1985), among whose many publications was the modern classic *How to Solve It*. In this book, Polya proposed a four-step method for problem solving.

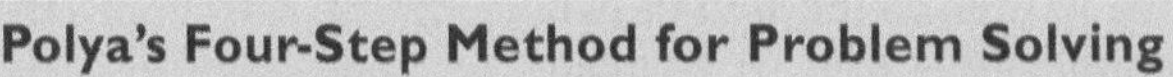

Polya's Four-Step Method for Problem Solving

Step 1 **Understand the problem.** You cannot solve a problem if you do not understand what you are asked to find. The problem must be read and analyzed carefully. You may need to read it several times. After you have done so, ask yourself, "What must I find?"

Step 2 **Devise a plan.** There are many ways to attack a problem. Decide what plan is appropriate for the particular problem you are solving.

Step 3 **Carry out the plan.** Once you know how to approach the problem, carry out your plan. You may run into "dead ends" and unforeseen roadblocks, but be persistent.

Step 4 **Look back and check.** Check your answer to see that it is reasonable. Does it satisfy the conditions of the problem? Have you answered all the questions the problem asks? Can you solve the problem a different way and come up with the same answer?

Granger Collection

Fibonacci (1170–1250) discovered the sequence named after him in a problem on rabbits. Fibonacci (son of Bonaccio) is one of several names for Leonardo of Pisa. His father managed a warehouse in present-day Bougie (or Bejaia), in Algeria. Thus it was that Leonardo Pisano studied with a Moorish teacher and learned the "Indian" numbers that the Moors and other Moslems brought with them in their westward drive.

Fibonacci wrote books on algebra, geometry, and trigonometry.

In Step 2 of Polya's problem-solving method, we are told to devise a plan. Here are some hints and strategies that may prove useful.

PROBLEM-SOLVING HINTS

- Make a table or a chart.
- Look for a pattern.
- Solve a similar, simpler problem.
- Draw a sketch.
- Use inductive reasoning.
- Write an equation and solve it.
- If a formula applies, use it.
- Work backward.
- Guess and check.
- Use trial and error.
- Use common sense.
- Look for a "catch" if an answer seems too obvious or impossible.

Using a Table or Chart

EXAMPLE 1 Solving Fibonacci's Rabbit Problem

A man put a pair of rabbits in a cage. During the first month the rabbits produced no offspring but each month thereafter produced one new pair of rabbits. If each new pair thus produced reproduces in the same manner, how many pairs of rabbits will there be at the end of 1 year? (This problem is a famous one in the history of mathematics and first appeared in *Liber Abaci,* a book written by the Italian mathematician Leonardo Pisano (also known as Fibonacci) in the year 1202.)

SOLUTION

Step 1 **Understand the problem.** We can reword the problem as follows:

How many pairs of rabbits will the man have at the end of one year if he starts with one pair, and they reproduce this way: During the first month of life, each pair produces no new rabbits, but each month thereafter each pair produces one new pair?

Step 2 **Devise a plan.** Because there is a definite pattern to how the rabbits will reproduce, we can construct **Table 2.**

Table 2

Month	Number of Pairs at Start	Number of New Pairs Produced	Number of Pairs at End of Month
1st			
2nd			
3rd			
4th			
5th			
6th			
7th			
8th			
9th			
10th			
11th			
12th			

The answer will go here.

Texas Instruments images used with permission/CBS/Paramount/Nationaly Council of Teachers of Mathematics

On January 23, 2005, the CBS television network presented the first episode of *NUMB3RS*, a show focusing on how mathematics is used in solving crimes. David Krumholtz plays Charlie Eppes, a brilliant mathematician who assists his FBI agent brother (Rob Morrow).

In the first-season episode "Sabotage" (2/25/2005), one of the agents admits that she "never saw how math relates to the real world," and Charlie uses the **Fibonacci sequence** and its relationship to nature to enlighten her.

The sequence shown in color in the table in **Example 1** is the Fibonacci sequence, mentioned in **Example 2(b)** of **Section 1.**

Step 3 **Carry out the plan.** At the start of the first month, there is only one pair of rabbits. No new pairs are produced during the first month, so there is $1 + 0 = 1$ pair present at the end of the first month. This pattern continues. In the table, we add the number in the first column of numbers to the number in the second column to get the number in the third.

Month	Number of Pairs at Start	+	Number of New Pairs Produced	=	Number of Pairs at End of Month	
1st	1		0		1	$1 + 0 = 1$
2nd	1		1		2	$1 + 1 = 2$
3rd	2		1		3	$2 + 1 = 3$
4th	3		2		5	•
5th	5		3		8	•
6th	8		5		13	•
7th	13		8		21	•
8th	21		13		34	•
9th	34		21		55	•
10th	55		34		89	•
11th	89		55		144	•
12th	144		89		233	$144 + 89 = 233$

The answer is the final entry.

There will be 233 pairs of rabbits at the end of one year.

Step 4 **Look back and check.** Go back and make sure that we have interpreted the problem correctly. Double-check the arithmetic. We have answered the question posed by the problem, so the problem is solved. ■■■

Working Backward

EXAMPLE 2 Determining a Wager at the Track

Ronnie Virgets goes to the racetrack with his buddies on a weekly basis. One week he tripled his money, but then lost \$12. He took his money back the next week, doubled it, but then lost \$40. The following week he tried again, taking his money back with him. He quadrupled it, and then played well enough to take that much home, a total of \$224. How much did he start with the first week?

SOLUTION

This problem asks us to find Ronnie's starting amount. Since we know his final amount, the method of working backward can be applied.

Because his final amount was \$224 and this represents four times the amount he started with on the third week, we *divide* \$224 by 4 to find that he started the third week with \$56. Before he lost \$40 the second week, he had this \$56 plus the \$40 he lost, giving him \$96. This represented double what he started with, so he started with \$96 *divided by* 2, or \$48, the second week. Repeating this process once more for the first week, before his \$12 loss he had

$$\$48 + \$12 = \$60,$$

which represents triple what he started with. Therefore, he started with

$$\$60 \div 3 = \$20. \quad \text{Answer}$$

To check, observe the following equations that depict winnings and losses.

First week: $(3 \times \$20) - \$12 = \$60 - \$12 = \$48$

Second week: $(2 \times \$48) - \$40 = \$96 - \$40 = \$56$

Third week: $(4 \times \$56) = \$224$ His final amount ■■■

Arteki/Shutterstock

Augustus De Morgan was an English mathematician and philosopher, who served as professor at the University of London. He wrote numerous books, one of which was *A Budget of Paradoxes*. His work in set theory and logic led to laws that bear his name. He died in the same year as Charles Babbage.

Using Trial and Error

Recall that $5^2 = 5 \cdot 5 = 25$. That is, 5 squared is 25. Thus, 25 is called a **perfect square.**

$$1, \quad 4, \quad 9, \quad 16, \quad 25, \quad 36, \quad \text{and so on}$$ Perfect squares

EXAMPLE 3 Finding Augustus De Morgan's Birth Year

The mathematician Augustus De Morgan lived in the nineteenth century. He made the following statement: "I was x years old in the year x^2." In what year was he born?

SOLUTION

We must find the year of De Morgan's birth. The problem tells us that he lived in the nineteenth century, which is another way of saying that he lived during the 1800s. One year of his life was a perfect square, so we must find a number between 1800 and 1900 that is a perfect square. Use trial and error.

$$42^2 = 42 \cdot 42 = 1764$$
$$43^2 = 43 \cdot 43 = 1849$$ 1849 is between 1800 and 1900.
$$44^2 = 44 \cdot 44 = 1936$$

The only natural number whose square is between 1800 and 1900 is 43, since $43^2 = 1849$. Therefore, De Morgan was 43 years old in 1849. The final step in solving the problem is to subtract 43 from 1849 to find the year of his birth.

$$1849 - 43 = 1806$$ He was born in 1806.

Although the following check may seem unorthodox, it works: Look up De Morgan's birth date in a book dealing with mathematics history, such as *An Introduction to the History of Mathematics*, Sixth Edition, by Howard W. Eves.

Guessing and Checking

As mentioned above, $5^2 = 25$. The inverse (opposite) of squaring a number is called taking the **square root.** We indicate the positive square root using a **radical symbol** $\sqrt{}$. Thus, $\sqrt{25} = 5$. Also,

$$\sqrt{4} = 2, \quad \sqrt{9} = 3, \quad \sqrt{16} = 4, \quad \text{and so on.}$$ Square roots

The next problem deals with a square root and dates back to Hindu mathematics, circa 850.

EXAMPLE 4 Finding the Number of Camels

One-fourth of a herd of camels was seen in the forest; twice the square root of that herd had gone to the mountain slopes; and 3 times 5 camels remained on the riverbank. What is the numerical measure of that herd of camels?

SOLUTION

The numerical measure of a herd of camels must be a counting number. Because the problem mentions "one-fourth of a herd" and "the square root of that herd," the number of camels must be both a multiple of 4 and a perfect square, so that only whole numbers are used. The least counting number that satisfies both conditions is 4. We write an equation where x represents the numerical measure of the herd, and then substitute 4 for x to see if it is a solution.

One-fourth of the herd	+	Twice the square root of that herd	+	3 times 5 camels	=	The numerical measure of the herd.
$\frac{1}{4}x$	+	$2\sqrt{x}$	+	$3 \cdot 5$	=	x

$$\frac{1}{4}(4) + 2\sqrt{4} + 3 \cdot 5 = 4 \qquad \text{Let } x = 4.$$

$$1 + 4 + 15 \stackrel{?}{=} 4 \qquad \sqrt{4} = 2$$

$$20 \neq 4$$

Because 4 is not the solution, try 16, the next perfect square that is a multiple of 4.

$$\frac{1}{4}(16) + 2\sqrt{16} + 3 \cdot 5 = 16 \qquad \text{Let } x = 16.$$

$$4 + 8 + 15 \stackrel{?}{=} 16 \qquad \sqrt{16} = 4$$

$$27 \neq 16$$

Because 16 is not a solution, try 36.

$$\frac{1}{4}(36) + 2\sqrt{36} + 3 \cdot 5 = 36 \qquad \text{Let } x = 36.$$

$$9 + 12 + 15 \stackrel{?}{=} 36 \qquad \sqrt{36} = 6$$

$$36 = 36$$

Thus, 36 is the numerical measure of the herd. *Check*: "One-fourth of 36, plus twice the square root of 36, plus 3 times 5" gives 9 plus 12 plus 15, which equals 36. ▮▮▮

Considering a Similar, Simpler Problem

EXAMPLE 5 Finding the Units Digit of a Power

The digit farthest to the right in a counting number is called the *ones* or *units* digit, because it tells how many ones are contained in the number when grouping by tens is considered. What is the ones (or units) digit in 2^{4000}?

SOLUTION

Recall that 2^{4000} means that 2 is used as a factor 4000 times.

$$2^{4000} = \underbrace{2 \times 2 \times 2 \times \ldots \times 2}_{4000 \text{ factors}}$$

To answer the question, we examine some smaller powers of 2 and then look for a pattern. We start with the exponent 1 and look at the first twelve powers of 2.

$2^1 = 2$	$2^5 = 32$	$2^9 = 512$
$2^2 = 4$	$2^6 = 64$	$2^{10} = 1024$
$2^3 = 8$	$2^7 = 128$	$2^{11} = 2048$
$2^4 = 16$	$2^8 = 256$	$2^{12} = 4096$

Notice that in any one of the four rows above, the ones digit is the same all the way across the row. The final row, which contains the exponents 4, 8, and 12, has the ones digit 6. Each of these exponents is divisible by 4, and because 4000 is divisible by 4, we can use inductive reasoning to predict that the units digit in 2^{4000} is 6.

(*Note*: The units digit for any other power can be found if we divide the exponent by 4 and consider the remainder. Then compare the result to the list of powers above. For example, to find the units digit of 2^{543}, divide 543 by 4 to get a quotient of 135 and a remainder of 3. The units digit is the same as that of 2^3, which is 8.) ▮▮▮

Krista Mackey/iStockphoto

The 1952 film *Hans Christian Andersen* features Danny Kaye as the Danish writer of fairy tales. In a scene outside a schoolhouse, he sings a song to an inchworm: "Inchworm, inchworm, measuring the marigolds, you and your arithmetic, you'll probably go far." Following the scene, students in the schoolhouse are heard singing arithmetic facts:

Two and two are four,
Four and four are eight,
Eight and eight are sixteen,
Sixteen and sixteen are thirty-two.

Their answers are all **powers of 2.**

Drawing a Sketch

EXAMPLE 6 Connecting the Dots

Figure 6

An array of nine dots is arranged in a 3×3 square, as shown in **Figure 6**. Is it possible to join the dots with exactly four straight line segments if you are not allowed to pick up your pencil from the paper and may not trace over a segment that has already been drawn? If so, show how.

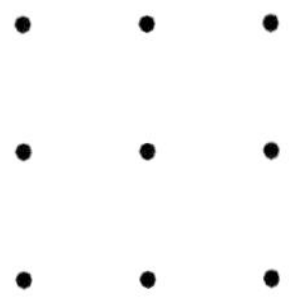

SOLUTION

Figure 7 shows three attempts. In each case, something is wrong. In the first sketch, one dot is not joined. In the second, the figure cannot be drawn without picking up your pencil from the paper or tracing over a line that has already been drawn. In the third figure, all dots have been joined, but you have used five line segments as well as retraced over the figure.

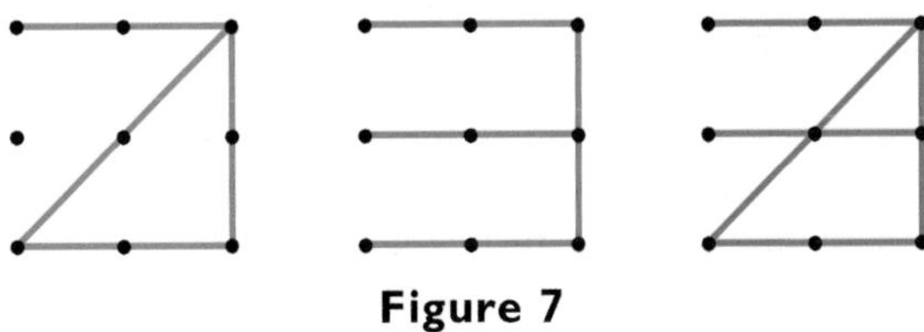

Figure 7

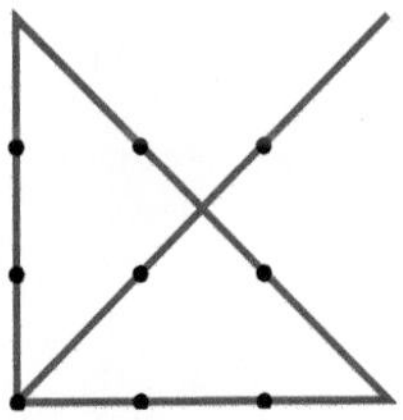

Figure 8

The conditions of the problem can be satisfied, as shown in **Figure 8**. We "went outside of the box," which was not prohibited by the conditions of the problem. This is an example of creative thinking—we used a strategy that often is not considered at first.

Using Common Sense

PROBLEM-SOLVING HINTS Some problems involve a "catch." They seem too easy or perhaps impossible at first because we tend to overlook an obvious situation. Look carefully at the use of language in such problems. And, of course, never forget to use common sense.

In *Die Hard: With a Vengeance* (see the **Chapter Opener**), Simon taunts McClane with a riddle that has its origins in Egyptian mathematics.

As I was going to St. Ives,
I met a man with seven wives.
Every wife had seven sacks,
Every sack had seven cats,
Every cat had seven kittens.
Kittens, cats, sacks, and wives,
How many were going to St. Ives?

"My phone number is 555 and the answer. Call me in 30 seconds or die."

By calling 555-0001, he was able to contact Simon. Do you see why 1 is the answer to this riddle? (Use **common sense.**)

EXAMPLE 7 Determining Coin Denominations

Two currently minted United States coins together have a total value of \$1.05. One is not a dollar. What are the two coins?

SOLUTION

Our initial reaction might be, "The only way to have two such coins with a total of \$1.05 is to have a nickel and a dollar, but the problem says that one of them is not a dollar." This statement is indeed true. What we must realize here is that the one that is not a dollar is the nickel, and the *other* coin is a dollar! So the two coins are a dollar and a nickel.

3 EXERCISES

One of the most popular features in the journal Mathematics Teacher, *published by the National Council of Teachers of Mathematics, is the monthly calendar. It provides an interesting, unusual, or challenging problem for each day of the month. Problems are contributed by the editors of the journal, teachers, and students, and the contributors are cited in each issue. Some of these exercises are problems chosen from these calendars over the past years, with the day, month, and year for the problem indicated. The authors want to thank the many contributors for permission to use these problems.*

Use the various problem-solving strategies to solve each problem. In many cases there is more than one possible approach, so be creative.

1. ***Class Members*** A classroom contains an equal number of boys and girls. If 8 girls leave, twice as many boys as girls remain. What was the original number of students present? (May 24, 2008)

2. ***Give Me a Digit*** Given a two-digit number, make a three-digit number by putting a 6 as the right-most digit. Then add 6 to the resulting three-digit number and remove the right-most digit to obtain another two digit number. If the result is 76, what is the original two-digit number? (October 18, 2009)

3. ***Missing Digit*** Look for a pattern and find the missing digit x.

$$\begin{array}{cccc} 3 & 2 & 4 & 8 \\ 7 & 2 & 1 & 3 \\ 8 & 4 & x & 5 \\ 4 & 3 & 6 & 9 \end{array}$$

(February 14, 2009)

4. ***Abundancy*** An integer $n > 1$ is **abundant** if the sum of its proper divisors (positive integer divisors smaller than n) is greater than n. Find the smallest abundant integer. (November 27, 2009)

5. ***Cross-Country Competition*** The schools in an athletic conference compete in a cross-country meet to which each school sends three participants. Erin, Katelyn, and Iliana are the three representatives from one school. Erin finished the race in the middle position; Katelyn finished after Erin, in the 19th position; and Iliana finished 28th. How many schools took part in the race? (May 27, 2008)

Webphotographer/iStockphoto

6. ***Gone Fishing*** Four friends go fishing one day and bring home a total of 11 fish. If each person caught at least 1 fish, then which of the following *must* be true?

A. One person caught exactly 2 fish.

B. One person caught exactly 3 fish.

C. One person caught fewer than 3 fish.

D. One person caught more than 3 fish.

E. Two people each caught more than 1 fish.

(May 24, 2008)

Digital Vision/Thinkstock

7. ***Cutting a Square in Half*** In how many ways can a single straight line cut a square in half? (October 2, 2008)

8. ***You Lie!*** Max, Sam, and Brett were playing basketball. One of them broke a window, and the other two saw him break it. Max said, "I am innocent." Sam said, "Max and I are both innocent." Brett said, "Max and Sam are both innocent." If only one of them is telling the truth, who broke the window? (September 21, 2008)

9. ***Bookworm Snack*** A 26-volume encyclopedia (one for each letter) is placed on a bookshelf in alphabetical order from left to right. Each volume is 2 inches thick, including the front and back covers. Each cover is $\frac{1}{4}$ inch thick. A bookworm eats straight through the encyclopedia, beginning inside the front cover of volume A and ending after eating through the back cover of volume Z. How many inches of book did the bookworm eat? (November 12, 2008)

10. ***Pick a Card, Any Card*** Three face cards from an ordinary deck of playing cards lie facedown in a horizontal row and are arranged such that immediately to the right of a king is a queen or two queens, immediately to the left of a queen is a queen or two queens, immediately to the left of a heart is a spade or two spades, and immediately to the right of a spade is a spade or two spades. Name the three cards in order. (April 23, 2008)

11. ***Catwoman's Cats*** If you ask Batman's nemesis, Catwoman, how many cats she has, she answers with a riddle: "Five-sixths of my cats plus seven." How many cats does Catwoman have? (April 20, 2003)

12. ***Pencil Collection*** Bob gave four-fifths of his pencils to Barbara, then he gave two-thirds of the remaining pencils to Bonnie. If he ended up with ten pencils for himself, with how many did he start? (October 12, 2003)

13. ***Adding Gasoline*** The gasoline gauge on a van initially read $\frac{1}{8}$ full. When 15 gallons were added to the tank, the gauge read $\frac{3}{4}$ full. How many more gallons are needed to fill the tank? (November 25, 2004)

14. ***Gasoline Tank Capacity*** When 6 gallons of gasoline are put into a car's tank, the indicator goes from $\frac{1}{4}$ of a tank to $\frac{5}{8}$. What is the total capacity of the gasoline tank? (February 21, 2004)

15. ***Number Pattern*** What is the relationship between the rows of numbers?

18, 38, 24, 46, 42
8, 24, 8, 24, 8

(May 26, 2005)

16. ***Unknown Number*** The number in an unshaded square is obtained by adding the numbers connected with it from the row above. (The 11 is one such number.) What is the value of x? (December 22, 2008)

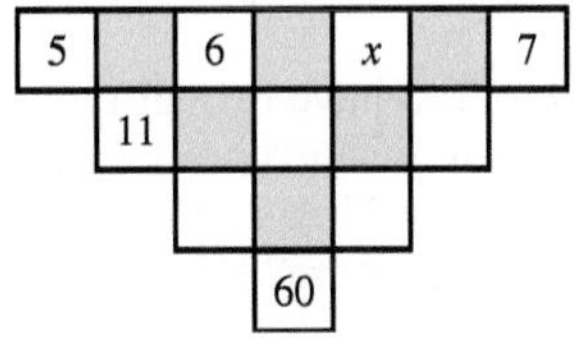

17. ***Locking Boxes*** You and I each have one lock and a corresponding key. I want to mail you a box with a ring in it, but any box that is not locked will be emptied before it reaches its recipient. How can I safely send you the ring? (Note that you and I each have keys to our own lock but not to the other lock.) (May 4, 2004)

18. ***Woodchuck Chucking Wood*** Nine woodchucks can chuck eight pieces of wood in 3 hours. How much wood can a woodchuck chuck in 1 hour? (May 24, 2004)

19. ***Number in a Sequence*** In the sequence 16, 80, 48, 64, A, B, C, D, each term beyond the second term is the arithmetic mean (average) of the two previous terms. What is the value of D? (April 26, 2004)

20. ***Unknown Number*** Cindy was asked by her teacher to subtract 3 from a certain number and then divide the result by 9. Instead, she subtracted 9 and then divided the result by 3, giving an answer of 43. What would her answer have been if she had worked the problem correctly? (September 3, 2004)

21. ***Labeling Boxes*** You are working in a store that has been very careless with the stock. Three boxes of socks are each incorrectly labeled. The labels say *red socks, green socks*, and *red and green socks*. How can you relabel the boxes correctly by taking only one sock out of one box, without looking inside the boxes? (October 22, 2001)

22. ***Vertical Symmetry in States' Names*** (If a vertical line is drawn through the center of a figure and the left and right sides are reflections of each other across this line, the figure is said to have vertical symmetry.) When spelled with all capital letters, each letter in HAWAII has vertical symmetry. Find the name of a state whose letters all have vertical and horizontal symmetry. (September 11, 2001)

23. ***Sum of Hidden Dots on Dice*** Three dice with faces numbered 1 through 6 are stacked as shown. Seven of the eighteen faces are visible, leaving eleven faces hidden on the back, on the bottom, and between dice. The total number of dots not visible in this view is _____.

A. 21
B. 22
C. 31
D. 41
E. 53

(September 17, 2001)

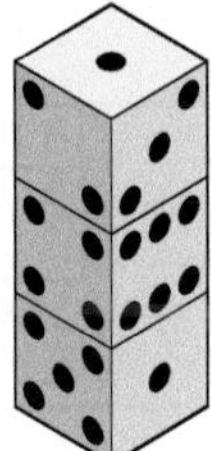

24. ***Mr. Green's Age*** At his birthday party, Mr. Green would not directly tell how old he was. He said, "If you add the year of my birth to this year, subtract the year of my tenth birthday and the year of my fiftieth birthday, and then add my present age, the result is eighty." How old was Mr. Green? (December 14, 1997)

25. ***Unfolding and Folding a Box*** An unfolded box is shown below.

Which figure shows the box folded up? (November 7, 2001)

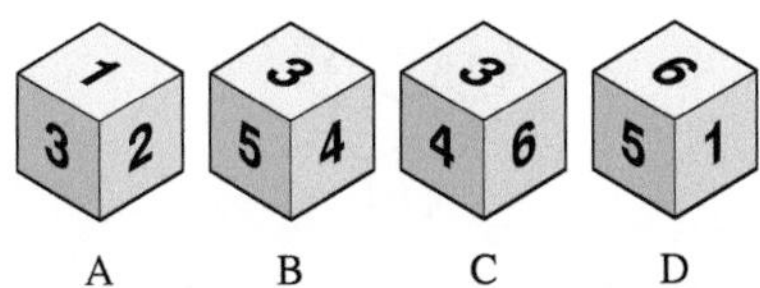

26. ***Age of the Bus Driver*** Today is your first day driving a city bus. When you leave downtown, you have twenty-three passengers. At the first stop, three people exit and five people get on the bus. At the second stop, eleven people exit and eight people get on the bus. At the third stop, five people exit and ten people get on. How old is the bus driver? (April 1, 2002)

27. ***Matching Triangles and Squares*** How can you connect each square with the triangle that has the same number? Lines cannot cross, enter a square or triangle, or go outside the diagram. (October 15, 1999)

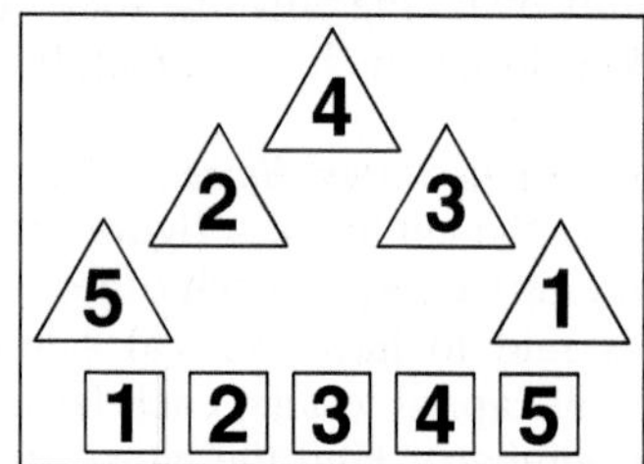

28. ***Squared Rectangle*** A **squared rectangle,** shown here, is a rectangle whose interior can be completely divided into two or more squares. The number written inside a square is the length of a side of that square. Compute the area of this squared rectangle. (September 22, 2009)

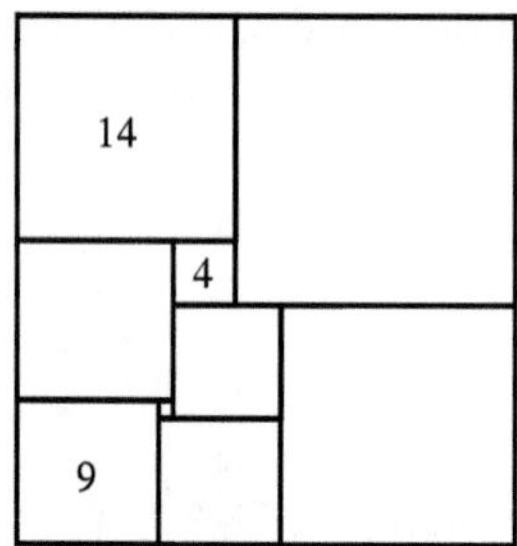

29. ***Forming Perfect Square Sums*** How must one place the integers from 1 to 15 in each of the spaces below in such a way that no number is repeated and the sum of the numbers in any two consecutive spaces is a perfect square? (November 11, 2001)

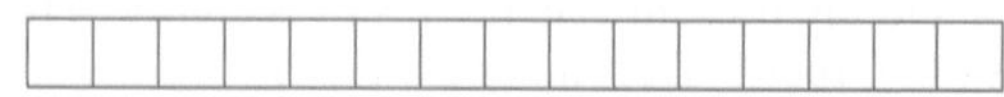

30. ***How Old?*** Pat and Chris have the same birthday. Pat is twice as old as Chris was when Pat was as old as Chris is now. If Pat is now 24 years old, how old is Chris? (December 3, 2001)

31. ***Difference Triangle*** Balls numbered 1 through 6 are arranged in a **difference triangle.** Note that in any row, the difference between the larger and the smaller of two successive balls is the number of the ball that appears below them. Arrange balls numbered 1 through 10 in a difference triangle. (May 6, 1998)

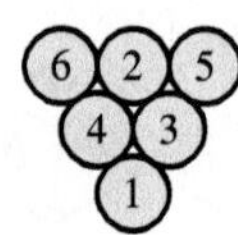

32. ***Clock Face*** By drawing two straight lines, divide the face of a clock into three regions such that the numbers in the regions have the same total. (October 28, 1998)

33. ***Alphametric*** If a, b, and c are digits for which

$$\begin{array}{r} 7\ a\ 2 \\ -4\ 8\ b \\ \hline c\ 7\ 3, \end{array}$$

then $a + b + c =$ _____.

A. 14 **B.** 15 **C.** 16 **D.** 17 **E.** 18

(September 22, 1999)

34. ***Perfect Square*** Only one of these numbers is a perfect square. Which one is it? (October 8, 1997)

329476 389372 964328
326047 724203

35. ***Sleeping on the Way to Grandma's House*** While traveling to his grandmother's for Christmas, George fell asleep halfway through the journey. When he awoke, he still had to travel half the distance that he had traveled while sleeping. For what part of the entire journey had he been asleep? (December 25, 1998)

36. ***Counting Puzzle (Rectangles)*** How many rectangles of any size are in the figure shown? (September 10, 2001)

37. ***Buckets of Water*** You have brought two unmarked buckets to a stream. The buckets hold 7 gallons and 3 gallons of water, respectively. How can you obtain exactly 5 gallons of water to take home? (October 19, 1997)

38. ***Multiples of 9*** The first two of three consecutive multiples of 9 sum to 2511. What are the numbers? (January 4, 2010)

39. ***Counting Puzzle (Rectangles)*** How many rectangles are in the figure? (March 27, 1997)

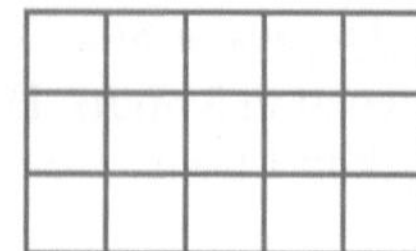

40. ***Digit Puzzle*** Place each of the digits 1, 2, 3, 4, 5, 6, 7, and 8 in separate boxes so that boxes that share common corners do not contain successive digits. (November 29, 1997)

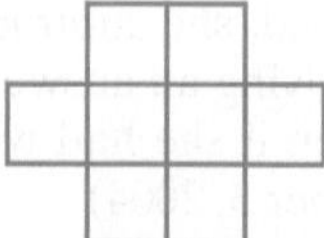

41. ***Palindromic Number*** (*Note:* A **palindromic number** is a number whose digits read the same left to right as right to left. For example, 383, 12321, and 9876789 are palindromic.) The odometer of the family car read 15951 when the driver noticed that the number was palindromic. "Curious," said the driver to herself. "It will be a long time before that happens again." But 2 hours later, the odometer showed a new palindromic number. (*Author's note:* Assume it was the next possible one.) How fast was the car driving in those 2 hours? (December 26, 1998)

42. ***How Much Is That Doggie in the Window?*** A man wishes to sell a puppy for \$11. A customer who wants to buy it has only foreign currency. The exchange rate for the foreign currency is as follows: 11 round coins = \$15, 11 square coins = \$16, 11 triangular coins = \$17. How many of each coin should the customer pay? (April 20, 2008)

Photos.com/Thinkstock

43. ***Final Digits of a Power of 7*** What are the final two digits of 7^{1997}? (November 29, 1997)

44. ***Consecutive Whole Numbers*** The sum of nine consecutive whole numbers is 123,456,789,987,654,321. What is the difference between the largest and smallest of these numbers? (October 4, 2008)

45. ***Summing the Digits*** When $10^{50} - 50$ is expressed as a single whole number, what is the sum of its digits? (April 7, 2008)

46. ***Units Digit of a Power of 3*** If you raise 3 to the 324th power, what is the units digit of the result?

47. ***Units Digit of a Power of 7*** What is the units digit in 7^{491}?

48. ***Frog Climbing up a Well*** A frog is at the bottom of a 20-foot well. Each day it crawls up 4 feet, but each night it slips back 3 feet. After how many days will the frog reach the top of the well?

Andrii Muzyka/Shutterstock

49. ***Going Postal*** Joanie wants to mail a package that requires \$1.53 in postage. If she has only 5-cent and 8-cent stamps, what is the smallest number of stamps she could use that would total exactly \$1.53? (August 20, 2008)

50. ***Money Spent at a Bazaar*** Christine O'Brien bought a book for \$10 and then spent half her remaining money on a train ticket. She then bought lunch for \$4 and spent half her remaining money at a bazaar. She left the bazaar with \$8. How much money did she start with?

51. ***Matching Socks*** A drawer contains 20 black socks and 20 white socks. If the light is off and you reach into the drawer to get your socks, what is the minimum number of socks you must pull out in order to be sure that you have a matching pair?

52. ***Counting Puzzle (Squares)*** How many squares are in the figure?

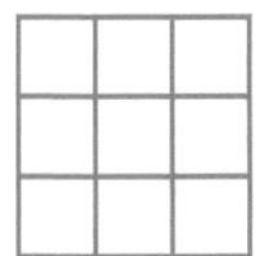

53. ***Counting Puzzle (Triangles)*** How many triangles are in the figure?

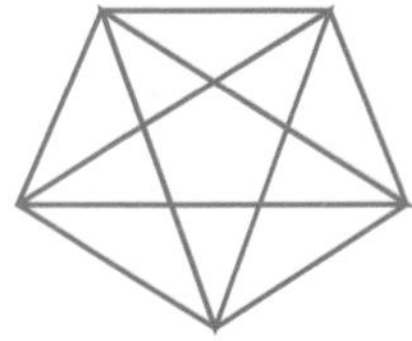

54. ***Fun with Fractions*** A strip of paper is $\frac{2}{3}$ meter long. Can a strip exactly $\frac{1}{2}$ meter long be made without the use of a ruler? If so, how? (September 8, 2008)

55. ***Perfect Number*** A **perfect number** is a counting number that is equal to the sum of all its counting number divisors except itself. For example, 28 is a perfect number because its divisors other than itself are 1, 2, 4, 7, and 14, and $1 + 2 + 4 + 7 + 14 = 28$. What is the least perfect number?

56. ***Naming Children*** Becky's mother has three daughters. She named her first daughter Penny and her second daughter Nichole. What did she name her third daughter?

57. ***Growth of a Lily Pad*** A lily pad grows so that each day it doubles its size. On the twentieth day of its life, it completely covers a pond. On what day was the pond half covered?

58. ***Interesting Property of a Sentence*** Comment on an interesting property of this sentence: "A man, a plan, a canal, Panama." (*Hint:* See **Exercise 41.**)

59. ***High School Graduation Year of Author*** One of the authors of this book graduated from high school in the year that satisfies these conditions: (1) The sum of the digits is 23; (2) The hundreds digit is 3 more than the tens digit; (3) No digit is an 8. In what year did he graduate?

60. ***Analyzing Units*** A day is divided into 24 hours. Each hour has 60 minutes, and each minute has 60 seconds. In another system of measurement, each day has 20 naps and each nap has 40 winks. How many seconds are in a wink? (November 10, 2008)

61. ***Adam and Eve's Assets*** Eve said to Adam, "If you give me one dollar, then we will have the same amount of money." Adam then replied, "Eve, if you give me one dollar, I will have double the amount of money you are left with." How much does each have?

62. ***Missing Digits Puzzle*** In the addition problem below, some digits are missing as indicated by the blanks. If the problem is done correctly, what is the sum of the missing digits?

$$\begin{array}{rcccc} & \_ & 3 & 5 \\ & 8 & \_ & 6 \\ + & 1 & 4 & \_ \\ \hline \_ & 4 & 0 & 8 \end{array}$$

63. ***Missing Digits Puzzle*** Fill in the blanks so that the multiplication problem below uses all digits 0, 1, 2, 3, ..., 9 exactly once, and is correctly worked.

$$\begin{array}{rrrrr} & & \_ & 0 & 2 \\ \times & & & 3 & \_ \\ \hline \_ & 5, & \_ & \_ & \_ \end{array}$$

64. ***Magic Square*** A **magic square** is a square array of numbers that has the property that the sum of the numbers in any row, column, or diagonal is the same. Fill in the square below so that it becomes a magic square, and all digits 1, 2, 3, . . . , 9 are used exactly once.

6		8
	5	
		4

65. ***Magic Square*** Refer to **Exercise 64.** Complete the magic square below so that all counting numbers 1, 2, 3, . . . , 16 are used exactly once, and the sum in each row, column, or diagonal is 34.

6			9
	15		14
11		10	
16		13	

66. ***Decimal Digit*** What is the 100th digit in the decimal representation for $\frac{1}{7}$?

67. ***Pitches in a Baseball Game*** What is the minimum number of pitches that a baseball player who pitches a complete game can make in a regulation 9-inning baseball game?

68. ***Weighing Coins*** You have eight coins. Seven are genuine and one is a fake, which weighs a little less than the other seven. You have a balance scale, which you may use only three times. Tell how to locate the bad coin in three weighings. (Then show how to detect the bad coin in only *two* weighings.)

69. ***Geometry Puzzle*** When the diagram shown is folded to form a cube, what letter is opposite the face marked Z?

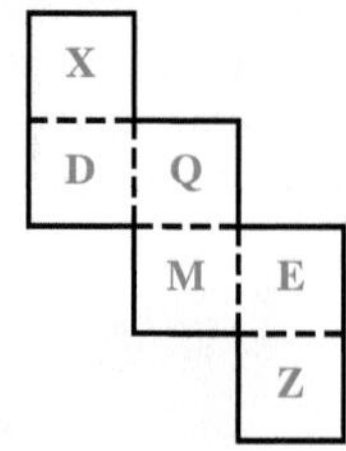

70. ***Number Pattern*** If the pattern below continues, where would the number 289 appear?

$$\begin{array}{ccccc} & & 1 & & \\ & 3 & & 5 & \\ 7 & & 9 & & 11 \end{array}$$

(November 11, 2008)

71. ***Geometry Puzzle*** Draw the following figure without picking up your pencil from the paper and without tracing over a line you have already drawn.

72. ***Geometry Puzzle*** Repeat **Exercise 71** for this figure.

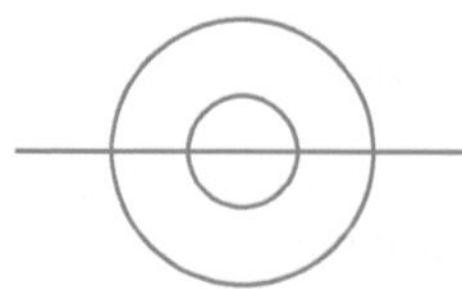

73. ***Paying for a Mint*** Brian Altobello has an unlimited number of cents (pennies), nickels, and dimes. In how many different ways can he pay 15¢ for a chocolate mint? (For example, one way is 1 dime and 5 pennies.)

74. ***Books on a Shelf*** Volumes 1 and 2 of *The Complete Works of Wally Smart* are standing in numerical order from left to right on your bookshelf. Volume 1 has 450 pages and Volume 2 has 475 pages. Excluding the covers, how many pages are between page 1 of Volume 1 and page 475 of Volume 2?

75. ***Area and Perimeter*** Triangle ABC has sides 10, 24, and 26 cm long. A rectangle that has an area equal to that of the triangle is 3 cm wide. Find the perimeter of the rectangle. (November 13, 2008)

76. ***Teenager's Age*** A teenager's age increased by 2 gives a perfect square. Her age decreased by 10 gives the square root of that perfect square. She is 5 years older than her brother. How old is her brother?

77. ***Ages*** James, Dan, Jessica, and Cathy form a pair of married couples. Their ages are 36, 31, 30, and 29. Jessica is married to the oldest person in the group. James is older than Jessica but younger than Cathy. Who is married to whom, and what are their ages?

78. ***Making Change*** In how many different ways can you make change for a half dollar using currently minted U.S. coins, if cents (pennies) are not allowed?

79. ***Days in a Month*** Some months have 30 days and some have 31 days. How many months have 28 days?

80. ***Dirt in a Hole*** How much dirt is there in a cubical hole, 6 feet on each side?

81. ***Final Digit*** What is the last digit of $49{,}327^{1783}$? (April 11, 2009)

82. ***Missing Digit*** Find the missing digit, x, in the product given by

$$(172195)(572167) = 985242x6565.$$

(May 3, 2009)

83. ***Geometry Puzzle*** What is the maximum number of small squares in which we may place crosses (×) and not have any row, column, or diagonal completely filled with crosses? Illustrate your answer.

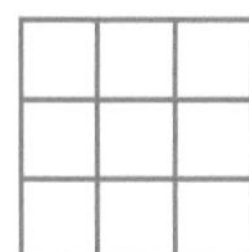

84. ***Making Change*** Webster has some pennies, dimes, and quarters in his pocket. When Josefa asks him for change for a dollar, Webster discovers that he cannot make the change exactly. What is the largest possible total value of the coins in his pocket? (October 5, 2009)

85. ***Fibonacci Property*** Refer to **Example 1**, and observe the sequence of numbers in color. Choose any four successive terms. Multiply the first one chosen by the fourth. Then multiply the two middle terms. Repeat this process. What do you notice when the two products are compared?

4 CALCULATING, ESTIMATING, AND READING GRAPHS

Calculation • Estimation • Interpretation of Graphs

Karl Pawlewicz/Sharp Electronics

The photograph shows the **Sharp EL-2139 HB,** a typical four-function calculator.

Since the introduction of hand-held calculators in the early 1970s, the methods of everyday arithmetic have been drastically altered. One of the first consumer models available was the Texas Instruments SR-10, which sold for nearly $150 in 1973. It could perform the four operations of arithmetic and take square roots, but could do very little more.

Calculation

The search for easier ways to calculate and compute has culminated in the development of hand-held calculators and computers. For the general population, a calculator that performs the operations of arithmetic and a few other functions is sufficient. These are known as **four-function calculators.** Students who take higher mathematics courses (engineers, for example) usually need the added power of **scientific calculators. Graphing calculators,** which actually plot graphs on small screens, are also available. ***Always refer to your owner's manual if you need assistance in performing an operation with your calculator. If you need further help, ask your instructor or another student who is using the same model.***

Current models of calculators differ from earlier versions in that they can display both the information the user inputs and the result generated on the same screen. In this way, the user can verify that the information entered into the calculator is correct. Although it is not necessary to have a graphing calculator to study the material presented in this text, we occasionally include graphing calculator screens to support results obtained or to provide supplemental information.*

*Because they are the most popular models of graphing calculators, we include screens similar to those generated by TI-83 Plus and TI-84 Plus models from Texas Instruments.

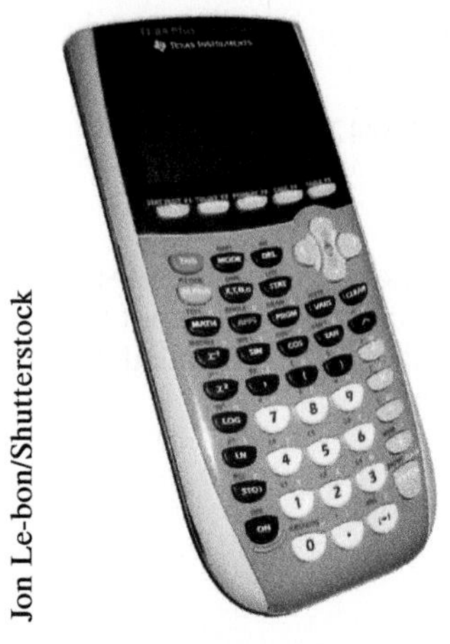

Jon Le-bon/Shutterstock

The popular **TI-84 Plus** graphing calculator is shown here.

The screens that follow illustrate some common entries and operations.

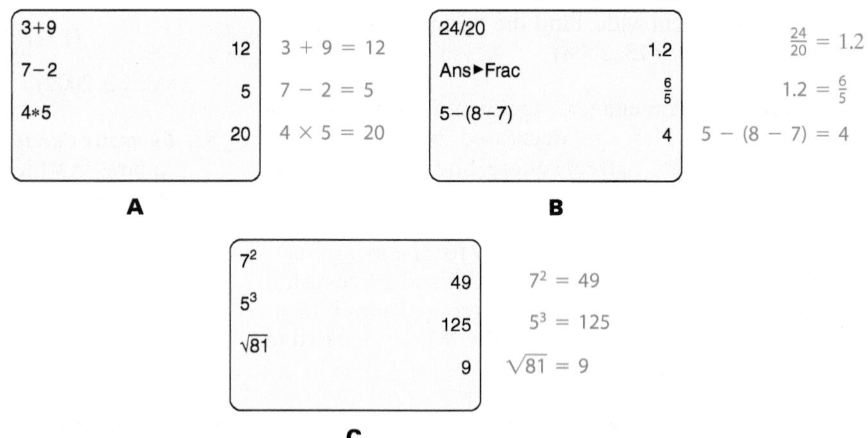

Screen A illustrates how two numbers can be added, subtracted, or multiplied. Screen B shows how two numbers can be divided, how the decimal quotient (stored in the memory cell Ans) can be converted into a fraction, and how parentheses can be used in a computation. Screen C shows how a number can be squared, how it can be cubed, and how its square root can be taken.

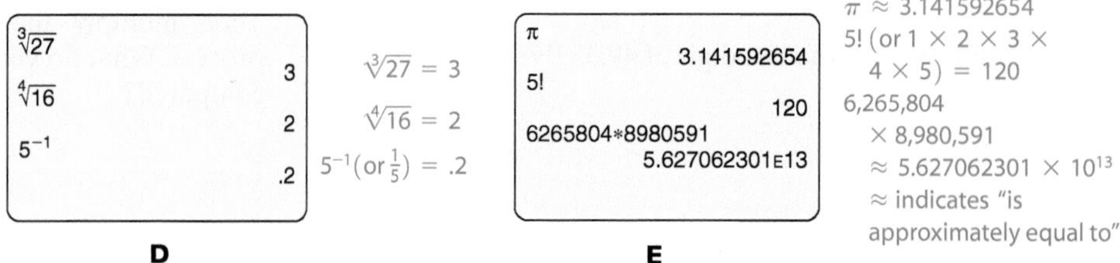

Screen D shows how other roots (cube root and fourth root) can be found, and how the reciprocal of a number can be found using -1 as an exponent. Screen E shows how π can be accessed with its own special key, how a **factorial** (as indicated by !) can be found and how a result might be displayed in **scientific notation.** (The "E13" following 5.627062301 means that this number is multiplied by 10^{13}. This answer is still only an approximation, because the product $6{,}265{,}804 \times 8{,}980{,}591$ contains more digits than the calculator can display.)

Estimation

Although calculators can make life easier when it comes to computations, many times we need only estimate an answer to a problem, and in these cases a calculator may not be necessary or appropriate.

EXAMPLE 1 Estimating an Appropriate Number of Birdhouses

A birdhouse for swallows can accommodate up to 8 nests. How many birdhouses would be necessary to accommodate 58 nests?

Beth Anderson/Pearson

SOLUTION

If we divide 58 by 8 either by hand or with a calculator, we get 7.25. Can this possibly be the desired number? Of course not, because we cannot consider fractions of birdhouses. Do we need 7 or 8 birdhouses? To provide nesting space for the nests left over after the 7 birdhouses (as indicated by the decimal fraction), we should plan to use 8 birdhouses. In this problem, we must round our answer *up* to the next counting number. ∎

EXAMPLE 2 Approximating Average Number of Yards per Carry

In 2009, Cedric Benson carried the football 301 times for 1251 yards (*Source:* www.nfl.com). Approximate his average number of yards per carry that year.

SOLUTION

Because we are are asked only to find Cedric's approximate average, we can say that he carried about 300 times for about 1200 yards, and his average was about $\frac{1200}{300} = 4$ yards per carry. (A calculator shows that his average to the nearest tenth was 4.2 yards per carry. Verify this.) ∎∎∎

EXAMPLE 3 Comparing Proportions of Workers by Age Groups

In a recent year, there were approximately 127,000 males in the 25–29-year age bracket working on farms. This represented part of the total of 238,000 farm workers in that age bracket. Of the 331,000 farm workers in the 40–44-year age bracket, 160,000 were males. Without using a calculator, determine which age bracket had a larger proportion of males.

SOLUTION

Think in terms of thousands instead of dealing with all the zeros. First, we analyze the age bracket 25–29 years. Because there were a total of 238 thousand workers, of which 127 thousand were males, there were

$$238 - 127 = 111 \text{ thousand female workers.}$$ More than half were males.

In the 40–44-year age bracket, of the 331 thousand workers, there were 160 thousand males, giving

$$331 - 160 = 171 \text{ thousand female workers.}$$ Fewer than half were males.

The 25–29-year age bracket had the larger proportion of males. ∎∎∎

Interpretation of Graphs

In a **circle graph,** or **pie chart,** a circle is used to indicate the total of all the data categories represented. The circle is divided into sectors, or wedges (like pieces of a pie), whose sizes show the relative magnitudes of the categories. The sum of all the fractional parts must be 1 (for 1 whole circle).

EXAMPLE 4 Interpreting Information in a Circle Graph

Use the circle graph in **Figure 9** to determine how much of the amount spent for a \$3.50 gallon of gasoline in California goes to refinery margin and to crude oil cost.

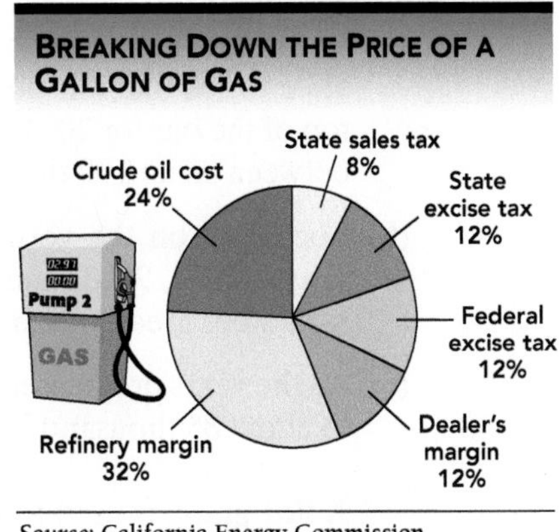

Source: California Energy Commission.

Figure 9

SOLUTION

The sectors in the circle graph in **Figure 9** are sized to match how the price is divided. For example, the greatest portion of the price (32%) goes to the refinery, while the least portion (8%) goes for state sales tax. As expected, the percents total 100%. The price of gasoline is \$3.50 per gallon.

$$\text{Refinery margin: } \$3.50 \times \underbrace{0.32}_{\text{32\% converted to a decimal}} = \$1.12$$

$$\text{Crude oil cost: } \$3.50 \times \underbrace{0.24}_{\text{24\% converted to a decimal}} = \$0.84$$

A **bar graph** is used to show comparisons. It consists of a series of bars (or simulations of bars) arranged either vertically or horizontally. In a bar graph, values from two categories are paired with each other (for example, years with sales).

EXAMPLE 5 Interpreting Information in a Bar Graph

The bar graph in **Figure 10** shows U.S. sales of motor scooters, which have gained popularity due to their fuel efficiency. The graph compares sales in thousands.

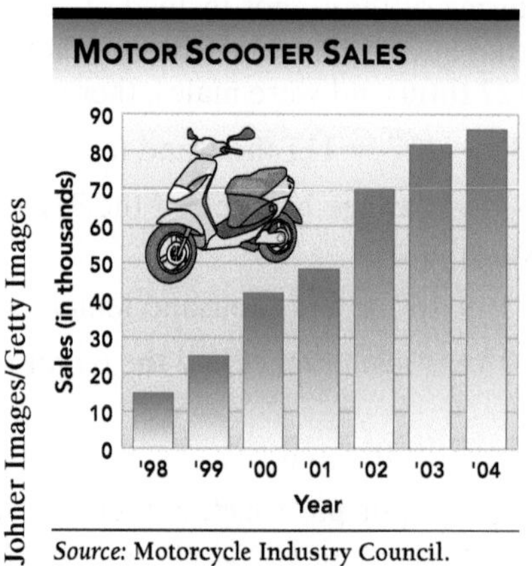

Source: Motorcycle Industry Council.

Johner Images/Getty Images

Figure 10

(a) Estimate sales in 2000 and 2004.

(b) In what years were sales greater than 50 thousand?

(c) Describe the change in sales as the years progressed.

SOLUTION

(a) Locate the top of the bar for 2000, and move horizontally across to the vertical scale to see that it is about 40. Sales in 2000 were about 40 thousand. Follow the top of the bar for 2004 across to the vertical scale to see that it lies about halfway between 80 and 90 thousand, so sales in 2004 were about 85,000.

(b) Locate 50 on the vertical scale and follow the line across to the right. Three years—2002, 2003, and 2004—have bars that extend above the line for 50, so sales were greater than 50 thousand in those years.

(c) As the years progressed, sales increased steadily, from about 15 thousand in 1998 to about 85 thousand in 2004.

A **line graph** is used to show changes or trends in data over time. To form a line graph, we connect a series of points representing data with line segments.

EXAMPLE 6 Interpreting Information in a Line Graph

Current projections indicate that funding for Medicare will not cover its costs unless the program changes. The line graph in **Figure 11** shows Medicare funds in billions of dollars for the years 2004 through 2013.

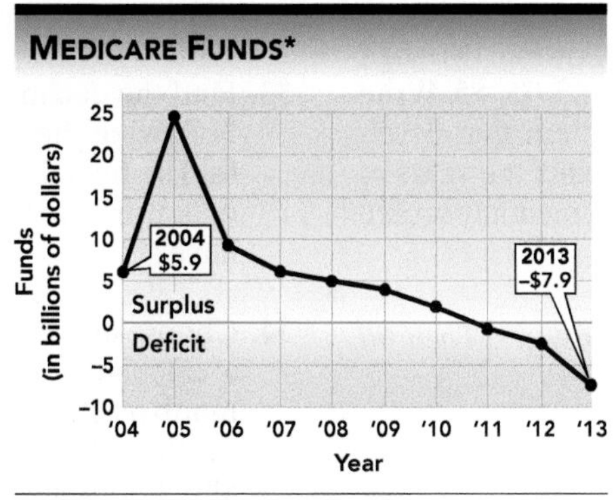

Source: Centers for Medicare and Medicaid Services.
*Projected

Stockbyte/Getty Images

Figure 11

(a) Estimate the funds in the years 2005 and 2006. About how much did the funding decrease from 2005 to 2006?

(b) Which is the only period in which Medicare funds increased? What is the projected trend from 2005 to 2013?

(c) In which year is it projected that funds will first show a deficit?

SOLUTION

(a) At the bottom of the graph, locate 2005, and read up to find that the point has a height of about 25 (billion dollars). Similarly, the point for 2006 has height about 10 (billion dollars). The funding *decreased* by about

$$25 - 10 = 15 \text{ billion dollars.} \quad \text{2005 amount} - \text{2006 amount}$$

(b) The graph *rises* from 2004 to 2005, so funds increased between these two years. The graph *falls* during 2005 to 2013, so funds will decrease.

(c) From 2004 to 2010, the graph is always above 0, but in 2011, it falls slightly below 0 for the first time, indicating a deficit. ■■■

4 EXERCISES

Perform the indicated operations and give as many digits in your answer as shown on your calculator display. (The number of displayed digits may vary depending on the model used.)

1. $39.7 + (8.2 - 4.1)$

2. $2.8 \times (3.2 - 1.1)$

3. $\sqrt{5.56440921}$

4. $\sqrt{37.38711025}$

5. $\sqrt[3]{418.508992}$

6. $\sqrt[3]{700.227072}$

7. 2.67^2

8. 3.49^3

9. 5.76^5

10. 1.48^6

11. $\dfrac{14.32 - 8.1}{2 \times 3.11}$

12. $\dfrac{12.3 + 18.276}{3 \times 1.04}$

13. $\sqrt[5]{1.35}$

14. $\sqrt[6]{3.21}$

15. $\dfrac{\pi}{\sqrt{2}}$

16. $\dfrac{2\pi}{\sqrt{3}}$

17. $\sqrt[4]{\dfrac{2143}{22}}$

18. $\dfrac{12{,}345{,}679 \times 72}{\sqrt[3]{27}}$

19. $\dfrac{\sqrt{2}}{\sqrt[3]{6}}$

20. $\dfrac{\sqrt[3]{12}}{\sqrt{3}}$

21. Choose any number consisting of five digits. Multiply it by 9 on your calculator. Now add the digits in the answer. If the sum is more than 9, add the digits of this sum, and repeat until the sum is less than 10. Your answer will always be 9. Repeat the exercise with a number consisting of six digits. Does the same result hold?

22. Use your calculator to *square* the following two-digit numbers ending in 5: 15, 25, 35, 45, 55, 65, 75, 85. Write down your results, and examine the pattern that develops. Then use inductive reasoning to predict the value of 95^2. Write an explanation of how you can mentally square a two-digit number ending in 5.

Perform each calculation and observe the answers. Then fill in the blank with the appropriate response.

23. $\frac{-3}{-8}$; $\frac{-5}{-4}$; $\frac{-2.7}{-4.3}$

Dividing a negative number by another negative number gives a _______________ product.
(negative/positive)

24. $5 \cdot -4$; $-3 \cdot 8$; $2.7 \cdot -4.3$

Multiplying a negative number by a positive number gives a _______________ product.
(negative/positive)

25. 5.6^0; π^0; 2^0; 120^0

Raising a nonzero number to the power 0 gives a result of ______.

26. 1^2; 1^3; 1^{-3}; 1^0

Raising 1 to any power gives a result of ______.

27. $\frac{1}{7}$; $\frac{1}{-9}$; $\frac{1}{3}$; $\frac{1}{-8}$

The sign of the reciprocal of a number is _____________________ the sign of the number.
(the same as/different from)

28. $5 \div 0$; $9 \div 0$; $0 \div 0$

Dividing a number by 0 gives a(n) _______________ on a calculator.

29. $0 \div 8$; $0 \div -2$; $0 \div \pi$

Zero divided by a nonzero number gives a quotient of ______.

30. $\sqrt{-3}$; $\sqrt{-4}$; $\sqrt{-10}$

Taking the square root of a negative number gives a(n) ___________________ on a calculator.

31. $-3 \cdot -4 \cdot -5$; $-3 \cdot -4 \cdot -5 \cdot -6 \cdot -7$;

$-3 \cdot -4 \cdot -5 \cdot -6 \cdot -7 \cdot -8 \cdot -9$

Multiplying an *odd* number of negative numbers gives a _______________ product.
(positive/negative)

32. $-3 \cdot -4$; $-3 \cdot -4 \cdot -5 \cdot -6$;

$-3 \cdot -4 \cdot -5 \cdot -6 \cdot -7 \cdot -8$

Multiplying an *even* number of negative numbers gives a _______________ product.
(positive/negative)

33. Find the decimal representation of $\frac{1}{6}$ on your calculator. Following the decimal point will be a 1 and a string of 6s. The final digit will be a 7 if your calculator *rounds off* or a 6 if it *truncates*. Which kind of calculator do you have?

34. Choose any three-digit number and enter the digits into a calculator. Then enter them again to get a six-digit number. Divide this six-digit number by 7. Divide the result by 13. Divide the result by 11. What is interesting about your answer? Explain why this happens.

35. Choose any digit except 0. Multiply it by 429. Now multiply the result by 259. What is interesting about your answer? Explain why this happens.

36. Choose two natural numbers. Add 1 to the second and divide by the first to get a third. Add 1 to the third and divide by the second to get a fourth. Add 1 to the fourth and divide by the third to get a fifth. Continue this process until you discover a pattern. What is the pattern?

Give an appropriate counting number answer to each question in Exercises 37–40. (Find the least counting number that will work.)

37. ***Pages to Store Trading Cards*** A plastic page designed to hold trading cards will hold up to 9 cards. How many pages will be needed to store 563 cards?

38. ***Drawers for DVDs*** A sliding drawer designed to hold DVD cases has 20 compartments. If Chris wants to house his collection of 408 Disney DVDs, how many such drawers will he need?

39. ***Containers for African Violets*** A gardener wants to fertilize 800 African violets. Each container of fertilizer will supply up to 60 plants. How many containers will she need to do the job?

iStockphoto/Thinkstock

40. ***Fifth-Grade Teachers Needed*** False River Academy has 155 fifth-grade students. The principal, Butch LeBeau, has decided that each fifth-grade teacher should have a maximum of 24 students. How many fifth-grade teachers does he need?

In Exercises 41–46, use estimation to determine the choice closest to the correct answer.

41. ***Price per Acre of Land*** To build a "millennium clock" on Mount Washington in Nevada that would tick once each year, chime once each century, and last at least 10,000 years, the nonprofit Long Now Foundation purchased 80 acres of land for $140,000. Which one of the following is the closest estimate to the price per acre?

A. $1000 **B.** $2000 **C.** $4000 **D.** $11,200

42. ***Time of a Round-Trip*** The distance from Seattle, Washington, to Springfield, Missouri, is 2009 miles. About how many hours would a roundtrip from Seattle to Springfield and back take a bus that averages 50 miles per hour for the entire trip?

A. 60 **B.** 70 **C.** 80 **D.** 90

43. ***People per Square Mile*** Buffalo County in Nebraska has a population of 40,249 and covers 968 square miles. About how many people per square mile live in Buffalo County?

A. 40 **B.** 400 **C.** 4000 **D.** 40,000

44. ***Revolutions of Mercury*** The planet Mercury takes 88.0 Earth days to revolve around the sun once. Pluto takes 90,824.2 days to do the same. When Pluto has revolved around the sun once, about how many times will Mercury have revolved around the sun?

A. 100,000 **B.** 10,000 **C.** 1000 **D.** 100

45. ***Reception Average*** In 2009, Brandon Marshall of the Denver Broncos caught 101 passes for 1120 yards. His approximate number of yards gained per catch was ________.

A. $\frac{1}{11}$ **B.** 110 **C.** 1.1 **D.** 11

46. ***Area of the Sistine Chapel*** The Sistine Chapel in Vatican City measures 40.5 meters by 13.5 meters.

Photos.com/Thinkstock

Which is the closest approximation to its area?

A. 110 meters **B.** 55 meters
C. 110 square meters **D.** 600 square meters

Immigration *The circle graph below shows the approximate percent of immigrants admitted into the United States during the 1990s. Use the graph to answer the questions in Exercises 47–50.*

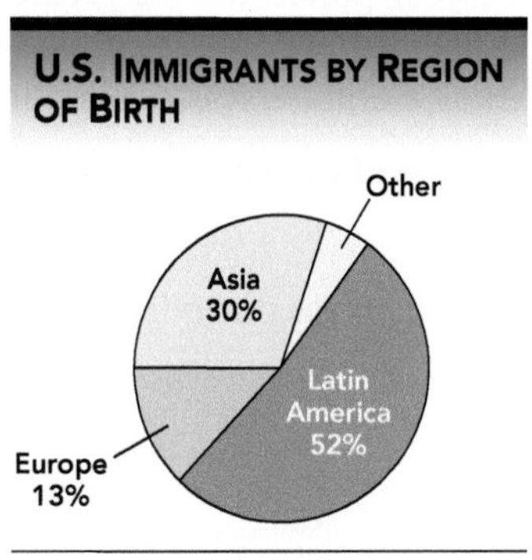

Source: U.S. Bureau of the Census.

47. What percent of the immigrants were from the "Other" group of countries?

48. What percent of the immigrants were not from Asia?

49. In a group of 2,000,000 immigrants, how many would you expect to be from Europe?

50. In a group of 4,000,000 immigrants, how many more would there be from Latin America than all the other regions combined?

Milk Production *The bar graph shows total U.S. milk production in billions of pounds for the years 2001 through 2007. Use the bar graph to work Exercises 51–54.*

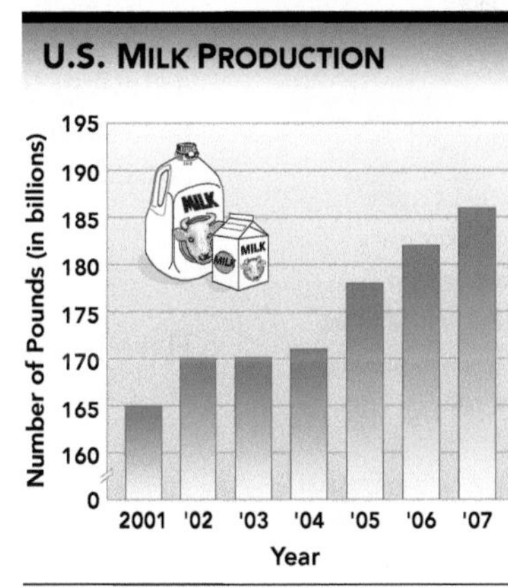

Source: U.S. Department of Agriculture.

51. In what years was U.S. milk production greater than 175 billion pounds?

52. In what two years was U.S. milk production about the same?

53. Estimate U.S. milk production in 2001 and 2007.

54. Describe the change in U.S. milk production from 2001 to 2007.

***Gasoline Prices** The line graph shows the average price, adjusted for inflation, that Americans have paid for a gallon of gasoline for selected years since 1970. Use the line graph to work Exercises 55–58.*

55. Over which 5-year period did the greatest increase in the price of a gallon of gas occur? About how much was this increase?

56. Estimate the price of a gallon of gas during 1985, 1990, 1995, and 2000.

57. Describe the trend in gas prices from 1980 to 1995.

58. During which year(s) did a gallon of gas cost approximately $1.50?

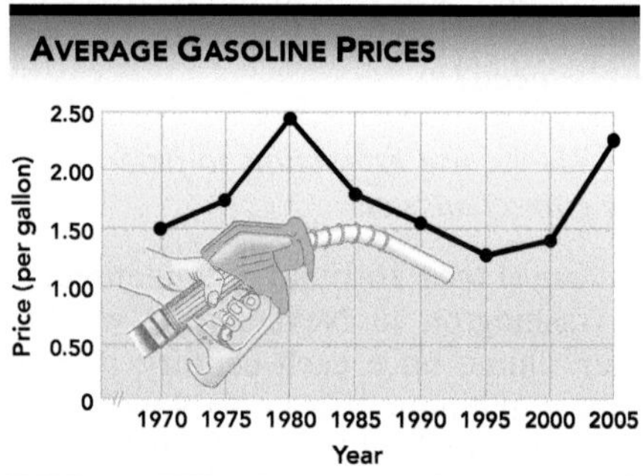

Source: Energy Information Administration.

EXTENSION

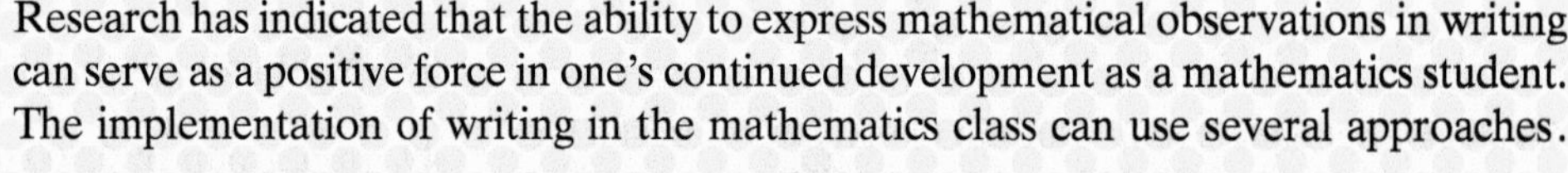

Using Writing to Learn about Mathematics

Journals • Learning Logs • Reports on Articles • Term Papers

Research has indicated that the ability to express mathematical observations in writing can serve as a positive force in one's continued development as a mathematics student. The implementation of writing in the mathematics class can use several approaches.

Kobal Collection

Mathematical writing takes many forms. One of the most famous author/mathematicians was **Charles Dodgson** (1832–1898), who used the pen name **Lewis Carroll.**

Dodgson was a mathematics lecturer at Oxford University in England. Queen Victoria told Dodgson how much she enjoyed *Alice's Adventures in Wonderland* and how much she wanted to read his next book; he is said to have sent her *Symbolic Logic,* his most famous mathematical work.

The *Alice* books made Carroll famous. Late in life, however, Dodgson shunned attention and denied that he and Carroll were the same person, even though he gave away hundreds of signed copies to children and children's hospitals.

Journals One way of using writing in mathematics is to keep a journal in which you spend a few minutes explaining what happened in class that day. The journal entries may be general or specific, depending on the topic covered, the degree to which you understand the topic, your interest level at the time, and so on. Journal entries are usually written in informal language and are often an effective means of communicating to yourself, your classmates, and your instructor what feelings, perceptions, and concerns you are having at the time.

Learning Logs Although journal entries are for the most part unstructured writings in which the student's thoughts are allowed to roam freely, entries in learning logs are typically more structured. An instructor may pose a specific question for a student to answer in a learning log. In this text, we intersperse writing exercises in each exercise set that are appropriate for answering in a learning log. For example, consider **Exercise 13** in the exercise set for the opening section in this chapter.

Discuss the differences between inductive and deductive reasoning. Give an example of each.

Here is a possible response to this exercise.

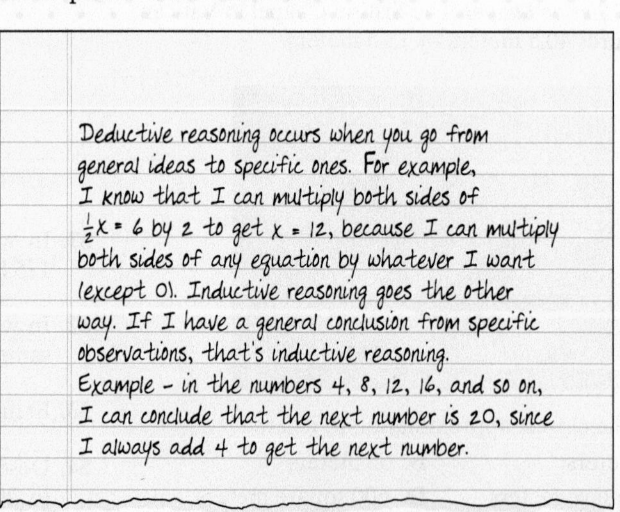

Deductive reasoning occurs when you go from general ideas to specific ones. For example, I know that I can multiply both sides of $\frac{1}{2}x = 6$ by 2 to get $x = 12$, because I can multiply both sides of any equation by whatever I want (except 0). Inductive reasoning goes the other way. If I have a general conclusion from specific observations, that's inductive reasoning. Example – in the numbers 4, 8, 12, 16, and so on, I can conclude that the next number is 20, since I always add 4 to get the next number.

Reports on Articles The motto "Publish or perish" has long been around, implying that a scholar in pursuit of an academic position must publish in a journal in his or her field. There are numerous journals that publish papers in mathematics research and/or mathematics education. In Activity 3, we suggest some articles that have appeared within the last few years. A report on such an article can help you understand what mathematicians do and what ideas mathematics teachers use to convey concepts to their students.

Term Papers Professors in mathematics survey courses are, in increasing numbers, requiring short term papers of their students. In this way, you can become aware of the plethora of books and articles on mathematics and mathematicians, many written specifically for the layperson. In Activities 5 and 6, we provide a list of possible term paper topics.

EXTENSION ACTIVITIES

Rather than include a typical exercise set, we list some suggested activities in which writing can be used to enhance awareness and learning of mathematics.

Activity 1 Keep a journal. After each class, write for a few minutes on your perceptions about the class, the topics covered, or whatever you feel is appropriate.

Activity 2 Keep a learning log, answering at least one writing exercise from each exercise set covered in your class syllabus. Ask your teacher for suggestions of other types of specific writing assignments.

Activity 3 The National Council of Teachers of Mathematics publishes journals in mathematics education: *Teaching Children Mathematics* and *Mathematics Teacher* are two that can be found online or in the periodicals section of most college and university libraries. We have chosen several recent articles in each of these journals. Write a short report on one of these articles according to guidelines specified by your instructor.

From *Mathematics Teacher*

2004

Devaney, Robert L. "Fractal Patterns and Chaos Games." November 2004, p. 228.

Francis, Richard L. "New Worlds to Conquer." October 2004, p. 166.

Hansen, Will. "War and Pieces." September 2004, p. 70.

Mahoney, John F. "How Many Votes Are Needed to Be Elected President?" October 2004, p. 154.

2005

Clausen, Mary C. "Did You 'Code'?" November 2005, p. 260.

Comstock, Jocelyne M., Sean P. Madden, and James P. Downing. "Paper Moon: Simulating a Total Solar Eclipse." December 2005/January 2006, p. 312.

Parker, Dennis. "Partitioning the Interior of a Circle with Chords." September 2005, p. 120.

Quinn, Jennifer J., and Arthur T. Benjamin. "Revisiting Fibonacci and Related Sequences." December 2005/January 2006, p. 357.

2006

Cline, Kelly S. "Classroom Voting in Mathematics." September 2006, p. 100.

Gordon, Sheldon P. "Placement Tests: The Shaky Bridge Connecting School and College Mathematics." October 2006, p. 174.

Johnson, Iris DeLoach. "Grandfather Tang Goes to High School." March 2006, p. 522.

Wong, Michael. "The Human Body's Built-In Range Finder: The Thumb Method of Indirect Distance Measurement." May 2006, p. 622.

From *Teaching Children Mathematics*

2004

Anthony, Glenda J., and Margaret A. Walshaw. "Zero: A 'None' Number?" August 2004, p. 38.

Buschman, Larry. "Teaching Problem Solving in Mathematics." February 2004, p. 302.

Joram, Elana, Christina Hartman, and Paul R. Trafton. "'As People Get Older, They Get Taller': An Integrated Unit on Measurement, Linear Relationships, and Data Analysis." March 2004, p. 344.

Mann, Rebecca L. "Balancing Act: The Truth Behind the Equals Sign." September 2004, p. 65.

2005

Flores, Alfinio, Erin E. Turner, and Renee C. Bachman. "Posing Problems to Develop Conceptual Understanding: Two Teachers Make Sense of Division of Fractions." October 2005, p. 17.

Hansen, Laurie E. "ABCs of Early Mathematics Experiences." November 2005, p. 208.

Sherrill, Carl M. "Math Riddles: Helping Children Connect Words and Numbers." March 2005, p. 368.

Thompson, Tony, and Stephen Sproule. "Calculators for Students with Special Needs." March 2005, p. 391.

2006

Barnes, Mary Kathleen. "How Many Days 'til My Birthday? Helping Kindergarten Students Understand Calendar Connections and Concepts." February 2006, p. 290.

Cassel, Darlinda, Anne Reynolds, and Eileen Lillard. "A Mathematical Exploration of Grandpa's Quilt." March 2006, p. 340.

de Groot, Cornelis, and Timothy Whalen. "Longing for Division." April 2006, p. 410.

Nugent, Christina M. "How Many Blades of Grass Are on a Football Field?" February 2006, p. 282.

© Disney Enterprises, Inc.

Activity 4 One of the most popular mathematical films of all time is *Donald in Mathmagic Land*, a 1959 Disney short that is available on DVD. Spend an entertaining half-hour watching this film, and write a report on it according to the guidelines of your instructor.

Activity 5 Write a report according to the guidelines of your instructor on one of the following mathematicians, philosophers, and scientists.

Abel, N.
Agnesi, M. G.
Agnesi, M. T.
Al-Khowârizmi
Apollonius
Archimedes
Aristotle
Babbage, C.
Bernoulli, Jakob
Bernoulli, Johann
Cantor, G.
Cardano, G.
Copernicus, N.
De Morgan, A.
Descartes, R.
Euler, L.
Fermat, P.
Fibonacci (Leonardo of Pisa)
Galileo (Galileo Galilei)
Galois, E.
Gauss, C.
Hilbert, D.
Kepler, J.
Kronecker, L.
Lagrange, J.
Leibniz, G.
L'Hôspital, G.
Lobachevsky, N.
Mandelbrot, B.
Napier, J.
Nash, J.
Newton, I.
Noether, E.
Pascal, B.
Plato
Polya, G.
Pythagoras
Ramanujan, S.
Riemann, G.
Russell, B.
Somerville, M.
Tartaglia, N.
Whitehead, A.
Wiles, A.

Activity 6 Write a term paper on one of the following topics in mathematics according to the guidelines of your instructor.

Babylonian mathematics
Egyptian mathematics
The origin of zero
Plimpton 322
The Rhind papyrus
Origins of the Pythagorean theorem
The regular (Platonic) solids
The Pythagorean brotherhood
The Golden Ratio (Golden Section)
The three famous construction problems of the Greeks
The history of the approximations of π
Euclid and his "Elements"
Early Chinese mathematics
Early Hindu mathematics
Origin of the word *algebra*
Magic squares
Figurate numbers
The Fibonacci sequence
The Cardano/Tartaglia controversy
Historical methods of computation (logarithms, the abacus, Napier's rods, the slide rule, etc.)
Pascal's triangle
The origins of probability theory
Women in mathematics
Mathematical paradoxes
Unsolved problems in mathematics
The four-color theorem
The proof of Fermat's Last Theorem
The search for large primes
Fractal geometry
The co-inventors of calculus
The role of the computer in the study of mathematics
Mathematics and music
Police mathematics
The origins of complex numbers
Goldbach's conjecture
The use of the Internet in mathematics education
The development of graphing calculators
Mathematics education reform movement
Multicultural mathematics
The Riemann Hypothesis

Activity 7 Investigate a computer program that focuses on teaching children elementary mathematics, and write a critical review of it as if you were writing for a journal that contains software reviews of educational material. Be sure to address the higher-level thinking skills in addition to drill and practice.

Activity 8 The following Web sites provide a fascinating list of mathematics-related topics. Go to one of them, choose a topic that interests you, and report on it, according to the guidelines of your instructor.

www.mathworld.wolfram.com

www.world.std.com/~reinhold/mathmovies.html

www.maths.surrey.ac.uk/hosted-sites/R.Knott/

http://dir.yahoo.com/Science/Mathematics/

www.cut-the-knot.com/

www.ics.uci.edu/~eppstein/recmath.html

Activity 9 A theme of mathematics-related scenes in movies and television is found throughout this text. Prepare a report on one or more such scenes, and determine whether the mathematics involved is correct or incorrect. If correct, show why. If incorrect, find the correct answer. See www.math.harvard.edu/~knill/mathmovies/ and www.mathclassgoestohollywood.com.

Activity 10 The longest running animated television series is *The Simpsons*, having begun in 1989. The Web site www.simpsonsmath.com explores the occurrence of mathematics in the episodes on a season-by-season basis. Watch several episodes and elaborate on the mathematics found in them.

COLLABORATIVE INVESTIGATION

Discovering Patterns in Pascal's Triangle

One fascinating array of numbers, **Pascal's triangle,** consists of rows of numbers, each of which contains one more entry than the one before. The first six rows are shown here.

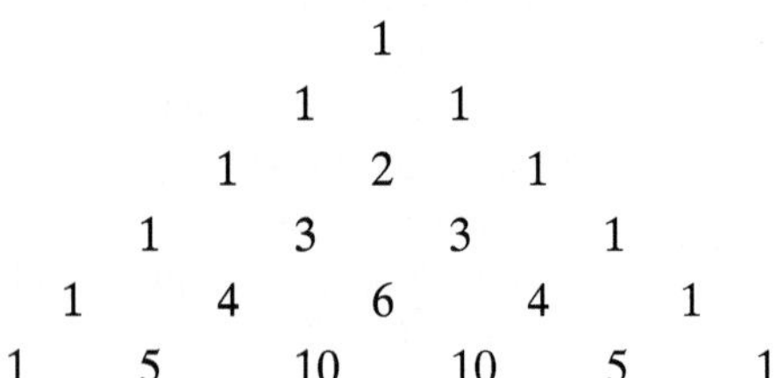

To discover some of its patterns, divide the class into groups of four students each. Within each group designate one student as A, one as B, one as C, and one as D. Then perform the following activities in order.

1. Discuss among group members some of the properties of the triangle that are obvious from observing the first six rows shown.

2. It is fairly obvious that each row begins and ends with 1. Discover a method whereby the other entries in a row can be determined from the entries in the row immediately above it. (*Hint*: In the fifth row, $6 = 3 + 3$.) Then, as a group, find the next three rows of the triangle, and have each member prepare his or her own copy of the entire first nine rows for later reference.

3. Now each student in the group will investigate a particular property of the triangle. In some cases, a calculator will be helpful. All students should begin working at the same time. (A discussion follows.)

Student A: Find the sum of the entries in each row. Notice the pattern that emerges. Now write the tenth row of the triangle.

Student B: Investigate the successive differences in the diagonals from upper left to lower right. For example, in the diagonal that begins 1, 2, 3, 4, . . . , the successive differences are all 1; in the diagonal that begins 1, 3, 6, . . . , the successive differences are 2, 3, 4, and so on. Do this up through the diagonal that begins 1, 6, 21, ...

Student C: Find the values of the first five powers of the number 11, starting with 11^0 (recall $11^0 = 1$).

Student D: Arrange these nine rows of the triangle with all rows "flush left," and then draw lightly dashed arrows as shown:

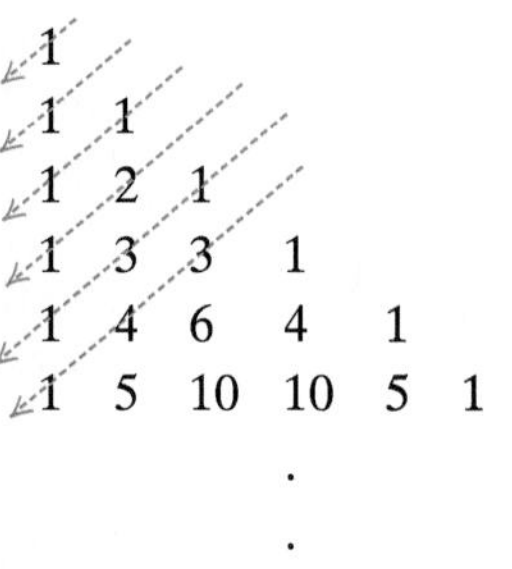

and so on. Then add along the diagonals. Write these sums in order from left to right.

4. After all students have concluded their individual investigations in Item 3, return to a group discussion.

(a) Have student A report the result found in Item 3, and then make a prediction concerning the sum of the entries in the tenth row.

(b) Have student B report the successive differences discovered in the diagonals. Then have all students in the group investigate the successive differences in the diagonal that begins 1, 7, 28 . . . . (It may be necessary to write a few more rows of the triangle.)

(c) Have student C report the relationship between the powers of 11 found, and then determine the value of 11^5. Why does the pattern not continue here?

(d) Have student D report the sequence of numbers found. Then, as a group, predict what the next sum will be by observing the pattern in the sequence. Confirm your prediction by actual computation.

5. Choose a representative from each group to report to the entire class the observations made throughout this investigation.

6. Find a reference to Pascal's triangle on the Internet and prepare a report.

CHAPTER TEST

In Exercises 1 and 2, decide whether the reasoning involved is an example of inductive or deductive reasoning.

1. Carol Britz is a sales representative for a publishing company. For the past 16 years, she has exceeded her annual sales goal, primarily by selling mathematics textbooks. Therefore, she will also exceed her annual sales goal this year.

2. For all natural numbers n, n^2 is also a natural number. 176 is a natural number. Therefore, 176^2 is a natural number.

3. ***Magic Hexagon*** (A **magic hexagon** has all entries in the columns and diagonals adding up to the same sum.) Find the constant sum for the magic hexagon, and fill in the numbers so that every column or diagonal has that sum. (From *Mathematics Teacher* monthly calendar, November 20, 2007.)

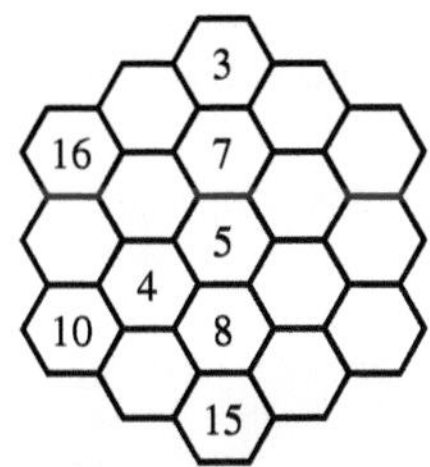

4. Use the list of equations and inductive reasoning to predict the next equation, and then verify your conjecture.

$$65{,}359{,}477{,}124{,}183 \times 17 = 1{,}111{,}111{,}111{,}111{,}111$$
$$65{,}359{,}477{,}124{,}183 \times 34 = 2{,}222{,}222{,}222{,}222{,}222$$
$$65{,}359{,}477{,}124{,}183 \times 51 = 3{,}333{,}333{,}333{,}333{,}333$$

5. Use the method of successive differences to find the next term in the sequence

$$3, 11, 31, 69, 131, 223, \ldots.$$

6. Find the sum $1 + 2 + 3 + \cdots + 250$.

7. Consider the following equations, where the left side of each is an octagonal number.

$$1 = 1$$
$$8 = 1 + 7$$
$$21 = 1 + 7 + 13$$
$$40 = 1 + 7 + 13 + 19$$

Use the pattern established on the right sides to predict the next octagonal number. What is the next equation in the list?

8. Use the result of **Exercise 7** and the method of successive differences to find the first eight octagonal numbers. Then divide each by 4 and record the remainder. What is the pattern obtained?

9. Describe the pattern used to obtain the terms of the Fibonacci sequence

$$1, 1, 2, 3, 5, 8, 13, 21, \ldots.$$

Use problem-solving strategies to solve each problem, taken from the date indicated in the monthly calendar of Mathematics Teacher.

10. ***Building a Fraction*** Each of the four digits 2, 4, 6, and 9 is placed in one of the boxes to form a fraction. The numerator and the denominator are both two-digit whole numbers. What is the smallest value of all the common fractions that can be formed? Express your answer as a common fraction. (November 17, 2004)

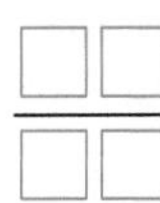

11. ***Units Digit of a Power of 9*** What is the units digit (ones digit) in the decimal representation of 9^{1997}? (January 27, 1997)

12. ***Counting Puzzle (Triangles)*** How many triangles are in this figure? (January 6, 2000)

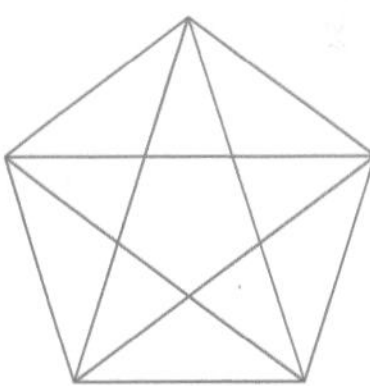

13. ***Make Them Equal*** Consider the following:

$$1\ 2\ 3\ 4\ 5\ 6\ 7\ 8\ 9\ 0 = 100.$$

Leaving all the numerals in the order given, insert addition and subtraction signs into the expression to make the equation true. (March 23, 2008)

14. ***Shrinkage*** Dr. Small is 36 inches tall, and Ms. Tall is 96 inches tall. If Dr. Small shrinks 2 inches per year and Ms. Tall grows $\frac{2}{3}$ of an inch per year, how tall will Ms. Tall be when Dr. Small disappears altogether? (November 2, 2007)

15. ***Units Digit of a Sum*** Find the units digit (ones digit) of the decimal numeral representing the number $11^{11} + 14^{14} + 16^{16}$. (February 14, 1994)

16. Based on your knowledge of elementary arithmetic, describe the pattern that can be observed when the following operations are performed:

$$9 \times 1, \quad 9 \times 2, \quad 9 \times 3, \ldots, 9 \times 9.$$

(*Hint:* Add the digits in the answers. What do you notice?)

Use your calculator to evaluate each of the following. Give as many decimal places as the calculator displays.

17. $\sqrt{98.16}$

18. 3.25^3

19. ***Basketball Scoring Results*** During the 2008–09 NCAA women's basketball season, Destini Hughes of LSU made 28 of her 96 field goal attempts. This means that for every 10 attempts, she made approximately ______ of them.

A. 4 **B.** 3 **C.** 2 **D.** 1

20. ***Unemployment Rate*** The line graph shows the overall unemployment rate in the U.S. civilian labor force for the years 1998 through 2005.

UNEMPLOYMENT RATE

Rate (percent): 0, 1, 2, 3, 4, 5, 6, 7

Year: '98 '99 '00 '01 '02 '03 '04 '05

Source: U.S. Department of Labor.

(a) Between which pairs of consecutive years did the unemployment rate decrease?

(b) What was the general trend in the unemployment rate between 2000 and 2003?

(c) Estimate the overall unemployment rate in 2003 and 2004. About how much did the unemployment rate decline between 2003 and 2004?

ANSWERS TO SELECTED EXERCISES

1 Exercises

1. deductive **3.** inductive **5.** deductive **7.** deductive **9.** inductive **11.** inductive **13.** Answers will vary. **15.** 21 **17.** 3072 **19.** 63 **21.** $\frac{11}{12}$ **23.** 216 **25.** 52 **27.** 5 **29.** One such list is 10, 20, 30, 40, 50, ... **31.** $(98{,}765 \times 9) + 3 = 888{,}888$ **33.** $3367 \times 15 = 50{,}505$ **35.** $33{,}334 \times 33{,}334 = 1{,}111{,}155{,}556$ **37.** $3 + 6 + 9 + 12 + 15 = \frac{15(6)}{2}$ **39.** $5(6) + 5(36) + 5(216) + 5(1296) + 5(7776) = 6(7776 - 1)$ **41.** $\frac{1}{2} + \frac{1}{4} + \frac{1}{8} + \frac{1}{16} + \frac{1}{32} = 1 - \frac{1}{32}$ **43.** 20,100 **45.** 320,400 **47.** 15,400 **49.** 2550 **51.** 1 (These are the numbers of chimes a clock rings, starting with 12 o'clock, if it rings the number of hours on the hour, and 1 chime on the half-hour.) **53. (a)** The middle digit is always 9, and the sum of the first and third digits is always 9 (considering 0 as the first digit if the difference has only two digits). **(b)** Answers will vary. **55.** 142,857; 285,714; 428,571; 571,428; 714,285; 857,142. Each result consists of the same six digits, but in a different order. $142{,}857 \times 7 = 999{,}999$

2 Exercises

1. arithmetic; 56 **3.** geometric; 1215 **5.** neither **7.** geometric; 8 **9.** neither **11.** arithmetic; 22 **13.** 79 **15.** 450 **17.** 4032 **19.** 32,758 **21.** 57; 99 **23.** $(4321 \times 9) - 1 = 38{,}888$ **25.** $999{,}999 \times 4 = 3{,}999{,}996$ **27.** $21^2 - 15^2 = 6^3$ **29.** $5^2 - 4^2 = 5 + 4$ **31.** $1 + 5 + 9 + 13 = 4 \times 7$ **33.** 45,150 **35.** 228,150 **37.** 2601 **39.** 250,000 **41.** $S = n(n + 1)$ **43.** Answers will vary. **45.** *row 1*: 28, 36; *row 2*: 36, 49, 64; *row 3*: 35, 51, 70, 92; *row 4*: 28, 45, 66, 91, 120; *row 5*: 18, 34, 55, 81, 112, 148; *row 6*: 8, 21, 40, 65, 96, 133, 176 **47.** $8(1) + 1 = 9 = 3^2$; $8(3) + 1 = 25 = 5^2$; $8(6) + 1 = 49 = 7^2$; $8(10) + 1 = 81 = 9^2$ **49.** The pattern is 1, 0, 1, 0, 1, 0, ... **51.**

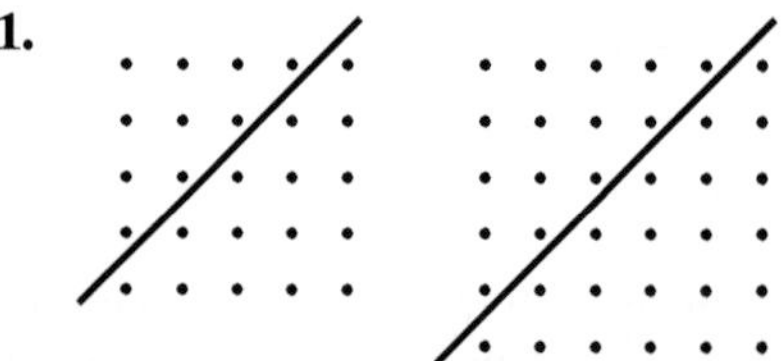

53. 256 **55.** 117 **57.** 235 **59.** $N_n = \frac{n(7n-5)}{2}$
61. a square number **63.** a perfect cube **65.** 42
67. 419 **69.** $\frac{101}{2}$ **71.** 2048 **73.** $\frac{1}{2048}$ **75.** $\frac{5}{2048}$

3 Exercises

1. 32 **3.** 0 (The product of the first and last digits is the two-digit number between them.) **5.** 11 **7.** infinitely many (Any line through the center of the square will do this.) **9.** 48.5 in. **11.** 42 **13.** 6 **15.** If you multiply the two digits in the numbers in the first row, you will get the second row of numbers. The second row of numbers is a pattern of two numbers (8 and 24) repeating. **17.** I put the ring in the box and put my lock on the box. I send you the box. You put your lock on, as well, and send it back to me. I then remove my lock with my key and send the box (with your lock still on) back to you, so you can remove your lock with your key and get the ring. **19.** 59
21. You should choose a sock from the box labeled *red and green socks.* Because it is mislabeled, it contains only red socks or only green socks, determined by the sock you choose. If the sock is green, relabel this box *green socks.* Since the other two boxes were mislabeled, switch the remaining label to the other box and place the label that says *red and green socks* on the unlabeled box. No other choice guarantees a correct relabeling because you can remove only one sock.
23. D **25.** A
27. One example of a solution follows.

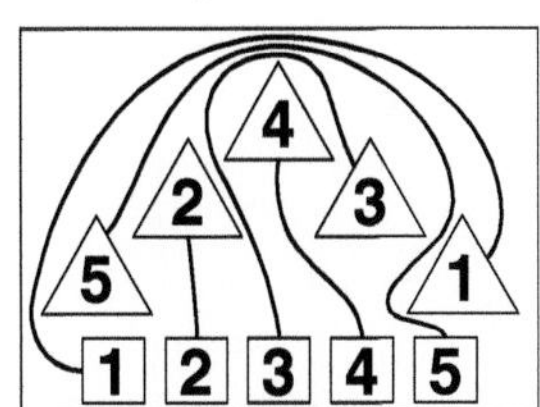

29.

9	7	2	14	11	5	4	12	13	3	6	10	15	1	8

(or the same arrangement reading right to left)
31. Here is one solution. **33.** D **35.** $\frac{1}{3}$

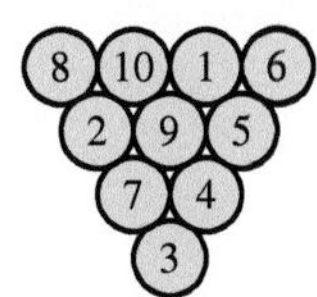

37. One possible sequence is shown here. The numbers represent the number of gallons in each bucket in each successive step.

Big	7	4	4	1	1	0	7	5	5
Small	0	3	0	3	0	1	1	3	0

39. 90 **41.** 55 mph **43.** 07 **45.** 437 **47.** 3
49. 21 stamps (5 five-cent stamps and 16 eight-cent stamps) **51.** 3 socks **53.** 35 **55.** 6
57. the nineteenth day **59.** 1967
61. Eve has \$5, and Adam has \$7.
63.

```
      4  0  2
  ×      3  9
 ------------
  1  5, 6  7  8
```

65.

6	12	7	9
1	15	4	14
11	5	10	8
16	2	13	3

67. 25 pitches (The visiting team's pitcher retires 24 consecutive batters through the first eight innings, using only one pitch per batter. His team does not score either. Going into the bottom of the ninth tied 0–0, the first batter for the home team hits his first pitch for a home run. The pitcher threw 25 pitches and loses the game by a score of 1–0.) **69.** Q
71. Here is one solution.

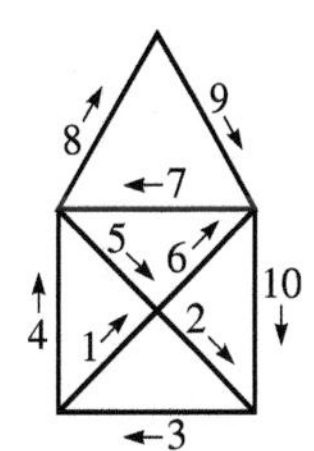

73. 6 ways **75.** 86 cm
77. Dan (36) is married to Jessica (29); James (30) is married to Cathy (31).
79. 12; All months have 28 days.
81. 3
85. The products always differ by 1.

83. 6

	X	X
X		X
X	X	

One of two possibilities

4 Exercises

1. 43.8 **3.** 2.3589 **5.** 7.48 **7.** 7.1289 **9.** 6340.338097
11. 1 **13.** 1.061858759 **15.** 2.221441469
17. 3.141592653 **19.** 0.7782717162 **21.** yes
23. positive **25.** 1 **27.** the same as **29.** 0
31. negative **33.** Answers will vary.
35. Answers will vary. **37.** 63 **39.** 14 **41.** B **43.** A
45. D **47.** 5% **49.** 260,000 **51.** 2005, 2006, 2007
53. 2001: about 165 billion lb; 2007: about 185 billion lb
55. from 2000 to 2005; about \$0.85
57. The price of a gallon of gas was decreasing.

Chapter Test

1. inductive **2.** deductive
3. The magic sum is 38.

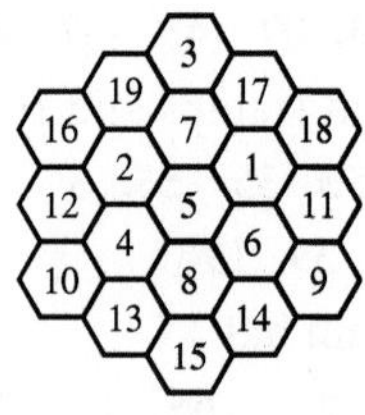

4. 65,359,477,124,183 × 68 = 4,444,444,444,444,444

5. 351 **6.** 31,375 **7.** 65; 65 = 1 + 7 + 13 + 19 + 25

8. 1, 8, 21, 40, 65, 96, 133, 176; The pattern is 1, 0, 1, 0, 1, 0, 1, 0, ...

9. The first two terms are both 1. Each term after the second is found by adding the two previous terms.

10. $\frac{1}{4}$ **11.** 9 **12.** 35

13. Answers will vary. One possible solution is 1 + 2 + 3 − 4 + 5 + 6 + 78 + 9 + 0 = 100.

14. 108 in., or 9 ft **15.** 3

16. The sum of the digits is always 9.

17. 9.907572861 (Answers may vary due to the model of calculator used.) **18.** 34.328125 **19.** B

20. **(a)** between 1998 and 1999, 1999 and 2000, and 2003 and 2004 **(b)** The unemployment rate was increasing. **(c)** 2003: 6.0%; 2004: 5.5%; decline: 0.5%

The Art of Problem Solving

1 Exercises

1. This is an example of a deductive argument because a specific conclusion, "you can expect it to be ready in ten days," is drawn from the two given premises.

3. This is an example of inductive reasoning because you are reasoning from a specific pattern to the conclusion that "It will also rain tomorrow."

5. This represents deductive reasoning since you are moving from a general rule (addition) to a specific result (the sum of 85 and 20).

7. This is a deductive argument where you are reasoning from the two given premises. The first, "If you build it, they will come" is a general statement and the conclusion, "they will come" is specific.

9. This is an example of inductive reasoning because you are reasoning from a specific pattern of all previous attendees to a conclusion that the next one "I" will also be accepted into graduate school.

11. This is an example of inductive reasoning because you are reasoning from a specific pattern to a generalization as to what is the next element in the sequence.

13. Writing exercise; answers will vary.

15. Each number in the list is obtained by adding 3 to the previous number. The most probable next term is $18+3=21$.

17. Each number in the list is obtained by multiplying the previous number by 4. The most probable next term is $4\times 768=3072$.

19. Beginning with the third term, each number in the sequence is the sum of the two previous terms.

$$9=(3+6)$$
$$15=(6+9)$$
$$24=(9+15)$$
$$39=(15+24)$$

The most probable next term is $63=(24+39)$.

21. The numerators and denominators are consecutive counting numbers. The probable next term is $\frac{11}{12}$.

23. The most probable next term is $6^3=216$. Observe the sequence:

$$1=1^3$$
$$8=2^3$$
$$27=3^3$$
$$64=4^3$$
$$125=5^3$$

This sequence is made up of the cubes of each counting number.

25. The probable next term is 52. Note that each term (after the first) may be computed by adding successively 5, 7, 9, and 11 to each preceding term. Thus, it follows that a probable next term would be $39+13=52$.

27. The probable next term is 5 since the sequence of numbers seems to add one more 5 each time the 5's precede the number 3.

29. There are many possibilities. One such list is 10, 20, 30, 40, 50, … .

31.

$$(9\times 9)+7=88$$
$$(98\times 9)+6=888$$
$$(987\times 9)+5=8888$$
$$(9876\times 9)+4=88{,}888$$

Observe that on the left, the pattern suggests that the digit 5 will be appended to the first number. Thus, we get (98,765 × 9) which is added to 3. On the right, the pattern suggests appending another digit 8 to obtain 888,888. Therefore,
$(98{,}765\times 9)+3=888{,}885+3=888{,}888$
By computation, the conjecture is verified.

33.

$$3367\times 3=10{,}101$$
$$3367\times 6=20{,}202$$
$$3367\times 9=30{,}303$$
$$3367\times 12=40{,}404$$

Observe that on the left, the pattern suggests that 3367 will be multiplied by the next multiple of 3, which is 15. On the right, the pattern suggests the result 50,505. The pattern suggests the following equation: $3367\times 15=50{,}505$.
Multiply 3367×15 to verify the conjecture.

35.
$$34 \times 34 = 1156$$
$$334 \times 334 = 111,556$$
$$3334 \times 3334 = 11,115,556$$
The pattern suggests the following equation: $33,334 \times 33,334 = 1,111,155,556$.
Multiply $33,334 \times 33,334$ to verify the conjecture.

37.
$$3 = \frac{3(2)}{2}$$
$$3 + 6 = \frac{6(3)}{2}$$
$$3 + 6 + 9 = \frac{9(4)}{2}$$
$$3 + 6 + 9 + 12 = \frac{12(5)}{2}$$
The pattern suggests the following equation:
$$3 + 6 + 9 + 12 + 15 = \frac{15(6)}{2}.$$
Since both the left and right sides equal 45, the conjecture is verified.

39.
$$5(6) = 6(6-1)$$
$$5(6) + 5(36) = 6(36-1)$$
$$5(6) + 5(36) + 5(216) = 6(216-1)$$
$$5(6) + 5(36) + 5(216) + 5(1296) = 6(1296-1)$$
Observe that the last equation may be written as:
$$5(6^1) + 5(6^2) + 5(6^3) + 5(6^4) = 6(6^4 - 1).$$
Thus, the next equation would likely be:
$$5(6) + 5(36) + 5(216) + 5(1296) + 5(6^5) = 6(6^5 - 1)$$
or,
$$5(6) + 5(36) + 5(216) + 5(1296) + 5(7776) = 6(7776 - 1).$$

41.
$$\frac{1}{2} = 1 - \frac{1}{2}$$
$$\frac{1}{2} + \frac{1}{4} = 1 - \frac{1}{4}$$
$$\frac{1}{2} + \frac{1}{4} + \frac{1}{8} = 1 - \frac{1}{8}$$
$$\frac{1}{2} + \frac{1}{4} + \frac{1}{8} + \frac{1}{16} = 1 - \frac{1}{16}$$
Observe that the last equation may be written as
$$\frac{1}{2^1} + \frac{1}{2^2} + \frac{1}{2^3} + \frac{1}{2^4} = 1 - \frac{1}{2^4}.$$
The next equation would be
$$\frac{1}{2^1} + \frac{1}{2^2} + \frac{1}{2^3} + \frac{1}{2^4} + \frac{1}{2^5} = 1 - \frac{1}{2^5}, \text{ or}$$
$$\frac{1}{2} + \frac{1}{4} + \frac{1}{8} + \frac{1}{16} + \frac{1}{32} = 1 - \frac{1}{32}.$$
Using the common denominator 32 for each fraction, the left and right side add (in each case) to $\frac{31}{32}$. The conjecture is, therefore, verified.

43. 1 + 2 + 3 + … +200
Pairing and adjoining the first term to the last term, the second term to the second-to-last term, etc., we have:
1 + 200 = 201, 2 + 199 = 201,
3 + 198 = 201, …
There are 100 of these sums. Therefore, $100 \times 201 = 20,100$.

45. 1 + 2 + 3 + … + 800
Pairing and adjoining the first term to the last term, the second term to the second-to-last term, etc., we have:
1 + 800 = 801, 2 + 799 = 801,
3 + 798 = 801, …
There are 400 of these sums. Therefore, $400 \times 801 = 320,400$.

47. 1 + 2 + 3 + … + 175
Note that there are an odd number of terms. So consider omitting, for the moment, the last term and take 1 + 174 = 175, 2 + 173 = 175, 3 + 172 = 175, etc. There are $\frac{174}{2} = 87$ of these pairs in addition to the last term. Thus, $(87 \times 175) + 175$, or $88 \times 175 = 15,400$.

49.
$$\begin{aligned} 2 + 4 + 6 + \ldots + 100 &= 2(1 + 2 + 3 + \cdots + 50) \\ &= 2[25(1 + 50)] \\ &= 2(1275) \\ &= 2550 \end{aligned}$$

51. These are the number of chimes a clock rings, starting with 12 o'clock, if the clock rings the number of hours on the hour and 1 chime on the half-hour. The next most probable number is the number of chimes at 3:30, which is 1.

53. **(a)** Here are three examples.

623	841	584
−326	−148	−485
297	693	99

In each result, the middle digit is always 9, and the sum of the first and third digits is always 9 (considering 0 as the first digit if the difference has only two digits).

(b) Writing exercise; answers will vary.

55. $142,857 \times 1 = 142,857$
$142,857 \times 2 = 285,714$
$142,857 \times 3 = 428,571$
$142,857 \times 4 = 571,428$
$142,857 \times 5 = 714,285$
$142,857 \times 6 = 857,142$
Each result consists of the same six digits, but in a different order. But $142,857 \times 7 = 999,999$. Thus, the pattern doesn't continue.

2 Exercises

1. If we choose any term after the first term, and subtract the preceding term, the common difference is 10. Therefore, this is an arithmetic sequence. The next term in the sequence is $46 + 10 = 56$.

3. If any term after the first is multiplied by 3, the following term is obtained. Therefore, this is a geometric sequence. The next term in the sequence is $405 \cdot 3 = 1215$.

5. There is neither a common difference nor a common ratio. This is neither an arithmetic nor a geometric sequence.

7. If any term after the first is multiplied by $\frac{1}{2}$, the following term is obtained.
Therefore, this is a geometric sequence. The next term in the sequence is $16 \cdot \frac{1}{2} = 8$.

9. There is neither a common difference nor a common ratio. This is neither an arithmetic nor a geometric sequence.

11. If we choose any term after the first term, and subtract the preceding term, the common difference is 2. Therefore, this is an arithmetic sequence. The next term in the sequence is $20 + 2 = 22$.

13.
1 4 11 22 37 56 79
3 7 11 15 19 23
4 4 4 4 (4)

Each line represents the difference of the two numbers above it. The number 23 is found from adding the predicted difference, (4), in line three to 19 in line 2. And 79 is found by adding 23, in line two, to 56 in line one. Thus, our next term in the sequence is 79.

15.
6 20 50 102 182 296 450
14 30 52 80 114 154
16 22 28 34 40
6 6 6 (6)

Thus, our next term in the sequence is 154 = 296 = 450.

17.
0 12 72 240 600 1260 2352 4032
12 60 168 360 660 1092 1680
48 108 192 300 432 588
60 84 108 132 156
24 24 24 (24)

Thus, our next term in the sequence is $1680 + 2352 = 4032$.

19.
5 34 243 1022 3121 7770 16799 32758
29 209 779 2099 4649 9029 15959
180 570 1320 2550 4380 6930
390 750 1230 1830 2550
360 480 600 720
120 120 (120)

Thus, our next term in the sequence is $15959 + 16799 = 32,758$.

21.
1 2 4 8 16 31 (57) 99
1 2 4 8 15 26 42
1 2 4 7 11 16
1 2 3 4 5
1 1 1 (1)

The next term of the sequence is 57. Following this pattern, we predict that the number of regions determined by 8 points is 99. Use $n = 8$ in the formula

$$\frac{n^4 - 6n^3 + 23n^2 - 18n + 24}{24}.$$

$$\frac{8^4 - 6 \times 8^3 + 23 \times 8^2 - 18 \times 8 + 24}{24}$$
$$= \frac{4096 - 3072 + 1472 - 144 + 24}{24}$$
$$= \frac{2376}{24}$$
$$= 99$$

Thus, the result agrees with our prediction.

23. By the pattern, the next equation is $(4321 \times 9) - 1 = 38,888$.
To verify, calculate left side and compare, $38,889 - 1 = 38,888$.

25. $999,999 \times 2 = 1,999,998$
$999,999 \times 3 = 2,999,997$
By the pattern, the next equation is $999,999 \times 4 = 3,999,996$.
To verify, multiply left side to get $3,999,996 = 3,999,996$.

27. $3^2 - 1^2 = 2^3$
$6^2 - 3^2 = 3^3$
$10^2 - 6^2 = 4^3$
$15^2 - 10^2 = 5^3$

Following this pattern, we see that the next equation will start with 21^2 since $15 + 6 = 21$. This equation will be $21^2 - 15^2 = 6^3$. The left side is $441 - 225 = 216$. The right side also equals 216.

29. $2^2 - 1^2 = 2 + 1$
$3^2 - 2^2 = 3 + 2$
$4^2 - 3^2 = 4 + 3$

Following this pattern, we see that the next equation will be $5^2 - 4^2 = 5 + 4$.
To verify, the left side is $25 - 16 = 9$. The right side also equals 9.

31. $1 = 1 \times 1$
$1 + 5 = 2 \times 3$
$1 + 5 + 9 = 3 \times 5$
The last term on the left side is 4 more than the previous last term. The first factor on the right side is the next counting number; the second factor is the next odd number. Thus, the probable next equation is $1 + 5 + 9 + 13 = 4 \times 7$.
To verify, calculate both sides to arrive at 28 = 28.

33. $1 + 2 + 3 + ... + 300$

$$S = \frac{300(300+1)}{2} = \frac{90300}{2} = 45{,}150$$

35. $1 + 2 + 3 + ... + 675$

$$S = \frac{675(675+1)}{2} = \frac{456300}{2} = 228{,}150$$

37. $1 + 3 + 5 + 7 + ... + 101$
Note that

$n = \frac{1+101}{2} = 51$ terms, so that $S = 51^2 = 2601$.

39. $1 + 3 + 5 + ... + 999$
Observe that

$n = \frac{1+999}{2} = 500$ terms, so that

$S = 500^2 = 250{,}500$.

41. Since each term in the second series is twice that of the first series, we might expect the sum to be twice as large or

$$S = 2 \times \frac{n(n+1)}{2} = n(n+1).$$

43. Writing exercise; answers will vary.

45.

Figurate Number	1st	2nd	3rd	4th	5th	6th	7th	8th
Triangular	1	3	6	10	15	21	28	36
Square	1	4	9	16	25	36	49	64
Pentagonal	1	5	12	22	35	51	70	92
Hexagonal	1	6	15	28	45	66	91	120
Heptagonal	1	7	18	34	55	81	112	148
Octagonal	1	8	21	40	65	96	133	176

47. $8(1)+1=9=3^2$; $8(3)+1=25=5^2$; $8(6)+1=49=7^2$; $8(10)+1=81=9^2$

49. The square numbers are 1, 4, 9, 25, 36, … .
$1 \div 4 = 0$, remainder 1
$4 \div 4 = 1$, remainder 0
$9 \div 4 = 2$, remainder 1
$16 \div 4 = 4$, remainder 0
$25 \div 4 = 6$, remainder 1
$36 \div 4 = 9$, remainder 0
The pattern of remainders is 1, 0, 1, 0, 1, 0, … .

51. The square number 25 may be represented by the sum of the two triangular numbers 10 and 15. The square number 36 may be represented by the sum of the two triangular numbers 15 and 21.

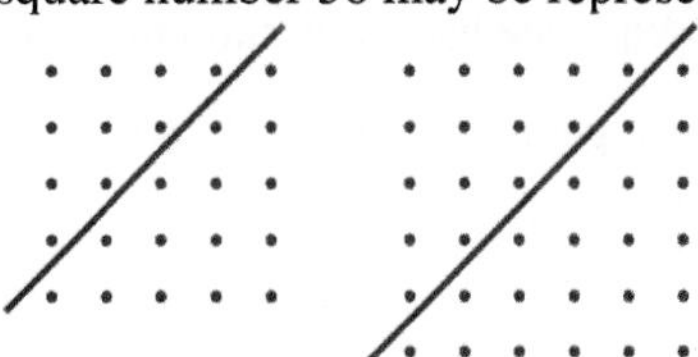

53. To find the sixteenth square number, use
$S_n = n^2$ with $n = 16$.
$S_{16} = 16^2 = 256$

55. To find the ninth pentagonal number, use
$P_n = \dfrac{n(3n-1)}{2}$ with $n = 9$.
$P_9 = \dfrac{9(26)}{2} = 117.$

57. To find the tenth heptagonal number, use
$Hp_n = \dfrac{n(5n-3)}{2}$ with $n = 10$.
$Hp_{10} = \dfrac{10(47)}{2} = 235$

59. Since each coefficient in parentheses appears to step up by 1, we would predict:

$N_n = \dfrac{n(7n-5)}{2}$.

$N_6 = \dfrac{6(37)}{2} = 111$

This verifies our prediction for $n = 6$.

61. The triangular numbers are 1, 3, 6, 10, 15, 21, 28, 36, 45, … . Adding consecutive triangular numbers, for example, 1 + 3 = 4, 3 + 6 = 9, 6 + 10 = 16, … , will give square numbers.

63. In each case, you get a perfect cube number. That is, if we take the 2nd and 3rd triangular numbers 3 and 6, $6^2 - 3^2 = 36 - 9 = 27$ which is the perfect cube number 3^3.

65. This sequence has a common difference of 4, so it is an arithmetic sequence with

$n = 11$

$a_1 = 2$

$d = 4$.

Using the formula,

$a_n = a_1 + (n-1)d$

$a_{11} = 2 + (11-1)\cdot 4$

$a_{11} = 2 + 10\cdot 4$

$a_{11} = 42$

The eleventh term in the sequence is 42.

67. This sequence has a common difference of 20, so it is an arithmetic sequence with

$n = 21$

$a_1 = 19$

$d = 20$.

Using the formula,

$a_n = a_1 + (n-1)d$

$a_{21} = 19 + (21-1)\cdot 20$

$a_{21} = 19 + 20\cdot 20$

$a_{21} = 419$

The 21st term in the sequence is 419.

69. This sequence has a common difference of $\frac{1}{2}$, so it is an arithmetic sequence with

$n = 101$

$a_1 = \frac{1}{2}$

$d = \frac{1}{2}$.

Using the formula,

$a_n = a_1 + (n-1)d$

$a_{101} = \frac{1}{2} + (101-1)\cdot\frac{1}{2}$

$a_{101} = \frac{1}{2} + 100\cdot\frac{1}{2}$

$a_{101} = \frac{101}{2}$

The 101st term in the sequence is $\frac{101}{2}$.

71. This sequence has a common ration of 2, so it is a geometric sequence with

$n = 11$

$a_1 = 2$

$r = 2$.

Using the formula,

$a_n = a_1 \cdot r^{n-1}$

$a_{11} = 2\cdot 2^{11-1}$

$a_{11} = 2\cdot 2^{10}$

$a_{11} = 2048$

The eleventh term in the sequence is 2048.

73. This sequence has a common ration of $\frac{1}{2}$, so it is a geometric sequence with

$n = 12$

$a_1 = 1$

$r = \frac{1}{2}$.

Using the formula,

$a_n = a_1 \cdot r^{n-1}$

$a_{12} = 1\cdot\left(\frac{1}{2}\right)^{12-1}$

$a_{12} = 1\cdot\left(\frac{1}{2}\right)^{11}$

$a_{12} = \frac{1}{2048}$

The 12th term in the sequence is $\frac{1}{2048}$.

75. This sequence has a common ration of $\frac{1}{4}$, so it is a geometric sequence with

$n = 8$

$a_1 = 40$

$r = \frac{1}{4}$.

Using the formula,

$$a_n = a_1 \cdot r^{n-1}$$
$$a_8 = 40 \cdot \left(\frac{1}{4}\right)^{8-1}$$
$$a_8 = 40 \cdot \left(\frac{1}{4}\right)^{7}$$
$$a_8 = \frac{40}{16384}$$
$$a_8 = \frac{5}{2048}$$

The 8th term in the sequence is $\frac{5}{2048}$.

3 Exercises

1. When 8 girls leave, twice as many boys as girls remain. Because we started with an equal number of boys and girls, 8 is half the number of boys in the classroom. Thus, there are 16 boys, so there are 16 girls, for a total of 32 students.

3. In each row, multiply the first digit by the last digit. The result is the two-digit number between them.
$3 \times 8 = 24$
$7 \times 3 = 21$
$8 \times 5 = 40$
$4 \times 9 = 36$
The x is the digit in the ones place in the result $8 \times 4 = 40,$ so x is 0.

5. Let X = the number of schools that took part in the race. Then there were $3x$ participants in the race. Erin finished in the middle position, so $3x$ is an odd number that is divisible by 3. Also, $3x > 28$, since Iliana finished 28th. The smallest odd number that is divisible by 3 and greater than 28 is 33. This must be the number of participants in the race because if there were 39 participants, then the middle position would have been 20, and Erin would have finished after Katelyn. So $3x = 33$, and $x = 11$. 11 schools sent participants to the cross-country meet.

7. Draw several squares, and for each square draw a different line that goes through the center of the square. Any line through the center of the square will divide the square into two halves that have the same size and shape. There are infinitely many lines that can be drawn through the center of a square, so there are infinitely many ways to cut a square in half.

9. The key to this problem is to think about the way the books are placed on the shelf. When they are placed in alphabetical order from left to right, that means volume A is on the far left and volume Z is on the far right. But think about where the covers for these volumes are. The front cover for volume A is on its right side, touching the back cover of volume B. The back cover for volume Z is on its left side, touching the front cover for volume Y. So the bookworm starts with the front cover of volume A $\left(\frac{1}{4}\text{ inch}\right)$ and eats through the entire volumes B through Y (24 books, 2 inches each, 48 inches total), then finishes by eating the back cover of volume Z $\left(\frac{1}{4}\text{ inch}\right)$. So the total amount eaten is 48.5 inches.

11. If we let n = the number of cats she has, then we can interpret her response as $n = \left(\frac{5}{6}n + 7\right)$ and solve for n.
$$n = \left(\frac{5}{6}n + 7\right)$$
$$6n = 5n + 42$$
$$n = 42$$

13. Let f = the number of gallons in a full tank. Then
$$\frac{1}{8}f + 15 = \frac{3}{4}f$$
$$8\left(\frac{1}{8}f + 15\right) = 8\left(\frac{3}{4}f\right)$$
$$f + 120 = 6f$$
$$120 = 5f$$
$$f = 24 \text{ gallons}$$
Thus a full tank is 24 gallons. The van started with $\frac{1}{8}$ of a full tank or $\frac{1}{8} \cdot 24 = 3$ gallons. Then 15 gallons were added for a total of (3 + 15 = 18) gallons. So (24 – 18) = 6 gallons are needed to fill the tank.

15. 18, 38, 24, 46, 42
8, 24, 8, 24, 8
By trial and error we might notice that if we multiply the two digits of each of the numbers in the first row, we get the corresponding number in the second row of numbers (8 and 24, which repeat).

17. I put the ring in the box and put my lock on the box. I send you the box. You put your lock on, as well, and send it back to me. I then remove my lock with my key and send you the box (with your lock still on) back to you, so you can remove your lock with your key and get the ring.

19. Given the sequence 16, 80, 48, 64, A, B, C, D, where each term is the arithmetic mean of the previous two terms: e.g. $48 = \frac{16+64}{2}$. We therefore know that $A = \frac{48+64}{2} = 56$; $B = \frac{64+56}{2} = 60$; $C = \frac{56+60}{2} = 58$; $D = \frac{60+58}{2} = 59$.

21. Choose a sock from the box labeled *red and green socks.* Since it is mislabeled, it contains only *red* socks or only *green* socks, determined by the sock you choose. If the sock is green, relabel this box *green socks.* Since the other two boxes were mislabeled, switch the remaining label to the other box and place the label that says *red and green socks* on the unlabeled box. No other choice guarantees a correct relabeling, since you can remove only one sock.

23. The total number of dots on each die is 1 + 2 + 3 + 4 + 5 + 6 = 21. Thus the top die has (21 – dots showing), unseen dots, or 21 – (1 + 2 + 3) = 21 – 6 = 15. The middle die has $21-(4+6)=21-10=11$. The bottom die has $21-(5+1)=21-6=15$ dots not shown. The total is $15+11+15=41$ dots not shown. This is option D.
Alternatively, since each die has 21 dots, there are $21\times 3=63$ total dots. Thus, there are $63-22=41$ unseen dots.

25. Visualize (or create unfolded box strip) with "1" on top, and folding "2," "3," and "4" around the middle. Option A satisfies this result.

27. One example of a solution follows.

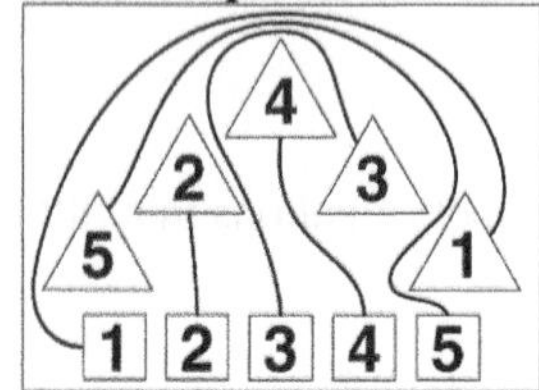

29. By trial and error, the following arrangement will work:

9 7 2 14 11 5 4 12 13 3 6 10 15 1 8

31. Use trial and error. One possible solution is as follows.

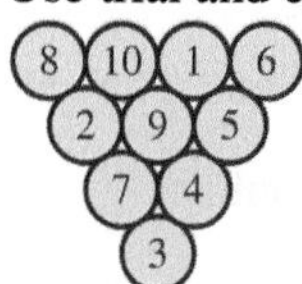

33. For units column assume that 1 is borrowed from the a digit. This suggests that $b=9$ since $12-9=3$. To arrive at 7 in the tens column, we know that 8 must be subtracted from 15. Thus, $a=6$ (remember that we borrowed one from that column, also). We borrowed one from the 7, as well, so that $c=6-4=2$ in the hundreds column. Thus, $a+b+c=6+9+2=17$.
This is represented by option D.

35. This exercise can be solved algebraically. If we let D = the total distance of the trip, and x = the distance traveled while asleep, then

$$x+\frac{1}{2}x=\frac{1}{2}D$$
$$2x+x=D$$
$$3x=D$$
$$x=\frac{1}{3}D$$

Thus, the distance traveled while asleep is $\frac{1}{3}$ of the total distance traveled.

37. Fill the big bucket. Pour into the small bucket. This leaves 4 gallons in the larger bucket. Empty the small bucket. Pour from the big bucket to fill up the small bucket. This leaves 1 gallon in the big bucket. Empty the small bucket. Pour 1 gallon from the big bucket to the small bucket. Fill up the big bucket. Pour into the small bucket. This leaves 5 gallons in the big bucket. Pour out the small bucket. This leaves exactly 5 gallons in the big bucket to take home. The above sequence is indicated by the following table.

Big bucket	7	4	4	1	1	0	7	5	5
Small bucket	0	3	0	3	0	1	1	3	0

39. Count systematically.

	No. of rows × No. of columns
15	1×1 rectangles
12	1×2 rectangles
9	1×3 rectangles
10	2×1 rectangles
8	2×2 rectangles
6	2×3 rectangles
5	3×1 rectangles
4	3×2 rectangles
3	3×3 rectangles
6	1×4 rectangles
4	2×4 rectangles
2	3×4 rectangles
3	1×5 rectangles
2	2×5 rectangles
1	3×5 rectangles
90	total rectangles

This gives a total of 90 rectangles.

41. One strategy is to assume the car was driving near usual highway speed limits (55-75 mph). We begin by trying 55 mph. In two hours the car would have traveled 110 miles. Adding 110 miles to the odometer reading, 15951, we get $110+15951=16061$ miles, which is palindromic. Thus, the speed of the car was 55 miles per hour.

43. Similar to Example 5 in the text, we might examine the units place and tens place for repetitive powers of 7 in order to explore possible patterns.

$7^1 = 07$ $\quad 7^5 = 16,807$

$7^2 = 49$ $\quad 7^6 = 117,649$

$7^3 = 343$ $\quad 7^7 = 823,543$

$7^4 = 2401$ $\quad 7^8 = 5,764,801$

Since the final two digits cycle over four values, we might consider dividing the successive exponents by 4 and examining their remainders. (Note: We are using inductive reasoning when we assume that this pattern will continue and will apply when the exponent is 1997.) Dividing the exponent 1997 by 4, we get a remainder of 1. This is the same remainder we get when dividing the exponent 1 (on 7^1) and 5 (on 7^5). Thus, we expect that the last two digits for 7^{1997} would be 07 as well.

45. Start with a smaller problem.

1000	10,000	100,000	1,000,000
− 50	− 50	− 50	− 50
950	9950	99,950	999,950

Following this pattern, the number that is the result of $10^{50} - 50$ has one zero, one 5, and $(50-2) = 48$ 9's. Thus, $(48 \times 9) + 5 + 0 = 432 + 5 + 0 = 437$.

47. Similar to Example 5 in the text (and Exercise 46 above), we might examine the units place for repetitive powers of 7 in order to explore possible patterns.

$7^1 = 7 \qquad 7^5 = 16{,}807$

$7^2 = 49 \qquad 7^6 = 117{,}649$

$7^3 = 343 \qquad 7^7 = 823{,}543$

$7^4 = 2401 \qquad 7^8 = 5{,}764{,}801$

Since the units digit cycles over four values, we might consider dividing the successive exponents by 4 and examining their remainders. Divide the exponent 491 by 4 to get a quotient of 122 and a remainder of 3. Reasoning inductively, the units digit would be the same as that of 7^3 and 7^7, which is 3.

49. Joanie will want to use as many eight-cent stamps as possible. Since no multiple of 8 has 3 as its last digit, she will need an odd number of five-cent stamps. Working backward, find the largest multiple of 8 that is less than 153 and has 8 as its last digit. The number is 128, or $8 \cdot 16$. So Joanie should use 16 eight-cent stamps and 5 five-cent stamps, for a total of 21 stamps.

51. To find the minimum number of socks to pull out, guess and check. There are two colors of socks. If you pull out 2 socks, you could have 2 of one color or 1 of each color. You must pull out more than 2 socks. If you pull out 3 socks, you might have 3 of one color or 1 of one color and 2 of the other. In either case, you have a matching pair, so 3 is the minimum number of socks to pull out.

53. To count the triangles, it helps to draw sketches of the figure several times. There are 5 triangles formed by two sides of the pentagon and a diagonal. There are 4 triangles formed with each side of the pentagon as a base, so there are $4 \times 5 = 20$ triangles formed in this way. Each point of the star forms a small triangle, so there are 5 of these. Finally, there are 5 triangles formed with a diagonal as a base. In each, the other two sides are inside the pentagon. (None of these triangles has a side common to the pentagon.) Thus, the total number of triangles in the figure is $5 + 20 + 5 + 5 = 35$.

55. Use trial and error to find the smallest perfect number. Try making a chart such as the following one.

Number	Divisors other than itself	Sum
1	None	
2	1	1
3	1	1
4	1, 2	3
5	1	1
6	1, 2, 3	6

Six is the smallest perfect number.

57. Working backward, we see that if the lily pad doubles its size each day so that it completely covers the pond on the twentieth day, the pond was half-covered on the previous (or nineteenth) day.

59. From condition (2), we can figure that since the author is living now, the year must be 196_, since $9 - 3 = 6$. Then, from condition (1), $23 - (1 + 9 + 6) = 7$, so the year is 1967.

61. By Eve's statement, Adam must have $2 more than Eve. But according to Adam, a loss of $1 from Eve to Adam gives Adam twice the amount that Eve has. By trial and error, the counting numbers 5 and 7 are the first to satisfy both conditions. Thus Eve has $5, and Adam has $7.

63. The first digit in the answer cannot be 0, 2, 3, or 5, since these digits have already been used. It cannot be more than 3, since one of the factors is a number in the 30's, making it impossible to get a product over 45,000. Thus, the first digit of the answer must be 1. To find the first digit in the 3-digit factor, use estimation. Dividing a number between 15,000 and 16,000 by a number between 30 and 40 could give a result with a first digit of 3, 4, or 5. Since 3 and 5 have already been used, this first digit must be 4. Thus, the 3-digit factor is 402. We now have the following.

$$\begin{array}{r} \underline{4}\ 0\ 2 \\ \times \quad 3\_ \\ \hline \underline{1}\ 5,\_\ \_\ \_ \end{array}$$

To find the units digit of the 2-digit factor, use trial and error with the digits that have not yet been used: 6, 7, 8, and 9.

$36 \times 402 = 14,472$ (too small and reuses 2 and 4)
$37 \times 402 = 14,874$ (too small and reuses 4)
$38 \times 402 = 15,276$ (reuses 2)
$39 \times 402 = 15,678$ (correct)

The correct problem is as follows.

$$\begin{array}{r} 4\ 0\ 2 \\ \times \quad 3\ 9 \\ \hline 1\ 5,\ 6\ 7\ 8 \end{array}$$

Notice that a combination of strategies was used to solve this problem.

65. Notice that the first column has three given numbers. Thus, $34-(6+11+16)=1$ is the first number in the second row. (Note: You could use the diagonal to solve for missing number in the same manner.) Then, $34-(1+15+14)=4$ is in the second row, third column. The diagonal from upper left to lower right has three given numbers. Therefore, $34-(6+15+10)=3$ is in the fourth row, fourth column. Continue filling in the missing numbers until the magic square is completed.

6	12	7	9
1	15	4	14
11	5	10	8
16	2	13	3

67. 25 pitches: Game tied 0 to 0 going into the 9th inning. Each pitcher has pitched a minimum of 24 pitches (three per inning). The winning pitcher pitches 3 more (fly ball/out) pitches for a total of 27. The losing (visiting team) pitcher pitches 1 more (for a total of 25) which happens to be a home run, thus, losing the game by a score of 1-0. (Note: the same result occurs if the losing pitcher gives up one homerun in any inning.)

69. Draw a sketch, visualize, or cut a piece of paper to build the cube. The cube may be folded with Z on the front.

Then, E is on top and M is on the left face. This places Q opposite the face marked Z. (D is on the bottom and X is on the right face.)

71. A solution, found by trial and error, is shown here.

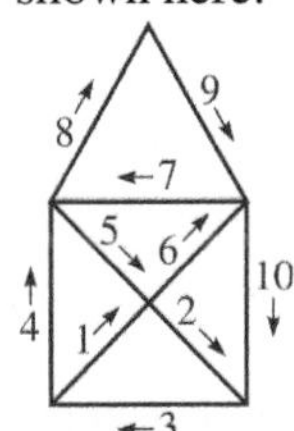

73. Solve this problem by making a list. First, find the ways he can use pennies to make 15 cents.
15 pennies
10 pennies, 1 nickel
5 pennies, 1 dime
5 pennies, 2 nickels
Find additional ways he can use nickels.
3 nickels
1 nickel, 1 dime
There are 6 ways to make 15 cents, so there are 6 ways he can pay 15 cents for a chocolate mint.

75. The triangle is a right triangle because $10^2+24^2=26^2$. The area of the triangle is $\frac{1}{2}(24)(10)=120$ sq cm. The rectangle has the same area as the triangle, with width 3 cm, so the length of the rectangle is $\frac{120}{3}=40$ cm. Then the perimeter of the rectangle is $2(40)+2(3)=80+6=86$ cm.

77. Jessica is married to James or Dan. Since Jessica is married to the oldest person in the group, she is not married to James, who is younger than Cathy. So Jessica is married to Dan, and Cathy is married to James. Since Jessica is married to the oldest person, we know that Dan is 36. Since James is older than Jessica but younger than Cathy, we conclude that Cathy is 31, James is 30, and Jessica is 29.

79. This is a problem with a "catch." The obvious answer is that only one month, February, has 28 days. However, the problem does not specify exactly 28 days, so any month with at least 28 days qualifies. All 12 months have 28 days.

81. Find the pattern in the last digit by repeatedly multiplying 7 by itself:

$7^1 = 7$

$7^2 = 49$

$7^3 = 343$

$7^4 = 2401$

$7^5 = 16{,}807$

$7^6 = 117{,}649$

The pattern in the last digit of each power of 7 is 7, 9, 3, 1 and then the pattern repeats. Divide the exponent 1783 by 4, the number of digits in the pattern: $1783 \div 4 = 445$ with a remainder of 3. The third digit in the pattern is 3, so the last digit of $49{,}327^{1783}$ is 3.

83. The maximum number of squares is 6. One possible array is as follows.

	X	X
X		X
X	X	

85. The sequence of numbers is 1, 1, 2, 3, 5, 8, 13, 21, 34, 55, 89, 144, ... Look at several examples of four successive terms.

Terms	Product of first and fourth	Product of middle terms
1, 1, 2, 3	$1 \cdot 3 = 3$	$1 \cdot 2 = 2$
5, 8, 13, 21	$5 \cdot 21 = 105$	$8 \cdot 13 = 104$
2, 3, 5, 8	$2 \cdot 8 = 16$	$3 \cdot 5 = 15$
8, 13, 21, 34	$8 \cdot 34 = 272$	$13 \cdot 21 = 273$

The products in each row differ by 1.

4 Exercises

Using a graphing calculator, such as the TI-84, we would enter the expressions as indicated on the left side of the equality then push [Enter] to arrive at the answer. When using scientific or other types of calculators some adjustments will have to be made. See observations related to the solutions for Exercise 13 below. It is a good idea to review your calculator handbook for related examples.

1. $39.7 + (8.2 - 4.1) = 43.8$

3. $\sqrt{5.56440921} = 2.3589$

5. $\sqrt[3]{418.508992} = 7.48$

7. $2.67^2 = 7.1289$

9. $5.76^5 \approx 6340.338097$

Observe that when using a calculator, the numerator must be grouped in parentheses as must the denominator. This will make the last operation (the indicated) division.

11. $\dfrac{(14.32 - 8.1)}{(2 \times 3.11)} = 1$

13. $\sqrt[5]{1.35} \approx 1.061858759$. Observe that many scientific calculators have only the $\sqrt[2]{\ }$ function built into the calculator. For an index larger than 2, you might want to think of the nth root of a number b as equivalent to the exponential expression $b^{1/n}$. For example, $\sqrt[5]{1.35} = (1.35)^{1/5}$. Then use your exponentiation function (button) to calculate the 5th root of 1.35. Note that you will enter the exponent $\frac{1}{5}$ on the calculator in parentheses as $(1 \div 5)$.

15. $\frac{\pi}{\sqrt{2}} \approx 2.221441469$

17. $\sqrt[4]{\frac{2143}{22}} \approx 3.141592653$

19. $\frac{\sqrt{2}}{\sqrt[3]{6}} \approx 0.7782717162$

21. Choose a five-digit number such as 73,468.
$73468 \times 9 = 661212$
$6+6+1+2+1+2=18$
$1+8=9$
Choose a six-digit number such as 739,216.
$739216 \times 9 = 6652944$
$6+6+5+2+9+4+4=36$
$3+6=9$
Yes, the same result holds.

23. $(-3) \div (-8) = 0.375$
$(-5) \div (-4) = 1.25$
$(-2.7) \div (-4.3) \approx 0.6279069767$
Dividing a negative number by another negative number gives a positive number.

25. $5.6^0 = 1;\ \pi^0 = 1;\ 2^0 = 1;\ 120^0 = 1;$
Raising a nonzero number to the power 0 gives a result of 1.

27. $\frac{1}{7} \approx .1428571$
$\frac{1}{(-9)} \approx -.1111111$
$\frac{1}{3} \approx .3333333$
$\frac{1}{(-8)} = -.125$
The sign of the reciprocal of a number is the same as the sign of the number.

29. $(0/8) = 0;\ (0/-2) = 0;\ (0/\pi) = 0$
Zero divided by a nonzero number gives a quotient of 0.

31. $(-3)\times(-4)\times(-5) = -60$
$(-3)\times(-4)\times(-5)\times(-6)\times(-7) = -2520$
$(-3)\times(-4)\times(-5)\times(-6)\times(-7)\times(-8)\times(-9)$
$= -181440$
Multiplying an *odd* number of negative numbers gives a negative product.

33. Writing exercise; answers will vary.

35. Writing exercise; answers will vary.

37. $563 \div 9 \approx 62.555556$. Since more than 62 are needed, we require 63 pages.

39. $800 \div 60 \approx 13.333$. Since more than 13 are needed, we require 14 containers.

41. $140{,}000 \div 80 \approx 160{,}000 \div 80 = \$2000$; option B

43. $40{,}249 \div 968 \approx \left(\frac{40{,}000}{1000}\right) = 40$; option A

45. Approximating the numbers for ease of calculation we have
1100 yards $\div$ 100 passes = 11 yards/catch; option D

47. Add the given percentages of known countries (52% + 13% + 30%) to get 95%. Subtract from 100% to get remaining area of pie chart:
100% − 95% = 5%

49. Thirteen percent of the 2,000,000 immigrants we would expect to arrive from Europe. Thus,
$13\% \times 2{,}000{,}000 = 0.13 \times 2{,}000{,}000$
$= 260{,}000$

51. U.S. milk production was greater than 175 billion pounds in 2005, 2006, and 2007.

53. 2001: about 165 billion pounds;
2007: about 185 billion pounds

55. The greatest increase in price occurred from 2000 to 2005. The increase was about \$2.25 − \$1.40 = \$0.85.

57. The price of a gallon of gas was decreasing.

Chapter Test

1. This is an example of inductive reasoning, since you are reasoning from a specific pattern to the general conclusion that she will again exceed her annual sales goal.

2. This is a deductive argument because you are reasoning from the stated general property to the specific result, 176^2 is a natural number.

3. Add the elements in the center column together to get 38. Each column and diagonal must also add to 38. This yields the following magic hexagon.

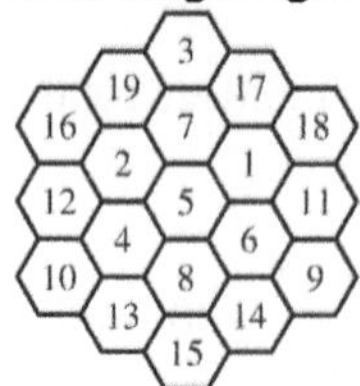

4. The specific pattern seems to indicate that the second factor in the product is a multiple of 17 and the digits on the right side of the equation increase by 1. If this pattern is correct, then the next term in the sequence would be
$65{,}359{,}477{,}124{,}183 \times 68$
$= 4{,}444{,}444{,}444{,}444{,}444$
since $4 \times 17 = 68$. This can be verified by multiplying $65{,}359{,}477{,}124{,}183 \times 68$ on your calculator.

5.
3 11 31 69 131 223 <u>351</u>
8 20 38 62 92 <u>128</u>
12 18 24 30 <u>36</u>
6 6 6 (6)
Thus, our next term in the sequence is $128 + 223 = 351$.

6. Using the method of Gauss, we have
1 + 250 = 251, 2 + 249 = 251, etc.
There are $\frac{250}{2} = 125$ such pairs, so the sum can be calculated as $125 \times 251 = 31{,}375$.

7. The next predicted octagonal number is 65, since the next equation on the list would be $65 = 1 + 7 + 13 + 19 + 25$, where 25 = 19 + 6.

8. Beginning with the first five octagonal numbers and applying the method of successive differences, we get
1 8 21 40 65 96 133 176
7 13 19 25 31 37 43
6 6 6 6 (6) (6)
Dividing each octagonal number by 4 we get the following pattern of remainders: 1, 0, 1, 0, 1, 0, 1, 0, … .

9. After the first two terms (both of which are 1), we can find the next by adding the two proceeding terms. That is, to get the 3rd term, add 1 + 1 = 2; the 4th term, 1 + 2 = 3; the 5th term, 2 + 3 = 5; and so forth.

10. To make the fraction as small as possible we want the smallest possible numerator (24) and the largest possible denominator (96).
Thus, we get the fraction $\frac{24}{96}$, which reduces to $\frac{1}{4}$.

11. Examine the units place for repetitive powers of 9 in order to explore possible patterns.
$9^1 = 9$ $9^3 = 729$ $9^5 = 59049$
$9^2 = 81$ $9^4 = 6561$ $9^6 = 531441$
If we divide the exponent 1997 by 2 (since the pattern of the units digit cycles after every 2nd power), we get a remainder of 1. Noting that in the line of 9^1, where each exponent when divided by 2 yields a remainder of 1, there is a units digit of 9, we reason inductively that 9^{1997} has the same units digit, 9.

12. There are 5 smaller triangles representing the extremities of the inside star. There are 5 triangles outside (between) the extremities of the star. Each (outside) line segment forms the base of (5) isosceles triangles that have their apex at each point of the star. Using the line segment connecting two points of the star as a base, two triangles can be formed; one (outside) with a point on the star as an opposite vertex; and one (inside) with opposite vertex at the intersection of any two lines forming the star. There is a total of 10 of these isosceles triangles. This gives a complete total of 35 triangles.

13. Answers will vary. One possible solution is $1 + 2 + 3 - 4 + 5 + 6 + 78 + 9 + 0 = 100$.

14. Dr. Small is 36 inches tall, and he shrinks 2 inches per year. So he will disappear after 36/2 = 18 years. In 18 years, Ms. Tall will grow $18 \cdot \frac{2}{3} = 12$ inches, so she will be 96 + 12 = 108 inches tall, or 9 ft.

15. Observe the following patterns on successive powers of 11, 14, and 16 in order to determine the units value of each term in the sum $11^{11} + 14^{14} + 16^{16}$.

$11^1 = 11$	$14^1 = 14$	$16^1 = 16$
$11^2 = 121$	$14^2 = 196$	$16^2 = 256$
$11^3 = 1331$	$14^3 = 2744$	$16^3 = 4096$
	$14^4 = 38146$	

Thus, we would expect 11^{11} to have the same unit digit value of 1. Since powers of 14 have units digits which cycles between 4 and 6, we observe that division of the exponents by 2 yield remainders of 1 or 0. We might expect the same pattern to continue to 14^{14}. Division of the exponent by 2 gives a remainder of 0. We get the same remainder, 0, for all even powers on 14, and each of these numbers has a units digit of 6. The powers of 16 seem to all have the same unit value of 6. Thus, if we add the units digits 1 + 6 + 6 = 13, we see that the units digit of this sum is 3.

16. Making the following observations

$9 \times 1 = 9$

$9 \times 2 = 18 \ (1 + 8 = 9)$

$9 \times 3 = 27 \ (2 + 7 = 9)$

$9 \times 4 = 36 \ (3 + 6 = 9)$

$9 \times 5 = 45 \ (4 + 5 = 9)$

suggests that the sum of the digits in the product will always be 9.

17. $\sqrt{98.16} \approx 9.907572861$ But answers may vary depending upon what calculator you are using.

18. $3.25^3 = 34.328125$

19. The ratio of made shots to those attempted is approximately $\frac{30}{100} = \frac{3}{10}$. So in 10 attempts, we would expect her to make about 3 shots; option B

20. **(a)** The unemployment rate decreased between 1998 and 1999, between 199 and 2000, and between 2003 and 2004.

(b) Between 2000 and 2003, the unemployment rate was increasing.

(c) 2003: 6.0%; 2004: 5.5%; The unemployment rate declined by 0.5%.

THE BASIC CONCEPTS OF SET THEORY

Picture Desk/Kobal Collection

In the movie *I.Q.*, Meg Ryan plays Catherine Boyd, Alfred Einstein's brilliant niece, who is attracted to blue-collar worker Ed Walters (Tim Robbins). Ed pretends to be a physicist.

ED: I think your uncle wants us to dance.

CATHERINE: Oh, now, don't be irrelevant, Ed. You can't get from there to here.

ED: Why not?

CATHERINE: Now don't tell me that a famous and brilliant scientist such as yourself doesn't know about Zeno's paradox.

ED: Remind me.

CATHERINE: You can't get from there to here because you always have to cover half the remaining distance, like from me to you. I have to cover half of it. Then, see, I still have half of that remaining, so I cover half that . . . and since there are infinite halves left, I can't ever get there.

ED (taking her in his arms and starting to dance): So how did that happen?

CATHERINE: I don't know.

Prior to the twentieth century, some ideas in *set theory* were considered *paradoxes* (wrong opinions). *Zeno's paradox,* as described by Catherine and seen in **Exercises 51 and 52** of the **Extension,** has been around in several forms for thousands of years.

1 SYMBOLS AND TERMINOLOGY

Designating Sets • Sets of Numbers and Cardinality • Finite and Infinite Sets • Equality of Sets

Bettmann/Corbis

The basic ideas of set theory were developed by the German mathematician **Georg Cantor** (1845–1918) in about 1875. Cantor created a new field of theory and at the same time continued the long debate over infinity that began in ancient times. He developed counting by one-to-one correspondence to determine how many objects are contained in a set. Infinite sets differ from finite sets by not obeying the familiar law that the whole is greater than any of its parts.

Designating Sets

A **set** is a collection of objects. The objects belonging to the set are called the **elements,** or **members,** of the set. Sets are designated using the following three methods: (1) *word description,* (2) the *listing method,* and (3) *set-builder notation.*

The set of even counting numbers less than 10	Word description
$\{2, 4, 6, 8\}$	Listing method
$\{x \mid x \text{ is an even counting number less than } 10\}$	Set-builder notation

The set-builder notation above is read "the set of all x such that x is an even counting number less than 10." Set-builder notation uses the algebraic idea of a *variable.* (Any symbol would do, but just as in other algebraic applications, the letter x is a common choice.)

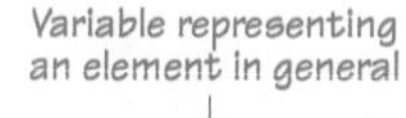

$$\{x \mid x \text{ is an even counting number less than } 10\}$$

Criteria by which an element qualifies for membership in the set

Sets are commonly given names (usually capital letters), such as E for the set of all letters of the English alphabet.

$$E = \{\text{a, b, c, d, e, f, g, h, i, j, k, l, m, n, o, p, q, r, s, t, u, v, w, x, y, z}\}$$

The listing notation can often be shortened by establishing the pattern of elements included and using ellipsis points to indicate a continuation of the pattern.

$$E = \{\text{a, b, c, d}, \ldots, \text{x, y, z}\}, \quad \text{or} \quad E = \{\text{a, b, c, d, e}, \ldots, \text{z}\}.$$

The set containing no elements is called the **empty set,** or **null set.** The symbol $\emptyset$ is used to denote the empty set, so $\emptyset$ and $\{\ \}$ have the same meaning. We do *not* denote the empty set with the symbol $\{\emptyset\}$ because this notation represents a set with one element (that element being the empty set).

EXAMPLE 1 Listing Elements of Sets

Give a complete listing of all the elements of each set.

(a) the set of counting numbers between six and thirteen

(b) $\{5, 6, 7, \ldots, 13\}$

(c) $\{x \mid x \text{ is a counting number between 6 and 7}\}$

SOLUTION

(a) This set can be denoted $\{7, 8, 9, 10, 11, 12\}$. (Notice that the word *between* excludes the endpoint values.)

(b) This set begins with the element 5, then 6, then 7, and so on, with each element obtained by adding 1 to the previous element in the list. This pattern stops at 13, so a complete listing is $\{5, 6, 7, 8, 9, 10, 11, 12, 13\}$.

(c) There are no counting numbers between 6 and 7, so this is the empty set $\{\ \}$, or $\emptyset$.

For a set to be useful, it must be well defined. For example, the preceding set E of the letters of the English alphabet is well defined. Given the letter q, we know that q is an element of E. Given the Greek letter θ (theta), we know that it is not an element of set E.

However, given the set C of all good singers, and a particular singer, Raeanna, it may not be possible to say whether

Raeanna is an element of C or Raeanna is *not* an element of C.

The problem is the word "good"; how good is good? Because we cannot necessarily decide whether a given singer belongs to set C, set C is not well defined.

The letter q is an element of set E, where E is the set of all the letters of the English alphabet. To show this, the symbol $\in$ is used.

$$\text{q} \in E$$ This is read "q is an element of set E."

The letter θ is not an element of E. To show this, $\in$ with a slash mark is used.

$$\theta \notin E$$ This is read "θ is not an element of set E."

EXAMPLE 2 Applying the Symbol ∈

Decide whether each statement is *true* or *false*.

(a) $3 \in \{1, 2, 5, 9, 13\}$ **(b)** $0 \in \{0, 1, 2, 3\}$ **(c)** $\frac{1}{5} \notin \left\{\frac{1}{3}, \frac{1}{4}, \frac{1}{6}\right\}$

SOLUTION

(a) Because 3 is *not* an element of the set $\{1, 2, 5, 9, 13\}$, the statement is *false*.

(b) Because 0 is indeed an element of the set $\{0, 1, 2, 3\}$, the statement is *true*.

(c) This statement says that $\frac{1}{5}$ is not an element of the set $\left\{\frac{1}{3}, \frac{1}{4}, \frac{1}{6}\right\}$, which is *true*.

Sets of Numbers and Cardinality

Important categories of numbers are summarized below.

Sets of Numbers

Natural or Counting numbers $\{1, 2, 3, 4, \ldots\}$

Whole numbers $\{0, 1, 2, 3, 4, \ldots\}$

Integers $\{\ldots, -3, -2, -1, 0, 1, 2, 3, \ldots\}$

Rational numbers $\left\{\frac{p}{q} \,\middle|\, p \text{ and } q \text{ are integers, and } q \neq 0\right\}$

(*Examples:* $\frac{3}{5}$, $-\frac{7}{9}$, 5, 0. Any rational number may be written as a terminating decimal number, such as 0.25, or a repeating decimal number, such as 0.666 . . . .)

Real numbers $\{x \mid x \text{ is a number that can be expressed as a decimal}\}$

Irrational numbers $\{x \mid x \text{ is a real number and } x \text{ cannot be expressed as a quotient of integers}\}$

(*Examples:* $\sqrt{2}$, $\sqrt[3]{4}$, π. Decimal representations of irrational numbers are neither terminating nor repeating.)

The number of elements in a set is called the **cardinal number,** or **cardinality,** of the set. The symbol

$$n(A), \quad \text{which is read "}n \text{ of } A\text{,"}$$

represents the cardinal number of set A. If elements are repeated in a set listing, they should not be counted more than once when determining the cardinal number of the set.

EXAMPLE 3 Finding Cardinal Numbers

Find the cardinal number of each set.

(a) $K = \{2, 4, 8, 16\}$ **(b)** $M = \{0\}$ **(c)** $B = \{1, 1, 2, 2, 3\}$

(d) $R = \{4, 5, \ldots, 12, 13\}$ **(e)** $\emptyset$

SOLUTION

(a) Set K contains four elements, so the cardinal number of set K is 4, and $n(K) = 4$.

(b) Set M contains only one element, 0, so $n(M) = 1$.

(c) If elements are repeated in a set listing, they should not be counted more than once when determining the cardinal number of the set. Set B has only three *distinct* elements, so $n(B) = 3$.

(d) Although only four elements are listed, the ellipsis points indicate that there are other elements in the set. Counting them all, we find that there are ten elements, so $n(R) = 10$.

(e) The empty set, $\emptyset$, contains no elements, so $n(\emptyset) = 0$. ■■■

Beth Anderson/Pearson

A close-up of a camera lens shows the **infinity symbol,** ∞, defined in this case as any distance greater than 1000 times the focal length of a lens.

The sign was invented by the mathematician John Wallis in 1655. Wallis used $1/\infty$ to represent an infinitely small quantity.

Finite and Infinite Sets

If the cardinal number of a set is a particular whole number (0 or a counting number), as in all parts of **Example 3,** we call that set a **finite set.** Given enough time, we could finish counting all the elements of any finite set and arrive at its cardinal number.

Some sets, however, are so large that we could never finish the counting process. The counting numbers themselves are such a set. Whenever a set is so large that its cardinal number is not found among the whole numbers, we call that set an **infinite set.**

EXAMPLE 4 Designating an Infinite Set

Designate all odd counting numbers by the three common methods of set notation.

SOLUTION

The set of all odd counting numbers	Word description
$\{1, 3, 5, 7, 9, \ldots\}$	Listing method
$\{x \mid x \text{ is an odd counting number}\}$	Set-builder notation

■■■

Equality of Sets

Set Equality

Set A is **equal** to set B provided the following two conditions are met:

1. Every element of A is an element of B, and
2. Every element of B is an element of A.

Two sets are equal if they contain exactly the same elements, regardless of order.

$$\{a, b, c, d\} = \{a, c, d, b\}$$ Both sets contain exactly the same elements.

Repetition of elements in a set listing does not add new elements.

$$\{1, 0, 1, 2, 3, 3\} = \{0, 1, 2, 3\}$$ Both sets contain exactly the same elements.

EXAMPLE 5 Determining Whether Two Sets Are Equal

Are $\{-4, 3, 2, 5\}$ and $\{-4, 0, 3, 2, 5\}$ equal sets?

SOLUTION

Every element of the first set is an element of the second. However, 0 is an element of the second and not of the first. The sets do not contain exactly the same elements, so they are not equal.

$$\{-4, 3, 2, 5\} \neq \{-4, 0, 3, 2, 5\}$$

EXAMPLE 6 Determining Whether Two Sets Are Equal

Decide whether each statement is *true* or *false*.

(a) $\{3\} = \{x \mid x$ is a counting number between 1 and 5$\}$

(b) $\{x \mid x$ is a negative natural number$\} = \{y \mid y$ is a number that is both rational and irrational$\}$

SOLUTION

(a) The set on the right contains *all* counting numbers between 1 and 5, namely 2, 3, and 4, while the set on the left contains *only* the number 3. Because the sets do not contain exactly the same elements, they are not equal. The statement is *false*.

(b) All natural numbers are positive, so the set on the left is $\emptyset$. By definition, if a number is rational, it cannot be irrational, so the set on the right is also $\emptyset$. Because each set is the empty set, the sets are equal. The statement is *true*.

1 EXERCISES

Match each set in Column I with the appropriate description in Column II.

I	II
1. $\{1, 3, 5, 7, 9\}$	**A.** the set of all even integers
2. $\{x \mid x$ is an even integer greater than 4 and less than 6$\}$	**B.** the set of the five least positive integer powers of 2
3. $\{\ldots, -4, -3, -2, -1\}$	**C.** the set of even positive integers less than 10
4. $\{\ldots, -5, -3, -1, 1, 3, 5, \ldots\}$	**D.** the set of all odd integers
5. $\{2, 4, 8, 16, 32\}$	**E.** the set of all negative integers
6. $\{\ldots, -4, -2, 0, 2, 4, \ldots\}$	**F.** the set of odd positive integers less than 10
7. $\{2, 4, 6, 8, 10\}$	**G.** $\emptyset$
8. $\{2, 4, 6, 8\}$	**H.** the set of the five least positive integer multiples of 2

List all the elements of each set. Use set notation and the listing method to describe the set.

9. the set of all counting numbers less than or equal to 6

10. the set of all whole numbers greater than 8 and less than 18

11. the set of all whole numbers not greater than 4

12. the set of all counting numbers between 4 and 14

13. $\{6, 7, 8, \ldots, 14\}$

14. $\{3, 6, 9, 12, \ldots, 30\}$

15. $\{-15, -13, -11, \ldots, -1\}$

16. $\{-4, -3, -2, \ldots, 4\}$

17. $\{2, 4, 8, \ldots, 256\}$

18. $\{90, 87, 84, \ldots, 69\}$

19. $\{x \mid x \text{ is an even whole number less than } 11\}$

20. $\{x \mid x \text{ is an odd integer between } -8 \text{ and } 7\}$

Denote each set by the listing method. There may be more than one correct answer.

21. the set of all counting numbers greater than 20

22. the set of all integers between −200 and 500

23. the set of Great Lakes

24. the set of U.S. presidents who served after Richard Nixon and before Barack Obama

25. $\{x \mid x \text{ is a positive multiple of } 5\}$

26. $\{x \mid x \text{ is a negative multiple of } 6\}$

27. $\{x \mid x \text{ is the reciprocal of a natural number}\}$

28. $\{x \mid x \text{ is a positive integer power of } 4\}$

Denote each set by set-builder notation, using x as the variable. There may be more than one correct answer.

29. the set of all rational numbers

30. the set of all even natural numbers

31. $\{1, 3, 5, \ldots, 75\}$

32. $\{35, 40, 45, \ldots, 95\}$

Give a word description for each set. There may be more than one correct answer.

33. $\{-9, -8, -7, \ldots, 7, 8, 9\}$

34. $\left\{1, \frac{1}{2}, \frac{1}{3}, \frac{1}{4}, \ldots\right\}$

35. {Alabama, Alaska, Arizona, . . . , Wisconsin, Wyoming}

36. {Alaska, California, Hawaii, Oregon, Washington}

Identify each set as finite *or* infinite.

37. $\{2, 4, 6, \ldots, 932\}$

38. $\{6, 12, 18\}$

39. $\left\{\frac{1}{2}, \frac{2}{3}, \frac{3}{4}, \ldots\right\}$

40. $\{\ldots, -100, -80, -60, -40, \ldots\}$

41. $\{x \mid x \text{ is a natural number greater than } 50\}$

42. $\{x \mid x \text{ is a natural number less than } 50\}$

43. $\{x \mid x \text{ is a rational number}\}$

44. $\{x \mid x \text{ is a rational number between } 0 \text{ and } 1\}$

Find n(A) for each set.

45. $A = \{0, 1, 2, 3, 4, 5, 6, 7\}$

46. $A = \{-3, -1, 1, 3, 5, 7, 9\}$

47. $A = \{2, 4, 6, \ldots, 1000\}$

48. $A = \{0, 1, 2, 3, \ldots, 3000\}$

49. $A = \{\text{a, b, c}, \ldots, \text{z}\}$

50. $A = \{x \mid x \text{ is a vowel in the English alphabet}\}$

51. $A =$ the set of integers between −20 and 20

52. $A =$ the set of sanctioned U.S. senate seats

53. $A = \left\{\frac{1}{3}, \frac{2}{4}, \frac{3}{5}, \frac{4}{6}, \ldots, \frac{27}{29}, \frac{28}{30}\right\}$

54. $A = \left\{\frac{1}{2}, -\frac{1}{2}, \frac{1}{3}, -\frac{1}{3}, \ldots, \frac{1}{10}, -\frac{1}{10}\right\}$

55. Although *x* is a consonant, why can we write "*x* is a vowel in the English alphabet" in **Exercise 50?**

56. Explain how **Exercise 53** can be answered without actually listing and then counting all the elements.

Identify each set as well defined *or* not well defined.

57. $\{x \mid x \text{ is a real number}\}$

58. $\{x \mid x \text{ is a good athlete}\}$

59. $\{x \mid x \text{ is a difficult course}\}$

60. $\{x \mid x \text{ is a counting number less than } 2\}$

Fill each blank with either $\in$ *or* $\notin$ *to make each statement true.*

61. 5 ____ $\{2, 4, 5, 7\}$

62. -4 ____ $\{4, 7, 8, 12\}$

63. -12 ____ $\{3, 8, 12, 18\}$

64. 0 ____ $\{-2, 0, 5, 9\}$

65. $\{3\}$ ____ $\{2, 3, 4, 6\}$

66. $\{6\}$ ____ $\{5 + 1, 6 + 1\}$

67. 8 ____ $\{11 - 2, 10 - 2, 9 - 2, 8 - 2\}$

68. The statement $3 \in \{9 - 6, 8 - 6, 7 - 6\}$ is true even though the *symbol* 3 does not appear in the set. Explain.

Write true *or* false *for each statement.*

69. $3 \in \{2, 5, 6, 8\}$

70. $6 \in \{-2, 5, 8, 9\}$

71. $b \in \{h, c, d, a, b\}$

72. $m \in \{l, m, n, o, p\}$

73. $9 \notin \{6, 3, 4, 8\}$

74. $2 \notin \{7, 6, 5, 4\}$

75. $\{k, c, r, a\} = \{k, c, a, r\}$

76. $\{e, h, a, n\} = \{a, h, e, n\}$

77. $\{5, 8, 9\} = \{5, 8, 9, 0\}$

78. $\{3, 7, 12, 14\} = \{3, 7, 12, 14, 0\}$

79. $\{4\} \in \{\{3\}, \{4\}, \{5\}\}$

80. $4 \in \{\{3\}, \{4\}, \{5\}\}$

81. $\{x \mid x \text{ is a natural number less than } 3\} = \{1, 2\}$

82. $\{x \mid x \text{ is a natural number greater than } 10\} = \{11, 12, 13, \ldots\}$

Write true *or* false *for each statement.*

Let $A = \{2, 4, 6, 8, 10, 12\}$, $B = \{2, 4, 8, 10\}$, *and* $C = \{4, 10, 12\}$.

83. $4 \in A$

84. $8 \in B$

85. $4 \notin C$

86. $8 \notin B$

87. Every element of C is also an element of A.

88. Every element of C is also an element of B.

89. The human mind likes to create collections. Why do you suppose this is so? In your explanation, use one or more particular "collections," mathematical or otherwise.

90. Explain the difference between a well-defined set and a not well-defined set. Give examples and use terms introduced in this section.

Two sets are ***equal*** *if they contain identical elements. However, two sets are* ***equivalent*** *if they contain the same number of elements (but not necessarily the same elements). For each condition, give an example or explain why it is impossible.*

91. two sets that are neither equal nor equivalent

92. two sets that are equal but not equivalent

93. two sets that are equivalent but not equal

94. two sets that are both equal and equivalent

95. ***Overpaid Actors*** A *Forbes* magazine survey of a recent five-year period considered 100 featured Hollywood actors. The table shows the "worst" ten actors, in terms of how much their films returned per dollar that the actor earned.

Most Overpaid Actors

Rank	Actor	Return per Dollar to Actor
1.	Will Ferrell	\$3.29
2.	Ewan McGregor	\$3.75
3.	Billy Bob Thornton	\$4.00
4.	Eddie Murphy	\$4.43
5.	Ice Cube	\$4.77
6.	Tom Cruise	\$7.18
7.	Drew Barrymore	\$7.43
8.	Leonardo DiCaprio	\$7.52
9.	Samuel L. Jackson	\$8.59
10.	Jim Carrey	\$8.62

Source: Forbes.com

(a) List the set of actors with a return of at least \$7.40.

(b) List the set of actors with a return of at most \$3.75.

96. ***Burning Calories*** Candice Cotton likes cotton candy, each serving of which contains 220 calories. To burn off unwanted calories, Candice participates in her favorite activities, shown below, in increments of 1 hour and never repeats a given activity on a given day.

Activity	Symbol	Calories Burned per Hour
Volleyball	v	160
Golf	g	260
Canoeing	c	340
Swimming	s	410
Running	r	680

(a) On Monday, Candice has time for no more than two hours of activities. List all possible sets of activities that would burn off at least the number of calories obtained from three cotton candies.

(b) Assume that Candice can afford up to three hours of time for activities on Wednesday. List all sets of activities that would burn off at least the number of calories in five cotton candies.

(c) Candice can spend up to four hours in activities on Saturday. List all sets of activities that would burn off at least the number of calories in seven cotton candies.

2 VENN DIAGRAMS AND SUBSETS

Venn Diagrams • Complement of a Set • Subsets of a Set • Proper Subsets • Counting Subsets

Venn Diagrams

In the statement of a problem, there is either a stated or implied **universe of discourse.** The universe of discourse includes all things under discussion at a given time. For example, in studying reactions to a proposal that a certain campus raise the minimum age of individuals to whom beer may be sold, the universe of discourse might be all the students at the school, the nearby members of the public, the board of trustees of the school, or perhaps all these groups of people.

In set theory, the universe of discourse is called the **universal set,** typically designated by the letter U. The universal set might change from problem to problem.

Also in set theory, we commonly use **Venn diagrams,** developed by the logician John Venn (1834–1923). In these diagrams, the universal set is represented by a rectangle, and other sets of interest within the universal set are depicted by circular regions (sometimes ovals or other shapes). See **Figure 1**.

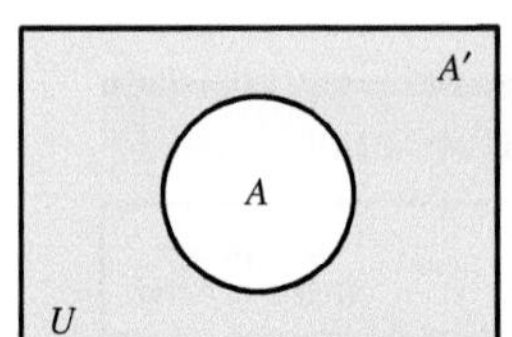

The entire region bounded by the rectangle represents the universal set U, while the portion bounded by the circle represents set A.

Figure 1

Complement of a Set

The colored region inside U and outside the circle in **Figure 1** is labeled A' (read "**A prime**"). This set, called the *complement* of A, contains all elements that are contained in U but not contained in A.

The Complement of a Set

For any set A within the universal set U, the **complement** of A, written A', is the set of elements of U that are not elements of A. That is,

$$A' = \{x \mid x \in U \text{ and } x \notin A\}.$$

EXAMPLE 1 Finding Complements

Find each set.

Let $U = \{a, b, c, d, e, f, g, h\}$, $M = \{a, b, e, f\}$, and $N = \{b, d, e, g, h\}$.

(a) M' **(b)** N'

SOLUTION

(a) Set M' contains all the elements of set U that are *not* in set M. Because set M contains a, b, e, and f, these elements will be disqualified from belonging to set M'.

$$M' = \{c, d, g, h\}$$

(b) Set N' contains all the elements of U that are not in set N, so $N' = \{a, c, f\}$.

Consider the complement of the universal set, U'. The set U' is found by selecting all the elements of U that do not belong to U. There are no such elements, so there can be no elements in set U'. This means that for any universal set U,

$$U' = \emptyset.$$

Now consider the complement of the empty set, $\emptyset'$. Because $\emptyset' = \{x \mid x \in U \text{ and } x \notin \emptyset\}$ and set $\emptyset$ contains no elements, every member of the universal set U satisfies this description. Therefore, for any universal set U,

$$\emptyset' = U.$$

Subsets of a Set

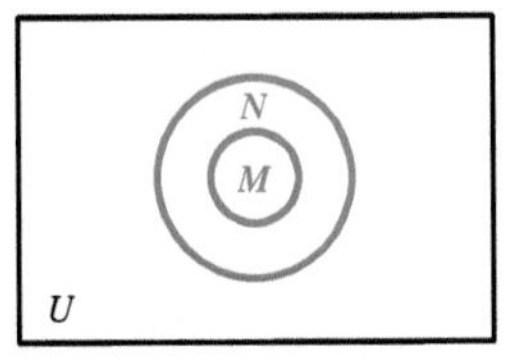

Figure 2

Suppose that we are given the universal set $U = \{1, 2, 3, 4, 5\}$, while $A = \{1, 2, 3\}$. Every element of set A is also an element of set U. Because of this, set A is called a *subset* of set U, written

$$A \subseteq U.$$

("A is not a subset of set U" would be written $A \nsubseteq U$.)

A Venn diagram showing that set M is a subset of set N is shown in **Figure 2**.

Subset of a Set

Set A is a **subset** of set B if every element of A is also an element of B. In symbols, this is written $\boldsymbol{A \subseteq B}$.

EXAMPLE 2 Determining Whether One Set is a Subset of Another

Write $\subseteq$ or $\nsubseteq$ in each blank to make a true statement.

(a) $\{3, 4, 5, 6\}$ ____ $\{3, 4, 5, 6, 8\}$ **(b)** $\{1, 2, 6\}$ ____ $\{2, 4, 6, 8\}$

(c) $\{5, 6, 7, 8\}$ ____ $\{5, 6, 7, 8\}$

SOLUTION

(a) Because every element of $\{3, 4, 5, 6\}$ is also an element of $\{3, 4, 5, 6, 8\}$, the first set is a subset of the second, so $\subseteq$ goes in the blank.

$$\{3, 4, 5, 6\} \subseteq \{3, 4, 5, 6, 8\}$$

(b) $\{1, 2, 6\} \nsubseteq \{2, 4, 6, 8\}$ 1 does not belong to $\{2, 4, 6, 8\}$.

(c) $\{5, 6, 7, 8\} \subseteq \{5, 6, 7, 8\}$ ∎

As **Example 2(c)** suggests, every set is a subset of itself.

$$\boldsymbol{B \subseteq B}, \quad \textbf{for any set } \boldsymbol{B}.$$

The statement of set equality in **Section 1** can be formally presented.

Set Equality (Alternative definition)

Suppose A and B are sets. Then $A = B$ if $A \subseteq B$ and $B \subseteq A$ are both true.

Proper Subsets

Suppose that we are given the following sets.

$$B = \{5, 6, 7, 8\} \quad \text{and} \quad A = \{6, 7\}$$

A is a subset of B, but A is not all of B. There is at least one element in B that is not in A. (Actually, in this case there are two such elements, 5 and 8.) In this situation, A is called a *proper subset* of B. To indicate that A is a proper subset of B, write

$$A \subset B.$$

Notice the similarity of the subset symbols, $\subset$ and $\subseteq$, to the inequality symbols from algebra, $<$ and $\leq$.

Proper Subset of a Set

Set A is a **proper subset** of set B if $A \subseteq B$ and $A \neq B$. In symbols, this is written $\boldsymbol{A \subset B}$.

EXAMPLE 3 Determining Subset and Proper Subset Relationships

Decide whether $\subset$, $\subseteq$, or both could be placed in each blank to make a true statement.

(a) $\{5, 6, 7\}$ ____ $\{5, 6, 7, 8\}$ **(b)** $\{a, b, c\}$ ____ $\{a, b, c\}$

SOLUTION

(a) Every element of $\{5, 6, 7\}$ is contained in $\{5, 6, 7, 8\}$, so $\subseteq$ could be placed in the blank. Also, the element 8 belongs to $\{5, 6, 7, 8\}$ but not to $\{5, 6, 7\}$, making $\{5, 6, 7\}$ a proper subset of $\{5, 6, 7, 8\}$. Place $\subset$ in the blank.

(b) The set $\{a, b, c\}$ is a subset of $\{a, b, c\}$. Because the two sets are equal, $\{a, b, c\}$ is not a proper subset of $\{a, b, c\}$. Only $\subseteq$ may be placed in the blank. ▮▮▮

Set A is a subset of set B if every element of set A is also an element of set B. This definition can be reworded by saying that set A is a subset of set B if there are no elements of A that are not also elements of B. This second form of the definition shows that the empty set is a subset of any set.

$$\emptyset \subseteq B, \quad \textbf{for any set } B.$$

This is true because it is not possible to find any elements of $\emptyset$ that are not also in B. (There are no elements in $\emptyset$.) The empty set $\emptyset$ is a proper subset of every set except itself.

$$\emptyset \subset B \quad \textbf{if } B \textbf{ is any set other than } \emptyset.$$

Every set (except ∅) has at least two subsets, ∅ and the set itself.

EXAMPLE 4 Listing All Subsets of a Set

Find all possible subsets of each set.

(a) $\{7, 8\}$ **(b)** $\{a, b, c\}$

SOLUTION

(a) By trial and error, the set $\{7, 8\}$ has four subsets: $\emptyset$, $\{7\}$, $\{8\}$, $\{7, 8\}$.

(b) Here, trial and error leads to eight subsets for $\{a, b, c\}$:

$$\emptyset, \{a\}, \{b\}, \{c\}, \{a, b\}, \{a, c\}, \{b, c\}, \{a, b, c\}.$$ ▮▮▮

Counting Subsets

In **Example 4,** the subsets of $\{7, 8\}$ and the subsets of $\{a, b, c\}$ were found by trial and error. An alternative method involves drawing a **tree diagram,** a systematic way of listing all the subsets of a given set. See **Figure 3**.

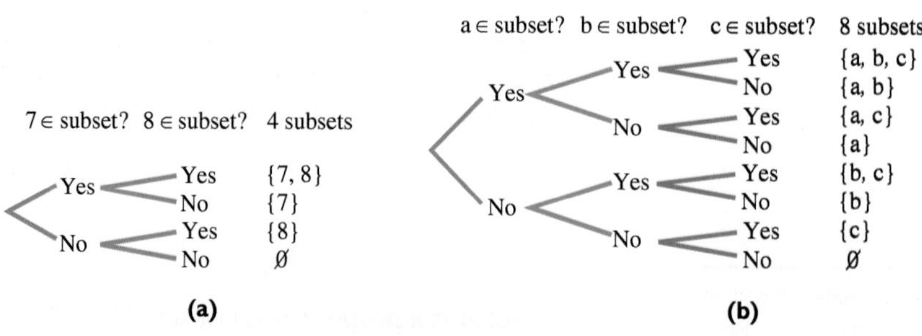

Figure 3

Powers of 2

$2^0 = 1$
$2^1 = 2$
$2^2 = 2 \cdot 2 = 4$
$2^3 = 2 \cdot 2 \cdot 2 = 8$
$2^4 = 2 \cdot 2 \cdot 2 \cdot 2 = 16$
$2^5 = 32$
$2^6 = 64$
$2^7 = 128$
$2^8 = 256$
$2^9 = 512$
$2^{10} = 1024$
$2^{11} = 2048$
$2^{12} = 4096$
$2^{15} = 32{,}768$
$2^{20} = 1{,}048{,}576$
$2^{25} = 33{,}554{,}432$
$2^{30} = 1{,}073{,}741{,}824$

In **Example 4,** we determined the number of subsets of a given set by making a list of all such subsets and then counting them. The tree diagram method also produced a list of all possible subsets. To obtain a formula for finding the number of subsets, we use inductive reasoning. That is, we observe particular cases to try to discover a general pattern.

Begin with the set containing the least number of elements possible—the empty set. This set, $\emptyset$, has only one subset, $\emptyset$ itself. Next, a set with one element has only two subsets, itself and $\emptyset$. These facts, together with those obtained in **Example 4** for sets with two and three elements, are summarized here.

Number of elements	0	1	2	3
Number of subsets	1	2	4	8

This chart suggests that as the number of elements of the set increases by one, the number of subsets doubles. If so, then the number of subsets in each case might be a power of 2. Since every number in the second row of the chart is indeed a power of 2, add this information to the chart.

Number of elements	0	1	2	3
Number of subsets	$1 = 2^0$	$2 = 2^1$	$4 = 2^2$	$8 = 2^3$

This chart shows that the number of elements in each case is the same as the exponent on the base 2. Inductive reasoning gives the following generalization.

Number of Subsets

The number of subsets of a set with n elements is $\mathbf{2^n}$.

Because the value 2^n includes the set itself, we must subtract 1 from this value to obtain the number of proper subsets of a set containing n elements.

Number of Proper Subsets

The number of proper subsets of a set with n elements is $\mathbf{2^n - 1}$.

Although inductive reasoning is a good way of *discovering* principles or arriving at a *conjecture,* it does not provide a proof that the conjecture is true in general. The two formulas above are true, by observation, for $n = 0, 1, 2,$ or 3. (For a general proof, see **Exercise 69** at the end of this section.)

EXAMPLE 5 Finding the Numbers of Subsets and Proper Subsets

Find the number of subsets and the number of proper subsets of each set.

(a) $\{3, 4, 5, 6, 7\}$ **(b)** $\{1, 2, 3, 4, 5, 9, 12, 14\}$

SOLUTION

(a) This set has 5 elements and $2^5 = 2 \cdot 2 \cdot 2 \cdot 2 \cdot 2 = 32$ subsets. Of these, $2^5 - 1 = 32 - 1 = 31$ are proper subsets.

(b) This set has 8 elements. There are $2^8 = 256$ subsets and 255 proper subsets. ∎

2 EXERCISES

Match each set or sets in Column I with the appropriate description in Column II.

I	II
1. $\{p\}, \{q\}, \{p, q\}, \emptyset$	**A.** the proper subsets of $\{p, q\}$
2. $\{p\}, \{q\}, \emptyset$	**B.** the complement of $\{c, d\}$, if $U = \{a, b, c, d\}$
3. $\{a, b\}$	**C.** the complement of U
4. $\emptyset$	**D.** the subsets of $\{p, q\}$

Insert $\subseteq$ *or* $\not\subseteq$ *in each blank so that the resulting statement is true.*

5. $\{-2, 0, 2\}$ ____ $\{-2, -1, 1, 2\}$

6. $\{M, W, F\}$ ____ $\{S, M, T, W, Th\}$

7. $\{2, 5\}$ ____ $\{0, 1, 5, 3, 7, 2\}$

8. $\{a, n, d\}$ ____ $\{r, a, n, d, y\}$

9. $\emptyset$ ____ $\{a, b, c, d, e\}$

10. $\emptyset$ ____ $\emptyset$

11. $\{-5, 2, 9\}$ ____ $\{x \mid x \text{ is an odd integer}\}$

12. $\left\{1, 2, \frac{9}{3}\right\}$ ____ the set of rational numbers

Decide whether $\subset$, $\subseteq$, both, *or* neither *can be placed in each blank to make the statement true.*

13. $\{P, Q, R\}$ ____ $\{P, Q, R, S\}$

14. $\{\text{red, blue, yellow}\}$ ____ $\{\text{yellow, blue, red}\}$

15. $\{9, 1, 7, 3, 5\}$ ____ $\{1, 3, 5, 7, 9\}$

16. $\{S, M, T, W, Th\}$ ______ $\{W, E, E, K\}$

17. $\emptyset$ ____ $\{0\}$

18. $\emptyset$ ____ $\emptyset$

19. $\{0, 1, 2, 3\}$ ______ $\{1, 2, 3, 4\}$

20. $\left\{\frac{5}{6}, \frac{9}{8}\right\}$ ______ $\left\{\frac{6}{5}, \frac{8}{9}\right\}$

For Exercises 21–40, tell whether each statement is true *or* false. *U is the universal set.*

$$\text{Let } U = \{a, b, c, d, e, f, g\},\ A = \{a, e\},$$
$$B = \{a, b, e, f, g\},\ C = \{b, f, g\},\ \text{and } D = \{d, e\}.$$

21. $A \subset U$

22. $C \not\subset U$

23. $D \subseteq B$

24. $D \not\subseteq A$

25. $A \subset B$

26. $B \subseteq C$

27. $\emptyset \not\subset A$

28. $\emptyset \subseteq D$

29. $\emptyset \subseteq \emptyset$

30. $D \subset B$

31. $D \not\subseteq B$

32. $A \not\subseteq B$

33. There are exactly 6 subsets of C.

34. There are exactly 31 subsets of B.

35. There are exactly 3 proper subsets of A.

36. There are exactly 4 subsets of D.

37. There is exactly 1 subset of $\emptyset$.

38. There are exactly 128 proper subsets of U.

39. The Venn diagram below correctly represents the relationship among sets A, D, and U.

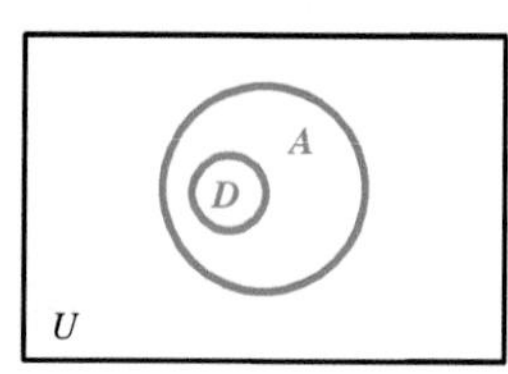

40. The Venn diagram below correctly represents the relationship among sets B, C, and U.

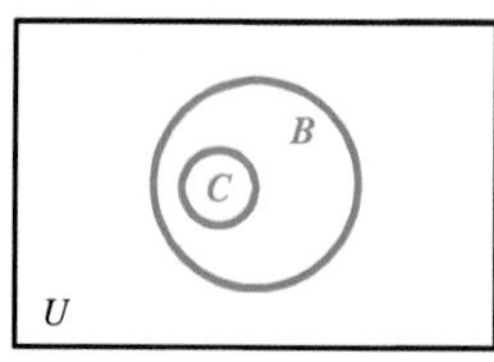

Find **(a)** *the number of subsets and* **(b)** *the number of proper subsets of each set.*

41. $\{a, b, c, d, e, f\}$

42. the set of days of the week

43. $\{x \mid x \text{ is an odd integer between } -4 \text{ and } 6\}$

44. $\{x \mid x \text{ is an odd whole number less than } 4\}$

Let $U = \{1, 2, 3, 4, 5, 6, 7, 8, 9, 10\}$ *and find the complement of each set.*

45. $\{1, 2, 3, 4, 6, 8\}$

46. $\{2, 5, 9, 10\}$

47. $\{1, 3, 4, 5, 6, 7, 8, 9, 10\}$

48. $\{1, 2, 3, 4, 5, 6, 7, 8, 9\}$

49. U

50. $\emptyset$

Vacationing in California *Terry McGinnis is planning a trip with her two sons to California. In weighing her options concerning whether to fly or drive from their home in Iowa, she has listed the following characteristics.*

Fly to California	Drive to California
Higher cost	Lower cost
Educational	Educational
More time to see the sights in California	Less time to see the sights in California
Cannot visit relatives along the way	Can visit relatives along the way

Refer to these characteristics in Exercises 51–56.

51. Find the smallest universal set U that contains all listed characteristics of both options.

Let F represent the set of characteristics of the flying option and let D represent the set of characteristics of the driving option. Use the universal set from ***Exercise 51.***

52. Give the set F'.

53. Give the set D'.

Find the set of elements common to both sets in Exercises 54–56.

54. F and D

55. F' and D'

56. F and D'

Meeting in a Hospitality Suite *Amie Carobrese, Bruce Collin, Corey Chapman, Dwayne Coy, and Eric Cobbe plan to meet at the hospitality suite after the CEO makes his speech at the January sales meeting of their publishing company. Denoting these five people by* A, B, C, D, *and* E, *list all the possible sets of this group in which the given number of them can gather.*

57. five people

58. four people

59. three people

60. two people

61. one person

62. no people

63. Find the total number of ways that members of this group can gather in the suite. (*Hint:* Find the total number of sets in your answers to **Exercises 57–62.**)

64. How does your answer in **Exercise 63** compare with the number of subsets of a set of five elements? Interpret the answer to **Exercise 63** in terms of subsets.

65. The twenty-five members of the mathematics club must send a delegation to a meeting for student groups at their school. The delegation can include as many members of the club as desired, but at least one member must attend. How many different delegations are possible? (*Mathematics Teacher* calendar problem)

66. In **Exercise 65,** suppose ten of the club members say they do not want to be part of the delegation. Now how many delegations are possible?

67. ***Selecting Bills*** Suppose you have the bills shown here.

Beth Anderson/Pearson

(a) If you must select at least one bill, and you may select up to all of the bills, how many different sums of money could you make?

(b) In part (a), remove the condition "you must select at least one bill." How many sums are possible?

68. ***Selecting Coins*** The photo shows a group of obsolete U.S. coins, consisting of one each of the penny, nickel, dime, quarter, and half dollar. Repeat **Exercise 65,** replacing "bill(s)" with "coin(s)."

US Mint

69. In discovering the expression (2^n) for finding the number of subsets of a set with n elements, we observed that for the first few values of n, increasing the number of elements by one doubles the number of subsets. Here, you can prove the formula in general by showing that the same is true for any value of n. Assume set A has n elements and s subsets. Now add one additional element, say e, to the set A. (We now have a new set, say B, with $n + 1$ elements.) Divide the subsets of B into those that do not contain e and those that do.

(a) How many subsets of B do not contain e? (*Hint:* Each of these is a subset of the original set A.)

(b) How many subsets of B do contain e? (*Hint:* Each of these would be a subset of the original set A, with the element e inserted.)

(c) What is the total number of subsets of B?

(d) What do you conclude?

70. Explain why $\emptyset$ is both a subset and an element of $\{\emptyset\}$.

3 SET OPERATIONS AND CARTESIAN PRODUCTS

Intersection of Sets • Union of Sets • Difference of Sets • Ordered Pairs • Cartesian Product of Sets • Venn Diagrams • De Morgan's Laws

Intersection of Sets

Two candidates, Aimee Berger and Darien Estes, are running for a seat on the city council. A voter deciding for whom she should vote recalled the campaign promises, each given a code letter, made by the candidates.

Honest Aimee Berger	Determined Darien Estes
Spend less money, m	Spend less money, m
Emphasize traffic law enforcement, t	Crack down on crooked politicians, p
Increase service to suburban areas, s	Increase service to the city, c

Figure 4

The only promise common to both candidates is promise m, to spend less money. Suppose we take each candidate's promises to be a set. The promises of Berger give the set $\{m, t, s\}$, while the promises of Estes give $\{m, p, c\}$. The common element m belongs to the *intersection* of the two sets, as shown in color in the Venn diagram in **Figure 4**.

$$\{m, t, s\} \cap \{m, p, c\} = \{m\}$$ $\cap$ represents set intersection.

The intersection of two sets is itself a set.

Intersection of Sets

The **intersection** of sets A and B, written $A \cap B$, is the set of elements common to both A and B.

$$\mathbf{A \cap B = \{x \mid x \in A \text{ and } x \in B\}}$$

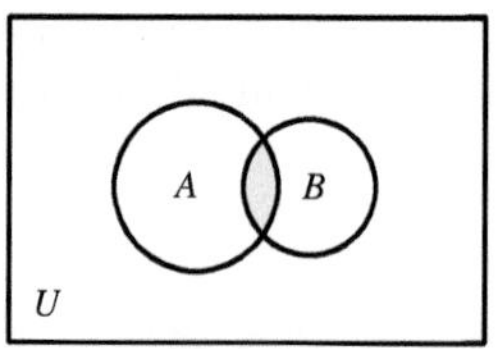

$A \cap B$

Figure 5

Form the intersection of sets A and B by taking all the elements included in both sets, as shown in color in **Figure 5**.

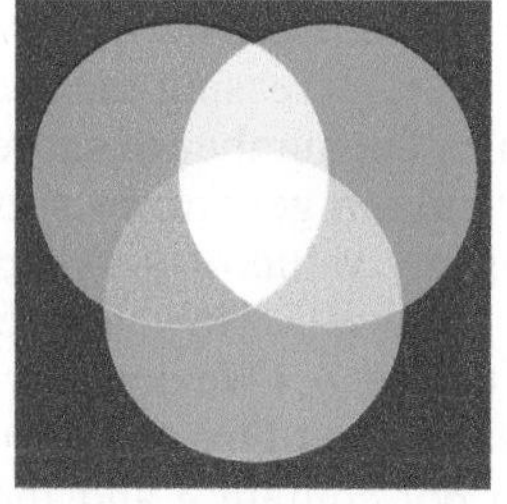

White light can be viewed as the intersection of the three primary colors.

EXAMPLE 1 Finding Intersections

Find each intersection.

(a) $\{3, 4, 5, 6, 7\} \cap \{4, 6, 8, 10\}$ **(b)** $\{9, 14, 25, 30\} \cap \{10, 17, 19, 38, 52\}$

(c) $\{5, 9, 11\} \cap \emptyset$

SOLUTION

(a) The elements common to both sets are 4 and 6.

$$\{3, 4, 5, 6, 7\} \cap \{4, 6, 8, 10\} = \{4, 6\}$$

(b) These two sets have no elements in common.

$$\{9, 14, 25, 30\} \cap \{10, 17, 19, 38, 52\} = \emptyset$$

(c) There are no elements in $\emptyset$, so there can be no elements belonging to both $\{5, 9, 11\}$ and $\emptyset$.

$$\{5, 9, 11\} \cap \emptyset = \emptyset$$

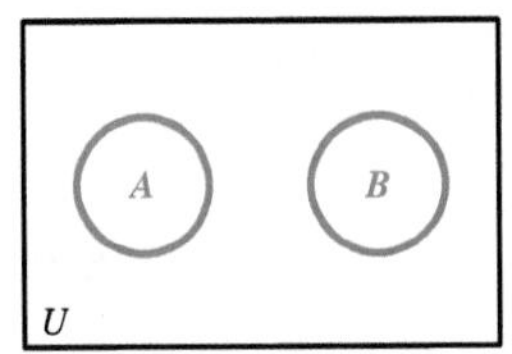

Disjoint sets

Figure 6

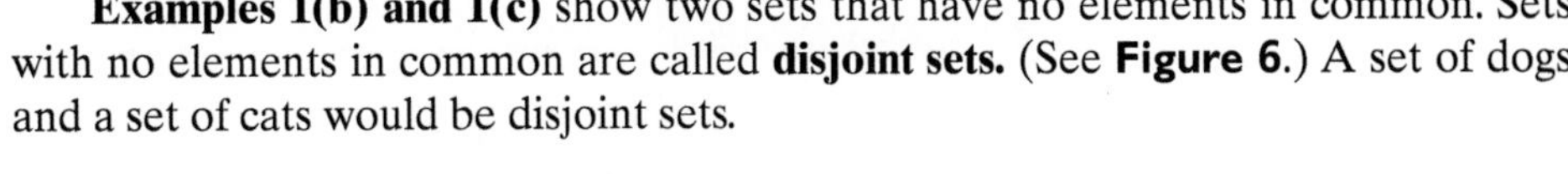

Examples 1(b) and 1(c) show two sets that have no elements in common. Sets with no elements in common are called **disjoint sets.** (See **Figure 6.**) A set of dogs and a set of cats would be disjoint sets.

Sets A and B are disjoint if $A \cap B = \emptyset$.

Union of Sets

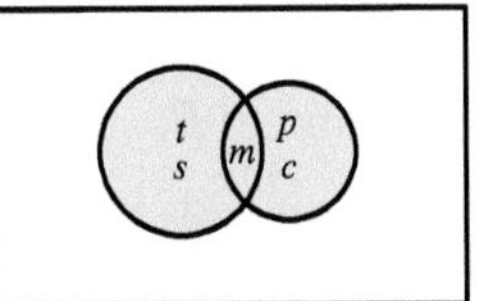

Figure 7

Referring again to the lists of campaign promises, suppose a pollster wants to summarize the types of promises made by the candidates. The pollster would need to study *all* the promises made by *either* candidate, or the set $\{m, t, s, p, c\}$. This set is the *union* of the sets of promises, as shown in color in the Venn diagram in **Figure 7**.

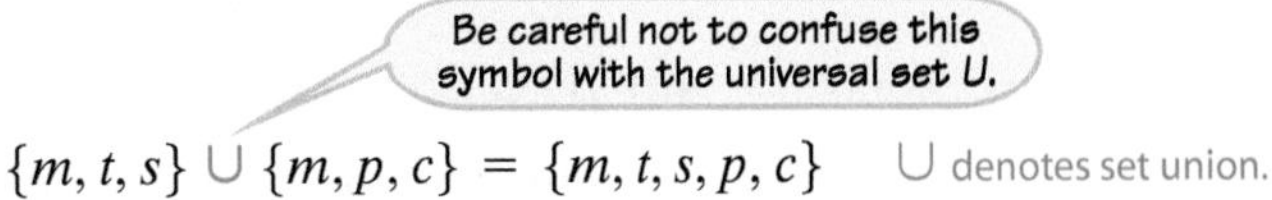

$$\{m, t, s\} \cup \{m, p, c\} = \{m, t, s, p, c\}$$ $\cup$ denotes set union.

Again, the union of two sets is a set.

Union of Sets

The **union** of sets A and B, written $A \cup B$, is the set of all elements belonging to either A or B.

$$\mathbf{A \cup B = \{x \mid x \in A \text{ or } x \in B\}}$$

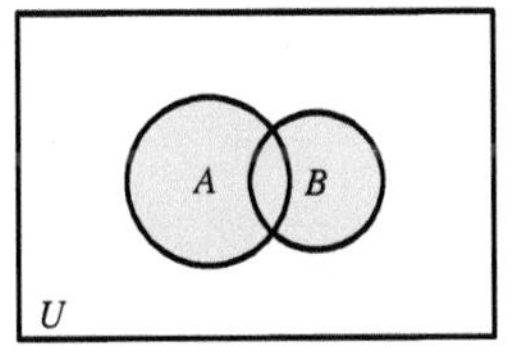

$A \cup B$

Figure 8

***Form the union of sets A and B by taking all the elements of set A and then including the elements of set B that are not already listed. See* Figure 8.**

EXAMPLE 2 Finding Unions

Find each union.

(a) $\{2, 4, 6\} \cup \{4, 6, 8, 10, 12\}$

(b) $\{a, b, d, f, g, h\} \cup \{c, f, g, h, k\}$

(c) $\{3, 4, 5\} \cup \emptyset$

SOLUTION

(a) Start by listing all the elements from the first set, 2, 4, and 6. Then list all the elements from the second set that are not in the first set, 8, 10, and 12. The union is made up of *all* these elements.

$$\{2, 4, 6\} \cup \{4, 6, 8, 10, 12\} = \{2, 4, 6, 8, 10, 12\}$$

(b) $\{a, b, d, f, g, h\} \cup \{c, f, g, h, k\} = \{a, b, c, d, f, g, h, k\}$

(c) Because there are no elements in $\emptyset$, the union of $\{3, 4, 5\}$ and $\emptyset$ contains only the elements 3, 4, and 5.

$$\{3, 4, 5\} \cup \emptyset = \{3, 4, 5\}$$

Recall from the previous section that A' represents the *complement* of set A. ***Set A' is formed by taking all the elements of the universal set U that are not in set A.***

EXAMPLE 3 Finding Intersections and Unions of Complements

Find each set. Let

$$U = \{1, 2, 3, 4, 5, 6, 9\},\ A = \{1, 2, 3, 4\},\ B = \{2, 4, 6\},\ \text{and}\ C = \{1, 3, 6, 9\}.$$

(a) $A' \cap B$ **(b)** $B' \cup C'$ **(c)** $A \cap (B \cup C')$ **(d)** $(A' \cup C') \cap B'$

SOLUTION

(a) First identify the elements of set A', the elements of U that are not in set A.

$$A' = \{5, 6, 9\}$$

Now, find $A' \cap B$, the set of elements belonging both to A' and to B.

$$A' \cap B = \{5, 6, 9\} \cap \{2, 4, 6\} = \{6\}$$

(b) $B' \cup C' = \{1, 3, 5, 9\} \cup \{2, 4, 5\} = \{1, 2, 3, 4, 5, 9\}$

(c) First find the set inside the parentheses.

$$B \cup C' = \{2, 4, 6\} \cup \{2, 4, 5\} = \{2, 4, 5, 6\}$$

Now, find the intersection of this set with A.

$$\begin{aligned} A \cap (B \cup C') &= A \cap \{2, 4, 5, 6\} \\ &= \{1, 2, 3, 4\} \cap \{2, 4, 5, 6\} \\ &= \{2, 4\} \end{aligned}$$

(d) $A' = \{5, 6, 9\}$ and $C' = \{2, 4, 5\}$, so

$$A' \cup C' = \{5, 6, 9\} \cup \{2, 4, 5\} = \{2, 4, 5, 6, 9\}.$$

$B' = \{1, 3, 5, 9\}$, so

$$(A' \cup C') \cap B' = \{2, 4, 5, 6, 9\} \cap \{1, 3, 5, 9\} = \{5, 9\}.$$

For Further Thought

Comparing Properties

The arithmetic operations of addition and multiplication, when applied to numbers, have some familiar properties. If a, b, and c are *real numbers*, then the **commutative property of addition** says that the order of the numbers being added makes no difference:

$$a + b = b + a.$$

(Is there a **commutative property of multiplication**?) The **associative property of addition** says that when three numbers are added, the grouping used makes no difference:

$$(a + b) + c = a + (b + c).$$

(Is there an **associative property of multiplication**?) The number 0 is called the **identity element for addition** since adding it to any number does not change that number:

$$a + 0 = a.$$

(What is the **identity element for multiplication**?) Finally, the **distributive property of multiplication over addition** says that

$$a(b + c) = ab + ac.$$

(Is there a distributive property of addition over multiplication?)

For Group or Individual Investigation

Now consider the operations of union and intersection, applied to sets. By recalling definitions, or by trying examples, answer the following questions.

1. Is set union commutative? Set intersection?
2. Is set union associative? Set intersection?
3. Is there an identity element for set union? If so, what is it? How about set intersection?
4. Is set intersection distributive over set union? Is set union distributive over set intersection?

EXAMPLE 4 Describing Sets in Words

Describe each set in words.

(a) $A \cap (B \cup C')$ **(b)** $(A' \cup C') \cap B'$

SOLUTION

(a) This set might be described as "the set of all elements that are in A, and also are in B or not in C."

(b) One possibility is "the set of all elements that are not in A or not in C, and also are not in B."

Difference of Sets

Suppose that $A = \{1, 2, 3, \ldots, 10\}$ and $B = \{2, 4, 6, 8, 10\}$. If the elements of B are excluded (or taken away) from A, the set $C = \{1, 3, 5, 7, 9\}$ is obtained. C is called the *difference* of sets A and B.

Difference of Sets

The **difference** of sets A and B, written $A - B$, is the set of all elements belonging to set A and not to set B.

$$\mathbf{A - B = \{x | x \in A \text{ and } x \notin B\}}$$

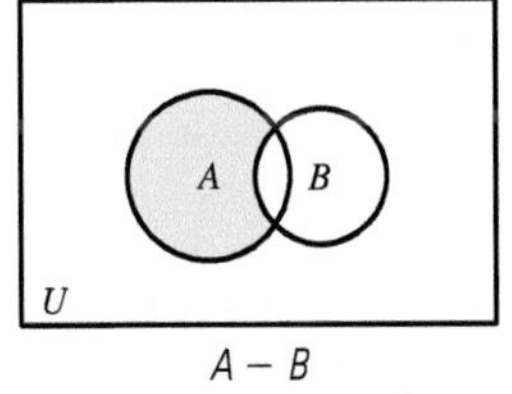

$A - B$

Figure 9

Because $x \notin B$ has the same meaning as $x \in B'$ the set difference $A - B$ can also be described as

$$\{x | x \in A \text{ and } x \in B'\}, \quad \text{or} \quad A \cap B'.$$

Figure 9 illustrates the idea of set difference. The region in color represents $A - B$.

EXAMPLE 5 Finding Set Differences

Find each set.

$$\text{Let } U = \{1, 2, 3, 4, 5, 6, 7\}, \quad A = \{1, 2, 3, 4, 5, 6\},$$
$$B = \{2, 3, 6\}, \quad \text{and} \quad C = \{3, 5, 7\}.$$

(a) $A - B$ **(b)** $B - A$ **(c)** $(A - B) \cup C'$

SOLUTION

(a) Begin with set A and exclude any elements found also in set B.

$$A - B = \{1, 2, 3, 4, 5, 6\} - \{2, 3, 6\} = \{1, 4, 5\}$$

(b) To be in $B - A$, an element must be in set B and not in set A. But all elements of B are also in A. Thus, $B - A = \emptyset$.

(c) From part (a), $A - B = \{1, 4, 5\}$. Also, $C' = \{1, 2, 4, 6\}$.

$$(A - B) \cup C' = \{1, 2, 4, 5, 6\}$$

The results in **Examples 5(a) and 5(b)** illustrate that, in general,

$$\mathbf{A - B \neq B - A.}$$

Ordered Pairs

When writing a set that contains several elements, the order in which the elements appear is not relevant. For example,

$$\{1, 5\} = \{5, 1\}.$$

However, there are many instances in mathematics where, when two objects are paired, the order in which the objects are written is important. This leads to the idea of the *ordered pair.* When writing ordered pairs, use parentheses rather than braces, which are reserved for writing sets.

Ordered Pairs

In the **ordered pair** (a, b), a is called the **first component** and b is called the **second component.** In general, $(a, b) \neq (b, a)$.

Two ordered pairs (a, b) and (c, d) are **equal** provided that their first components are equal and their second components are equal.

$$(a, b) = (c, d) \quad \textit{if and only if} \quad a = c \text{ and } b = d.$$

EXAMPLE 6 Determining Equality of Sets and of Ordered Pairs

Decide whether each statement is *true* or *false*.

(a) $(3, 4) = (5 - 2, 1 + 3)$ **(b)** $\{3, 4\} \neq \{4, 3\}$ **(c)** $(7, 4) = (4, 7)$

SOLUTION

(a) Because $3 = 5 - 2$ and $4 = 1 + 3$, the first components are equal and the second components are equal. The statement is *true.*

(b) Because these are sets and not ordered pairs, the order in which the elements are listed is not important. Because these sets are equal, the statement is *false.*

(c) The ordered pairs $(7, 4)$ and $(4, 7)$ are not equal because they do not satisfy the requirements for equality of ordered pairs. The statement is *false.* ■■■

Cartesian Product of Sets

A set may contain ordered pairs as elements. If A and B are sets, then each element of A can be paired with each element of B, and the results can be written as ordered pairs. The set of all such ordered pairs is called the *Cartesian product* of A and B, written $A \times B$ and read **"*A* cross *B*."** The name comes from that of the French mathematician René Descartes.

Cartesian Product of Sets

The **Cartesian product** of sets A and B is defined as follows.

$$A \times B = \{(a, b) \mid a \in A \text{ and } b \in B\}$$

EXAMPLE 7 Finding Cartesian Products

Let $A = \{1, 5, 9\}$ and $B = \{6, 7\}$. Find each set.

(a) $A \times B$ **(b)** $B \times A$

SOLUTION

(a) Pair each element of A with each element of B. Write the results as ordered pairs, with the element of A written first and the element of B written second. Write as a set.

$$A \times B = \{(1, 6), (1, 7), (5, 6), (5, 7), (9, 6), (9, 7)\}$$

(b) Because B is listed first, this set will consist of ordered pairs that have their components interchanged when compared to those in part (a).

$$B \times A = \{(6, 1), (7, 1), (6, 5), (7, 5), (6, 9), (7, 9)\}$$

The order in which the ordered pairs themselves are listed is not important. For example, another way to write $B \times A$ in **Example 7(b)** would be

$$\{(6, 1), (6, 5), (6, 9), (7, 1), (7, 5), (7, 9)\}.$$

EXAMPLE 8 Finding the Cartesian Product of a Set with Itself

Let $A = \{1, 2, 3, 4, 5, 6\}$. Find $A \times A$.

SOLUTION

Pair 1 with each element in the set, 2 with each element, and so on.

$$\begin{aligned} A \times A = \{&(1, 1), (1, 2), (1, 3), (1, 4), (1, 5), (1, 6), \\ &(2, 1), (2, 2), (2, 3), (2, 4), (2, 5), (2, 6), \\ &(3, 1), (3, 2), (3, 3), (3, 4), (3, 5), (3, 6), \\ &(4, 1), (4, 2), (4, 3), (4, 4), (4, 5), (4, 6), \\ &(5, 1), (5, 2), (5, 3), (5, 4), (5, 5), (5, 6), \\ &(6, 1), (6, 2), (6, 3), (6, 4), (6, 5), (6, 6)\} \end{aligned}$$

Michael Kempf/Shutterstock

The **Cartesian product** in **Example 8** represents all possible results that are obtained when two distinguishable dice are rolled. This Cartesian product is important when studying certain problems in counting techniques and probability.

From **Example 7** it can be seen that, in general,

$$\boldsymbol{A \times B \neq B \times A},$$

because they do not contain exactly the same ordered pairs. However, each set contains the same number of elements, six. Furthermore, $n(A) = 3$, $n(B) = 2$, and $n(A \times B) = n(B \times A) = 6$. Because $3 \cdot 2 = 6$, one might conclude that the cardinal number of the Cartesian product of two sets is equal to the product of the cardinal numbers of the sets. In general, this conclusion is correct.

Cardinal Number of a Cartesian Product

If $n(A) = a$ and $n(B) = b$, then the following is true.

$$\boldsymbol{n(A \times B) = n(B \times A) = n(A) \cdot n(B) = n(B) \cdot n(A) = ab = ba}$$

EXAMPLE 9 Finding Cardinal Numbers of Cartesian Products

Find $n(A \times B)$ and $n(B \times A)$ from the given information.

(a) $A = \{\text{a, b, c, d, e, f, g}\}$ and $B = \{2, 4, 6\}$ **(b)** $n(A) = 24$ and $n(B) = 5$

SOLUTION

(a) Because $n(A) = 7$ and $n(B) = 3$, $n(A \times B)$ and $n(B \times A)$ both equal $7 \cdot 3$, or 21.

(b) $n(A \times B) = n(B \times A) = 24 \cdot 5 = 5 \cdot 24 = 120$

An **operation** is a rule or procedure by which one or more objects are used to obtain another object. The most common operations on sets are summarized in the box on the next page.

Set Operations

Let A and B be any sets, with U the universal set.

The **complement** of A, written A', is

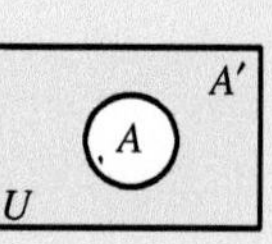

$$A' = \{x \mid x \in U \text{ and } x \notin A\}.$$

The **intersection** of A and B is

$$A \cap B = \{x \mid x \in A \text{ and } x \in B\}.$$

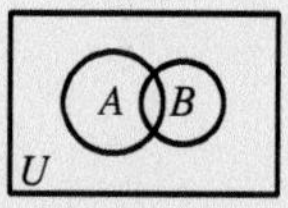

The **union** of A and B is

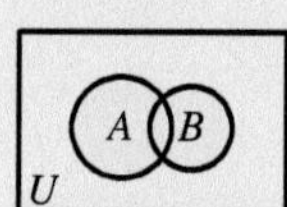

$$A \cup B = \{x \mid x \in A \text{ or } x \in B\}.$$

The **difference** of A and B is

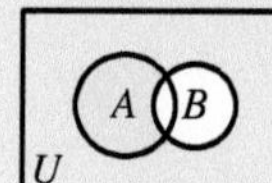

$$A - B = \{x \mid x \in A \text{ and } x \notin B\}.$$

The **Cartesian product** of A and B is

$$A \times B = \{(x, y) \mid x \in A \text{ and } y \in B\}.$$

Venn Diagrams

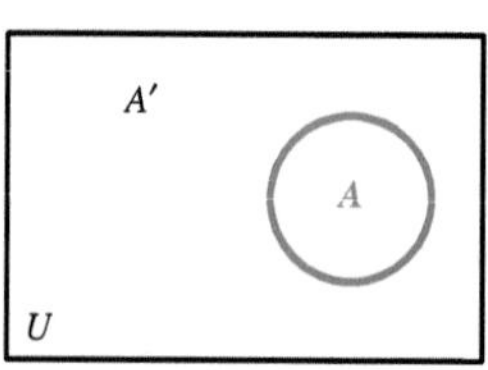

Figure 10

With a single set, we can use a Venn diagram as in **Figure 10.** The universal set U is divided into two regions, one representing set A and the other representing set A'.

Two sets A and B within the universal set suggest a Venn diagram as in **Figure 11.** Region 1 includes those elements outside of both set A and set B. Region 2 includes the elements belonging to A but not to B. Region 3 includes those elements belonging to both A and B. How would you describe the elements of region 4?

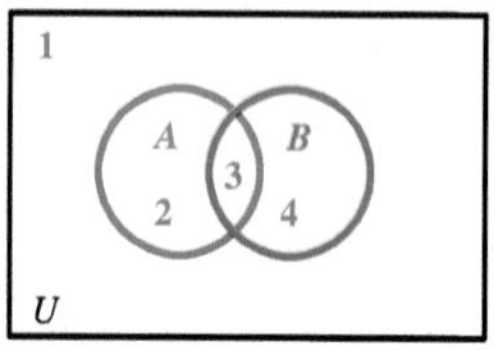

Numbering is arbitrary. The numbers indicate four regions, not cardinal numbers or elements.

Figure 11

EXAMPLE 10 Shading Venn Diagrams to Represent Sets

Draw a Venn diagram similar to **Figure 11** and shade the region or regions representing each set.

(a) $A' \cap B$ **(b)** $A' \cup B'$

SOLUTION

(a) Refer to **Figure 11**. Set A' contains all the elements outside of set A—in other words, the elements in regions 1 and 4. Set B is made up of the elements in regions 3 and 4. The intersection of sets A' and B is made up of the elements in the region common to (1 and 4) and (3 and 4), which is region 4. Thus, $A' \cap B$ is represented by region 4, shown in color in **Figure 12.** This region can also be described as $B - A$.

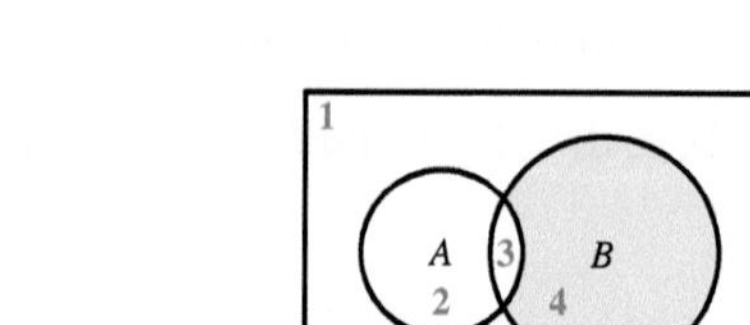

Figure 12

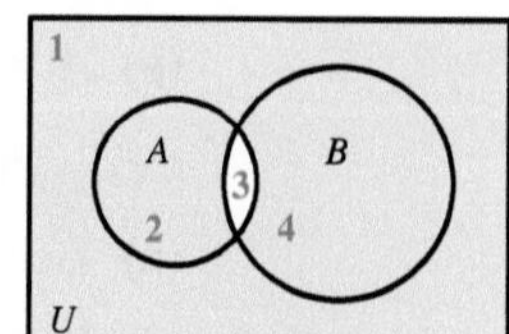

Figure 13

(b) Again, set A' is represented by regions 1 and 4, while B' is made up of regions 1 and 2. The union of A' and B', the set $A' \cup B'$, is made up of the elements belonging to the union of regions 1, 2, and 4, which are in color in **Figure 13.** ▪▪▪

EXAMPLE 11 Locating Elements in a Venn Diagram

Place the elements of the sets in their proper locations in a Venn diagram.

Let $U = \{q, r, s, t, u, v, w, x, y, z\}$, $A = \{r, s, t, u, v\}$, and $B = \{t, v, x\}$.

SOLUTION

Because $A \cap B = \{t, v\}$, elements t and v are placed in region 3 in **Figure 14**. The remaining elements of A, that is r, s, and u, go in region 2. The figure shows the proper placement of all other elements.

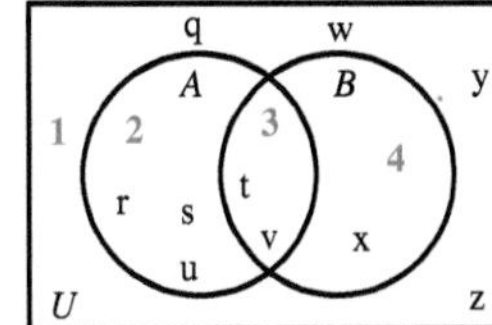

Figure 14

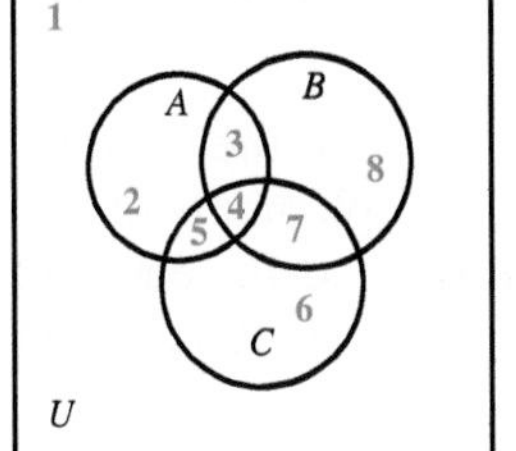

Numbering is arbitrary. The numbers indicate regions, not cardinal numbers or elements.

Figure 15

To include three sets A, B, and C within a universal set, draw a Venn diagram as in **Figure 15**, where again an arbitrary numbering of the regions is shown.

EXAMPLE 12 Shading a Set in a Venn Diagram

Shade the set $(A' \cap B') \cap C$ in a Venn diagram similar to the one in **Figure 15**.

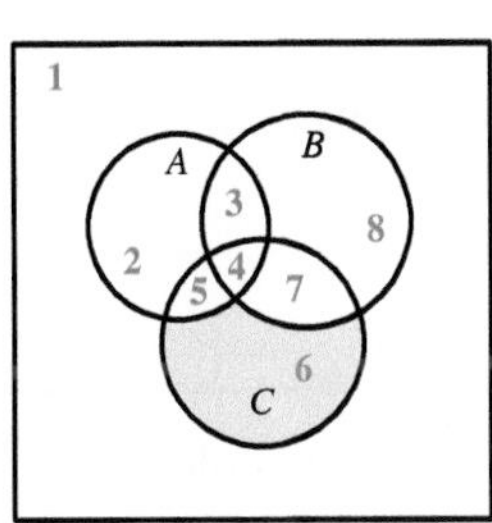

$(A' \cap B') \cap C$

Figure 16

SOLUTION

Work first inside the parentheses. As shown in **Figure 16**, set A' is made up of the regions outside set A, or regions 1, 6, 7, and 8. Set B' is made up of regions 1, 2, 5, and 6. The intersection of these sets is given by the overlap of regions 1, 6, 7, 8 and 1, 2, 5, 6, or regions 1 and 6.

For the final Venn diagram, find the intersection of regions 1 and 6 with set C. As seen in **Figure 16**, set C is made up of regions 4, 5, 6, and 7. The overlap of regions 1, 6 and 4, 5, 6, 7 is region 6, the region in color in **Figure 16**.

EXAMPLE 13 Verifying a Statement Using a Venn Diagram

Is the statement $(A \cap B)' = A' \cup B'$ true for every choice of sets A and B?

SOLUTION

To help decide, use the regions labeled in **Figure 11**. Set $A \cap B$ is made up of region 3, so that $(A \cap B)'$ is made up of regions 1, 2, and 4. These regions are in color in **Figure 17(a)**.

To find a Venn diagram for set $A' \cup B'$, first check that A' is made up of regions 1 and 4, while set B' includes regions 1 and 2. Finally, $A' \cup B'$ is made up of regions 1 and 4, or 1 and 2, that is, regions 1, 2, and 4. These regions are in color in **Figure 17(b)**.

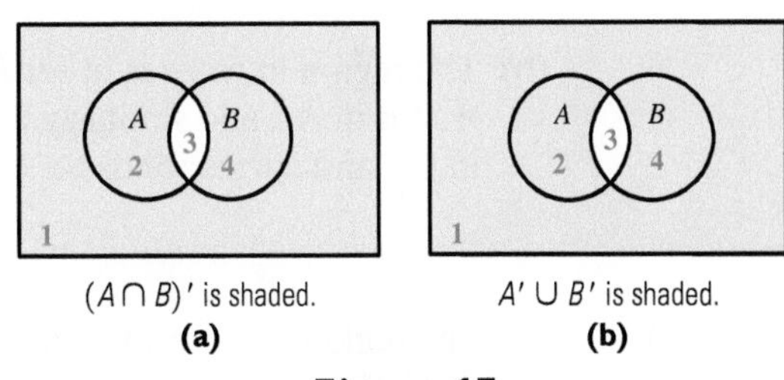

$(A \cap B)'$ is shaded.
(a)

$A' \cup B'$ is shaded.
(b)

Figure 17

The fact that the same regions are in color in both Venn diagrams suggests that

$$(A \cap B)' = A' \cup B'.$$

De Morgan's Laws

The result of **Example 13** can be stated in words.

The complement of the intersection of two sets is equal to the union of the complements of the two sets.

As a result, it is natural to ask ourselves whether it is also true that the complement of the *union* of two sets is equal to the *intersection* of the complements of the two sets (where the words "intersection" and "union" are substituted for each other). This was investigated by the British logician Augustus De Morgan (1806–1871) and was found to be true. DeMorgan's two laws for sets follow.

De Morgan's Laws for Sets

For any sets A and B,

$$(A \cap B)' = A' \cup B' \quad \text{and} \quad (A \cup B)' = A' \cap B'.$$

The Venn diagrams in **Figure 17** strongly suggest the truth of the first of De Morgan's laws. They provide a *conjecture*. Actual proofs of De Morgan's laws would require methods used in more advanced courses on set theory.

EXAMPLE 14 Describing Regions in Venn Diagrams Using Symbols

For the Venn diagrams, write a symbolic description of the region in color, using A, B, C, $\cap$, $\cup$, $-$, and $'$ as necessary.

(a)

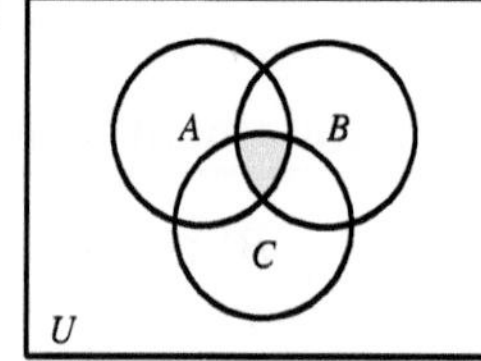

(b)

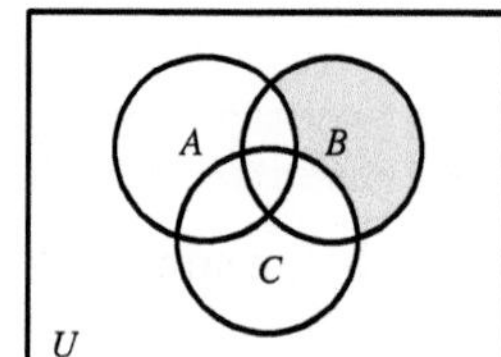

(c) Refer to the figure in part (b) and give two additional ways of describing the region in color.

SOLUTION

(a) The region in color belongs to all three sets, A and B and C. Therefore, the region corresponds to

$$A \cap B \cap C.$$

(b) The region in color is in set B and is not in A and is not in C. Because it is not in A, it is in A', and similarly it is in C'. The region is, therefore, in B and in A' and in C', and corresponds to

$$B \cap A' \cap C'.$$

(c) The region in color includes all of B, except for the regions belonging to either A or C. This suggests the idea of set difference. The region may be described as

$$B - (A \cup C), \quad \text{or equivalently,} \quad B \cap (A \cup C)'.$$

3 EXERCISES

Match each term in Group I with the appropriate description A–F in Group II. Assume that A and B are sets.

I

1. the intersection of A and B

2. the union of A and B

3. the difference of A and B

4. the complement of A

5. the Cartesian product of A and B

6. the difference of B and A

II

A. the set of elements in A that are not in B

B. the set of elements common to both A and B

C. the set of elements in the universal set that are not in A

D. the set of elements in B that are not in A

E. the set of ordered pairs such that each first element is from A and each second element is from B, with every element of A paired with every element of B

F. the set of elements that are in A or in B or in both A and B

Perform the indicated operations, and designate each answer using the listing method.

$$\text{Let } U = \{\text{a, b, c, d, e, f, g}\}, \quad X = \{\text{a, c, e, g}\},$$
$$Y = \{\text{a, b, c}\}, \quad \text{and} \quad Z = \{\text{b, c, d, e, f}\}.$$

7. $X \cap Y$ **8.** $X \cup Y$ **9.** $Y \cup Z$

10. $Y \cap Z$ **11.** $X \cup U$ **12.** $Y \cap U$

13. X' **14.** Y'

15. $X' \cap Y'$ **16.** $X' \cap Z$

17. $X \cup (Y \cap Z)$ **18.** $Y \cap (X \cup Z)$

19. $(Y \cap Z') \cup X$ **20.** $(X' \cup Y') \cup Z$

21. $(Z \cup X')' \cap Y$ **22.** $(Y \cap X')' \cup Z'$

23. $X - Y$ **24.** $Y - X$

25. $X \cap (X - Y)$ **26.** $Y \cup (Y - X)$

27. $X' - Y$ **28.** $Y' - X$

29. $(X \cap Y') \cup (Y \cap X')$ **30.** $(X \cap Y') \cap (Y \cap X')$

Describe each set in words.

31. $A \cup (B' \cap C')$ **32.** $(A \cap B') \cup (B \cap A')$

33. $(C - B) \cup A$ **34.** $B \cap (A' - C)$

35. $(A - C) \cup (B - C)$ **36.** $(A' \cap B') \cup C'$

Adverse Effects of Alcohol and Tobacco *The table lists some common adverse effects of prolonged tobacco and alcohol use.*

Tobacco	Alcohol
Emphysema, e	Liver damage, l
Heart damage, h	Brain damage, b
Cancer, c	Heart damage, h

Let T be the set of listed effects of tobacco and A be the set of listed effects of alcohol. Find each set.

37. the smallest possible universal set U that includes all the effects listed

38. A' **39.** T' **40.** $T \cap A$

41. $T \cup A$ **42.** $T \cap A'$

Describe in words each set in Exercises 43–48.

Let U = the set of all tax returns,
A = the set of all tax returns with itemized deductions,
B = the set of all tax returns showing business income,
C = the set of all tax returns filed in 2009,
D = the set of all tax returns selected for audit.

43. $B \cup C$ **44.** $A \cap D$ **45.** $C - A$

46. $D \cup A'$ **47.** $(A \cup B) - D$ **48.** $(C \cap A) \cap B'$

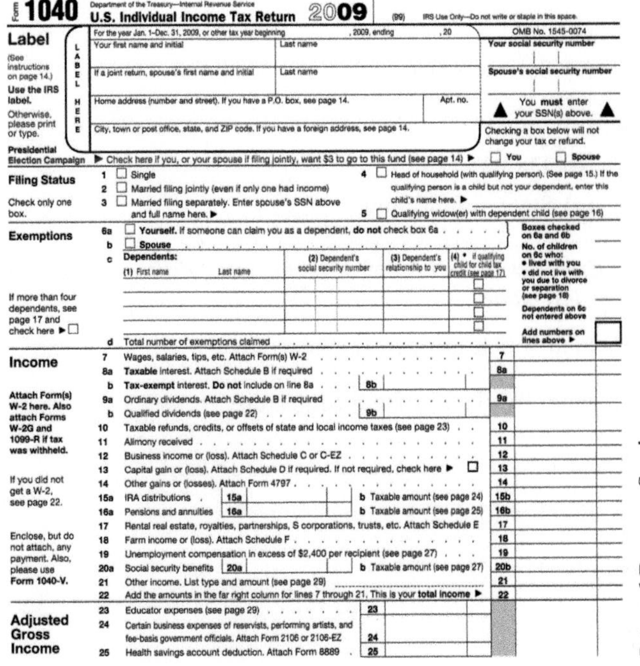
Form 1040 Department of the Treasury—Internal Revenue Service
U.S. Individual Income Tax Return 2009 (99) IRS Use Only—Do not write or staple in this space.

Label (See instructions on page 14.) Use the IRS label. Otherwise, please print or type.
LABEL HERE
For the year Jan. 1–Dec. 31, 2009, or other tax year beginning , 2009, ending , 20 OMB No. 1545-0074
Your first name and initial | Last name | Your social security number
If a joint return, spouse's first name and initial | Last name | Spouse's social security number
Home address (number and street). If you have a P.O. box, see page 14. | Apt. no. | ▲ You must enter your SSN(s) above. ▲
City, town or post office, state, and ZIP code. If you have a foreign address, see page 14. | Checking a box below will not change your tax or refund.

Presidential Election Campaign ▶ Check here if you, or your spouse if filing jointly, want $3 to go to this fund (see page 14) ▶ ☐ You ☐ Spouse

Filing Status
Check only one box.
1 ☐ Single
2 ☐ Married filing jointly (even if only one had income)
3 ☐ Married filing separately. Enter spouse's SSN above and full name here. ▶
4 ☐ Head of household (with qualifying person). (See page 15.) If the qualifying person is a child but not your dependent, enter this child's name here. ▶
5 ☐ Qualifying widow(er) with dependent child (see page 16)

Exemptions
6a ☐ Yourself. If someone can claim you as a dependent, do not check box 6a
b ☐ Spouse
Boxes checked on 6a and 6b
c Dependents: (1) First name Last name | (2) Dependent's social security number | (3) Dependent's relationship to you | (4) ✓ if qualifying child for child tax credit (see page 17)
No. of children on 6c who: • lived with you • did not live with you due to divorce or separation (see page 18)
Dependents on 6c not entered above
If more than four dependents, see page 17 and check here ▶ ☐
d Total number of exemptions claimed
Add numbers on lines above ▶

Income
Attach Form(s) W-2 here. Also attach Forms W-2G and 1099-R if tax was withheld.
If you did not get a W-2, see page 22.
Enclose, but do not attach, any payment. Also, please use Form 1040-V.
7 Wages, salaries, tips, etc. Attach Form(s) W-2 — 7
8a Taxable interest. Attach Schedule B if required — 8a
b Tax-exempt interest. Do not include on line 8a — 8b
9a Ordinary dividends. Attach Schedule B if required — 9a
b Qualified dividends (see page 22) — 9b
10 Taxable refunds, credits, or offsets of state and local income taxes (see page 23) — 10
11 Alimony received — 11
12 Business income or (loss). Attach Schedule C or C-EZ — 12
13 Capital gain or (loss). Attach Schedule D if required. If not required, check here ▶ ☐ — 13
14 Other gains or (losses). Attach Form 4797 — 14
15a IRA distributions 15a | b Taxable amount (see page 24) — 15b
16a Pensions and annuities 16a | b Taxable amount (see page 25) — 16b
17 Rental real estate, royalties, partnerships, S corporations, trusts, etc. Attach Schedule E — 17
18 Farm income or (loss). Attach Schedule F — 18
19 Unemployment compensation in excess of $2,400 per recipient (see page 27) — 19
20a Social security benefits 20a | b Taxable amount (see page 27) — 20b
21 Other income. List type and amount (see page 29) — 21
22 Add the amounts in the far right column for lines 7 through 21. This is your total income ▶ — 22

Adjusted Gross Income
23 Educator expenses (see page 29) — 23
24 Certain business expenses of reservists, performing artists, and fee-basis government officials. Attach Form 2106 or 2106-EZ — 24
25 Health savings account deduction. Attach Form 8889 — 25

Internal Revenue Service

Assuming that A and B represent any two sets, identify each statement as either always true *or* not always true.

49. $A \subseteq (A \cup B)$

50. $A \subseteq (A \cap B)$

51. $(A \cap B) \subseteq A$

52. $(A \cup B) \subseteq A$

53. $n(A \cup B) = n(A) + n(B)$

54. $n(A \cup B) = n(A) + n(B) - n(A \cap B)$

For Exercises 55–60, use your results in parts (a) and (b) to answer part (c).

Let $U = \{1, 2, 3, 4, 5\}$, $X = \{1, 3, 5\}$, $Y = \{1, 2, 3\}$, *and* $Z = \{3, 4, 5\}$.

55. (a) Find $X \cup Y$.
(b) Find $Y \cup X$.
(c) State a conjecture.

56. (a) Find $X \cap Y$.
(b) Find $Y \cap X$.
(c) State a conjecture.

57. (a) Find $X \cup (Y \cup Z)$.
(b) Find $(X \cup Y) \cup Z$.
(c) State a conjecture.

58. (a) Find $X \cap (Y \cap Z)$.
(b) Find $(X \cap Y) \cap Z$.
(c) State a conjecture.

59. (a) Find $(X \cup Y)'$.
(b) Find $X' \cap Y'$.
(c) State a conjecture.

60. (a) Find $(X \cap Y)'$.
(b) Find $X' \cup Y'$.
(c) State a conjecture.

In Exercises 61 and 62, let X be the set of different letters in your last name.

61. Find $X \cup \emptyset$ and state a conjecture.

62. Find $X \cap \emptyset$ and state a conjecture.

Decide whether each statement is true or false.

63. $(3, 2) = (5 - 2, 1 + 1)$

64. $(10, 4) = (7 + 3, 5 - 1)$

65. $(6, 3) = (3, 6)$

66. $(2, 13) = (13, 2)$

67. $\{6, 3\} = \{3, 6\}$

68. $\{2, 13\} = \{13, 2\}$

69. $\{(1, 2), (3, 4)\} = \{(3, 4), (1, 2)\}$

70. $\{(5, 9), (4, 8), (4, 2)\} = \{(4, 8), (5, 9), (4, 2)\}$

Find $A \times B$ and $B \times A$, for A and B defined as follows.

71. $A = \{2, 8, 12\}$, $B = \{4, 9\}$

72. $A = \{3, 6, 9, 12\}$, $B = \{6, 8\}$

73. $A = \{\text{d, o, g}\}$, $B = \{\text{p, i, g}\}$

74. $A = \{\text{b, l, u, e}\}$, $B = \{\text{r, e, d}\}$

For the sets specified in Exercises 75–78, use the given information to find $n(A \times B)$ and $n(B \times A)$.

75. the sets in **Exercise 71**

76. the sets in **Exercise 73**

77. $n(A) = 35$ and $n(B) = 6$

78. $n(A) = 13$ and $n(B) = 5$

Find the cardinal number specified.

79. If $n(A \times B) = 72$ and $n(A) = 12$, find $n(B)$.

80. If $n(A \times B) = 300$ and $n(B) = 30$, find $n(A)$.

Place the elements of these sets in the proper locations in the given Venn diagram.

81. Let $U = \{\text{a, b, c, d, e, f, g}\}$,
$A = \{\text{b, d, f, g}\}$,
$B = \{\text{a, b, d, e, g}\}$.

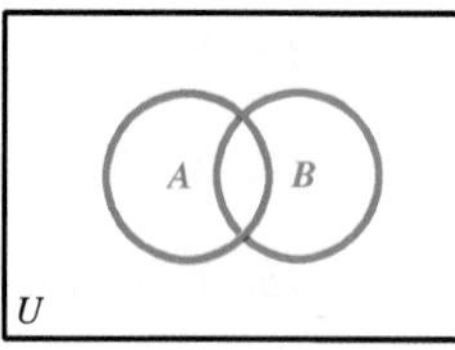

82. Let $U = \{5, 6, 7, 8, 9, 10, 11, 12, 13\}$,
$M = \{5, 8, 10, 11\}$,
$N = \{5, 6, 7, 9, 10\}$.

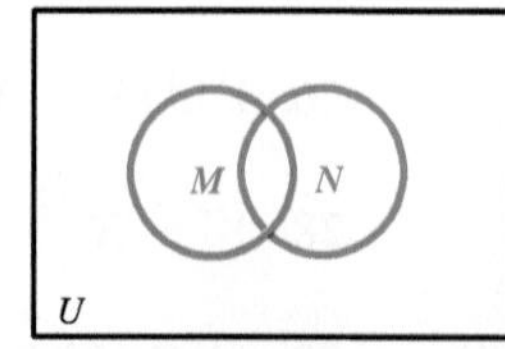

Use a Venn diagram similar to the one shown below to shade each set.

83. $B \cap A'$

84. $A \cup B$

85. $A' \cup B$

86. $A' \cap B'$

87. $B' \cup A$

88. $A' \cup A$

89. $B' \cap B$

90. $A \cap B'$

91. $B' \cup (A' \cap B')$

92. $(A \cap B) \cup B$

93. U'

94. $\emptyset'$

In Exercises 95 and 96, place the elements of the sets in the proper location in a Venn diagram similar to the one shown below.

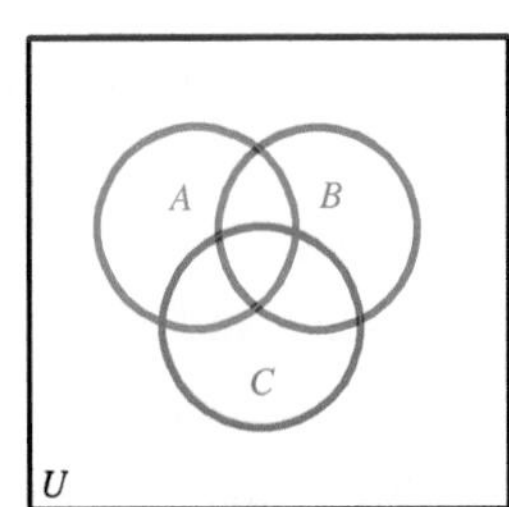

95. Let $U = \{\text{m, n, o, p, q, r, s, t, u, v, w}\}$,
$A = \{\text{m, n, p, q, r, t}\}$,
$B = \{\text{m, o, p, q, s, u}\}$,
$C = \{\text{m, o, p, r, s, t, u, v}\}$.

96. Let $U = \{1, 2, 3, 4, 5, 6, 7, 8, 9\}$,
$A = \{1, 3, 5, 7\}$,
$B = \{1, 3, 4, 6, 8\}$,
$C = \{1, 4, 5, 6, 7, 9\}$.

Use a Venn diagram to shade each set.

97. $(A \cap B) \cap C$

98. $(A \cap C') \cup B$

99. $(A \cap B) \cup C'$

100. $(A' \cap B) \cap C$

101. $(A' \cap B') \cap C$

102. $(A \cup B) \cup C$

103. $(A \cap B') \cup C$

104. $(A \cap C') \cap B$

105. $(A \cap B') \cap C'$

106. $(A' \cap B') \cup C$

107. $(A' \cap B') \cup C'$

108. $(A \cap B)' \cup C$

Write a symbolic description of each shaded area. Use the symbols A, B, C, $\cap$, $\cup$, $-$, and $'$ as necessary. More than one answer may be possible.

109.

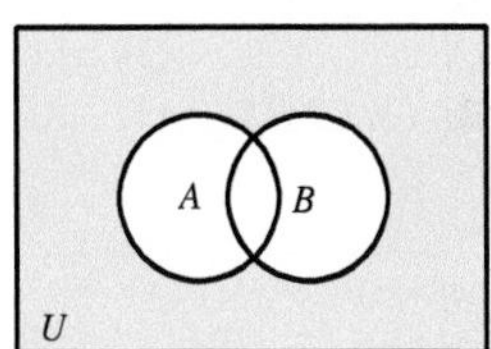

110.

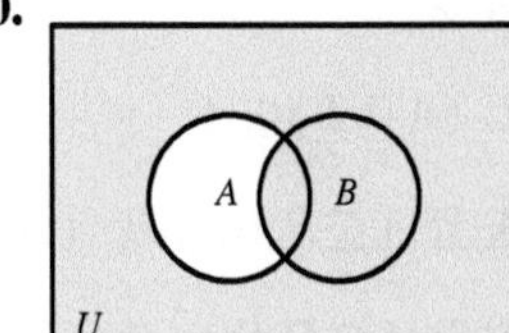

111.

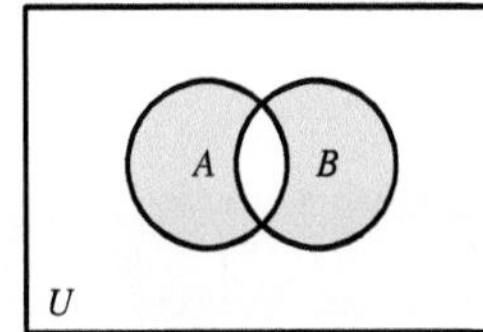

112.

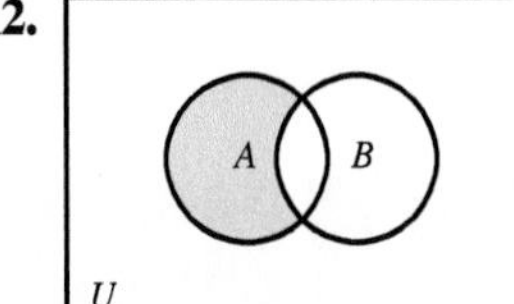

113.

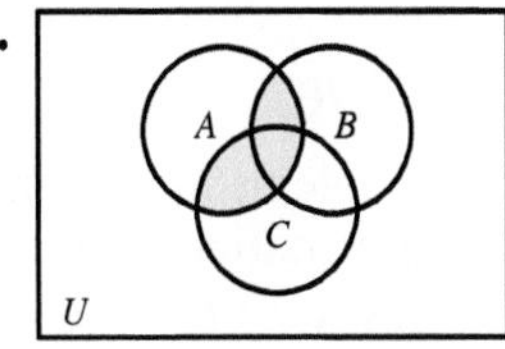

114.

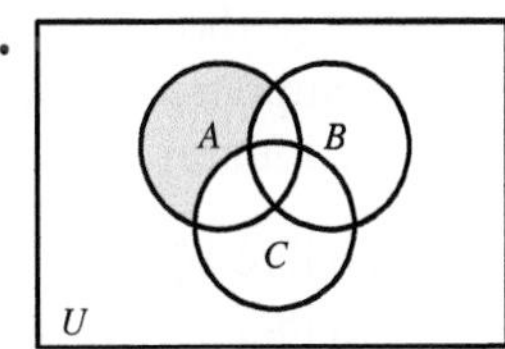

115.

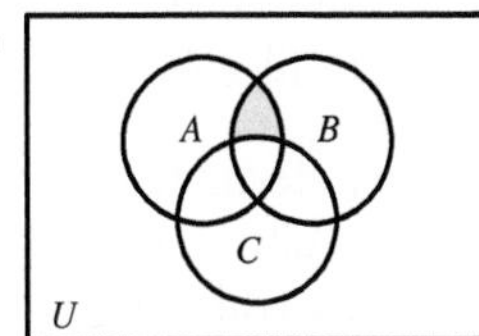

116.

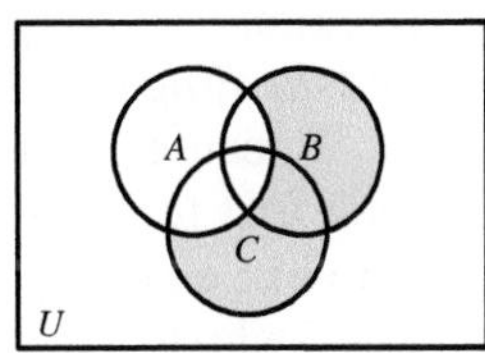

Suppose A and B are sets. Describe the conditions under which each statement would be true.

117. $A = A - B$

118. $A = B - A$

119. $A = A - \emptyset$

120. $A = \emptyset - A$

121. $A \cup \emptyset = \emptyset$

122. $A \cap \emptyset = \emptyset$

123. $A \cap \emptyset = A$

124. $A \cup \emptyset = A$

125. $A \cup A = \emptyset$

126. $A \cap A = \emptyset$

127. $A \cup B = A$

128. $A \cap B = B$

For Exercises 129–135, draw two appropriate Venn diagrams to decide whether the given statement is always true *or* not always true.

129. $A \cap A' = \emptyset$

130. $A \cup A' = U$

131. $(A \cap B) \subseteq A$

132. $(A \cup B) \subseteq A$

133. If $A \subseteq B$, then $A \cup B = A$.

134. If $A \subseteq B$, then $A \cap B = B$.

135. $(A \cup B)' = A' \cap B'$
(De Morgan's second law)

136. If A and B are sets, is it necessarily true that $n(A - B) = n(A) - n(B)$?

137. If $Q = \{x \mid x \text{ is a rational number}\}$ and $H = \{x \mid x \text{ is an irrational number}\}$, describe each set.

(a) $Q \cup H$

(b) $Q \cap H$

4 SURVEYS AND CARDINAL NUMBERS

Surveys • Cardinal Number Formula • Tables

Walt Disney Co./Everett Collection

Surveys

Problems involving sets of people (or objects) sometimes require analyzing known information about certain subsets to obtain cardinal numbers of other subsets. In this section, we apply three problem-solving techniques to such problems: Venn diagrams, cardinal number formulas, and tables. The "known information" is quite often (although not always) obtained by conducting a survey.

Suppose a group of students on a college campus is asked to compare some animated feature films, and the following information is produced.

34 like *Up*	12 like *Up* and *Mr. Fox*
29 like *The Princess and the Frog*	10 like *Princess* and *Mr. Fox*
26 like *Fantastic Mr. Fox*	4 like all three films
16 like *Up* and *Princess*	5 like none of these films.

To determine the total number of students surveyed, we cannot just add the eight numbers above because there is some overlap. For example, in **Figure 18**, the 34 students who like *Up* should not be positioned in region b but should be distributed among regions b, c, d, and e, in a way that is consistent with all of the given data. (Region b actually contains those students who like *Up* but do not like *The Princess and the Frog* and do not like *Fantastic Mr. Fox*.)

Because, at the start, we do not know how to distribute the 34 who like *Up*, we look first for some more manageable data. The smallest total listed, the 4 students who like all three films, can be placed in region d (the intersection of the three sets). The 5 who like none of the three must go into region a. Then, the 16 who like *Up* and *Princess* must go into regions d and e. Because region d already contains 4 students, we must place

$$16 - 4 = 12 \quad \text{in region } e.$$

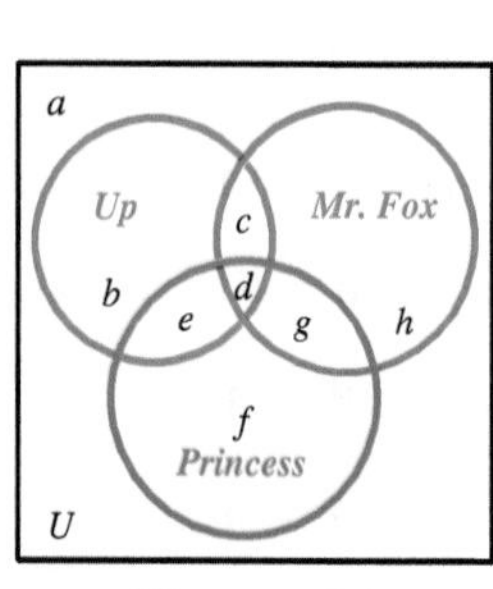

Figure 18

Because 12 like *Up* and *Mr. Fox* (regions c and d), we place

$$12 - 4 = 8 \quad \text{in region } c.$$

Now that regions c, d, and e contain 8, 4, and 12 students, respectively, we must place

$$34 - 8 - 4 - 12 = 10 \quad \text{in region } b.$$

By similar reasoning, all regions are assigned their correct numbers. See **Figure 19** on the next page.

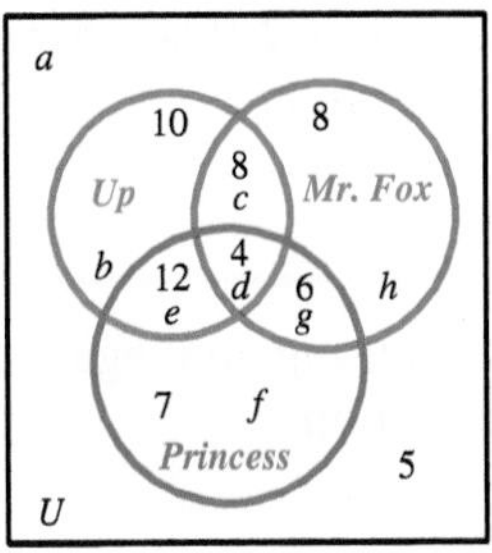

Figure 19

EXAMPLE 1 Analyzing a Survey

Using the survey data on student preferences for animated feature films, as summarized in **Figure 19**, answer each question.

(a) How many students like *Fantastic Mr. Fox* only?

(b) How many students like exactly two films?

(c) How many students were surveyed?

SOLUTION

(a) A student who likes *Mr. Fox* only does not like *Up* and does not like *Princess*. These students are inside the regions for *Mr. Fox* and outside the regions for *Up* and *Princess*. Region h is the appropriate region in **Figure 19**, and we see that eight students like *Fantastic Mr. Fox* only.

(b) The students in regions c, e, and g like exactly two films. The total number of such students is

$$8 + 12 + 6 = 26.$$

(c) Each student surveyed has been placed in exactly one region of **Figure 19**, so the total number surveyed is the sum of the numbers in all eight regions:

$$5 + 10 + 8 + 4 + 12 + 7 + 6 + 8 = 60.$$

Cardinal Number Formula

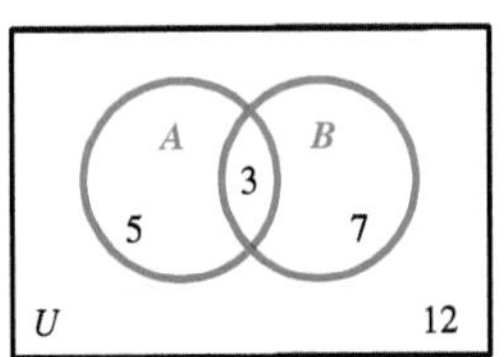

Figure 20

If the numbers shown in **Figure 20** are the cardinal numbers of the individual regions, then

$$n(A) = 5 + 3 = 8, \quad n(B) = 3 + 7 = 10, \quad n(A \cap B) = 3,$$

and

$$n(A \cup B) = 5 + 3 + 7 = 15.$$

Notice that $n(A \cup B) = n(A) + n(B) - n(A \cap B)$ because $15 = 8 + 10 - 3$. This relationship is true for any two sets A and B.

Cardinal Number Formula

For any two sets A and B, the following is true.

$$\boldsymbol{n(A \cup B) = n(A) + n(B) - n(A \cap B)}$$

This formula can be rearranged to find any one of its four terms when the others are known.

EXAMPLE 2 Applying the Cardinal Number Formula

Find $n(A)$ if $n(A \cup B) = 22$, $n(A \cap B) = 8$, and $n(B) = 12$.

SOLUTION

We solve the cardinal number formula for $n(A)$.

$$\begin{aligned} n(A) &= n(A \cup B) - n(B) + n(A \cap B) \\ &= 22 - 12 + 8 \\ &= 18 \end{aligned}$$

Sometimes, even when information is presented as in **Example 2**, it is more convenient to fit that information into a Venn diagram as in **Example 1.**

EXAMPLE 3 Analyzing Data in a Report

Scott Heeren, who leads a group of software engineers who investigate illegal activities on social networking sites, reported the following information.

T = the set of group members following patterns on Twitter

F = the set of group members following patterns on Facebook

L = the set of group members following patterns on LinkedIn

$n(T) = 13$	$n(T \cap F) = 9$	$n(T \cap F \cap L) = 5$
$n(F) = 16$	$n(F \cap L) = 10$	$n(T' \cap F' \cap L') = 3$
$n(L) = 13$	$n(T \cap L) = 6$	

How many engineers are in Scott's group?

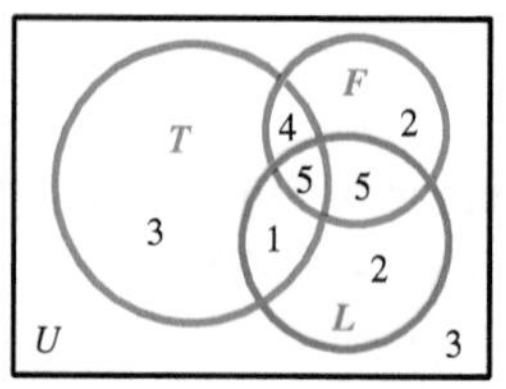

Figure 21

SOLUTION

The data supplied by Scott are reflected in **Figure 21.** The sum of the numbers in the diagram gives the total number of engineers in the group.

$$3 + 3 + 1 + 2 + 5 + 5 + 4 + 2 = 25$$

Tables

Sometimes information appears in a table rather than a Venn diagram, but the basic ideas of union and intersection still apply.

EXAMPLE 4 Analyzing Data in a Table

Melanie Cutler, the officer in charge of the cafeteria on a military base, wanted to know if the beverage that enlisted men and women preferred with lunch depended on their ages. On a given day, Melanie categorized her lunch patrons according to age and preferred beverage, recording the results in a table.

		Beverage			
		Cola (C)	**Iced Tea (I)**	**Sweet Tea (S)**	**Totals**
Age	**18–25 (Y)**	45	10	35	90
	26–33 (M)	20	25	30	75
	Over 33 (O)	5	30	20	55
	Totals	70	65	85	220

Using the letters in the table, find the number of people in each set.

(a) $Y \cap C$ **(b)** $O' \cup I$

SOLUTION

(a) The set Y includes all personnel represented across the top row of the table (90 in all), while C includes the 70 down the left column. The intersection of these two sets is just the upper left entry, 45 people.

(b) The set O' excludes the bottom row, so it includes the first and second rows. The set I includes the middle column only. The union of the two sets represents

$$45 + 10 + 35 + 20 + 25 + 30 + 30 = 195 \text{ people.}$$

4 EXERCISES

Use the numerals representing cardinalities in the Venn diagrams to give the cardinality of each set specified.

1. 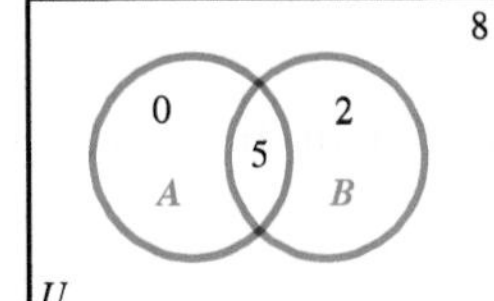

(a) $A \cap B$ **(b)** $A \cup B$
(c) $A \cap B'$ **(d)** $A' \cap B$
(e) $A' \cap B'$

2. 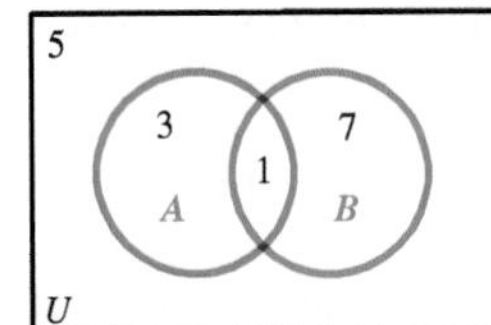

(a) $A \cap B$ **(b)** $A \cup B$
(c) $A \cap B'$ **(d)** $A' \cap B$
(e) $A' \cap B'$

3. 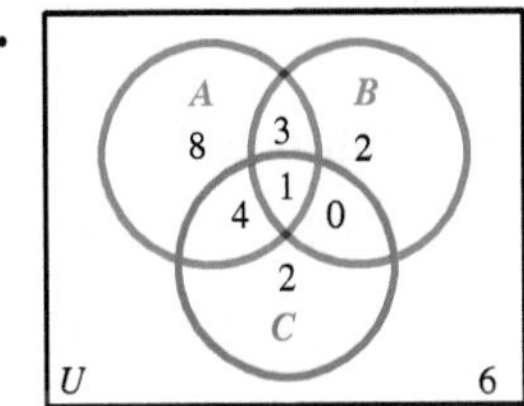

(a) $A \cap B \cap C$ **(b)** $A \cap B \cap C'$
(c) $A \cap B' \cap C$ **(d)** $A' \cap B \cap C$
(e) $A' \cap B' \cap C$ **(f)** $A \cap B' \cap C'$
(g) $A' \cap B \cap C'$ **(h)** $A' \cap B' \cap C'$

4. 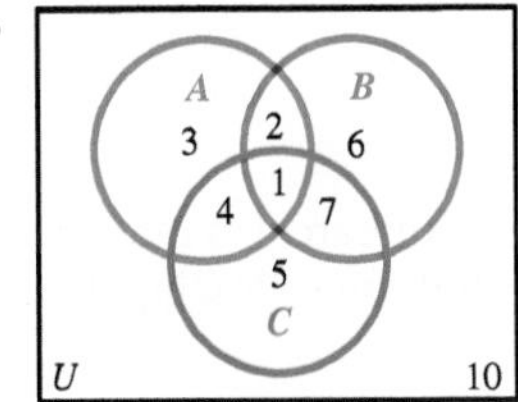

(a) $A \cap B \cap C$ **(b)** $A \cap B \cap C'$
(c) $A \cap B' \cap C$ **(d)** $A' \cap B \cap C$
(e) $A' \cap B' \cap C$ **(f)** $A \cap B' \cap C'$
(g) $A' \cap B \cap C'$ **(h)** $A' \cap B' \cap C'$

In Exercises 5–10, make use of an appropriate formula.

5. Find the value of $n(A \cup B)$ if $n(A) = 12, n(B) = 14$, and $n(A \cap B) = 5$.

6. Find the value of $n(A \cup B)$ if $n(A) = 16, n(B) = 28$, and $n(A \cap B) = 5$.

7. Find the value of $n(A \cap B)$ if $n(A) = 20, n(B) = 12$, and $n(A \cup B) = 25$.

8. Find the value of $n(A \cap B)$ if $n(A) = 20, n(B) = 24$, and $n(A \cup B) = 30$.

9. Find the value of $n(A)$ if $n(B) = 35, n(A \cap B) = 15$, and $n(A \cup B) = 55$.

10. Find the value of $n(B)$ if $n(A) = 20, n(A \cap B) = 6$, and $n(A \cup B) = 30$.

Draw an appropriate Venn diagram and use the given information to fill in the number of elements in each region.

11. $n(A) = 19,\ n(B) = 13,\ n(A \cup B) = 25,\ n(A') = 11$

12. $n(U) = 43,\ n(A) = 25,\ n(A \cap B) = 5,\ n(B') = 30$

13. $n(A') = 25,\ n(B) = 28,\ n(A' \cup B') = 40,\ n(A \cap B) = 10$

14. $n(A \cup B) = 15,\ n(A \cap B) = 8,\ n(A) = 13,\ n(A' \cup B') = 11$

15. $n(A) = 57,\ n(A \cap B) = 35,\ n(A \cup B) = 81,\ n(A \cap B \cap C) = 15,\ n(A \cap C) = 21,\ n(B \cap C) = 25,\ n(C) = 49,\ n(B') = 52$

16. $n(A) = 24,\ n(B) = 24,\ n(C) = 26,\ n(A \cap B) = 10,\ n(B \cap C) = 8,\ n(A \cap C) = 15,\ n(A \cap B \cap C) = 6,\ n(U) = 50$

17. $n(A) = 15,\ n(A \cap B \cap C) = 5,\ n(A \cap C) = 13,\ n(A \cap B') = 9,\ n(B \cap C) = 8,\ n(A' \cap B' \cap C') = 21,\ n(B \cap C') = 3,\ n(B \cup C) = 32$

18. $n(A \cap B) = 21,\ n(A \cap B \cap C) = 6,\ n(A \cap C) = 26,\ n(B \cap C) = 7,\ n(A \cap C') = 20,\ n(B \cap C') = 25,\ n(C) = 40,\ n(A' \cap B' \cap C') = 2$

Use Venn diagrams to work each problem.

19. ***Writing and Producing Music*** Joe Long worked on 9 music projects last year.

Everett Collection

Joe Long, Bob Gaudio, Tommy DeVito, and Frankie Valli
The Four Seasons

He wrote and produced 3 projects.
He wrote a total of 5 projects.
He produced a total of 7 projects.

(a) How many projects did he write but not produce?
(b) How many projects did he produce but not write?

20. ***Compact Disc Collection*** Gitti Lindner is a fan of the music of Paul Simon and Art Garfunkel. In her collection of 25 compact discs, she has the following:

5 on which both Simon and Garfunkel sing
7 on which Simon sings
8 on which Garfunkel sings
15 on which neither Simon nor Garfunkel sings.

(a) How many of her compact discs feature only Paul Simon?

(b) How many of her compact discs feature only Art Garfunkel?

(c) How many feature at least one of these two artists?

(d) How many feature at most one of these two artists?

21. ***Fan Response to Singers*** Julie Davis, a pop culture analyst, wanted to evaluate the relative appeal of different singers. She interviewed 65 fans and determined the following:

37 like Jazmine Sullivan
36 like Carrie Underwood
31 like Brad Paisley
14 like Jazmine and Carrie
21 like Jazmine and Brad
14 like Carrie and Brad
8 like all three singers.

How many of these fans like:

(a) exactly two of these singers?

(b) exactly one of these singers?

(c) none of these singers?

(d) Jazmine, but neither Carrie nor Brad?

(e) Brad and exactly one of the other two?

22. ***Financial Aid for Students*** At the University of Louisiana, half of the 48 mathematics majors were receiving federal financial aid as follows:

5 had Pell Grants
14 participated in the College Work Study Program
4 had TOPS scholarships
2 had TOPS scholarships and participated in Work Study.

Those with Pell Grants had no other federal aid.

How many of the 48 math majors had:

(a) no federal aid?

(b) more than one of these three forms of aid?

(c) federal aid other than these three forms?

(d) a TOPS scholarship or Work Study?

(e) exactly one of these three forms of aid?

23. ***Cooking Habits*** Eric Dangerfield interviewed 140 people in a suburban shopping center to find out some of their cooking habits. He obtained the results given at the top of the next column.

58 use microwave ovens
63 use electric ranges
58 use gas ranges
19 use microwave ovens and electric ranges
17 use microwave ovens and gas ranges
4 use both gas and electric ranges
1 uses all three

(a) How many use exactly two of these kinds of appliances?

(b) How many use at least two of these kinds of appliances?

24. ***Non-Mainline Religious Beliefs*** 140 U.S. adults were surveyed.

Let A = the set of respondents who believe in astrology,
R = the set of respondents who believe in reincarnation,
Y = the set of respondents who believe in the spirituality of yoga.

The survey revealed the following information:

$n(A) = 35$ $\quad n(R \cap Y) = 8$

$n(R) = 36$ $\quad n(A \cap Y) = 10$

$n(Y) = 32$ $\quad n(A \cap R \cap Y) = 6$

$n(A \cap R) = 19$

How many of the respondents believe in:

(a) astrology, but not reincarnation?

(b) at least one of these three things?

(c) reincarnation but neither of the others?

(d) exactly two of these three things?

(e) none of the three?

25. ***Survey on Attitudes Toward Religion*** Researchers interviewed a number of people and recorded the following data. Of all the respondents:

240 think Hollywood is unfriendly toward religion
160 think the media are unfriendly toward religion
181 think scientists are unfriendly toward religion
145 think both Hollywood and the media are unfriendly toward religion
122 think both scientists and the media are unfriendly toward religion
80 think exactly two of these groups are unfriendly toward religion
110 think all three groups are unfriendly toward religion
219 think none of these three groups is unfriendly toward religion.

How many respondents:

(a) were surveyed?

(b) think exactly one of these three groups is unfriendly toward religion?

26. ***Student Goals*** Carol Britz, who sells college textbooks, interviewed freshmen on a community college campus to find out the main goals of today's students.

Let W = the set of those who want to be wealthy,
F = the set of those who want to raise a family,
E = the set of those who want to become experts in their fields.

Carol's findings are summarized here.

$$n(W) = 160 \qquad n(E \cap F) = 90$$
$$n(F) = 140 \qquad n(W \cap F \cap E) = 80$$
$$n(E) = 130 \qquad n(E') = 95$$
$$n(W \cap F) = 95 \qquad n[(W \cup F \cup E)'] = 10$$

Find the total number of students interviewed.

27. ***Hospital Patient Symptoms*** Jesse Fisher conducted a survey among 75 patients admitted to the cardiac unit of a Santa Fe hospital during a two-week period.

Let B = the set of patients with high blood pressure,
C = the set of patients with high cholesterol levels,
S = the set of patients who smoke cigarettes.

Jesse's data are as follows.

$$n(B) = 47 \qquad n(B \cap S) = 33$$
$$n(C) = 46 \qquad n(B \cap C) = 31$$
$$n(S) = 52 \qquad n(B \cap C \cap S) = 21$$
$$n[(B \cap C) \cup (B \cap S) \cup (C \cap S)] = 51$$

Find the number of these patients who:

(a) had either high blood pressure or high cholesterol levels, but not both

(b) had fewer than two of the indications listed

(c) were smokers but had neither high blood pressure nor high cholesterol levels

(d) did not have exactly two of the indications listed.

28. ***Song Themes*** It was once said that country-western songs emphasize three basic themes: love, prison, and trucks. A survey of the local country-western radio station produced the following data.

12 songs about a truck driver who is in love while in prison
13 about a prisoner in love
28 about a person in love
18 about a truck driver in love
3 about a truck driver in prison who is not in love
2 about people in prison who are not in love and do not drive trucks
8 about people who are out of prison, are not in love, and do not drive trucks
16 about truck drivers who are not in prison

(a) How many songs were surveyed?

Find the number of songs about:

(b) truck drivers **(c)** prisoners

(d) truck drivers in prison

(e) people not in prison

(f) people not in love.

Everett Collection

29. Use the figure below to find the numbers of the regions belonging to each set.

(a) $A \cap B \cap C \cap D$

(b) $A \cup B \cup C \cup D$

(c) $(A \cap B) \cup (C \cap D)$

(d) $(A' \cap B') \cap (C \cup D)$

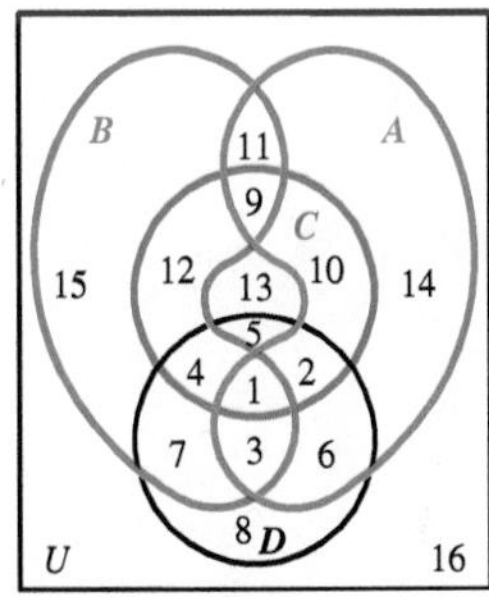

30. ***Sports Viewing*** A survey of 130 TV viewers was taken.

52 watch football
56 watch basketball
62 watch tennis
60 watch golf
21 watch football and basketball
19 watch football and tennis
22 watch basketball and tennis
27 watch football and golf
30 watch basketball and golf
21 watch tennis and golf
3 watch football, basketball, and tennis
15 watch football, basketball, and golf
10 watch football, tennis, and golf
10 watch basketball, tennis, and golf
3 watch all four of these sports
5 don't watch any of these four sports

Use a Venn diagram to answer each question.

(a) How many of these viewers watch football, basketball, and tennis, but not golf?

(b) How many watch exactly one of these four sports?

(c) How many watch exactly two of these four sports?

Solve each problem.

31. *Basketball Positions* Donna DePaulis runs a basketball program in California. On the first day of the season, 60 young women showed up and were categorized by age level and by preferred basketball position, as shown in the following table.

		Position			
		Guard (G)	Forward (F)	Center (N)	Totals
Age	Junior High (J)	9	6	4	19
	Senior High (S)	12	5	9	26
	College (C)	5	8	2	15
	Totals	26	19	15	60

Using the set labels (letters) in the table, find the number of players in each of the following sets.

(a) $J \cap G$ **(b)** $S \cap N$ **(c)** $N \cup (S \cap F)$

(d) $S' \cap (G \cup N)$ **(e)** $(S \cap N') \cup (C \cap G')$

(f) $N' \cap (S' \cap C')$

Brand X Pictures/Thinkstock

32. *Army Housing* A study of U.S. Army housing trends categorized personnel as commissioned officers (C), warrant officers (W), or enlisted (E), and categorized their living facilities as on-base (B), rented off-base (R), or owned off-base (O). One survey yielded the following data.

		Facilities			
		B	R	O	Totals
Personnel	C	12	29	54	95
	W	4	5	6	15
	E	374	71	285	730
	Totals	390	105	345	840

Find the number of personnel in each of the following sets.

(a) $W \cap O$ **(b)** $C \cup B$

(c) $R' \cup W'$ **(d)** $(C \cup W) \cap (B \cup R)$

(e) $(C \cap B) \cup (E \cap O)$ **(f)** $B \cap (W \cup R)'$

33. Could the information of **Example 4** have been presented in a Venn diagram similar to those in **Examples 1 and 3?** If so, construct such a diagram. Otherwise, explain the essential difference of **Example 4.**

34. Explain how a cardinal number formula can be derived for the case where *three* sets occur. Specifically, give a formula relating $n(A \cup B \cup C)$ to

$$n(A),\ n(B),\ n(C),\ n(A \cap B),\ n(A \cap C),\ n(B \cap C),\ \text{and}\ n(A \cap B \cap C).$$

Illustrate with a Venn diagram.

EXTENSION Infinite Sets and Their Cardinalities

One-to-One Correspondence and Equivalent Sets • The Cardinal Number $\aleph_0$ • Infinite Sets • Sets That Are Not Countable

One-to-One Correspondence and Equivalent Sets Georg Cantor met with much resistance in the late 1800s when he first developed modern set theory because of his ideas on infinite sets. The results discussed here, however, are commonly accepted today. Recall the following from **Section 1.**

1. The cardinal number of a set is the number of elements it contains.
2. Two sets are *equivalent* if their cardinal numbers are equal.
3. A set is *infinite* if its cardinal number is "too large" to be found among the whole numbers.

The word **paradox** in Greek originally meant "wrong opinion" as opposed to orthodox, which meant "right opinion." Over the years, the word came to mean self-contradiction.

Before the twentieth century it was considered a paradox that any set could be placed into one-to-one correspondence with a proper subset of itself. This paradox, called **Galileo's paradox** after the sixteenth-century mathematician and scientist **Galileo** (see the picture), is now explained by saying that the ability to make such a correspondence is how we distinguish infinite sets from finite sets. What is true for finite sets is not necessarily true for infinite sets.

We can easily establish the equivalence of two finite sets by counting their elements and comparing their cardinal numbers. But the elements of an infinite set cannot be counted in the same sense. Cantor addressed this difficulty using the idea of a **one-to-one correspondence** between sets. The sets $A = \{1, 2, 3\}$ and $B = \{3, 6, 9\}$, for example, can be placed in such correspondence as follows (among other ways):

$$\begin{array}{ccc} \{1, & 2, & 3\} \\ \updownarrow & \updownarrow & \updownarrow \\ \{3, & 6, & 9\}. \end{array}$$

This correspondence is "one-to-one" because each element of each set is paired with exactly one element of the other set. The equivalence of A and B is denoted $\boldsymbol{A \sim B}$.

On the other hand, the sets $C = \{1, 8, 12\}$ and $D = \{6, 11\}$ are *not* equivalent. Any correspondence between them, such as

$$\begin{array}{ccc} \{1, & 8, & 12\} \\ \updownarrow & \searrow & \swarrow \\ \{6, & & 11\} \end{array}$$

is not one-to-one. (Two different elements from C must be paired with a single element of D.)

Cantor extended this idea that one-to-one correspondence establishes equivalence to his study of infinite sets.

The Cardinal Number $\aleph_0$ The most basic infinite set is the set of counting numbers, $\{1, 2, 3, 4, 5, \ldots\}$. The counting numbers are said to have the infinite cardinal number $\aleph_0$ (the first Hebrew letter, aleph, with a zero subscript, read "aleph-null"). Think of $\aleph_0$ as being the "smallest" infinite cardinal number. To the question "How many counting numbers are there?", we answer "There are $\aleph_0$ of them."

Now, any set that can be placed in a one-to-one correspondence with the counting numbers will have the same cardinal number, or $\aleph_0$. There are many such sets.

EXAMPLE 1 Showing that $\{0, 1, 2, 3, \ldots\}$ Has Cardinal Number $\aleph_0$

Verify that the set of whole numbers $\{0, 1, 2, 3, \ldots\}$ has cardinal number $\aleph_0$.

SOLUTION

We know that $\aleph_0$ is the cardinal number of the set of counting numbers (by definition). To show that another set, such as the whole numbers, also has $\aleph_0$ as its cardinal number, we must show that set to be equivalent to the set of counting numbers. Equivalence is established by a one-to-one correspondence between the two sets.

$$\begin{array}{ccccccccl} \{1, & 2, & 3, & 4, & 5, & 6, \ldots, & n, & \ldots\} & \text{Counting numbers} \\ \updownarrow & \updownarrow & \updownarrow & \updownarrow & \updownarrow & \updownarrow & \updownarrow & \updownarrow & \\ \{0, & 1, & 2, & 3, & 4, & 5, \ldots, & n-1, & \ldots\} & \text{Whole numbers} \end{array}$$

The pairing of the counting number n with the whole number $n - 1$ continues indefinitely, with neither set containing any element not used up in the pairing process. Even though the set of whole numbers has an additional element (the number 0) compared to the set of counting numbers, the correspondence proves that both sets have the same cardinal number, $\aleph_0$. ■■■

The result in **Example 1** shows that intuition is a poor guide for dealing with infinite sets. Because the sets of counting numbers and whole numbers can be placed in a one-to-one correspondence, the two sets have the same cardinal number.

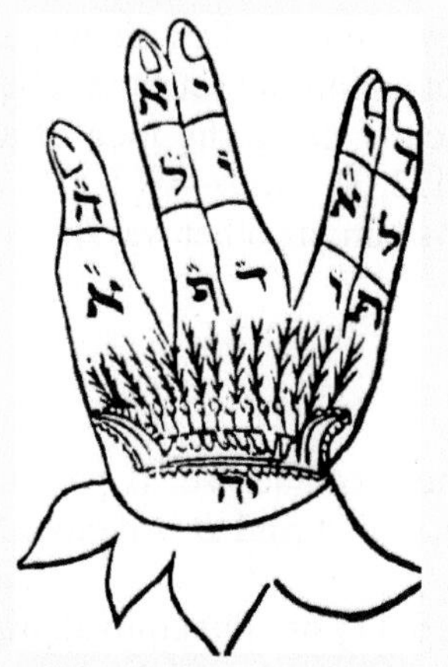

Aleph and other letters of the **Hebrew alphabet** are shown on a Kabbalistic diagram representing one of the ten emanations of God during Creation. Kabbalah, the ultramystical tradition within Judaism, arose in the fifth century and peaked in the sixteenth century in both Palestine and Poland.

Kabbalists believed that the Bible held mysteries that could be discovered in permutations, combinations, and anagrams of its very letters. Each letter in the aleph-bet has a numerical value (aleph = 1), and thus a numeration system exists. The letter Y stands for 10, so 15 should be YH (10 + 5). However, YH is a form of the Holy Name, so instead TW (9 + 6) is the symbol.

Infinite Sets The set $\{5, 6, 7\}$ is a proper subset of the set $\{5, 6, 7, 8\}$, and there is no way to place these two sets in a one-to-one correspondence. However, the set of counting numbers is a proper subset of the set of whole numbers, and **Example 1** showed that these two sets *can* be placed in a one-to-one correspondence. This important property is used in the formal definition of an infinite set.

Infinite Set

A set is **infinite** if it can be placed in a one-to-one correspondence with a proper subset of itself.

EXAMPLE 2 Showing that $\{\ldots, -3, -2, -1, 0, 1, 2, 3, \ldots\}$ Has Cardinal Number $\aleph_0$

Verify that the set of integers $\{\ldots, -3, -2, -1, 0, 1, 2, 3, \ldots\}$ has cardinal number $\aleph_0$.

SOLUTION

A one-to-one correspondence can be set up between the set of integers and the set of counting numbers.

$$\begin{array}{cccccccccc} \{1, & 2, & 3, & 4, & 5, & 6, & 7, & \ldots, & 2n, & 2n+1, & \ldots\} \\ \updownarrow & \updownarrow & \updownarrow & \updownarrow & \updownarrow & \updownarrow & \updownarrow & & \updownarrow & \updownarrow & \\ \{0, & 1, & -1, & 2, & -2, & 3, & -3, & \ldots, & n, & -n, & \ldots\} \end{array}$$

Because of this one-to-one correspondence, the cardinal number of the set of integers is the same as the cardinal number of the set of counting numbers, $\aleph_0$. ■■■

The one-to-one correspondence of **Example 2** proves that the set of integers is infinite—it was placed in one-to-one correspondence with a proper subset of itself.

As shown by **Example 2,** there are just as many integers as there are counting numbers. This result is not at all intuitive, and the next result is even less so. There is an infinite number of fractions between any two counting numbers. For example, there is an infinite set of fractions $\left\{\frac{1}{2}, \frac{3}{4}, \frac{7}{8}, \frac{15}{16}, \frac{31}{32}, \ldots\right\}$ between the counting numbers 0 and 1. This should imply that there are "more" fractions than counting numbers. However, there are just as many fractions as counting numbers.

EXAMPLE 3 Showing that the Set of Rational Numbers Has Cardinal Number $\aleph_0$

Verify that the cardinal number of the set of rational numbers is $\aleph_0$.

SOLUTION

First show that a one-to-one correspondence may be set up between the set of nonnegative rational numbers and the counting numbers. This is done by the following ingenious scheme, devised by Georg Cantor.

Look at **Figure 22** on the next page. The nonnegative rational numbers whose denominators are 1 are written in the first row. Those whose denominators are 2 are written in the second row, and so on. Every nonnegative rational number appears in this list sooner or later. For example, $\frac{327}{189}$ is in row 189 and column 327.

$\frac{0}{1}$	$\frac{1}{1}$	$\frac{2}{1}$	$\frac{3}{1}$	$\frac{4}{1}$	$\frac{5}{1}$	$\frac{6}{1}$	$\frac{7}{1}$ ...
	$\frac{1}{2}$	$\frac{2}{2}$	$\frac{3}{2}$	$\frac{4}{2}$	$\frac{5}{2}$	$\frac{6}{2}$	$\frac{7}{2}$ ...
	$\frac{1}{3}$	$\frac{2}{3}$	$\frac{3}{3}$	$\frac{4}{3}$	$\frac{5}{3}$	$\frac{6}{3}$	$\frac{7}{3}$ ...
	$\frac{1}{4}$	$\frac{2}{4}$	$\frac{3}{4}$	$\frac{4}{4}$	$\frac{5}{4}$	$\frac{6}{4}$	$\frac{7}{4}$ ...
	$\frac{1}{5}$	$\frac{2}{5}$	$\frac{3}{5}$	$\frac{4}{5}$	$\frac{5}{5}$	$\frac{6}{5}$	$\frac{7}{5}$ ...
	$\frac{1}{6}$	$\frac{2}{6}$	$\frac{3}{6}$	$\frac{4}{6}$	$\frac{5}{6}$	$\frac{6}{6}$	$\frac{7}{6}$ ...
	⋮	⋮	⋮	⋮	⋮	⋮	⋮

Figure 22

To set up a one-to-one correspondence between the set of nonnegative rationals and the set of counting numbers, follow the path drawn in **Figure 22.** Let $\frac{0}{1}$ correspond to 1, let $\frac{1}{1}$ correspond to 2, $\frac{2}{1}$ to 3, $\frac{1}{2}$ to 4 (skip $\frac{2}{2}$, since $\frac{2}{2} = \frac{1}{1}$), $\frac{1}{3}$ to 5, $\frac{1}{4}$ to 6, and so on. The numbers under the colored disks are omitted because they can be reduced to lower terms, and were thus included earlier in the listing.

This procedure sets up a one-to-one correspondence between the set of nonnegative rationals and the counting numbers, showing that both of these sets have the same cardinal number, $\aleph_0$. Now by using the method of **Example 2** (i.e., letting each negative number follow its corresponding positive number), we can extend this correspondence to include negative rational numbers as well. Thus, the set of all rational numbers has cardinal number $\aleph_0$. ■■■

A set is called **countable** if it is finite or if it has cardinal number $\aleph_0$. All the infinite sets of numbers discussed so far—the counting numbers, the whole numbers, the integers, and the rational numbers—are countable.

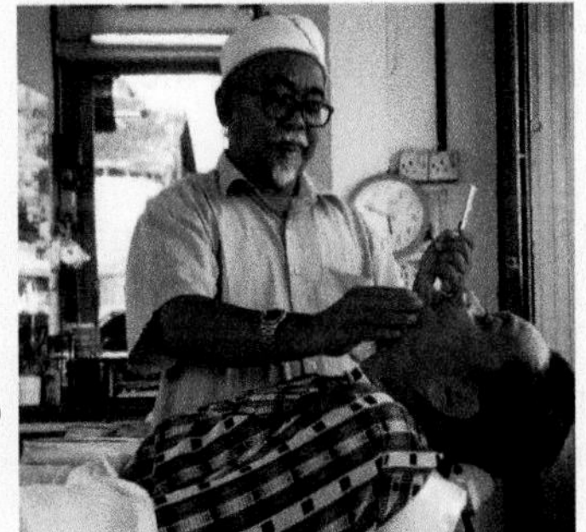

Koo Eng Yow/Shutterstock

The Barber Paradox is a version of a paradox of set theory that Bertrand Russell proposed in the early twentieth century.

1. The men in a village are of two types: men who do not shave themselves and men who do.
2. The village barber shaves all men who do not shave themselves and he shaves only those men.

But who shaves the barber? The barber cannot shave himself. If he did, he would fall into the category of men who shave themselves. However, (2) above states that the barber does not shave such men.

So the barber does not shave himself. But then he falls into the category of men who do not shave themselves. According to (2), the barber shaves all of these men; hence, the barber shaves himself, too.

We find that the barber cannot shave himself, yet the barber does shave himself—a paradox.

Sets That Are Not Countable

EXAMPLE 4 Showing that the Set of Real Numbers Does Not Have Cardinal Number $\aleph_0$

Verify that the set of all real numbers does not have cardinal number $\aleph_0$.

SOLUTION

There are two possibilities:

1. The set of real numbers has cardinal number $\aleph_0$.
2. The set of real numbers does not have cardinal number $\aleph_0$.

If we assume that the first statement is true, then a one-to-one correspondence can be set up between the set of real numbers and the set of counting numbers.

In a later chapter, we show that every real number can be written as a decimal number (or simply "decimal"). Thus, in the one-to-one correspondence we are assuming, some decimal corresponds to the counting number 1, some decimal corresponds to 2, and so on. Suppose the correspondence begins as follows:

$$1 \leftrightarrow 0.68458429006\ldots$$
$$2 \leftrightarrow 0.13479201038\ldots$$
$$3 \leftrightarrow 0.37291568341\ldots$$
$$4 \leftrightarrow 0.935223671611\ldots$$
and so on.

Getty Images/Digital Vision

Zeno's paradox of the Tortoise and Achilles was given in its original form by Zeno of Elea.

In the original story, the Tortoise is able to convince Achilles (the Greek hero of Homer's *The Illiad*) that in a race, given a small head start, the Tortoise is always able to defeat Achilles. (See the **Chapter Opener** and **Exercises 51 and 52** in this **Extension**.) The resolution of this paradox is discussed on the Web site www.mathacademy.com.

Assuming the existence of a one-to-one correspondence between the counting numbers and the real numbers means that every decimal is in the list above. Let's construct a new decimal K as follows. The first decimal in the above list has 6 as its first digit. Let K start as $K = 0.4\ldots$. We picked 4 because $4 \neq 6$. (We could have used any other digit except 6.) Because the second digit of the second decimal in the list is 3, we let $K = 0.45\ldots$ (because $5 \neq 3$). The third digit of the third decimal is 2, so let $K = 0.457\ldots$ (because $7 \neq 2$). The fourth digit of the fourth decimal is 2, so let $K = 0.4573\ldots$ (because $3 \neq 2$). Continue defining K in this way.

Is K in the list that we assumed to contain all decimals? The first decimal in the list differs from K in at least the first position (K starts with 4, and the first decimal in the list starts with 6). The second decimal in the list differs from K in at least the second position, and the nth decimal in the list differs from K in at least the nth position. Every decimal in the list differs from K in at least one position, so that K cannot possibly be in the list. In summary:

We assume every decimal is in the list above.
The decimal K is not in the list.

Because these statements cannot both be true, the original assumption has led to a contradiction. This forces the acceptance of the only possible alternative to the original assumption: It is not possible to set up a one-to-one correspondence between the set of reals and the set of counting numbers. The cardinal number of the set of reals is not equal to $\aleph_0$. ∎∎∎

The set of counting numbers is a proper subset of the set of real numbers. Because of this, it would seem reasonable to say that the cardinal number of the set of reals, commonly written c, is greater than $\aleph_0$. (The letter c here represents *continuum*.) Other, even larger, infinite cardinal numbers can be constructed. For example, the set of all subsets of the set of real numbers has a cardinal number larger than c. Continuing this process of finding cardinal numbers of sets of subsets, more and more, larger and larger infinite cardinal numbers are produced.

The six most important infinite sets of numbers were listed in **Section 1.** All of them have been dealt with in this **Extension,** except the irrational numbers. The irrationals have decimal representations, so they are all included among the real numbers. Because the irrationals are a subset of the reals, you might guess that the irrationals have cardinal number $\aleph_0$, just like the rationals. However, because the union of the rationals and the irrationals is all the reals, that would imply that the cardinality of the union of two disjoint countable sets is c. But **Example 2** showed that this is not the case. A better guess is that the cardinal number of the irrationals is c (the same as that of the reals). This is, in fact, true.

Cardinal Numbers of Infinite Number Sets

Infinite Set	Cardinal Number
Natural or counting numbers	$\aleph_0$
Whole numbers	$\aleph_0$
Integers	$\aleph_0$
Rational numbers	$\aleph_0$
Irrational numbers	c
Real numbers	c

EXTENSION EXERCISES

Match each set in Column I with the set in Column II that has the same cardinality. Give the cardinal number.

I	II
1. {6}	**A.** $\{x \mid x$ is a rational number$\}$
2. {−16, 14, 3}	**B.** {26}
3. $\{x \mid x$ is a natural number$\}$	**C.** $\{x \mid x$ is an irrational number$\}$
4. $\{x \mid x$ is a real number$\}$	**D.** {x, y, z}
5. $\{x \mid x$ is an integer between 5 and 6$\}$	**E.** $\{x \mid x$ is a real number that satisfies $x^2 = 25\}$
6. $\{x \mid x$ is an integer that satisfies $x^2 = 100\}$	**F.** $\{x \mid x$ is an integer that is both even and odd$\}$

Place each pair of sets into a one-to-one correspondence, if possible.

7. {I, II, III} and {x, y, z}

8. {a, b, c, d} and {2, 4, 6}

9. {a, d, d, i, t, i, o, n} and {a, n, s, w, e, r}

10. {Obama, Clinton, Bush} and {Michelle, Hillary, Laura}

Give the cardinal number of each set.

11. {a, b, c, d, . . . , k}

12. {9, 12, 15, . . . , 36}

13. ∅

14. {0}

15. {300, 400, 500, . . . }

16. {−35, −28, −21, . . . , 56}

17. $\left\{-\frac{1}{4}, -\frac{1}{8}, -\frac{1}{12}, \ldots\right\}$

18. $\{x \mid x$ is an even integer$\}$

19. $\{x \mid x$ is an odd counting number$\}$

20. {b, a, 1, 1, a, d}

21. {Jan, Feb, Mar, . . . , Dec}

22. {Alabama, Alaska, Arizona, . . . , Wisconsin, Wyoming}

23. Lew Lefton has revised the old song "100 Bottles of Beer on the Wall" to illustrate a property of infinite cardinal numbers. Fill in the blank in the first verse of Lefton's composition:

$\aleph_0$ bottles of beer on the wall, $\aleph_0$ bottles of beer,
take one down and pass it around, ____ bottles
of beer on the wall.
(*Source:* http://people.math.gatech.edu/~llefton)

$\aleph_0 - 1 = ?$

Joy Brown/Shutterstock

24. Two one-to-one correspondences are considered "different" if some elements are paired differently in one than in the other.

$$\begin{matrix}\{a, & b, & c\} \\ \updownarrow & \updownarrow & \updownarrow \\ \{a, & b, & c\}\end{matrix} \quad \text{and} \quad \begin{matrix}\{a, & b, & c\} \\ \updownarrow & \updownarrow & \updownarrow \\ \{c, & b, & a\}\end{matrix} \quad \text{are different,}$$

$$\text{while} \quad \begin{matrix}\{a, & b, & c\} \\ \updownarrow & \updownarrow & \updownarrow \\ \{c, & a, & b\}\end{matrix} \quad \text{and} \quad \begin{matrix}\{b, & c, & a\} \\ \updownarrow & \updownarrow & \updownarrow \\ \{a, & b, & c\}\end{matrix} \quad \text{are not.}$$

(a) How many *different* correspondences can be set up between the two sets {Jamie Foxx, Mike Myers, Madonna} and {Austin Powers, Ray Charles, Eva Peron}?

(b) Which one of these correspondences pairs each person with the appropriate famous movie role?

Determine whether each pair of sets is equal, equivalent, both, *or* neither.

25. {u, v, w}, {v, u, w}

26. {48, 6}, {4, 86}

27. {X, Y, Z}, {x, y, z}

28. {top}, {pot}

29. $\{x \mid x$ is a positive real number$\}$, $\{x \mid x$ is a negative real number$\}$

30. $\{x \mid x$ is a positive rational number$\}$, $\{x \mid x$ is a negative real number$\}$

Show that each set has cardinal number $\aleph_0$ by setting up a one-to-one correspondence between the given set and the set of counting numbers.

31. the set of positive even integers

32. {−10, −20, −30, −40, . . .}

33. $\{1{,}000{,}000,\ 2{,}000{,}000,\ 3{,}000{,}000, \ldots\}$

34. the set of odd integers

35. $\{2, 4, 8, 16, 32, \ldots\}$
(*Hint:* $4 = 2^2, 8 = 2^3, 16 = 2^4$, and so on)

36. $\{-17, -22, -27, -32, \ldots\}$

In Exercises 37–40, identify the given statement as always true *or* not always true. *If* not always true, *give a counterexample.*

37. If A and B are infinite sets, then A is equivalent to B.

38. If set A is an infinite set and set B can be put in a one-to-one correspondence with a proper subset of A, then B must be infinite.

39. If A is an infinite set and A is not equivalent to the set of counting numbers, then $n(A) = c$.

40. If A and B are both countably infinite sets, then $n(A \cup B) = \aleph_0$.

Exercises 41 and 42 are geometric applications of the concept of infinity.

41. The set of real numbers can be represented by an infinite line, extending indefinitely in both directions. Each point on the line corresponds to a unique real number, and each real number corresponds to a unique point on the line.

(a) Use the figure below, where the line segment between 0 and 1 has been bent into a semicircle and positioned above the line, to prove that

$\{x \mid x \text{ is a real number between 0 and 1}\}$ *is equivalent to* $\{x \mid x \text{ is a real number}\}$.

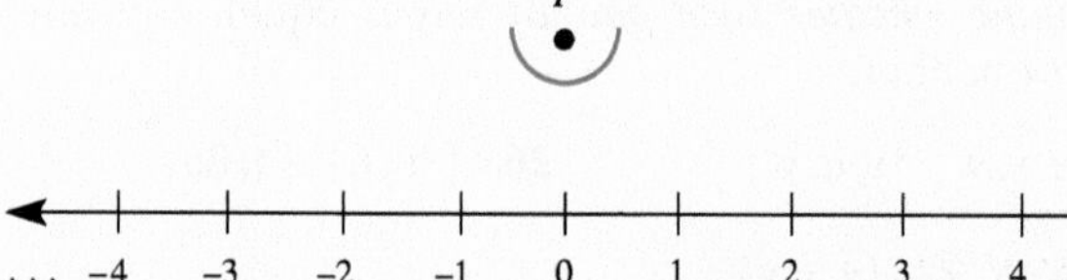

(b) What fact does part (a) establish about the set of real numbers?

42. Show that the two vertical line segments shown here both have the same number of points.

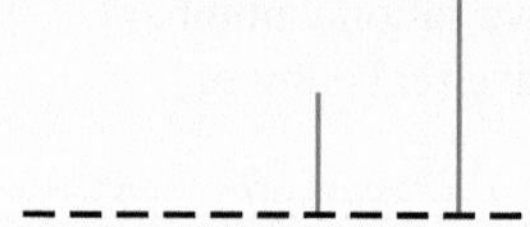

Show that each set can be placed in a one-to-one correspondence with a proper subset of itself to prove that the set is infinite.

43. $\{3, 6, 9, 12, \ldots\}$

44. $\{4, 7, 10, 13, 16, \ldots\}$

45. $\left\{\frac{3}{4}, \frac{3}{8}, \frac{3}{12}, \frac{3}{16}, \ldots\right\}$

46. $\left\{1, \frac{4}{3}, \frac{5}{3}, 2, \ldots\right\}$

47. $\left\{\frac{1}{9}, \frac{1}{18}, \frac{1}{27}, \frac{1}{36}, \ldots\right\}$

48. $\{-3, -5, -9, -17, \ldots\}$

49. Describe the distinction between *equal* and *equivalent* sets.

50. Explain how the correspondence suggested in **Example 4** shows that the set of real numbers between 0 and 1 is not countable.

The Paradoxes of Zeno *The* **Chapter Opener** *discussed the scene in the movie* I.Q. *that deals with Zeno's paradox. Zeno was born about 496* B.C. *in southern Italy. Two forms of his paradox are given below. What is your explanation for the following two examples of Zeno's paradoxes?*

51. Achilles, if he starts out behind a tortoise, can never overtake the tortoise even if he runs faster.

Suppose Tortoise has a head start of one meter and goes one-tenth as fast as Achilles. When Achilles reaches the point where Tortoise started, Tortoise is then one-tenth meter ahead. When Achilles reaches *that* point, Tortoise is one-hundredth meter ahead. And so on. Achilles gets closer but can never catch up.

52. Motion itself cannot occur.

You cannot travel one meter until after you have first gone a half meter. But you cannot go a half meter until after you have first gone a quarter meter. And so on. Even the tiniest motion cannot occur because a tinier motion would have to occur first.

COLLABORATIVE INVESTIGATION

Surveying the Members of Your Class

This group activity is designed to determine the number of students present in your class without actually counting the members one by one. This will be accomplished by having each member of the class determine one particular set in which he or she belongs, and then finding the sum of the cardinal numbers of the subsets.

For this activity, we designate three sets: X, Y, and Z.

$X = \{$students in the class registered with the Republican party$\}$

$Y = \{$students in the class 24 years of age or younger$\}$

$Z = \{$students who have never been married$\}$

Each student in the class will belong to one of the sets X, X', one of the sets Y, Y', and one of the sets Z, Z'. (The complement of a set consists of all elements in the universe (class) that are not in the set.)

As an example, suppose that a student is a 23-year-old divorced Democrat. The student belongs to the sets X', Y, and Z'. The set to which the student belongs is

$$X' \cap Y \cap Z'.$$

In the Venn diagram that follows, the eight subsets are identified by lowercase letters (*a*)–(*h*).

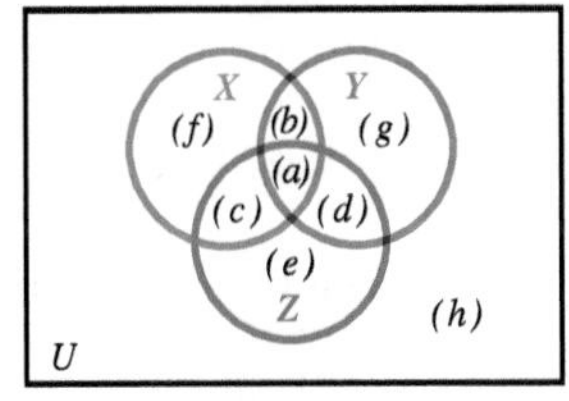

The final column in the following table will be completed when a survey is made. Each student should now determine to which set he or she belongs. (The student described earlier belongs to (*g*).)

Region	Description in Terms of Set Notation	Number of Class Members in the Set
(*a*)	$X \cap Y \cap Z$	
(*b*)	$X \cap Y \cap Z'$	
(*c*)	$X \cap Y' \cap Z$	
(*d*)	$X' \cap Y \cap Z$	
(*e*)	$X' \cap Y' \cap Z$	
(*f*)	$X \cap Y' \cap Z'$	
(*g*)	$X' \cap Y \cap Z'$	
(*h*)	$X' \cap Y' \cap Z'$	

The instructor will now poll the class to see how many members are in each set. *Remember that each class member will belong to one and only one set.*

After the survey is made, find the sum of the numbers in the final column. They should add up to *exactly* the number of students present. Count the class members individually to verify this.

Topics for Discussion

1. Suppose that the final column entries do not add up to the total number of class members. What might have gone wrong?
2. Why can't a class member be a member of more than one of the eight subsets listed?

CHAPTER TEST

In Exercises 1–14, let

$$U = \{a, b, c, d, e, f, g, h\}, \quad A = \{a, b, c, d\},$$

$$B = \{b, e, a, d\}, \quad \textit{and} \quad C = \{a, e\}.$$

Find each set.

1. $A \cup C$

2. $B \cap A$

3. B'

4. $A - (B \cap C')$

Identify each statement as true *or* false.

5. $b \in A$

6. $C \subseteq A$

7. $B \subset (A \cup C)$

8. $c \notin C$

9. $n[(A \cup B) - C] = 4$

10. $\emptyset \subset C$

11. $A \cap B'$ is equivalent to $B \cap A'$

12. $(A \cup B)' = A' \cap B'$

Find each of the following.

13. $n(A \times C)$

14. the number of proper subsets of A

Give a word description for each set.

15. $\{-3, -1, 1, 3, 5, 7, 9\}$

16. {January, February, March, . . . , December}

Express each set in set-builder notation.

17. $\{-1, -2, -3, -4, \ldots\}$

18. $\{24, 32, 40, 48, \ldots, 88\}$

Place ⊂, ⊆, both, *or* neither *in each blank to make a true statement.*

19. $\emptyset$ _____ $\{x \mid x$ is a counting number between 20 and 21$\}$

20. $\{4, 9, 16\}$ _______ $\{4, 5, 6, 7, 8, 9, 10\}$

Shade each set in an appropriate Venn diagram.

21. $X \cup Y'$

22. $X' \cap Y'$

23. $(X \cup Y) - Z$

24. $[(X \cap Y) \cup (Y \cap Z) \cup (X \cap Z)] - (X \cap Y \cap Z)$

Facts About Inventions *The table lists ten inventions, together with other pertinent data.*

Invention	Date	Inventor	Nation
Adding machine	1642	Pascal	France
Barometer	1643	Torricelli	Italy
Electric razor	1917	Schick	U.S.
Fiber optics	1955	Kapany	England
Geiger counter	1913	Geiger	Germany
Pendulum clock	1657	Huygens	Holland
Radar	1940	Watson-Watt	Scotland
Telegraph	1837	Morse	U.S.
Thermometer	1593	Galileo	Italy
Zipper	1891	Judson	U.S.

Let U = the set of all ten inventions,
A = the set of items invented in the United States,
and T = the set of items invented in the twentieth century.

List the elements of each set.

25. $A \cap T$

26. $(A \cup T)'$

27. $A - T'$

28. State De Morgan's laws for sets in words rather than symbols.

29. The numerals in the Venn diagram indicate the number of elements in each particular subset.

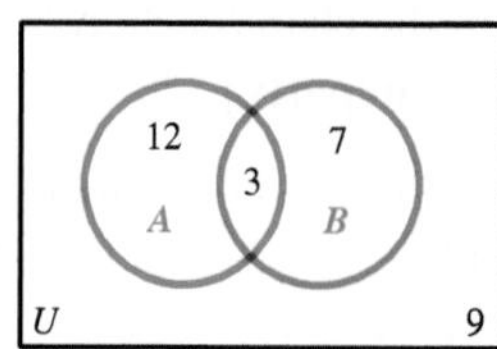

Determine the number of elements in each set.

(a) $A \cup B$ **(b)** $A \cap B'$ **(c)** $(A \cap B)'$

30. ***Financial Aid to College Students*** Three major sources of financial aid are government grants, private scholarships, and the colleges themselves. Susan Brilling, Financial Aid Director of a small private Southern college, surveyed the records of 100 sophomores and found the following:

49 receive government grants
55 receive private scholarships
43 receive aid from the college
23 receive government grants and private scholarships
18 receive government grants and aid from the college
28 receive private scholarships and aid from the college
8 receive help from all three sources.

How many of the students in the survey:

(a) have government grants only?

(b) have private scholarships but not government grants?

(c) receive financial aid from only one of these sources?

(d) receive aid from exactly two of these sources?

(e) receive no financial aid from any of these sources?

(f) receive no aid from the college or from the government?

ANSWERS TO SELECTED EXERCISES

1 Exercises

1. F **3.** E **5.** B **7.** H **9.** {1, 2, 3, 4, 5, 6} **11.** {0, 1, 2, 3, 4} **13.** {6, 7, 8, 9, 10, 11, 12, 13, 14} **15.** {−15, −13, −11, −9, −7, −5, −3, −1} **17.** {2, 4, 8, 16, 32, 64, 128, 256} **19.** {0, 2, 4, 6, 8, 10} **21.** {21, 22, 23, ...} **23.** {Lake Erie, Lake Huron, Lake Michigan, Lake Ontario, Lake Superior} **25.** {5, 10, 15, 20, 25, ...} **27.** $\{1, \frac{1}{2}, \frac{1}{3}, \frac{1}{4}, \frac{1}{5}, \ldots\}$

In Exercises 29 and 31, there are other ways to describe the sets. **29.** $\{x \mid x$ is a rational number$\}$ **31.** $\{x \mid x$ is an odd natural number less than 76$\}$ **33.** the set of single-digit integers **35.** the set of states of the United States **37.** finite **39.** infinite **41.** infinite **43.** infinite **45.** 8 **47.** 500 **49.** 26 **51.** 39 **53.** 28 **55.** Answers will vary. **57.** well defined **59.** not well defined **61.** $\in$ **63.** $\notin$ **65.** $\notin$ **67.** $\in$ **69.** false **71.** true **73.** true **75.** true **77.** false **79.** true **81.** true **83.** true **85.** false **87.** true **89.** Answers will vary. **91.** {2} and {3, 4} (Other examples are possible.) **93.** {a, b} and {a, c} (Other examples are possible.) **95. (a)** {Drew Barrymore, Leonardo DiCaprio, Samuel L. Jackson, Jim Carrey} **(b)** {Will Ferrell, Ewan McGregor}

2 Exercises

1. D **3.** B **5.** $\not\subseteq$ **7.** $\subseteq$ **9.** $\subseteq$ **11.** $\not\subseteq$ **13.** both **15.** $\subseteq$ **17.** both **19.** neither **21.** true **23.** false **25.** true **27.** false **29.** true **31.** true **33.** false **35.** true **37.** true **39.** false **41. (a)** 64 **(b)** 63 **43. (a)** 32 **(b)** 31 **45.** {5, 7, 9, 10} **47.** {2} **49.** $\emptyset$ **51.** {Higher cost, Lower cost, Educational, More time to see the sights in California, Less time to see the sights in California, Cannot visit relatives along the way, Can visit relatives along the way} **53.** {Higher cost, More time to see the sights in California, Cannot visit relatives along the way} **55.** $\emptyset$ **57.** {A, B, C, D, E} (All are present.) **59.** {A, B, C}, {A, B, D}, {A, B, E}, {A, C, D}, {A, C, E}, {A, D, E}, {B, C, D}, {B, C, E}, {B, D, E}, {C, D, E} **61.** {A}, {B}, {C}, {D}, {E} **63.** 32 **65.** $2^{25} - 1 = 33{,}554{,}431$ **67. (a)** 15 **(b)** 16; It is now possible to select *no* bills. **69. (a)** s **(b)** s **(c)** $2s$ **(d)** Adding one more element will always double the number of subsets, so the expression 2^n is true in general.

3 Exercises

1. B **3.** A **5.** E **7.** {a, c} **9.** {a, b, c, d, e, f} **11.** {a, b, c, d, e, f, g} **13.** {b, d, f} **15.** {d, f} **17.** {a, b, c, e, g} **19.** {a, c, e, g} **21.** {a} **23.** {e, g} **25.** {e, g} **27.** {d, f} **29.** {e, b, g}

In Exercises 31–35, there may be other acceptable descriptions.

31. the set of all elements that either are in A, or are not in B and not in C **33.** the set of all elements that are in C but not in B, or are in A **35.** the set of all elements that are in A but not in C, or in B but not in C **37.** $\{e, h, c, l, b\}$ **39.** $\{l, b\}$ **41.** $\{e, h, c, l, b\}$ **43.** the set of all tax returns showing business income or filed in 2009 **45.** the set of all tax returns filed in 2009 without itemized deductions **47.** the set of all tax returns with itemized deductions or showing business income, but not selected for audit **49.** always true **51.** always true **53.** not always true **55. (a)** {1, 3, 5, 2} **(b)** {1, 2, 3, 5} **(c)** For any sets X and Y, $X \cup Y = Y \cup X$. **57. (a)** {1, 3, 5, 2, 4} **(b)** {1, 3, 5, 2, 4} **(c)** For any sets X, Y, and Z, $X \cup (Y \cup Z) = (X \cup Y) \cup Z$. **59. (a)** {4} **(b)** {4} **(c)** For any sets X and Y, $(X \cup Y)' = X' \cap Y'$. **61.** $X \cup \emptyset = X$; For any set X, $X \cup \emptyset = X$. **63.** true **65.** false **67.** true **69.** true **71.** $A \times B = \{(2, 4), (2, 9), (8, 4), (8, 9), (12, 4), (12, 9)\}$; $B \times A = \{(4, 2), (4, 8), (4, 12), (9, 2), (9, 8), (9, 12)\}$ **73.** $A \times B = \{$(d, p), (d, i), (d, g), (o, p), (o, i), (o, g), (g, p), (g, i), (g, g)$\}$; $B \times A = \{$(p, d), (p, o), (p, g), (i, d), (i, o), (i, g), (g, d), (g, o), (g, g)$\}$ **75.** $n(A \times B) = 6$; $n(B \times A) = 6$ **77.** $n(A \times B) = 210$; $n(B \times A) = 210$ **79.** 6

81.

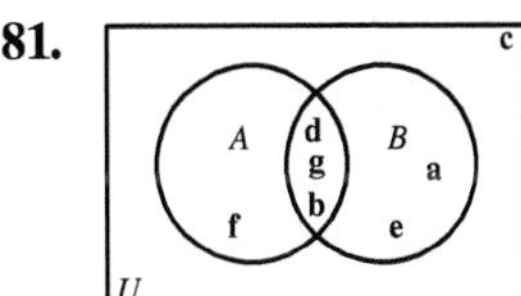

83.

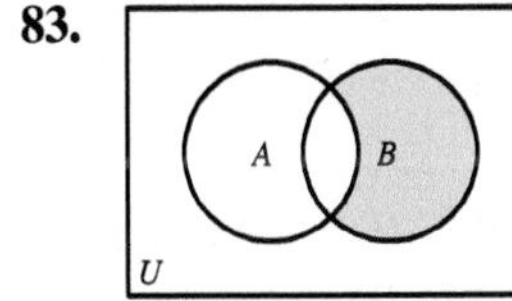

$B \cap A'$

85.

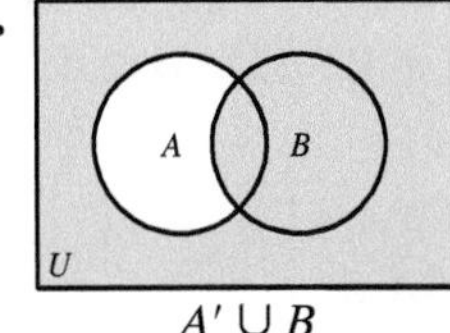

$A' \cup B$

87.

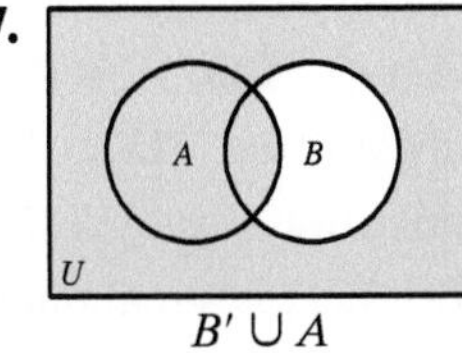

$B' \cup A$

89.
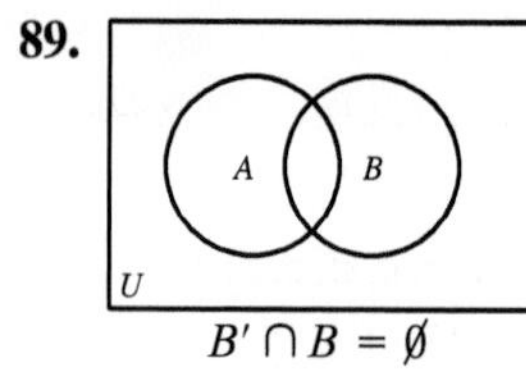

$B' \cap B = \emptyset$

91.
$B' \cup (A' \cap B')$

93.
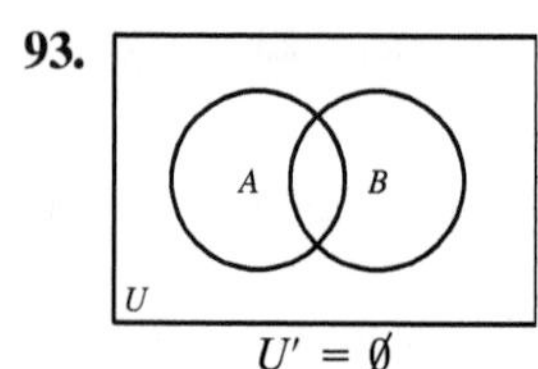

$U' = \emptyset$

95.
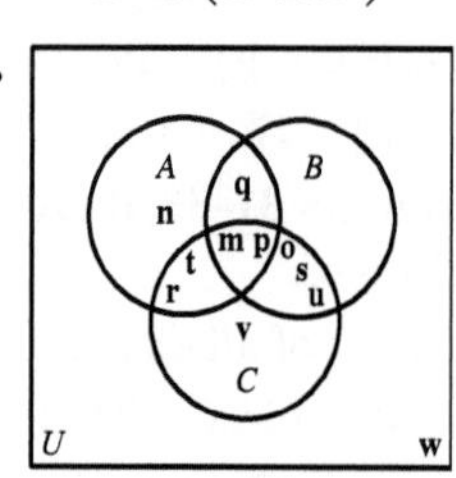

97.
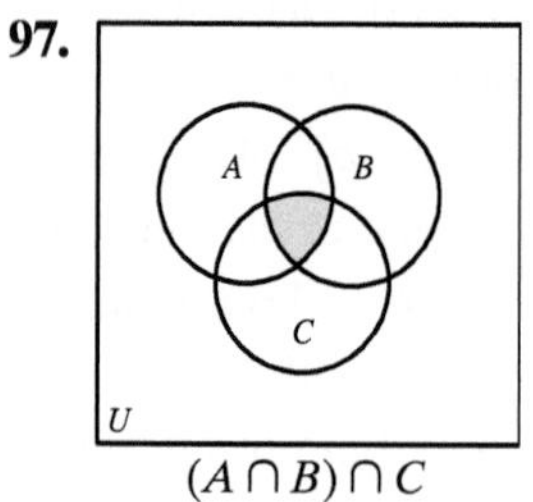

$(A \cap B) \cap C$

99.
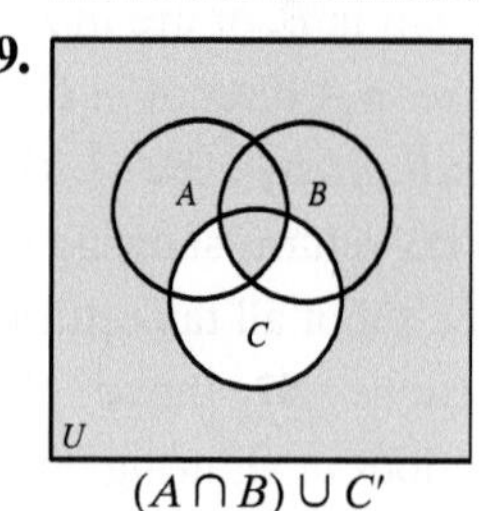

$(A \cap B) \cup C'$

101.
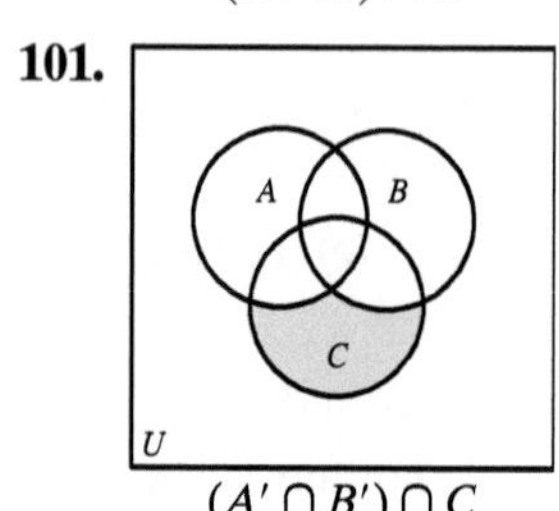

$(A' \cap B') \cap C$

103.
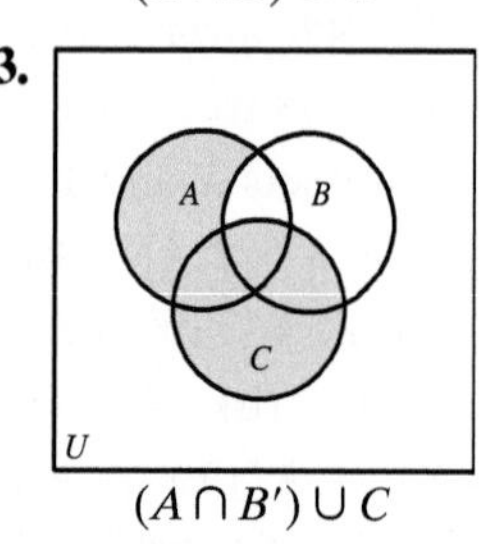

$(A \cap B') \cup C$

105.
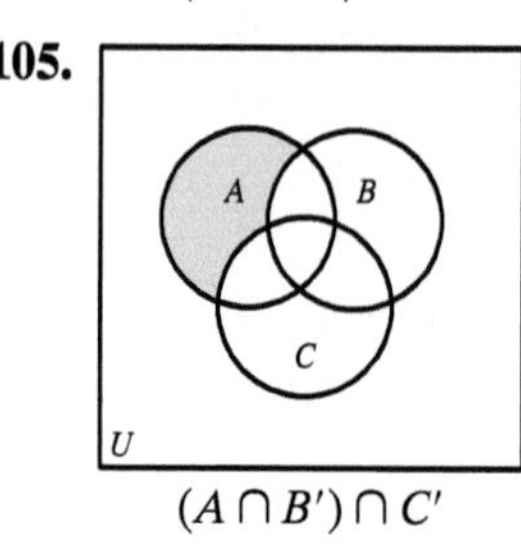

$(A \cap B') \cap C'$

107.
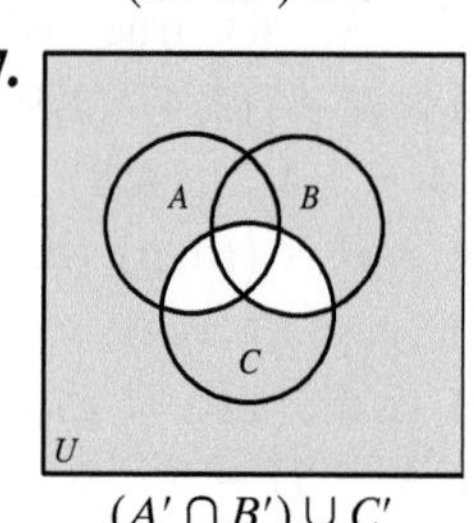

$(A' \cap B') \cup C'$

109. $A' \cap B'$, or $(A \cup B)'$
111. $(A \cup B) \cap (A \cap B)'$, or $(A \cup B) - (A \cap B)$, or $(A - B) \cup (B - A)$
113. $(A \cap B) \cup (A \cap C)$, or $A \cap (B \cup C)$
115. $(A \cap B) \cap C'$, or $(A \cap B) - C$
117. $A \cap B = \emptyset$ **119.** This statement is true for any set A.
121. $A = \emptyset$ **123.** $A = \emptyset$ **125.** $A = \emptyset$ **127.** $B \subseteq A$
129. always true **131.** always true
133. not always true **135.** always true
137. **(a)** $\{x \mid x \text{ is a real number}\}$ **(b)** $\emptyset$

4 Exercises

1. **(a)** 5 **(b)** 7 **(c)** 0 **(d)** 2 **(e)** 8 **3.** **(a)** 1 **(b)** 3 **(c)** 4 **(d)** 0 **(e)** 2 **(f)** 8 **(g)** 2 **(h)** 6 **5.** 21
7. 7 **9.** 35

11.
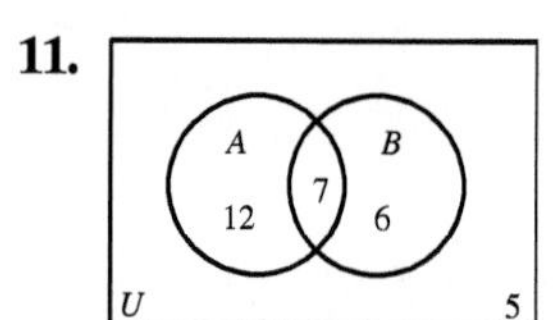

13.
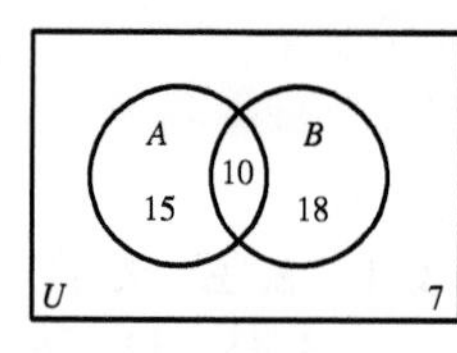

15.
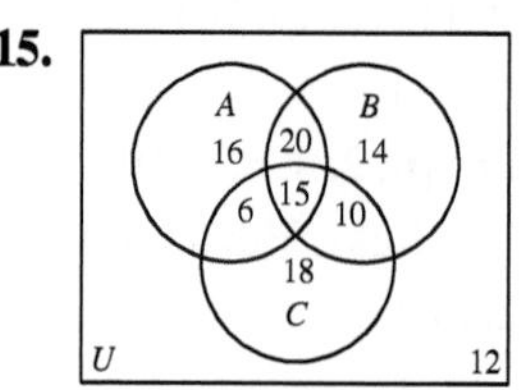

17.
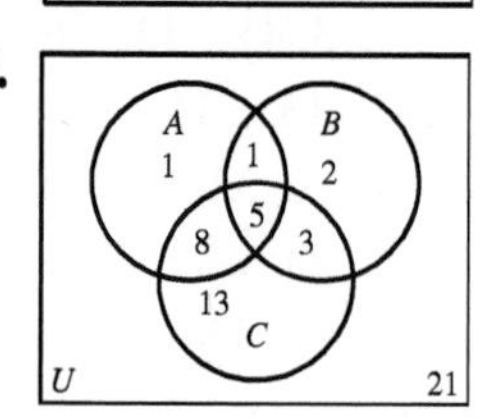

19. **(a)** 2 **(b)** 4 **21.** **(a)** 25 **(b)** 20 **(c)** 12 **(d)** 10 **(e)** 19 **23.** **(a)** 37 **(b)** 38 **25.** **(a)** 500 **(b)** 91 **27.** **(a)** 31 **(b)** 24 **(c)** 11 **(d)** 45 **29.** **(a)** 1 **(b)** 1, 2, 3, 4, 5, 6, 7, 8, 9, 10, 11, 12, 13, 14, 15 **(c)** 1, 2, 3, 4, 5, 9, 11 **(d)** 5, 8, 13 **31.** **(a)** 9 **(b)** 9 **(c)** 20 **(d)** 20 **(e)** 27 **(f)** 15 **33.** Answers will vary.

Extension Exercises

1. B; 1 **3.** A; $\aleph_0$ **5.** F; 0
7. (Other correspondences are possible.)

$$\begin{matrix} \{\text{I}, & \text{II}, & \text{III}\} \\ \updownarrow & \updownarrow & \updownarrow \\ \{x, & y, & z\} \end{matrix}$$

9. (Other correspondences are possible.)

$$\begin{matrix} \{a, & d, & i, & t, & o, & n\} \\ \updownarrow & \updownarrow & \updownarrow & \updownarrow & \updownarrow & \updownarrow \\ \{a, & n, & s, & w, & e, & r\} \end{matrix}$$

11. 11 **13.** 0 **15.** $\aleph_0$ **17.** $\aleph_0$ **19.** $\aleph_0$ **21.** 12
23. $\aleph_0$ **25.** both **27.** equivalent **29.** equivalent

31.
$$\begin{matrix} \{2, & 4, & 6, & 8, & \ldots, & 2n, & \ldots\} \\ \updownarrow & \updownarrow & \updownarrow & \updownarrow & & \updownarrow & \\ \{1, & 2, & 3, & 4, & \ldots, & n, & \ldots\} \end{matrix}$$

33.
$$\begin{matrix} \{1{,}000{,}000, & 2{,}000{,}000, & 3{,}000{,}000, & \ldots, & 1{,}000{,}000n, & \ldots\} \\ \updownarrow & \updownarrow & \updownarrow & & \updownarrow & \\ \{\ 1, & 2, & 3, & \ldots, & n, & \ldots\} \end{matrix}$$

35.
$$\begin{matrix} \{2, & 4, & 6, & 8, & \ldots, & 2n, & \ldots\} \\ \updownarrow & \updownarrow & \updownarrow & \updownarrow & & \updownarrow & \\ \{1, & 2, & 3, & 4, & \ldots, & n, & \ldots\} \end{matrix}$$

37. This statement is not always true. For example, let A = the set of counting numbers, B = the set of real numbers.
39. This statement is not always true. For example, A could be the set of all subsets of the set of reals. Then $n(A)$ would be an infinite number *greater* than c.
41. **(a)** Rays emanating from point P will establish a geometric pairing of the points on the semicircle with the points on the line.

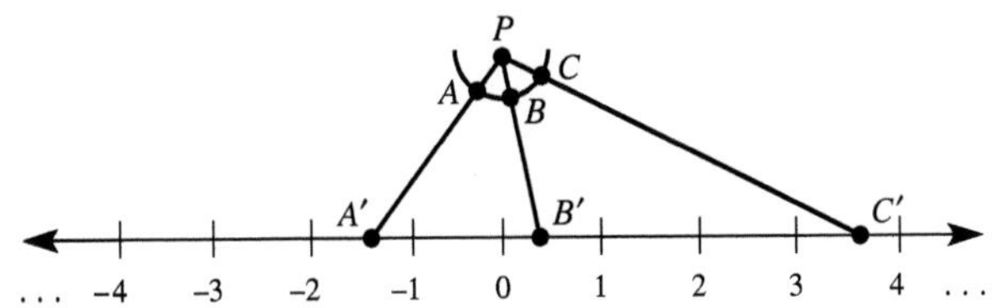

(b) The set of real numbers is infinite, having been placed in a one-to-one correspondence with a proper subset of itself.

43. $\{3, 6, 9, 12, \ldots, 3n, \ldots\}$
$\updownarrow$
$\{6, 9, 12, 15, \ldots, 3n + 3, \ldots\}$

45. $\left\{\frac{3}{4}, \frac{3}{8}, \frac{3}{12}, \frac{3}{16}, \ldots, \frac{3}{4n}, \ldots\right\}$
$\updownarrow$
$\left\{\frac{3}{8}, \frac{3}{12}, \frac{3}{16}, \frac{3}{20}, \ldots, \frac{3}{4n+4}, \ldots\right\}$

47. $\left\{\frac{1}{9}, \frac{1}{18}, \frac{1}{27}, \ldots, \frac{1}{9n}, \ldots\right\}$
$\updownarrow$
$\left\{\frac{1}{18}, \frac{1}{27}, \frac{1}{36}, \ldots, \frac{1}{9n+9}, \ldots\right\}$

49. Answers will vary. **51.** Answers will vary.

Chapter Test

1. {a, b, c, d, e} **2.** {a, b, d} **3.** {c, f, g, h} **4.** {a, c} **5.** true **6.** false **7.** true **8.** true **9.** false **10.** true **11.** true **12.** true **13.** 8 **14.** 15

Answers may vary in Exercises 15.–18. **15.** the set of odd integers between −4 and 10 **16.** the set of months of the year **17.** $\{x \mid x$ is a negative integer$\}$ **18.** $\{x \mid x$ is a multiple of 8 between 20 and 90$\}$ **19.** $\subseteq$ **20.** neither

21.

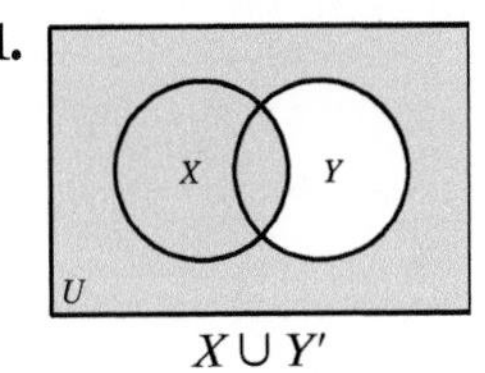

$X \cup Y'$

22.

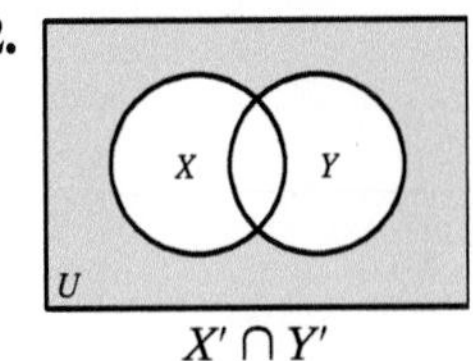

$X' \cap Y'$

23.

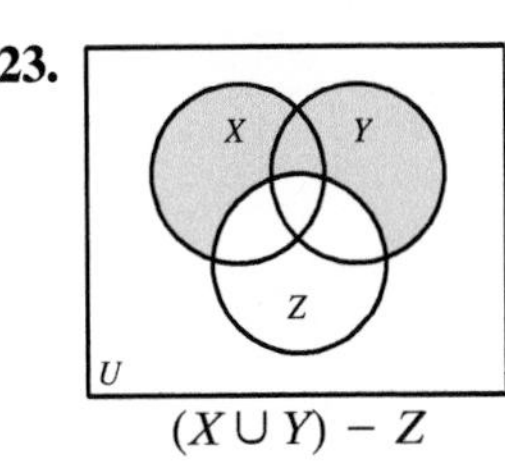

$(X \cup Y) - Z$

24.

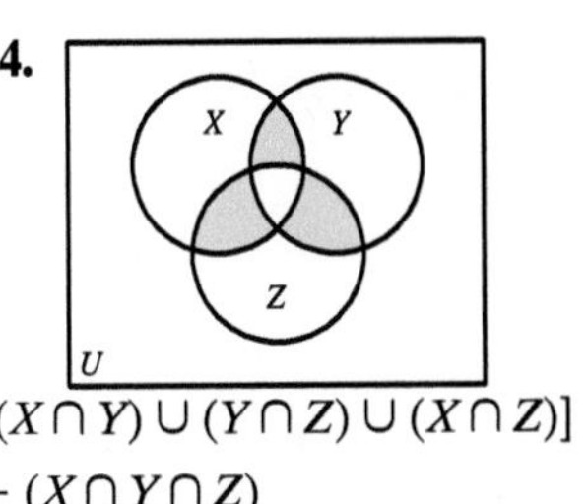

$[(X \cap Y) \cup (Y \cap Z) \cup (X \cap Z)] - (X \cap Y \cap Z)$

25. {Electric razor} **26.** {Adding machine, Barometer, Pendulum clock, Thermometer} **27.** {Electric razor} **28.** Answers will vary. **29. (a)** 22 **(b)** 12 **(c)** 28 **30. (a)** 16 **(b)** 32 **(c)** 33 **(d)** 45 **(e)** 14 **(f)** 26

The Basic Concepts of Set Theory

1 Exercises

1. {1, 3, 5, 7, 9} matches F, the set of odd positive integer less than 10.

3. {..., −4, −3, −2, −1} matches E, the set of all negative integers.

5. {2, 4, 8, 16, 32} matches B, the set of the five least positive integer powers of 2, since each element represents a successive power of 2 beginning with 2^1.

7. {2, 4, 6, 8, 10} matches H, the set of the five least positive integer multiples of 2, since this set represents the first five positive even integers. Remember that all even numbers are multiples of 2.

9. The set of all counting numbers less than or equal to 6 can be expressed as {1, 2, 3, 4, 5, 6}.

11. The set of all whole numbers not greater than 4 can be expressed as {0, 1, 2, 3, 4}.

13. In the set {6, 7, 8, ..., 14}, the ellipsis (three dots) indicates a continuation of the pattern. A complete listing of this set is {6, 7, 8, 9, 10, 11, 12, 13, 14}.

15. The set {−15, −13, −11, ..., −1} contains all integers from −15 to −1 inclusive. Each member is two larger than its predecessor. A complete listing of this set is {−15, −13, −11, −9, −7, −5, −3, −1}.

17. The set {2, 4, 8, ..., 256} contains all powers of two from 2 to 256 inclusive. A complete listing of this set is {2, 4, 8, 16, 32, 64, 128, 256}.

19. A complete listing of the set $\{x|x$ is an even whole number less than $11\}$ is {0, 2, 4, 6, 8, 10}. Remember that 0 is the first whole number.

21. The set of all counting numbers greater than 20 is represented by the listing {21, 22, 23, ...}.

23. The set of Great Lakes is represented by {Lake Erie, Lake Huron, Lake Michigan, Lake Ontario, Lake Superior}.

25. The set $\{x|x$ is a positive multiple of $5\}$ is represented by the listing {5, 10, 15, 20, ...}.

27. The set $\{x|x$ is the reciprocal of a natural number$\}$ is represented by the listing $\left\{1, \frac{1}{2}, \frac{1}{3}, \frac{1}{4}, \frac{1}{5}, \ldots\right\}$.

Note that in Exercises 29–31, there are other ways to describe the sets.

29. The set of all rational numbers may be represented using set-builder notation as $\{x|x$ is a rational number$\}$.

31. The set {1, 3, 5, ..., 75} may be represented using set-builder notation as $\{x|x$ is an odd natural number less than $76\}$.

33. {−9, −8, −7, ..., 7, 8, 9} is the set of single-digit integers.

35. {Alabama, Alaska, Arizona, ..., Wisconsin, Wyoming} is the set of states of the United States.

37. The set {2, 4, 6, ..., 932} is finite since the cardinal number associated with this set is a whole number.

39. The set $\left\{\frac{1}{2}, \frac{2}{3}, \frac{3}{4}, \ldots\right\}$ is infinite since there is no last element, and we would be unable to count all of the elements.

41. The set $\{x|x$ is a natural number greater than $50\}$ is infinite since there is no last element, and therefore its cardinal number is not a whole number.

43. The set $\{x|x$ is a rational number$\}$ is infinite since there is no last element, and therefore its cardinal number is not a whole number.

45. For any set A, $n(A)$ represents the cardinal number of the set, that is, the number of elements in the set. The set $A = \{0, 1, 2, 3, 4, 5, 6, 7\}$ contains 8 elements. Thus, $n(A) = 8$.

47. The set $A = \{2, 4, 6, \ldots, 1000)$ contains 500 elements. Thus, $n(A) = 500$.

49. The set $A = \{a, b, c, ..., z\}$ has 26 elements (letters of the alphabet). Thus, $n(A) = 26$.

51. The set A = the set of integers between −20 and 20 has 39 members. The set can be indicated as $\{-19, -18, ..., 18, 19\}$, or 19 negative integers, 19 positive integers, and 0. Thus, $n(A) = 39$.

53. The set $A = \left\{\frac{1}{3}, \frac{2}{4}, \frac{3}{5}, \frac{4}{6}, ..., \frac{27}{29}, \frac{28}{30}\right\}$ has 28 elements. Thus, $n(A) = 28$.

55. Writing exercise; answers will vary.

57. The set $\{x|x$ is a real number$\}$ is well defined since we can always tell if a number is real and belongs to this set.

59. The set $\{x|x$ is a difficult course$\}$ is not well defined since membership is a value judgment, and there is no clear-cut way to determine whether a particular course is "difficult."

61. $5 \boxed{\in} \{2, 4, 5, 7\}$ since 5 is a member of the set.

63. $-12 \boxed{\notin} \{3, 8, 12, 18\}$ because −12 is not a member of the set.

65. $\{3\} \boxed{\notin} \{2, 3, 4, 6\}$ since the elements are not sets themselves.

67. $8 \boxed{\in} \{11-2, 10-2, 9-2, 8-2\}$ since $8 = 10 - 2$.

69. The statement $3 \in \{2, 5, 6, 8\}$ is false since the element 3 is not a member of the set.

71. The statement $b \in \{h, c, d, a, b\}$ is true since b is contained in the set.

73. The statement $9 \notin \{6, 3, 4, 8\}$ is true since 9 is not a member of the set.

75. The statement $\{k, c, r, a\} = \{k, c, a, r\}$ is true since both sets contain exactly the same elements.

77. The statement $\{5, 8, 9\} = \{5, 8, 9, 0\}$ is false because the second set contains a different element from the first set, 0.

79. The statement $\{4\} \in \{\{3\}, \{4\}, \{5\}\}$ is true since the element, $\{4\}$, is a member of the set.

81. The statement $\{x|x$ is a natural number less than $3\} = \{1, 2\}$ is true since both represent sets with exactly the same elements.

83. The statement $4 \in A$ is true since 4 is a member of set A.

85. The statement $4 \notin C$ is false since 4 is a member of the set C.

87. Every element of C is also an element of A is true since the members, 4, 10, and 12 of set C, are also members of set A.

89. Writing exercise; answers will vary.

91. An example of two sets that are not equivalent and not equal would be $\{3\}$ and $\{c, f\}$. Other examples are possible.

93. An example of two sets that are equivalent but not equal would be $\{a, b\}$ and $\{a, c\}$. Other examples are possible.

95. (a) The actors with a return of at least $7.40 are those listed in the set {Drew Barrymore, Leonardo DiCaprio, Samuel L. Jackson, Jim Carrey}.

(b) The actors with a return of at most $3.75 are those listed in the set {Will Ferrell, Ewan McGregor}.

2 Exercises

1. $\{p\}, \{q\}, \{p, q\}, \varnothing$ matches D, the subsets of $\{p, q\}$.

3. $\{a, b\}$ matches B, the complement of $\{c, d\}$, if $U = \{a, b, c, d\}$.

5. $\{-2, 0, 2\} \boxed{\not\subseteq} \{-2, -1, 1, 2\}$

7. $\{2, 5\} \boxed{\subseteq} \{0, 1, 5, 3, 7, 2\}$

9. $\varnothing \boxed{\subseteq} \{a, b, c, d, e\}$, since the empty set is considered a subset of any given set.

11. $\{-5, 2, 9\} \boxed{\not\subseteq} \{x|x$ is an odd integer$\}$ since the element "2" is not an element of the second set.

13. $\{P, Q, R\} \boxed{\subseteq} \{P, Q, R, S\}$ and $\{P, Q, R\} \boxed{\subseteq} \{P, Q, R, S\}$, i.e. both.

15. $\{9, 1, 7, 3, 5\} \boxed{\subseteq} \{1, 3, 5, 7, 9\}$

17. $\emptyset \boxed{\subset} \{0\}$ or $\emptyset \boxed{\subseteq} \{0\}$, i.e., both.

19. $\{0, 1, 2, 3\} \boxed{\not\subseteq} \{1, 2, 3, 4\}$; therefore, neither. Note that if a set is not a subset of another set, it cannot be a proper subset either.

21. $A \subset U$ is true since all sets must be subsets of the universal set by definition, and U contains at least one more element than A.

23. $D \subseteq B$ is false since the element "d" in set D is not also a member of set B.

25. $A \subset B$ is true. All members of A are also members of B, and there are elements in set B not contained in set A.

27. $\emptyset \not\subset A$ is false since $\emptyset$ is a subset of all sets.

29. $\emptyset \subseteq \emptyset$ is true since the empty set, $\emptyset$, is considered a subset of all sets including itself. Note that all sets are subsets of themselves.

31. $D \not\subseteq B$ is true. Set D is not a subset of B because the element "d," though a member of set D, is not also a member of set B.

33. There are exactly 6 subsets of C is false. Since there are 3 elements in set C, there are $2^3 = 8$ subsets.

35. There are exactly 3 proper subsets of A is true. Since there are 2 elements in set A, there are $2^2 = 4$ subsets, and one of those is the set A itself, so there are 3 proper subsets of A.

37. There is exactly one subset of $\emptyset$ is true. The only subset of $\emptyset$ is $\emptyset$ itself.

39. The Venn diagram does not represent the correct relationships among the sets since D is not a subset of A. Thus, the answer is false.

41. Since the given set has 6 elements, there are
(a) $2^6 = 64$ subsets, and
(b) $2^6 - 1 = 63$ proper subsets.

43. The set $\{x|x$ is an odd integer between -4 and $6\}$ $= \{-3, -1, 1, 3, 5\}$. Since the set contains 5 elements, there are (a) $2^5 = 32$ subsets and (b) $2^5 - 1 = 32 - 1 = 31$ proper subsets.

45. The complement of $\{2, 3, 4, 6, 8\}$ is $\{5, 7, 9, 10\}$, that is, all of the elements in U not also in the given set.

47. The complement of $\{1, 3, 4, 5, 6, 7, 8, 9, 10\}$ is $\{2\}$.

49. The complement of the universal set, U, is the empty set, $\emptyset$.

51. In order to contain all of the indicated characteristics, the universal set $U =$ {Higher cost, Lower cost, Educational, More time to see the sights, Less time to see the sights, Cannot visit relatives along the way, Can visit relatives along the way}.

53. Since D contains the set of characteristics of the driving option, $D' =$ {Higher cost, More time to see the sights, Cannot visit relatives along the way}.

55. The set of element(s) common to F' and D' is $\emptyset$, the empty set, since there are no common elements.

57. The only possible set is $\{A, B, C, D, E\}$. (All are present.)

59. The possible subsets of three people would include $\{A, B, C\}$, $\{A, B, D\}$, $\{A, B, E\}$, $\{A, C, D\}$, $\{A, C, E\}$, $\{A, D, E\}$, $\{B, C, D\}$, $\{B, C, E\}$, $\{B, D, E\}$, and $\{C, D, E\}$.

61. The possible subsets consisting of one person would include $\{A\}$, $\{B\}$, $\{C\}$, $\{D\}$, and $\{E\}$.

63. Adding the number of subsets in Exercises 57–62, we have $1 + 5 + 10 + 10 + 5 + 1 = 32$ ways that the group can gather.

65. Because at least one member must attend, sending no members (the empty set) is not a possible subset of the members that can be sent. So the total number of different delegations that can possibly be sent is $2^{25} - 1 = 33{,}554{,}431$.

67. **(a)** Consider all possible subsets of a set with four elements (the number of bills). The number of subsets would be $2^4 = 16$. Since 16 includes also the empty set (and we must choose one bill), we will subtract one from this or $16 - 1 = 15$ possible sums of money.

(b) Removing the condition says, in effect, that we may also choose no bills. Thus, there are $2^4 = 16$ subsets or possible sums of money; it is now possible to select no bills.

69. (a) There are s subsets of B that do not contain e. These are the subsets of the original set A.

(b) There is one subset of B for each of the original subsets of set A, which is formed by including e as the element of that subset of A. Thus, B has s subsets which do contain e.

(c) The total number of subsets of B is the sum of the numbers of subsets containing e and of those not containing e. This number is $s + s$ or $2s$.

(d) Adding one more element will always double the number of subsets, so we conclude that the formula 2^n is true in general.

3 Exercises

1. The intersection of A and B, $A \cap B$, matches B, the set of elements common to both A and B.

3. The difference of A and B, $A - B$, matches A, the set of elements in A that are not in B.

5. The Cartesian product of A and B, $A \times B$, matches E, the set of ordered pairs such that each first element is from A and each second element is from B, with every element of A paired with every element of B.

7. $X \cap Y = \{a, c\}$ since these are the elements that are common to both X and Y.

9. $Y \cup Z = \{a, b, c, d, e, f\}$ since these are the elements that are contained in Y or Z (or both).

11. $X \cup U = \{a, b, c, d, e, f, g\} = U$. Observe that any set union with the universal set will give the universal set.

13. $X' = \{b, d, f\}$ since these are the only elements in U not contained in X.

15. $X' \cap Y' = \{b, d, f\} \cap \{d, e, f, g\} = \{d, f\}$

17. $X \cup (Y \cap Z) = \{a, c, e, g\} \cup \{b, c\}$
$= \{a, b, c, e, g\}$
Observe that the intersection must be done first.

19. $(Y \cap Z') \cup X$
$= (\{a, b, c\} \cap \{a, g\}) \cup \{a, c, e, g\}$
$= \{a\} \cup \{a, c, e, g\}$
$= \{a, c, e, g\}$
$= X$

21. $(Z \cup X')' \cap Y$
$= (\{b, c, d, e, f\} \cup \{b, d, f\})' \cap \{a, b, c\}$
$= \{b, c, d, e, f\}' \cap \{a, b, c\}$
$= \{a, g\} \cap \{a, b, c\}$
$= \{a\}$

23. $X - Y = \{e, g\}$
Since these are the only two elements that belong to X and not to Y.

25. $X \cap (X - Y) = \{a, c, e, g\} \cap \{e, g\} = \{e, g\}$
Observe that we must find $X - Y$ first.

27. $X' - Y = \{b, d, f\} - \{a, b, c\} = \{d, f\}$
Observe that we must find X' first.

29. $(X \cap Y') \cup (Y \cap X')$
$= (\{a, c, e, g\} \cap \{d, e, f, g\}) \cup (\{a, b, c\} \cap \{b, d, f\})$
$= \{e, g\} \cup \{b\}$
$= \{b, e, g\}$

31. $A \cup (B' \cap C')$ is the set of all elements that are in A, or are not in B and not in C.

33. $(C - B) \cup A$ is the set of all elements that are in C but not in B, or they are in A.

35. $(A - C) \cup (B - C)$ is the set of all elements that are in A but not C, or are in B but not in C.

37. The smallest set representing the universal set U is $\{e, h, c, l, b\}$.

39. T', the complement of T, is the set of effects in U that are not adverse effects of tobacco use: $T' = \{l, b\}$.

41. $T \cup A$ is the set of all adverse effects that are either tobacco related or alcohol related: $T \cup A = \{e, h, c, l, b\} = U$.

43. $B \cup C$ is the set of all tax returns showing business income or filed in 2009.

45. $C - A$ is the set of all tax returns filed in 2009 without itemized deductions.

47. $(A \cup B) - D$ is the set of all tax returns with itemized deductions or showing business income, but not selected for audit.

49. $A \subseteq (A \cup B)$ is always true since $A \cup B$ will contain all of the elements of A.

51. $(A \cap B) \subseteq A$ is always true since the elements of $A \cap B$ must be in A.

53. $n(A \cup B) = n(A) + n(B)$ is not always true. If there are any common elements to A and B, they will be counted twice.

55. **(a)** $X \cup Y = \{1, 2, 3, 5\}$

(b) $Y \cup X = \{1, 2, 3, 5\}$

(c) For any sets X and Y, $X \cup Y = Y \cup X$. This conjecture indicates that set union is a commutative operation.

57. **(a)** $X \cup (Y \cup Z)$

$$= \{1, 3, 5\} \cup (\{1, 2, 3\} \cup \{3, 4, 5\})$$
$$= \{1, 3, 5\} \cup \{1, 2, 3, 4, 5\}$$
$$= \{1, 3, 5, 2, 4\}$$

(b) $(X \cup Y) \cup Z$

$$= (\{1, 3, 5\} \cup \{1, 2, 3\}) \cup \{3, 4, 5\}$$
$$= \{1, 3, 5, 2\} \cup \{3, 4, 5\}$$
$$= \{1, 3, 5, 2, 4\}$$

(c) For any sets X, Y, and Z,
$X \cup (Y \cup Z) = (X \cup Y) \cup Z$.

This conjecture indicates that set union is an associative operation.

59. **(a)** $(X \cup Y)' = \{1, 3, 5, 2\}' = \{4\}$

(b) $X' \cap Y' = \{2, 4\} \cap \{4, 5\} = \{4\}$

(c) For any sets X and Y,
$(X \cup Y)' = X' \cap Y'$.

Observe that this conjecture is one form of De Morgan's Laws.

61. For example,

$$X \cup \emptyset = \{\text{N, A, M, E}\} \cup \emptyset$$
$$= \{\text{N, A, M, E}\}$$
$$= X;$$

for any set X, $X \cup \emptyset = X$.

63. The statement $(3, 2) = (5 - 2, 1 + 1)$ is true.

65. The statement $(6, 3) = (3, 6)$ is false. The parentheses indicate an ordered pair (where order is important) and corresponding elements in the ordered pairs must be equal.

67. The statement $\{6, 3\} = \{3, 6\}$ is true since order is not important when listing elements in sets.

69. The statement
$\{(1, 2), (3, 4)\} = \{(3, 4), (1, 2)\}$ is true. Each set contains the same two elements, the order of which is unimportant.

71. To form the Cartesian product $A \times B$, list all ordered pairs in which the first element belongs to A and the second element belongs to B:
With $A = \{2, 8, 12\}$ and $B = \{4, 9\}$,

$$A \times B = \{(2, 4), (2, 9), (8, 4), (8, 9), (12, 4), (12, 9)\}.$$

To form the Cartesian product $B \times A$, list all ordered pairs in which the first element belongs to B and the second element belongs to A:

$$B \times A = \{(4, 2), (4, 8), (4, 12), (9, 2), (9, 8), (9, 12)\}.$$

73. For $A = \{\text{d, o, g}\}$ and $B = \{\text{p, i, g}\}$,

$$A \times B = \{(\text{d, p}), (\text{d, i}), (\text{d, g}), (\text{o, p}), (\text{o, i}), (\text{o, g}), (\text{g, p}), (\text{g, i}), (\text{g, g})\};$$
$$B \times A = \{(\text{p, d}), (\text{p, o}), (\text{p, g}), (\text{i, d}), (\text{i, o}), (\text{i, g}), (\text{g, d}), (\text{g, o}), (\text{g, g})\}.$$

75. For $A = \{2, 8, 12\}$ and $B = \{4, 9\}$,
$n(A \times B) = n(A) \times n(B) = 3 \times 2 = 6$, or by counting the generated elements in Exercise 71 we also arrive at 6. In the same manner, $n(B \times A) = 2 \times 3 = 6$.

77. For $n(A) = 35$ and $n(B) = 6$,

$$n(A \times B) = n(A) \times n(B) = 35 \times 6 = 210$$
$$n(B \times A = n(B) \times n(A) = 6 \times 35 = 210$$

79. To find $n(B)$ when $n(A \times B) = 72$ and $n(A) = 12$, we have:

$$n(A \times B) = n(A) \times n(B)$$
$$72 = 12 \times n(B)$$
$$6 = n(B)$$

81. Let $U = \{a, b, c, d, e, f, g\}$, $A = \{b, d, f, g\}$, and $B = \{a, b, d, e, g\}$.

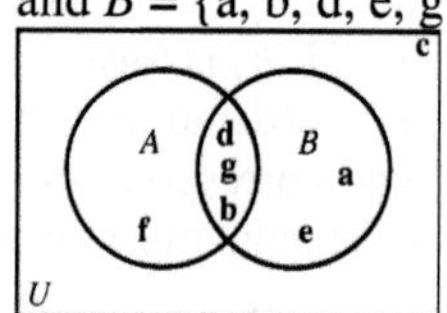

83. The set operations for $B \cap A'$ indicate those elements in B and not in A.

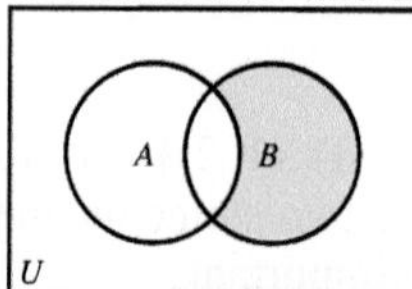

85. The set operations for $A' \cup B$ indicate those elements not in A or in B.

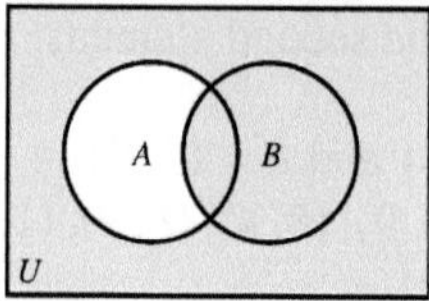

87. The set operations for $B' \cup A$ indicate those elements not in B or in A.

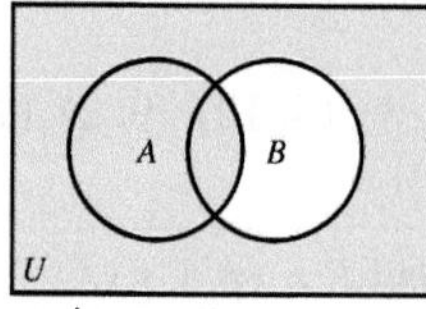

89. The set operations $B' \cap B$ indicate those elements not in B and in B at the same time, and since there are no elements that can satisfy both conditions, we get the null set (empty set), $\varnothing$.

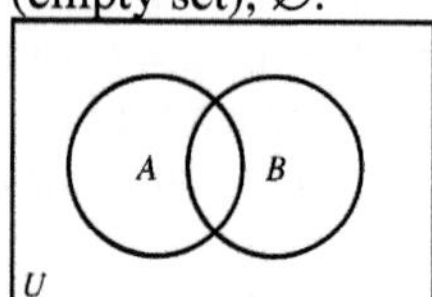

91. The indicated set operations mean those elements not in B or those not in A as long as they are also not in B. It is a help to shade the region representing "not in A" first, then that region representing "not in B." Identify the intersection of these regions (covered by both shadings). As in algebra, the general strategy when deciding which order to do operations is to begin inside parentheses and work out.

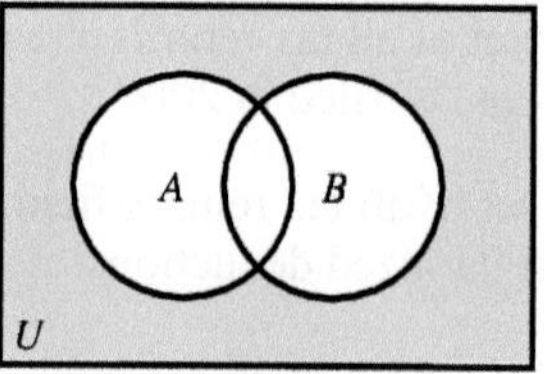

$A' \cap B'$

Finally, the region of interest will be that "not in B" along with (union of) the above intersection—$(A' \cap B')$. That is, the final region of interest is given by

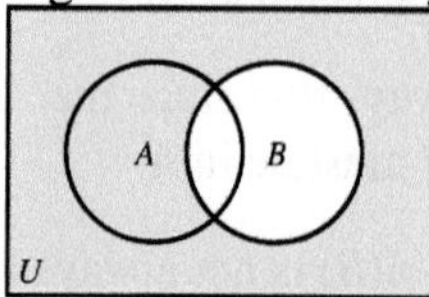

93. The complement of U, U', is the set of all elements not in U. But by definition, there can be no elements outside the universal set. Thus, we get the null (or empty) set, $\varnothing$, when we complement U.

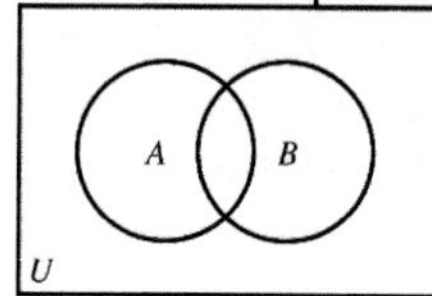

95. Let $U = \{m, n, o, p, q, r, s, t, u, v, w\}$, $A = \{m, n, p, q, r, t\}$, $B = \{m, o, p, q, s, u\}$, and $C = \{m, o, p, r, s, t, u, v\}$.
Placing the elements of these sets in the proper location on a Venn diagram will yield the following diagram.

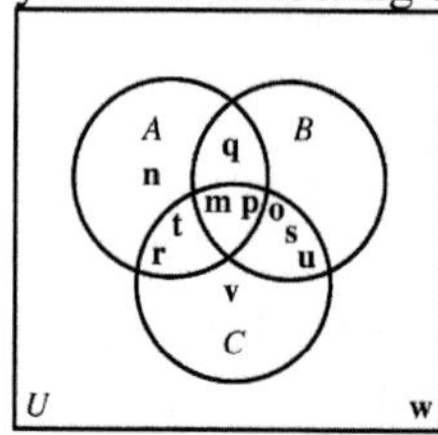

It helps to identify those elements in the intersection of A, B, and C first, then those elements not in this intersection but in each of the two set intersections (e.g., $A \cap B$, etc.), next, followed by elements that lie in only one set, etc.

97. The set operations $(A \cap B) \cap C$ indicate those elements common to all three sets.

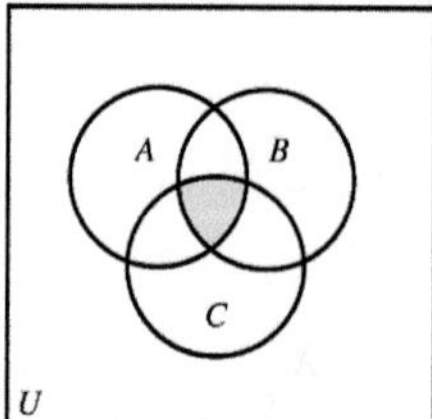

99. The set operations $(A \cap B) \cup C'$ indicate those elements in A and B at the same time along with those outside of C.

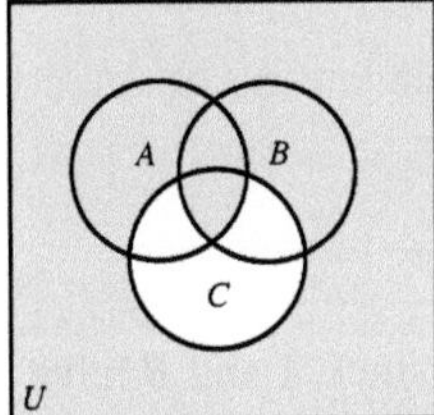

101. The set operations $(A' \cap B') \cap C$ indicate those elements that are in C while simultaneously outside of both A and B.

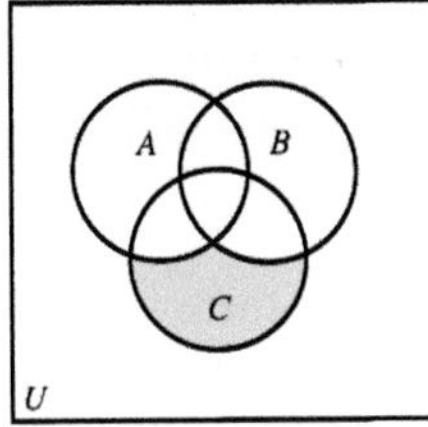

103. The set operations $(A \cap B') \cup C$ indicate those elements that are in A and at the same time outside of B, along with those in C.

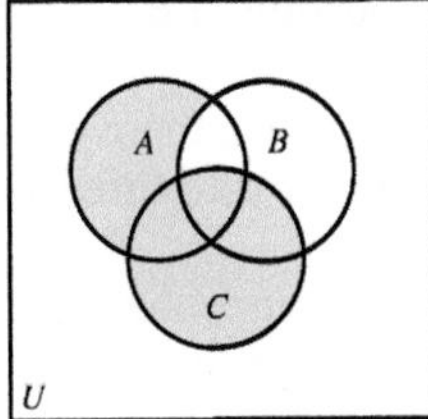

105. The set operations $(A \cap B') \cap C'$ indicate the region in A and outside B and at the same time outside C.

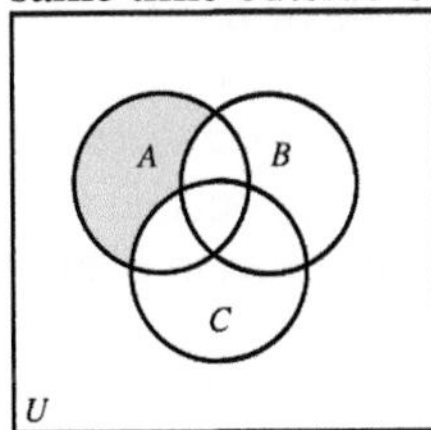

107. The set operations $(A' \cap B') \cup C'$ indicate the region that is both outside A and at the same time outside B, along with the region outside C.

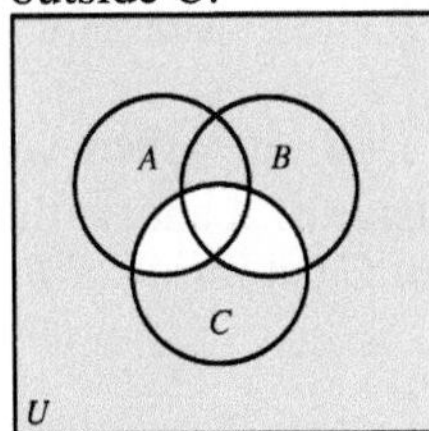

109. The shaded area indicates the region $(A \cup B)'$ or $A' \cap B'$.

111. Since this is the region in A or in B but, at the same time, outside of A and B, we have the set $(A \cup B) \cap (A \cap B)'$ or $(A \cup B) - (A \cap B)$.

113. The shaded area may be represented by the set $(A \cap B) \cup (A \cap C)$; that is, the region in the intersection of A and B along with the region in the intersection of A and C or, by the distributive property, $A \cap (B \cup C)$.

115. The region is represented by the set $(A \cap B) \cap C'$, that is, the region outside of C but inside both A and B, or $(A \cap B) - C$.

117. If $A = A - B$, then A and B must not have any common elements, or $A \cap B = \varnothing$.

119. $A = A - \varnothing$ is true for any set A.

121. $A \cup \varnothing = \varnothing$ is true only if A has no elements, or $A = \varnothing$.

123. $A\varnothing = A$ is true only if A has no elements, or $A = \varnothing$.

125. $A \cup A = \varnothing$ is true only if A has no elements, or $A = \varnothing$.

127. $A \cup B = A$ only if B is a subset of A, or $B \subseteq A$.

129. $A \cap A' = \varnothing$

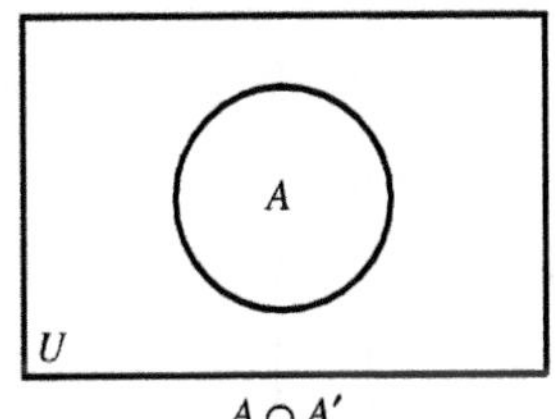

$A \cap A'$

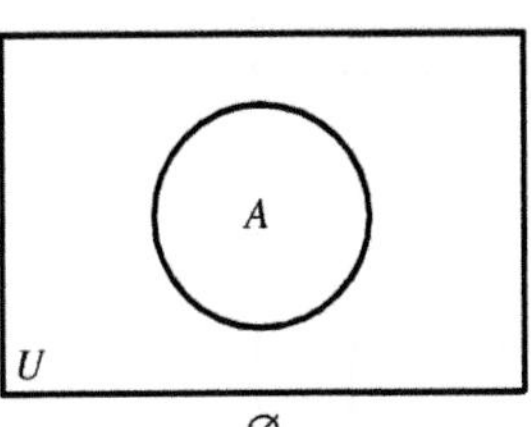

$\varnothing$

Thus, by the Venn diagrams, the statement is always true.

131. $(A \cap B) \subseteq A$

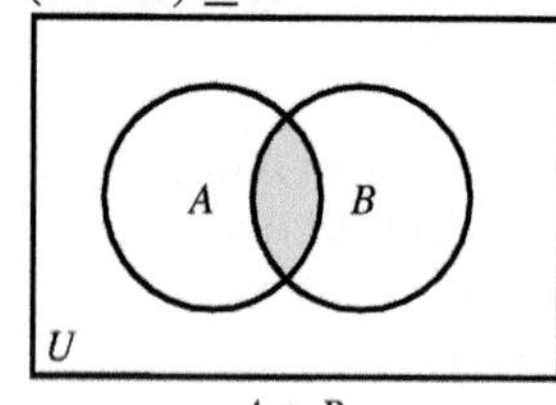

$A \cap B$

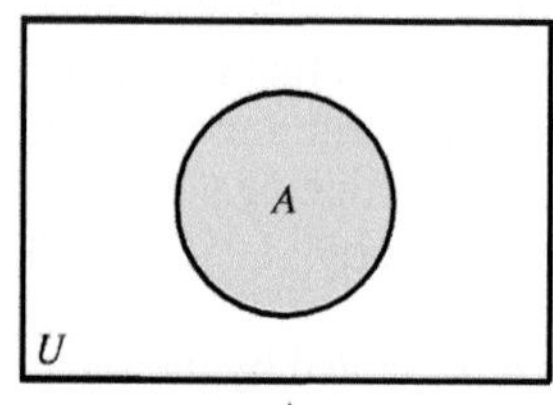

A

Thus, by the Venn diagrams, the shaded region is in A; therefore, the statement is always true.

133. If $A \subseteq B$, then $A \cup B = A$.

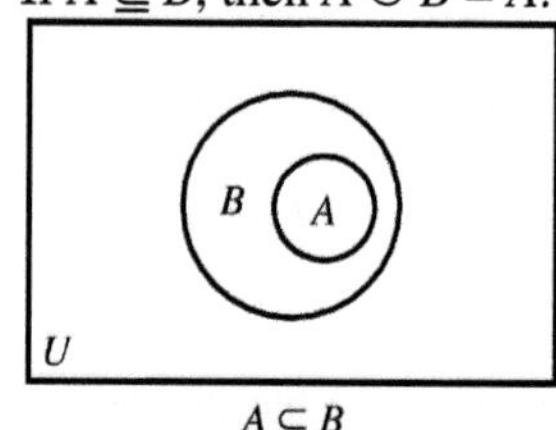

$A \subseteq B$

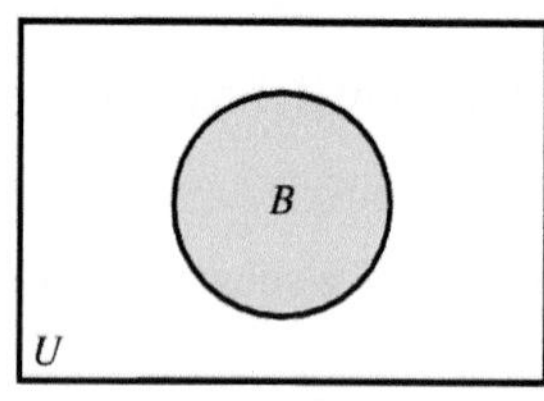

$A \cup B$

Thus, the statement is not always true.

135. $(A \cup B)' = A' \cap B'$ (De Morgan's second law).

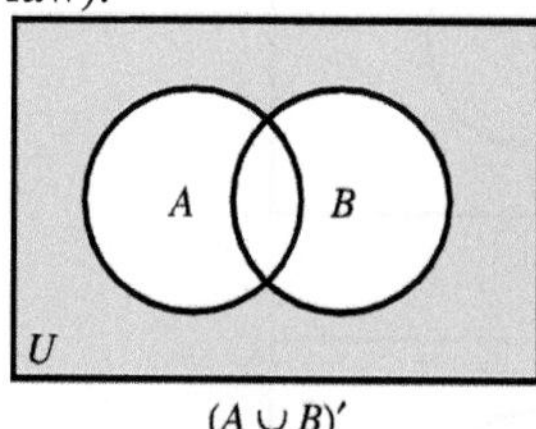

$(A \cup B)'$

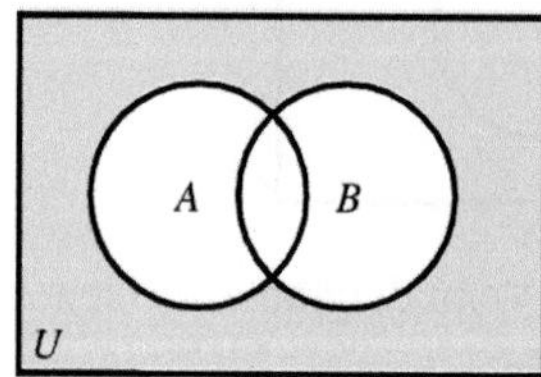

$A' \cap B'$

Thus, by the Venn diagrams, the statement is always true.

137. **(a)** $Q \cup H = \{x|x$ is a real number), since the real numbers are made up of all rational and all irrational numbers.

(b) $Q \cap H = \varnothing$, since there are no common elements.

4 Exercises

1. **(a)** $n(A \cap B) = 5$ since A and B have 5 elements in common.

(b) $n(A \cup B) = 7$ since there are a total of 7 elements in A or in B.

(c) $n(A \cap B') = 0$ since there are 0 elements which are in A and, at the same time, outside B.

(d) $n(A' \cap B) = 2$ since there are 2 elements which are in B and, at the same time, outside A.

(e) $n(A' \cap B') = 8$ since there are 8 elements which are outside of A and, at the same time, outside of B.

3. **(a)** $n(A \cap B \cap C) = 1$ since there is only one element shared by all three sets.

(b) $n(A \cap B \cap C') = 3$ since there are 3 elements in A and B while, at the same time, outside of C.

(c) $n(A \cap B' \cap C) = 4$ since there are 4 elements in A and C while, at the same time, outside of B.

(d) $n(A' \cap B \cap C) = 0$ since there are 0 elements which are outside of A while, at the same time, in B and C.

(e) $n(A' \cap B' \cap C) = 2$ since there are 2 elements outside of A and outside of B while, at the same time, in C.

(f) $n(A \cap B' \cap C') = 8$ since there are 8 elements in A which at the same time, are outside of B and outside of C.

(g) $n(A' \cap B \cap C') = 2$ since there are 2 elements outside of A and, at the same time, outside of C but inside of B.

(h) $n(A' \cap B' \cap C') = 6$ since there are 6 elements which are outside all three sets at the same time.

5. Using the Cardinal Number Formula, $n(A \cup B) = n(A) + n(B) - n(A \cap B)$, we have $n(A \cup B) = 12 + 14 - 5 = 21$.

7. Using the Cardinal Number Formula, $n(A \cup B) = n(A) + n(B) - n(A \cap B)$, we have $25 = 20 + 12 - n(A \cap B)$. Solving for $n(A \cap B)$, we get $n(A \cap B) = 7$.

9. Using the Cardinal Number Formula, $n(A \cup B) = n(A) + n(B) - n(A \cap B)$, we have $55 = n(A) + 35 - 15$. Solving for $n(A)$, we get $n(A) = 35$.

11. Using the Cardinal Number Formula, we find that

$$\begin{aligned} n(A \cup B) &= n(A) + n(B) - n(A \cap B) \\ 25 &= 19 + 13 - n(A \cap B) \\ n(A \cap B) &= 19 + 13 - 25 \\ &= 7. \end{aligned}$$

Then $n(A \cap B') = 19 - 17 = 12$ and $n(B \cap A') = 13 - 7 = 6$.
Since $n(A') = 11$ and $n(B \cap A') = 6$, we have $n(A \cup B)' = n(A' \cap B') = 11 - 6 = 5$.
Completing the cardinalities for each region, we arrive at the following Venn diagram.

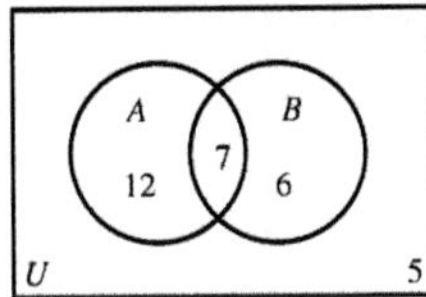

13. Since $n(B) = 28$ and $n(A \cap B) = 10$, we have $n(B \cap A') = 28 - 10 = 18$. Since $n(A') = 25$ and $n(B \cap A') = 18$, it follows that $n(A' \cap B') = 7$.
By De Morgan's laws, $A' \cup B' = (A \cap B)'$.
So, $n[(A \cap B)'] = 40$.
Thus, $n(A \cap B') = 40 - (18 + 7) = 15$.
Completing the cardinalities for each region, we arrive at the following Venn diagram.

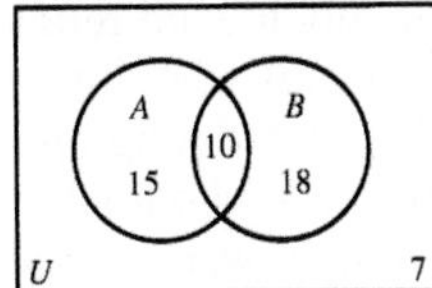

15. Fill in the cardinal numbers of the regions, beginning with $(A \cap B \cap C)$. Since $n(A \cap B \cap C) = 15$ and $n(A \cap B) = 35$, we have $n(A \cap B \cap C') = 35 - 15 = 20$. Since $n(A \cap C) = 21$, we have $n(A \cap C \cap B') = 21 - 15 = 6$. Since $n(B \cap C) = 25$, we have $n(B \cap C \cap A') = 25 - 15 = 10$. Since $n(C) = 49$, we have $n(C \cap A' \cap B') = 49 - (6 + 15 + 10) = 18$.
Since $n(A) = 57$, we have $n(A \cap B' \cap C') = 57 - (20 + 15 + 6) = 16$.
Since $n(B') = 52$, we have

$$\begin{aligned} n(A \cup B \cup C)' &= n(A' \cap B' \cap C') \\ &= 52 - (16 + 6 + 18) \\ &= 12. \end{aligned}$$

Completing the cardinalities for each region, we arrive at the following Venn diagram.

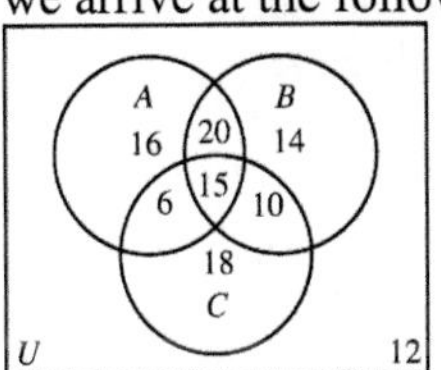

17. Fill in the cardinal numbers of the regions, beginning with the $(A \cap B \cap C)$.
$n(A \cap B \cap C) = 5$ and $n(A \cap C) = 13$, so $n(A \cap C \cap B') = 13 - 5 = 8$. $n(B \cap C) = 8$, so $n(B \cap C \cap A') = 8 - 5 = 3$. $n(A \cap B') = 9$, so $n(A \cap B' \cap C') = 9 - 8 = 1$. $n(A) = 15$, so $n(A \cap B \cap C') = 15 - (1 + 8 + 5) = 1$.
$n(B \cap C') = 3$, so
$n(B \cap A' \cap C') = 3 - 1 = 2$.
$n(A' \cap B' \cap C') = n(A \cup B \cup C)' = 21$.
$n(B \cup C) = 32$, so
$n(A' \cap B' \cap C) = 32 - (1 + 2 + 5 + 3) = 21$
Completing the cardinalities for each region, we arrive at the following Venn diagram.

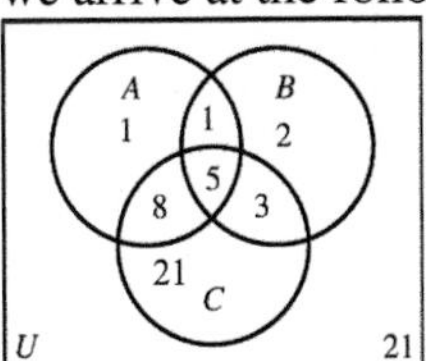

19. Complete a Venn diagram showing the cardinality for each region. Let W = set of projects Joe Long writes. Let P = set of projects Joe long produces.
Begin with $(W \cap P)$. $n(W \cap P) = 3$. Since $n(W) = 5$, $n(W \cap P') = 5 - 3 = 2$. Since $n(P) = 7$, $n(P \cap W') = 7 - 3 = 4$.

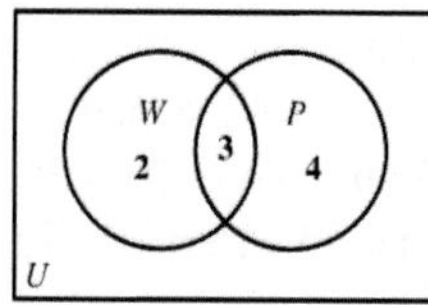

Interpreting the resulting cardinalities we see that:

(a) He wrote but did not produce $n(W \cap P') = 2$ projects.

(b) He produced but did not write $n(P \cap W') = 4$ projects.

21. Construct a Venn diagram and label the number of elements in each region. Let J = set of fans who like Jazmine Sullivan, C = set of fans who like Carrie Underwood, and B = set of fans who like Brad Paisley. Begin with the region indicating the intersection of all three sets,
$n(J \cap C \cap B) = 8$.
Since $n(J \cap C) = 14$,
$n(J \cap C \cap B') = 14 - 8 = 6$.
Since $n(C \cap B) = 14$,
$n(C \cap B \cap J') = 14 - 8 = 6$.
Since $n(J \cap B) = 21$,
$n(J \cap B \cap C') = 21 - 8 = 13$.
Since $n(J) = 37$, the number of elements inside J and not in C or B is $37 - (13 + 8 + 6) = 10$. Since $n(C) = 36$, the number of elements inside C and not in J or B is $36 - (6 + 8 + 6) = 16$. Since $n(B) = 31$, the number of elements inside B and not in J or C is $31 - (13 + 8 + 6) = 4$. Since $n(U) = 65$, there are $65 - (10 + 6 + 16 + 13 + 8 + 6 + 4)$ $= 2$ elements outside the three sets. That is, $n(J \cup C \cup B)' = 2$. The completed Venn diagram is as follows:

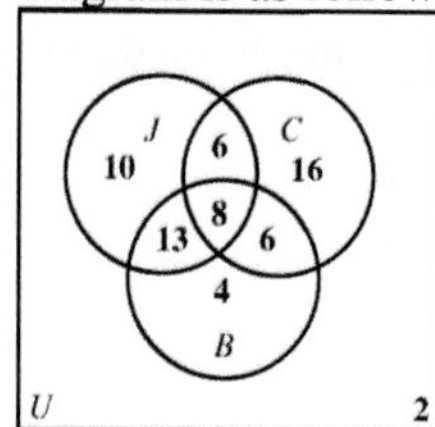

(a) There are $6 + 13 + 6 = 25$ fans that like exactly two of these singers.

(b) There are $10 + 16 + 4 = 30$ fans that like exactly one of these singers.

(c) There are 2 fans that like none of these singers.

(d) There are 10 fans that like Jazmine, but neither Carrie nor Brad.

(e) There are $13 + 6 = 19$ fans that like Brad and exactly one of the other two.

23. Let U be the set of people interviewed, and let M, E, and G represent the sets of people using microwave ovens, electric ranges, and gas ranges, respectively.
Construct a Venn diagram and label the cardinal number of each region, beginning with the region $(M \cap E \cap G)$.
$n(M \cap E \cap G) = 1$. Since $n(M \cap E) = 19$,
$n(M \cap E \cap G') = 19 - 1 = 18$. Since
$n(M \cap G) = 17$,
$n(M \cap G \cap E') = 17 - 1 = 16$. Since
$n(G \cap E) = 4$, $n(G \cap E \cap M') = 4 - 1 = 3$.
Since $n(M) = 58$,

$$\begin{aligned} n(M \cap G' \cap E') &= n(M \cap (G \cup E)') \\ &= 58 - (18 + 16 + 1) \\ &= 23. \end{aligned}$$

Since $n(E) = 63$,
$n(E \cap M' \cap G') = 63 - (18 + 3 + 1) = 41$.
Since $n(G) = 58$,

$$\begin{aligned} n(G \cap M' \cap E') &= n(G \cap (M \cup E)') \\ &= 58 - (16 + 3 + 1) \\ &= 38. \end{aligned}$$

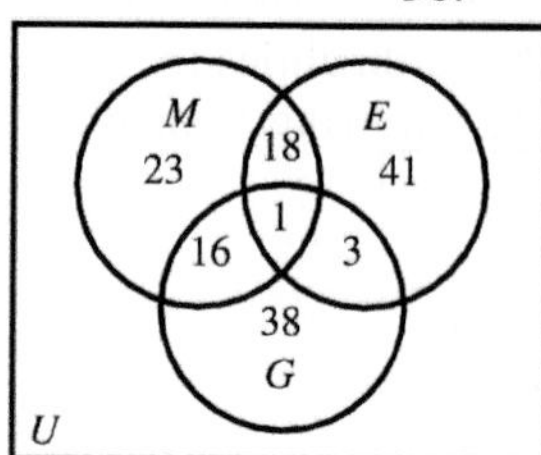

(a) The number of respondents that use exactly two of these appliances is $16 + 18 + 3 = 37$.

(b) The number of respondents that use at least two of these appliances is $37 + 1 = 38$.

25. Construct a Venn diagram and label the cardinal number of each region.
Let H = the set of respondents who think Hollywood is unfriendly toward religion, M = the set of respondents who think the media are unfriendly toward religion, S = the set of respondents who think scientists are unfriendly toward religion. Then we are given the following information.

$n(H) = 240$ $\quad n(H \cap M) = 145$
$n(M) = 160$ $\quad n(S \cap M) = 122$
$n(S) = 181$ $\quad n(H \cap M \cap S) = 110$
$n(H \cup M \cup S)' = 219$

Since $n(H \cap M) = 145$,
$n(H \cap M \cap S') = 145 - 110 = 35.$

Since $n(S \cap M) = 122$,
$n(S \cap M \cap H') = 122 - 110 = 12.$

The total number of respondents who think exactly two of these groups are unfriendly toward religion is 80, so
$n(H \cap S \cap M') = 80 - (35 + 12) = 33.$

Since $n(H) = 240$,
$n(H \cap S' \cap M') = 240 - (33 + 110 + 35) = 62.$

Since $n(M) = 160$,
$n(M \cap H' \cap S') = 160 - (35 + 110 + 12) = 3.$

Since $n(S) = 181$,
$n(S \cap H' \cap M') = 181 - (33 + 110 + 12) = 26.$

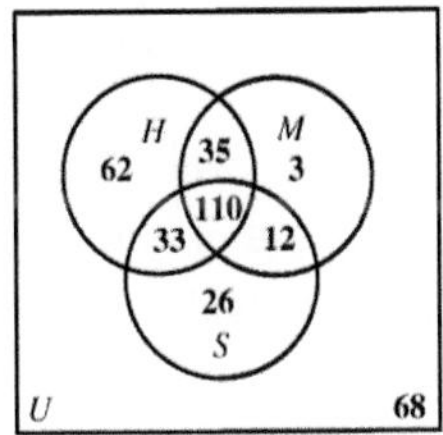

(a) The total number of respondents surveyed is
$62 + 33 + 110 + 35 + 3 + 12 + 26 + 219 = 500.$

(b) The number of respondents who think exactly one of these three groups is unfriendly toward religion is
$62 + 3 + 26 = 91.$

27. Construct a Venn diagram to represent the survey data beginning with the region representing the intersection of S, B, and C. Rather than representing each region as a combination of sets and set operations, we will label the regions a–h. There are 21 patients in Nadine's survey that are in the intersection of all three sets, i.e., in region d. Since there are 31 patients in $B \cap C$, we can deduce that there must be 10 patients in region c. Similarly since there are 33 patients in $B \cap S$, there must be 12 patients in region e. From the given information, there is a total of 51 patients in regions c, d, e, and g. Thus, there are $51 - (10 + 21 + 12) = 8$ patients in region g. Since there are 52 patients in S, we can deduce that there are $52 - (12 + 21 + 8) = 11$ patients in region f. Similarly, there are 4 patients in region b, and 7 patients in region h. There is a total of 73 patients found in regions b–h. Thus, there must be 2 patients in region a.

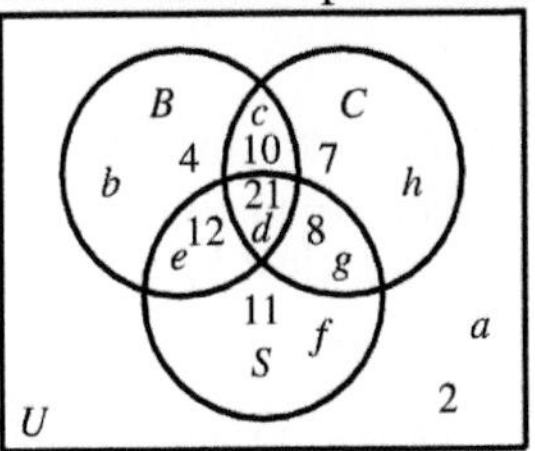

(a) The number of these patients who had either high blood pressure or high cholesterol levels, but not both is represented by regions b, e, g, and h for a total of 31 patients.

(b) The number of these patients who had fewer than two of the indications listed are found in regions a, b, f, and h for a total of 24 patients.

(c) The number of these patients who were smokers but had neither high blood pressure nor high cholesterol levels are found in region f, which has 11 members.

(d) The number of these patients who did not have exactly two of the indications listed would be those excluded from regions c, e, and g (representing patients with exactly two of the indications). We arrive at a total of 45 patients.

29. **(a)** The set $A \cap B \cap C \cap D$ is region 1 (in text).

(b) The set $A \cup B \cup C \cup D$ includes the regions 1, 2, 3, 4, 5, 6, 7, 8, 9, 10, 11, 12, 13, 14, and 15.

(c) The set $(A \cap B)\_ \cup (C \cap D)$ includes the set of regions $\{1, 3, 9, 11\} \cup \{1, 2, 4, 5\}$ or the regions 1, 2, 3, 4, 5, 9, and 11.

(d) The set $(A' \cap B') \cap (C \cup D)$ includes the set of regions $\{5, 13, 8, 16\} \cap \{1, 2, 3, 4, 5, 6, 7, 8, 9, 10, 12, 13\}$, which is represented by regions 5, 8, and 13.

31. (a) $n(J \cap G) = 9$, coming from the intersection of the first row with the first column.

(b) $n(S \cap N) = 9$, coming from the intersection of second row and the third column.

(c) $n(N \cup (S \cap F)) = 20$ since there are 20 players who are in either N(total of 15) or in S and F (just 5), at the same time.

(d) $n(S' \cap (G \cup N)) = 20$ since there are $9 + 4 + 5 + 2 = 20$ players who are not in S, but are in G or in N.

(e) $n((S \cap N') \cup (C \cap G')) = 27$
There are 27 players who are in S but not in N(12 + 5), or who are in C but not in G (8 + 2).

(f) $n(N' \cap (S' \cap C')) = 15$
There are 15 (9 + 6) players who are not in N and at the same time are not in S and not in C.

33. Writing exercise; answers will vary

EXTENSION: INFINITE SETS AND THEIR CARDINALITIES

1. The set {6} has the same cardinality as B, {26}. The cardinal number is 1.

3. The set $\{x|x$ is a natural number$\}$ has the same cardinality as A, $\aleph_0$.

5. The set $\{x|x$ is an integer between 5 and 6$\}$ has the same cardinality, 0, as F since there are no members in either set.

7. One correspondence is:
$\{I, II, III\}$
↕ ↕ ↕
$\{x, y, z\}$
Other correspondences are possible.

9. One correspondence is:
{a, d, i, t, o, n}
↕ ↕ ↕ ↕ ↕ ↕
{a, n, s, w, e, r}
Other correspondences are possible.

11. $n(\{a, b, c, d, ..., k\}) = 11$
By counting the number of letters a through k, we establish the cardinality to be 11.

13. $n(\emptyset) = 0$ since there are no members.

15. $n(\{300, 400, 500, ...\}) = \aleph_0$ since this set can be placed in a one-to-one correspondence with the counting numbers (i.e., is a countable infinite set).

17. $n\left(\left\{-\frac{1}{4}, -\frac{1}{8}, -\frac{1}{12}, ...\right\}\right) = \aleph_0$ since this set can be placed in a one-to-one correspondence with the counting numbers.

19. $n(\{x|x$ is an odd counting number$\}) = \aleph_0$ since this set can be placed in a one-to-one correspondence with the counting numbers.

21. $n(\{$Jan, Feb, Mar, ..., Dec$\}) = 12$ since there are twelve months indicated in the set.

23. "$\aleph_0$ bottles of beer on the wall, $\aleph_0$ bottles of beer, take one down and pass it around, $\boxed{\aleph_0}$ bottles of beer on the wall." This is true because $\aleph_0 - 1 = \aleph_0$.

25. The answer is both. Since the sets {u, v, w} and {v, u, w} are equal sets (same elements), they must then have the same number of elements and thus are equivalent.

27. The sets $\{X, Y, Z\}$ and $\{x, y, z\}$ are equivalent because they contain the same number of elements (same cardinality) but not the same elements.

29. The sets $\{x|x$ is a positive real number$\}$ and $\{x|x$ is a negative real number$\}$ are equivalent because they have the same cardinality, c. They are not equal since they contain different elements.

Note that each of the following answers shows only one possible correspondence.

31. $\{2, 4, 6, 8, 10, 12, ..., 2n, ...\}$
↕ ↕ ↕ ↕ ↕ ↕ ↕
$\{1, 2, 3, 4, 5, 6, ..., n, ...\}$

33. $\{1{,}000{,}000,\ 2{,}000{,}000,\ 3{,}000{,}000,\ ...,\ 1{,}000{,}000n,\ ...\}$
$\updownarrow \quad \updownarrow \quad \updownarrow \quad \updownarrow$
$\{1,\ 2,\ 3,\ ...,\ n,\ ...\}$

35. $\{2, 4, 8, 16, 32, ..., 2^n, ...\}$
$\updownarrow\ \updownarrow\ \updownarrow\ \updownarrow\ \updownarrow \quad \updownarrow$
$\{1, 2, 3, 4, 5, ..., n, ...\}$

37. The statement "If A and B are infinite sets, then A is equivalent to B" is not always true. For example, let A = the set of counting numbers and B = the set of real numbers. Each has a different cardinality.

39. The statement "If set A is an infinite set and A is not equivalent to the set of counting numbers, then $n(A) = c$" is not always true. For example, A could be the set of all subsets of the set of real numbers. Then, $n(A)$ would be an infinite number greater than c.

41. **(a)** Use the figure (in the text), where the line segment between 0 and 1 has been bent into a semicircle and positioned above the line, to prove that $\{x|x \text{ is a real number between 0 and 1}\}$ is equivalent to $\{x|x \text{ is a real number}\}$.

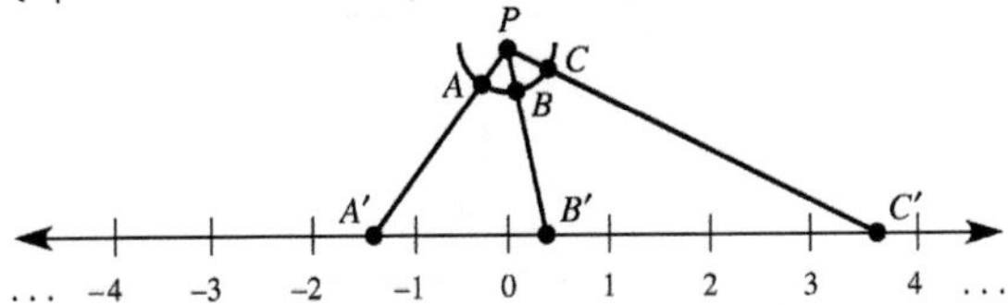

Rays emanating from point P will establish a geometric pairing for the points on the semicircle with the points on the line.

(b) The fact part (a) establishes about the set of real numbers is that the set of real numbers is infinite, having been placed in a one-to-one correspondence with a proper subset of itself.

43. $\{3, 6, 9, 12, ..., 3n, ...\}$
$\updownarrow\ \updownarrow\ \updownarrow\ \updownarrow \quad \updownarrow$
$\{6, 9, 12, 15, ..., 3n+3, ...\}$

45. $\left\{\frac{3}{4}, \frac{3}{8}, \frac{3}{12}, \frac{3}{16}, ..., \frac{3}{4n}, ...\right\}$
$\updownarrow\ \updownarrow\ \updownarrow\ \updownarrow \quad \updownarrow$
$\left\{\frac{3}{8}, \frac{3}{12}, \frac{3}{16}, \frac{3}{20}, ..., \frac{3}{4n+4}, ...\right\}$

47. $\left\{\frac{1}{9}, \frac{1}{18}, \frac{1}{27}, ..., \frac{1}{9n}, ...\right\}$
$\updownarrow\ \updownarrow\ \updownarrow \quad \updownarrow$
$\left\{\frac{1}{18}, \frac{1}{27}, \frac{1}{36}, ..., \frac{1}{9n+9}, ...\right\}$

49. Writing exercise; answers will vary.

51. Writing exercise; answers will vary.

Chapter Test

1. $A \cup C = \{a, b, c, d\} \cup \{a, e\}$
$= \{a, b, c, d, e\}$

2. $B \cap A = \{b, e, a, d\} \cap \{a, b, c, d\}$
$= \{a, b, d\}$

3. $B' = \{b, e, a, d\}' = \{c, f, g, h\}$

4. $A - (B \cap C')$
$= A - (\{b, e, a, d\} \cap \{b, c, d, f, g, h\})$
$= \{a, b, c, d\} - \{b, d\}$
$= \{a, c\}$

5. $b \in A$ is true since b is a member of set A.

6. $C \subseteq A$ is false since the element e, which is a member of set C, is not also a member of set A.

7. $B \subset (A \cup C)$ is true since all members of set B are also members of $A \cup C$.

8. $c \notin C$ is true because c is not a member of set C.

9. $n[(A \cup B) - C] = 4$ is false. Because,
$n[(a \cup B) - C] = n[\{a, b, c, d, e\} - \{a, e\}]$
$= n(\{b, c, d)\}$
$= 3$

10. $\varnothing \subset C$ is true. The empty set is considered a subset of any set. C has more elements than $\varnothing$ which makes $\varnothing$ a proper subset of C.

11. $(A \cap B')$ is equivalent to $(B \cap A')$ is true. Because, $n(A \cap B') = n(\{c\}) = 1$,
$n(B \cap A') = n(\{e\}) = 1$.

12. $(A \cup B)' = A' \cap B'$ is true by one of De Morgan's laws.

13. $n(A \times C) = n(A) \times n(C) = 4 \times 2 = 8$

14. The number of proper subsets of A is
$2^4 - 1 = 16 - 1 = 15$.

Answers may vary for Exercises 15–18.

15. A word description for $\{-3, -1, 1, 3, 5, 7, 9\}$ is the set of all odd integers between −4 and 10.

16. A word description for {January, February, March, ..., December} is the set of months of the year.

17. Set-builder notation for $\{-1, -2, -3, -4, ...\}$ would be $\{x|x$ is a negative integer$\}$.

18. Set-builder notation for $\{24, 32, 40, 48, ..., 88\}$ would be $\{x|x$ is a multiple of 8 between 20 and 90$\}$.

19. $\varnothing$ $\boxed{\subseteq}$ $\{x|x$ is a counting number between 20 and 21$\}$ since the empty set is a subset of any set.

20. $\{4, 9, 16\}$ $\boxed{\text{neither}}$ $\{4, 5, 6, 7, 8, 9, 10\}$ since the element 16 is not a member of the second set.

21. $X \cup Y'$

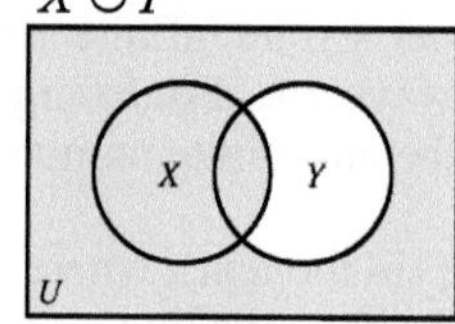

22. $X' \cap Y'$

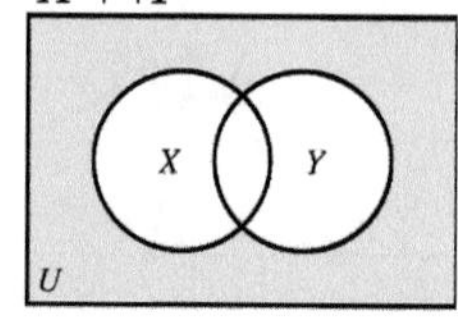

23. $(X \cup Y) - Z$

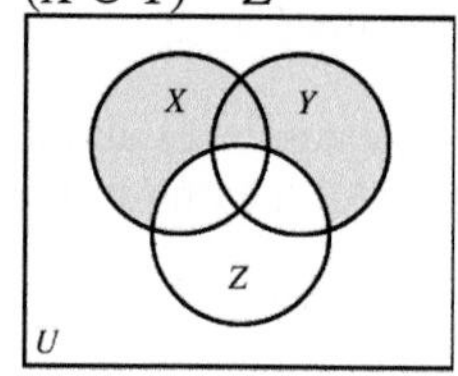

24. $[(X \cap Y) \cup (Y \cap Z) \cup (X \cap Z)]$
$- (X \cap Y \cap Z)$

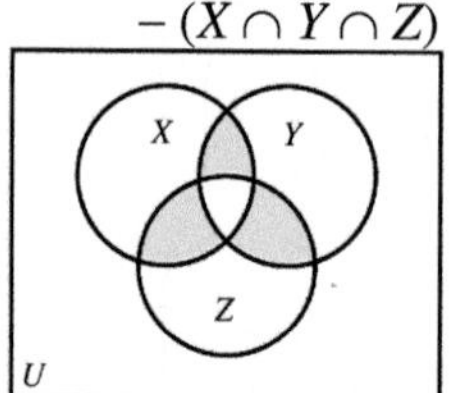

25. $A \cap T =$ {Electric razor, Telegraph, Zipper} $\cap$ {Electric razor, Fiber optics, Geiger counter, Radar} = {Electric Razor}

26. $(A \cup T)'$
= ({Electric razor, Telegraph, Zipper} $\cup$ {Electric razor, Fiber optics, Geiger counter, Radar})′
= {Electric razor, Fiber optics, Geiger counter, Radar, Telegraph, Zipper}′
= {Adding machine, Barometer, Pendulum clock, Thermometer}

27. $A - T'$
= {Electric razor, Telegraph, Zipper}
– {Electric razor, Fiber optics, Geiger counter, Radar}′
= {Electric razor, Telegraph, Zipper}
– {Adding machine, Barometer, Pendulum clock, Telegraph, Thermometer, Zipper}
= {Electric razor}

28. Writing exercise; answers will vary.

29. **(a)** $n(A \cup B) = 12 + 3 + 7 = 22$

(b) $n(A \cap B') = n(A - B) = 12$
These are the elements in A but outside of B.

30. Let G = set of students who are receiving government grants. Let S = set of students who are receiving private scholarships. Let A = set of students who are receiving aid from the college.
Complete a Venn diagram by inserting the appropriate cardinal number for each region in the diagram. Begin with the intersection of all three sets: $n(G \cap S \cap A) = 8$. Since $n(S \cap A) = 28$, $n(S \cap A \cap G') = 28 - 8 = 20$.
Since $n(G \cap A) = 18$,
$n(G \cap A \cap S') = 18 - 8 = 10$. Since
$n(G \cap S) = 23$, $n(G \cap S \cap A') = 23 - 8 = 15$.
Since $n(A) = 43$,

$$\begin{aligned} n(A \cap (G \cup S)') &= 43 - (10 + 8 + 20) \\ &= 43 - 38 \\ &= 5. \end{aligned}$$

Since $n(S) = 55$,

$$\begin{aligned} n(S \cap (G \cup A)') &= 55 - (15 + 8 + 20) \\ &= 55 - 43 \\ &= 12. \end{aligned}$$

Since $n(G) = 49$,

$$\begin{aligned} n(G \cap (S \cup A)') &= 49 - (10 + 8 + 15) \\ &= 49 - 33 \\ &= 16. \end{aligned}$$

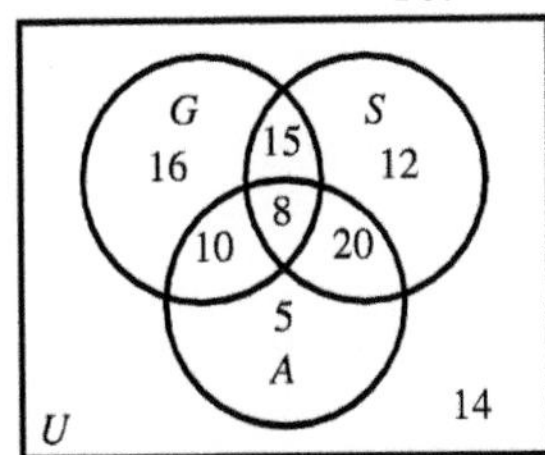

Thus,

(a) $n(G \cap (S \cup A)') = 16$ have a government grant only.

(b) $n(S \cap G') = 32$ have a private scholarship but not a government grant.

(c) $16 + 12 + 5 = 33$ receive financial aid from only one of these sources.

(d) $10 + 15 + 20 = 45$ receive aid from exactly two of these sources.

(e) $n(G \cup S \cup A)' = 14$ receive no financial aid from any of these sources.

(f)

$$\begin{aligned} &n(S \cap (A \cup G)') + n(A \cup G \cup S)' \\ &= 12 + 14 \\ &= 26 \end{aligned}$$

received private scholarships or no aid at all.

INTRODUCTION TO LOGIC

Dreamworks SKG/Everett Collection

In the 2007 movie *Shrek the Third*, Shrek searches for the rightful heir to the throne of the Kingdom of Far Far Away, while Prince Charming schemes to gain the throne for himself. The Prince, knowing that Pinocchio's nose grows if he lies, questions Pinocchio.

PRINCE CHARMING: So tell me puppet, where is Shrek?

PINOCCHIO: Well, I don't know where he's not.

PRINCE CHARMING: You're telling me you don't know where Shrek is?

PINOCCHIO: It wouldn't be inaccurate to assume that I couldn't exactly not say that is or isn't almost partially incorrect.

PRINCE CHARMING: So you do know where he is!

PINOCCHIO: On the contrary, I'm possibly more or less not definitely rejecting the idea that in no way, with any amount of uncertainty, that I undeniably do or do not know where he shouldn't probably be. If that indeed wasn't where he isn't. Even if he wasn't not where I knew he was, it could mean. . . .

Unable to contain his frustration with Pinocchio's roundabout answer, one of the Three Little Pigs blurts out that Shrek has gone to search for the rightful heir. The pig was unable to follow Pinocchio's logic, or lack of it. In this chapter, we examine the basics of the study of logic.

1 STATEMENTS AND QUANTIFIERS

Statements • Negations • Symbols • Quantifiers • Quantifiers and Number Sets

Bilwissedition Ltd. & Co. KG/Alamy

Gottfried Leibniz (1646–1716) was a wide-ranging philosopher and a universalist who tried to patch up Catholic–Protestant conflicts. He promoted cultural exchange between Europe and the East. Chinese ideograms led him to search for a universal symbolism. He was an early inventor of **symbolic logic.**

Statements

This section introduces the study of **symbolic logic,** which uses letters to represent statements, and symbols for words such as *and, or, not.* Logic is used in the study of the **truth value** (that is, the truth or falsity) of statements with multiple parts. The truth value of such statements depends on their components.

Many kinds of sentences occur in ordinary language, including factual statements, opinions, commands, and questions. Symbolic logic discusses only the type that involves facts. A **statement** is a declarative sentence that is either true or false, but not both simultaneously.

Electronic mail provides a means of communication. $12 + 6 = 13$	Statements Each is either true or false.
Access the file. Did the Saints win the Super Bowl? Tim Lincecum is a better baseball player than Cliff Lee. This sentence is false.	Not statements Each cannot be identified as being either true or false.

Of the sentences that are not statements, the first is a command, and the second is a question. The third is an opinion. "This sentence is false" is a paradox: If we assume it is true, then it is false, and if we assume it is false, then it is true.

A **compound statement** may be formed by combining two or more statements. The statements making up a compound statement are called **component statements.** Various **logical connectives,** or simply **connectives,** such as ***and, or, not,*** and ***if . . . then,*** can be used in forming compound statements. (While a statement such as "Today is not Tuesday" does not consist of two component statements, for convenience it is considered compound, because its truth value is determined by noting the truth value of a different statement, "Today is Tuesday.")

EXAMPLE 1 Deciding Whether a Statement Is Compound

Decide whether each statement is compound. If so, identify the connective.

(a) Lord Byron wrote sonnets, and the poem exhibits iambic pentameter.

(b) You can pay me now, or you can pay me later.

(c) If he said it, then it must be true.

(d) My pistol was made by Smith and Wesson.

SOLUTION

(a) This statement is compound, because it is made up of the component statements "Lord Byron wrote sonnets" and "the poem exhibits iambic pentameter." The connective is *and.*

(b) The connective here is *or.* The statement is compound.

(c) The connective here is *if . . . then,* discussed in more detail in **Section 3.** The statement is compound.

(d) While the word "and" is used in this statement, it is not used as a *logical* connective. It is part of the name of the manufacturer. The statement is not compound. ∎∎∎

Negations

The sentence "Anthony Mansella has a red truck" is a statement. The **negation** of this statement is "Anthony Mansella does not have a red truck." ***The negation of a true statement is false, and the negation of a false statement is true.***

EXAMPLE 2 Forming Negations

Form the negation of each statement.

(a) That city has a mayor. **(b)** The moon is not a planet.

SOLUTION

(a) To negate this statement, we introduce *not* into the sentence: "That city does not have a mayor."

(b) The negation is "The moon is a planet." ∎∎∎

One way to detect incorrect negations is to check truth values. ***A negation must have the opposite truth value from the original statement.***

The next example uses some of the inequality symbols in **Table 1**. In the case of an inequality involving a variable, the negation must have the opposite truth value for *any* replacement of the variable.

TEST LOGIC
1:=
2:≠
3:>
4:≥
5:<
6:≤

The TEST menu of the TI-83/84 Plus calculator allows the user to test the truth or falsity of statements involving =, ≠, >, ≥, <, and ≤. If a statement is true, it returns a 1. If it is false, it returns a 0.

Table 1

Symbolism	Meaning	Examples	
$a < b$	a is less than b	$4 < 9$	$\frac{1}{2} < \frac{3}{4}$
$a > b$	a is greater than b	$6 > 2$	$-5 > -11$
$a \leq b$	a is less than or equal to b	$8 \leq 10$	$3 \leq 3$
$a \geq b$	a is greater than or equal to b	$-2 \geq -3$	$-5 \geq -5$

EXAMPLE 3 Negating Inequalities

4<9
1
4>9
0

$4 < 9$ is true, as indicated by the 1.
$4 > 9$ is false, as indicated by the 0.

Give a negation of each inequality. Do *not* use a slash symbol.

(a) $x < 9$ **(b)** $7x + 11y \geq 77$

SOLUTION

(a) The negation of "x is less than 9" is "x is *not* less than 9." Because we cannot use "not," which would require writing $x \nless 9$, phrase the negation as "x is greater than or equal to 9," or

$$x \geq 9.$$

(b) The negation, with no slash, is

$$7x + 11y < 77.$$ ∎∎∎

```
TEST  LOGIC
1: and
2: or
3: xor
4: not(
```

The LOGIC menu of the TI-83/84 Plus calculator allows the user to test truth or falsity of statements involving *and, or, exclusive or* (see **Exercise 77** in **Section 2**), and *not.*

Symbols

The study of logic uses symbols. Statements are represented with letters, such as p, q, or r. Several symbols for connectives are shown in **Table 2**.

Table 2

Connective	Symbol	Type of Statement
and	$\wedge$	Conjunction
or	$\vee$	Disjunction
not	$\sim$	Negation

The symbol $\sim$ represents the connective *not.* If p represents the statement "Barack Obama was president in 2009" then $\sim p$ represents "Barack Obama was not president in 2009."

EXAMPLE 4 Translating from Symbols to Words

Let p represent "It is 70° today," and let q represent "It is Tuesday." Write each symbolic statement in words.

(a) $p \vee q$ **(b)** $\sim p \wedge q$ **(c)** $\sim(p \vee q)$ **(d)** $\sim(p \wedge q)$

SOLUTION

(a) From the table, $\vee$ symbolizes *or*. Thus, $p \vee q$ represents

It is 70° today or it is Tuesday.

(b) It is not 70° today and it is Tuesday.

(c) It is not the case that it is 70° today or it is Tuesday.

(d) It is not the case that it is 70° today and it is Tuesday. ∎

The statement in **Example 4(c)** usually is translated as **"Neither p nor q."**

Quantifiers

Quantifiers are used to indicate *how many* cases of a particular situation exist. The words ***all, each, every,*** and ***no(ne)*** are called **universal quantifiers,** while words and phrases such as ***some, there exists,*** and ***(for) at least one*** are called **existential quantifiers.** ***Be careful when forming the negation of a statement involving quantifiers.***

The negation of a statement must be false if the given statement is true and must be true if the given statement is false, in all possible cases. Consider this statement.

All girls in the group are named Mary.

Many people would write the negation of this statement as "No girls in the group are named Mary" or "All girls in the group are not named Mary." But neither of these is correct. To see why, look at the three groups below.

Group I: Mary Jane Payne, Mary Meyer, Mary O'Hara

Group II: Mary Johnson, Lisa Pollak, Margaret Watson

Group III: Donna Garbarino, Paula Story, Rhonda Alessi, Kim Falgout

These groups contain all possibilities that need to be considered. In Group I, *all* girls are named Mary. In Group II, *some* girls are named Mary (and some are not). In Group III, *no* girls are named Mary. Look at the truth values in **Table 3** on the next page, and keep in mind that "some" means "at least one (and possibly all)."

Erich Lessing/Art Resource, New York

Aristotle, the first to systematize the logic we use in everyday life, appears above in a detail from the painting *The School of Athens*, by Raphael. He is shown debating a point with his teacher **Plato.**

Table 3 Truth Value as Applied to:	Group I	Group II	Group III	
(1) All girls in the group are named Mary. (Given)	T	F	F	Negation
(2) No girls in the group are named Mary. (Possible negation)	**F**	**F**	**T**	
(3) All girls in the group are not named Mary. (Possible negation)	**F**	**F**	**T**	
(4) Some girls in the group are not named Mary. (Possible negation)	F	T	T	Negation

The negation of the given statement (1) must have opposite truth values in *all* cases. It can be seen that statements (2) and (3) do not satisfy this condition (for Group II), but statement (4) does. It may be concluded that the correct negation for "All girls in the group are named Mary" is "Some girls in the group are not named Mary." Other ways of stating the negation include the following.

Not all girls in the group are named Mary.

It is not the case that all girls in the group are named Mary.

At least one girl in the group is not named Mary.

Table 4 shows how to find the negation of a statement involving quantifiers.

Table 4 Negations of Quantified Statements

Statement	Negation
All do.	Some do not. (Equivalently: Not all do.)
Some do.	None do. (Equivalently: All do not.)

The negation of the negation of a statement is simply the statement itself. For instance, the negations of the statements in the Negation column are simply the corresponding original statements in the Statement column. As an example, the negation of "Some do not" is "All do."

EXAMPLE 5 Forming Negations of Quantified Statements

Form the negation of each statement.

(a) Some cats have fleas. **(b)** Some cats do not have fleas.

(c) No cats have fleas.

SOLUTION

(a) Because *some* means "at least one," the statement "Some cats have fleas" is really the same as "At least one cat has fleas." The negation of this is

"No cat has fleas."

(b) The statement "Some cats do not have fleas" claims that at least one cat, somewhere, does not have fleas. The negation of this is

"All cats have fleas."

(c) The negation is "Some cats have fleas."

Avoid the incorrect answer "All cats have fleas."

Quantifiers and Number Sets

Earlier we introduced sets of numbers.

Sets of Numbers

Natural or Counting numbers $\{1, 2, 3, 4, \ldots\}$

Whole numbers $\{0, 1, 2, 3, 4, \ldots\}$

Integers $\{\ldots, -3, -2, -1, 0, 1, 2, 3, \ldots\}$

Rational numbers $\left\{\frac{p}{q} \,\middle|\, p \text{ and } q \text{ are integers, and } q \neq 0\right\}$

(*Examples:* $\frac{3}{5}$, $-\frac{7}{9}$, 5, 0. Any rational number may be expressed as a terminating decimal number, such as 0.25, or a repeating decimal number, such as 0.666 . . . .)

Real numbers $\{x \mid x \text{ is a number that can be written as a decimal}\}$

Irrational numbers $\{x \mid x \text{ is a real number and } x \text{ cannot be written as a quotient of integers}\}$

(*Examples:* $\sqrt{2}$, $\sqrt[3]{4}$, π. Decimal representations of irrational numbers are neither terminating nor repeating.)

EXAMPLE 6 Deciding Whether Quantified Statements Are True or False

Decide whether each statement involving a quantifier is *true* or *false*.

(a) There exists a whole number that is not a natural number.

(b) Every integer is a natural number.

(c) Every natural number is a rational number.

(d) There exists an irrational number that is not real.

SOLUTION

(a) Because there is such a whole number (it is 0), this statement is true.

(b) This statement is false, because we can find at least one integer that is not a natural number. For example, −1 is an integer but is not a natural number.

(c) Because every natural number can be written as a fraction with denominator 1, this statement is true.

(d) In order to be an irrational number, a number must first be real. Because we cannot give an irrational number that is not real, this statement is false. (Had we been able to find at least one, the statement would have then been true.) ∎

1 EXERCISES

Decide whether each is a statement or is not a statement.

1. February 2, 2009, was a Monday.

2. The ZIP code for Oscar, LA, is 70762.

3. Listen, my children, and you shall hear of the midnight ride of Paul Revere.

4. Yield to oncoming traffic.

5. $5 + 9 \neq 14$ and $4 - 1 = 12$

6. $5 + 9 \neq 12$ or $4 - 2 = 5$

7. Some numbers are positive.

8. Millard Fillmore was president of the United States in 1851.

9. Accidents are the main cause of deaths of children under the age of 7.

10. *The Dark Knight* was the top-grossing movie of 2008.

Warner Bros./Everett Collection

11. Where are you going tomorrow?

12. Behave yourself and sit down.

13. Kevin "Catfish" McCarthy once took a prolonged continuous shower for 340 hours, 40 minutes.

14. One gallon of milk weighs more than 3 pounds.

Decide whether each statement is compound.

15. I read the *Detroit Free Press*, and I read the *Sacramento Bee*.

16. My brother got married in Copenhagen.

17. Tomorrow is Saturday.

18. Mamie Zwettler is younger than 18 years of age, and so is her friend Emma Lister.

19. Jay Beckenstein's wife loves Ben and Jerry's ice cream.

20. The sign on the back of the car read "Canada or bust!"

21. If Lorri Morgan sells her quota, then Michelle Cook will be happy.

22. If Bobby is a politician, then Mitch is a crook.

Write a negation for each statement.

23. Her aunt's name is Hermione.

24. The flowers are to be watered.

25. Every dog has its day.

26. No rain fell in southern California today.

27. Some books are longer than this book.

28. All students present will get another chance.

29. No computer repairman can play blackjack.

30. Some people have all the luck.

31. Everybody loves somebody sometime.

32. Everyone loves a winner.

Give a negation of each inequality. Do not use a slash symbol.

33. $x > 12$

34. $x < -6$

35. $x \geq 5$

36. $x \leq 19$

37. Try to negate the sentence "The exact number of words in this sentence is ten" and see what happens. Explain the problem that arises.

38. Explain why the negation of "$x > 5$" is not "$x < 5$."

Let p represent the statement "She has green eyes" *and let q represent the statement* "He is 60 years old." *Translate each symbolic compound statement into words.*

39. $\sim p$

40. $\sim q$

41. $p \wedge q$

42. $p \vee q$

43. $\sim p \vee q$

44. $p \wedge \sim q$

45. $\sim p \vee \sim q$

46. $\sim p \wedge \sim q$

47. $\sim(\sim p \wedge q)$

48. $\sim(p \vee \sim q)$

Let p represent the statement "Chris collects DVDs" *and let q represent the statement* "Josh is an art major." *Convert each compound statement into symbols.*

49. Chris collects DVDs and Josh is not an art major.

50. Chris does not collect DVDs or Josh is not an art major.

51. Chris does not collect DVDs or Josh is an art major.

52. Josh is an art major and Chris does not collect DVDs.

53. Neither Chris collects DVDs nor Josh is an art major.

54. Either Josh is an art major or Chris collects DVDs, and it is not the case that both Josh is an art major and Chris collects DVDs.

55. Incorrect use of quantifiers often is heard in everyday language. Suppose you hear that a local electronics chain is having a 40% off sale, and the radio advertisement states "All items are not available in all stores." Do you think that, literally translated, the ad really means what it says? What do you think is really meant? Explain your answer.

56. Repeat **Exercise 55** for the following: "All people don't have the time to devote to maintaining their vehicles properly."

Refer to the groups of art labeled A, B, *and* C, *and identify by letter the group or groups that are satisfied by the given statements involving quantifiers.*

A

B

C

57. All pictures have frames.

58. No picture has a frame.

59. At least one picture does not have a frame.

60. Not every picture has a frame.

61. At least one picture has a frame.

62. No picture does not have a frame.

63. All pictures do not have frames.

64. Not every picture does not have a frame.

Decide whether each statement in Exercises 65–74 involving a quantifier is true *or* false.

65. Every whole number is an integer.

66. Every natural number is an integer.

67. There exists a rational number that is not an integer.

68. There exists an integer that is not a natural number.

69. All rational numbers are real numbers.

70. All irrational numbers are real numbers.

71. Some rational numbers are not integers.

72. Some whole numbers are not rational numbers.

73. Each whole number is a positive number.

74. Each rational number is a positive number.

75. Explain the difference between the following statements.

All students did not pass the test.

Not all students passed the test.

76. The statement "For some real number x, $x^2 \geq 0$" is true. However, your friend does not understand why, because he claims that $x^2 \geq 0$ is true for *all* real numbers x (and not *some*). How would you explain his misconception to him?

77. Write the following statement using "every": There is no one here who has not done that at one time or another.

78. Only one of these statements is true. Which one is it?

A. For some real number x, $x \not< 0$.

B. For all real numbers x, $x^3 > 0$.

C. For all real numbers x less than 0, x^2 is also less than 0.

D. For some real number x, $x^2 < 0$.

2 TRUTH TABLES AND EQUIVALENT STATEMENTS

Conjunctions • Disjunctions • Negations • Mathematical Statements • Truth Tables • Alternative Method for Constructing Truth Tables • Equivalent Statements and De Morgan's Laws

Conjunctions

Truth values of component statements are used to find truth values of compound statements. To begin, we must decide on truth values of the **conjunction *p and q*,** symbolized $p \wedge q$. Here, the connective *and* implies the idea of "both." The following statement is true, because each component statement is true.

Monday immediately follows Sunday and March immediately follows February.

True

On the other hand, the following statement is false, even though part of the statement (Monday immediately follows Sunday) is true.

Monday immediately follows Sunday and March immediately follows January.

False

For the conjunction $p \wedge q$ to be true, both p and q must be true. This result is summarized by a table, called a **truth table,** which shows all four of the possible combinations of truth values for the conjunction *p and q*.

Truth Table for the Conjunction p and q

p and q

p	q	$p \wedge q$
T	T	T
T	F	F
F	T	F
F	F	F

EXAMPLE 1 Finding the Truth Value of a Conjunction

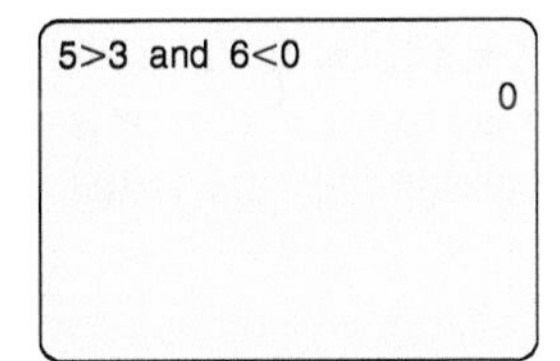

The calculator returns a "0" for $5 > 3$ *and* $6 < 0$, indicating that the statement is false.

Let p represent "$5 > 3$" and let q represent "$6 < 0$." Find the truth value of $p \wedge q$.

SOLUTION

Here p is true and q is false. Looking in the second row of the conjunction truth table shows that $p \wedge q$ is false. ■■■

In some cases, the logical connective *but* is used in compound statements.

He wants to go to the mountains but she wants to go to the beach.

Here, *but* is used in place of *and* to give a different emphasis to the statement. We consider this statement as we would consider the conjunction using the word *and.* The truth table for the conjunction, given above, would apply.

Disjunctions

In ordinary language, the word *or* can be ambiguous. The expression "this or that" can mean either "this or that or both," or "this or that but not both." For example, consider the following statement.

I will paint the wall or I will paint the ceiling.

This statement probably means: "I will paint the wall or I will paint the ceiling or I will paint both." On the other hand, consider the following statement.

I will drive the Lexus or the BMW to the store.

It probably means "I will drive the Lexus, or I will drive the BMW, but I will not drive both."

The symbol $\vee$ represents the first *or* described. That is,

$p \vee q$ **means** **"p or q or both."** Disjunction

With this meaning of *or*, $p \vee q$ is called the **inclusive disjunction,** or just the **disjunction** of p and q. In everyday language, the disjunction implies the idea of "either." For example, consider the following disjunction.

I have a quarter or I have a dime.

It is true whenever I have either a quarter, a dime, or both. The only way this disjunction could be false would be if I had neither coin. ***The disjunction $p \vee q$ is false only if both component statements are false.***

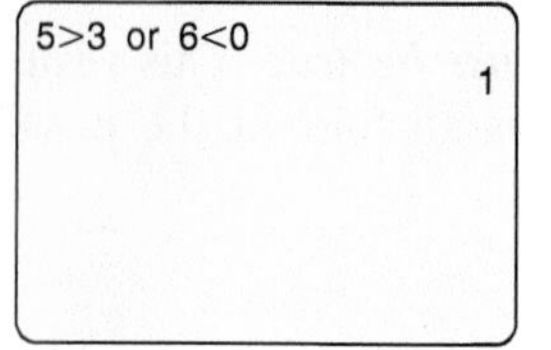

The calculator returns a "1" for $5 > 3$ *or* $6 < 0$, indicating that the statement is true.

Truth Table for the Disjunction ***p* or *q***

p* or *q

p	q	$p \vee q$
T	T	T
T	F	T
F	T	T
F	F	F

Table 5

Statement	Reason That It Is True
$8 \geq 8$	$8 = 8$
$3 \geq 1$	$3 > 1$
$-5 \leq -3$	$-5 < -3$
$-4 \leq -4$	$-4 = -4$

EXAMPLE 2 Finding the Truth Value of a Disjunction

Let p represent "$5 > 3$" and let q represent "$6 < 0$." Find the truth value of $p \vee q$.

SOLUTION

Here, as in **Example 1,** p is true and q is false. The second row of the disjunction truth table shows that $p \vee q$ is true.

The symbol $\geq$ is read **"is greater than or equal to,"** while $\leq$ is read **"is less than or equal to."** If a and b are real numbers, then $a \leq b$ is true if $a < b$ or $a = b$. **Table 5** in the margin shows several statements and the reasons they are true.

Negations

The **negation** of a statement p, symbolized $\sim p$**,** must have the opposite truth value from the statement p itself. This leads to the truth table for the negation.

Truth Table for the Negation **not *p***

not *p*

p	$\sim p$
T	F
F	T

EXAMPLE 3 Finding the Truth Value of a Compound Statement

Suppose p is false, q is true, and r is false. What is the truth value of the compound statement $\sim p \wedge (q \vee \sim r)$?

SOLUTION

Here parentheses are used to group q and $\sim r$ together. Work first inside the parentheses. Because r is false, $\sim r$ will be true. Because $\sim r$ is true and q is true, find the truth value of $q \vee \sim r$ by looking in the first row of the *or* truth table. This row gives the result T.

Because p is false, $\sim p$ is true, and the final truth value of $\sim p \wedge (q \vee \sim r)$ is found in the top row of the *and* truth table. From the *and* truth table, when $\sim p$ is true, and $q \vee \sim r$ is true, the statement

$$\sim p \wedge (q \vee \sim r) \quad \text{is true.}$$

We can use a short-cut symbolic method that involves replacing the statements with their truth values, letting T represent a true statement and F represent a false statement.

$$\sim p \wedge (q \vee \sim r)$$

$$\sim \mathrm{F} \wedge (\mathrm{T} \vee \sim \mathrm{F})$$ Work within parentheses first.

$$\mathrm{T} \wedge (\mathrm{T} \vee \mathrm{T})$$ ~F gives T.

$$\mathrm{T} \wedge \mathrm{T}$$ T ∨ T gives T.

The compound statement is true. → T   T ∧ T gives T.

Mathematical Statements

We can use truth tables to determine the truth values of compound mathematical statements.

EXAMPLE 4 Deciding Whether a Compound Mathematical Statement Is True or False

Let p represent the statement $3 > 2$, q represent $5 < 4$, and r represent $3 < 8$. Decide whether each statement is *true* or *false*.

(a) $\sim p \wedge \sim q$ **(b)** $\sim(p \wedge q)$ **(c)** $(\sim p \wedge r) \vee (\sim q \wedge \sim p)$

```
not(3>2) and not (5<4)
                              0
not((3>2) and (5<4))
                              1
```

Example 4(a) explains why

$$\sim(3 > 2) \wedge [\sim(5 < 4)]$$

is false. The calculator returns a 0. For a true statement such as

$$\sim[(3 > 2) \wedge (5 < 4)],$$

it returns a 1.

SOLUTION

(a) Because p is true, $\sim p$ is false. By the *and* truth table, if one part of an "and" statement is false, the entire statement is false.

$\sim p \wedge \sim q$ is false.

(b) For $\sim(p \wedge q)$, first work within the parentheses. Because p is true and q is false, $p \wedge q$ is false by the *and* truth table. Next, apply the negation. The negation of a false statement is true.

$\sim(p \wedge q)$ is true.

(c) Here p is true, q is false, and r is true. This makes $\sim p$ false and $\sim q$ true. By the *and* truth table, $\sim p \wedge r$ is false, and $\sim q \wedge \sim p$ is also false. By the *or* truth table,

$(\sim p \wedge r) \vee (\sim q \wedge \sim p)$ is false.

$$\downarrow \qquad \downarrow$$

$$\mathrm{F} \quad \vee \quad \mathrm{F}$$

(Alternatively, see **Example 8(b)**.)

Library of Congress Prints and Photographs Division (LC-USZ62-61664)

George Boole (1815–1864) grew up in poverty. His father, a London tradesman, gave him his first mathematics lessons and taught him to make optical instruments. Boole was largely self-educated. At 16 he worked in an elementary school and by age 20 had opened his own school. He studied mathematics in his spare time. He died of lung disease at age 49.

Boole's ideas have been used in the design of computers and telephone systems.

When a quantifier is used with a conjunction or a disjunction, we must be careful in determining the truth value, as shown in the following example.

EXAMPLE 5 Deciding Whether a Quantified Mathematical Statement Is True or False

Decide whether each statement is *true* or *false*.

(a) For some real number x, $x < 5$ and $x > 2$.

(b) For every real number x, $x > 0$ or $x < 1$.

(c) For all real numbers x, $x^2 > 0$.

SOLUTION

(a) Replacing x with 3 (as an example) gives $3 < 5$ and $3 > 2$. Because both $3 < 5$ and $3 > 2$ are true statements, the given statement is true by the *and* truth table. (Remember: *Some* means "at least one.")

(b) No matter which real number might be tried as a replacement for x, at least one of the two statements

$$x > 0, \quad x < 1$$

will be true. Because an "or" statement is true if one or both component statements are true, the entire statement as given is true.

(c) Because the quantifier is a universal quantifier, we need only find one case in which the inequality is false to make the entire statement false. Can we find a real number whose square is not positive (that is, not greater than 0)? Yes, we can—0 is the *only* real number whose square is not positive. This statement is false. ■■■

For Further Thought

Whose Picture Am I Looking At?

Raymond Smullyan is one of today's foremost writers of logic puzzles. This professor of mathematics and philosophy is now retired from Indiana University and has written several books on recreational logic, including *What Is the Name of This Book?*, *The Lady or the Tiger?*, and *Alice in Puzzleland*. The first of these includes the following puzzle, which has been around for many years.

For Group or Individual Investigation

A man is looking at a portrait. Someone asked him, "Whose picture are you looking at?" He replied: "Brothers and sisters, I have none, but this man's father is my father's son. ("This man's father" means, of course, the father of the man in the picture.)

Whose picture was the man looking at? (Turn the page to see the answer.)

p	q	Compound Statement
T	T	
T	F	
F	T	
F	F	

Truth Tables

In the preceding examples, the truth value for a given statement was found by going back to the basic truth tables. In the long run, it is easier to first create a complete truth table for the given statement itself. Then final truth values can be read directly from this table.

In this book we use the standard format shown in the margin for listing the possible truth values in compound statements involving two component statements.

EXAMPLE 6 Constructing a Truth Table

Consider the statement $(\sim p \wedge q) \vee \sim q$.

(a) Construct a truth table.

(b) Suppose both p and q are true. Find the truth value of the compound statement.

SOLUTION

(a) Begin by listing all possible combinations of truth values for p and q, as above. Then list the truth values of $\sim p$, which are the opposite of those of p, as shown in the table in the margin.

p	q	$\sim p$
T	T	F
T	F	F
F	T	T
F	F	T

Use only the "$\sim p$" column and the "q" column, along with the *and* truth table, to find the truth values of $\sim p \wedge q$. List them in a separate column.

p	q	$\sim p$	$\sim p \wedge q$
T	T	F	F
T	F	F	F
F	T	T	T
F	F	T	F

Next include a column for $\sim q$.

p	q	$\sim p$	$\sim p \wedge q$	$\sim q$
T	T	F	F	F
T	F	F	F	T
F	T	T	T	F
F	F	T	F	T

Finally, make a column for the entire compound statement. To find the truth values, use *or* to combine $\sim p \wedge q$ with $\sim q$.

p	q	$\sim p$	$\sim p \wedge q$	$\sim q$	$(\sim p \wedge q) \vee \sim q$
T	T	F	F	F	F
T	F	F	F	T	T
F	T	T	T	F	T
F	F	T	F	T	T

(b) Look in the first row of the final truth table above, where both p and q have truth value T. Read across the row to find that the compound statement is false.

EXAMPLE 7 Constructing a Truth Table

Construct the truth table for $p \wedge (\sim p \vee \sim q)$.

SOLUTION

Proceed as shown.

p	q	$\sim p$	$\sim q$	$\sim p \vee \sim q$	$p \wedge (\sim p \vee \sim q)$
T	T	F	F	F	F
T	F	F	T	T	T
F	T	T	F	T	F
F	F	T	T	T	F

Mary Evans Picture Library/Alamy

Emilie, Marquise du Châtelet (1706–1749) participated in the scientific activity of the generation after Newton and Leibniz. Educated in science, music, and literature, she was studying mathematics at the time (1733) she began a long intellectual relationship with the philosopher **François Voltaire** (1694–1778). She and Voltaire competed independently in 1738 for a prize offered by the French Academy on the subject of fire. Although du Châtelet did not win, her dissertation was published by the academy in 1744.

If a compound statement involves three component statements p, q, and r, we will use the following standard format in setting up the truth table.

p	q	r	**Compound Statement**
T	T	T	
T	T	F	
T	F	T	
T	F	F	
F	T	T	
F	T	F	
F	F	T	
F	F	F	

EXAMPLE 8 Constructing a Truth Table

Consider the statement $(\sim p \wedge r) \vee (\sim q \wedge \sim p)$.

(a) Construct a truth table.

(b) Suppose p is true, q is false, and r is true. Find the truth value of this statement.

SOLUTION

(a) There are three component statements: p, q, and r. The truth table thus requires eight rows to list all possible combinations of truth values of p, q, and r. The final truth table can be found in much the same way as the ones earlier.

p	q	r	$\sim p$	$\sim p \wedge r$	$\sim q$	$\sim q \wedge \sim p$	$(\sim p \wedge r) \vee (\sim q \wedge \sim p)$
T	T	T	F	F	F	F	F
T	T	F	F	F	F	F	F
T	F	T	F	F	T	F	F
T	F	F	F	F	T	F	F
F	T	T	T	T	F	F	T
F	T	F	T	F	F	F	F
F	F	T	T	T	T	T	T
F	F	F	T	F	T	T	T

(b) By the third row of the truth table in part (a), the compound statement is false. (This is an alternative method for working part (c) of **Example 4.**) ∎

Answer to the problem of *Whose Picture Am I Looking At?*

Most people give the incorrect answer that the man is looking at his own picture. The correct answer is that the man is looking at a picture of his son.

Smullyan helps the reader to understand why this is correct. Because he has no siblings, "my father's son" must refer to the man himself, so the second part of the problem can be reworded "This man's father is myself." Thus, the man in the picture must be his own son.

PROBLEM-SOLVING HINT One strategy for problem solving is to notice a pattern and use inductive reasoning. This strategy is applied in the next example.

EXAMPLE 9 Using Inductive Reasoning

If n is a counting number, and a logical statement is composed of n component statements, how many rows will appear in the truth table for the compound statement?

SOLUTION

To answer this question, we examine some of the earlier truth tables in this section. The truth table for the negation has one statement and two rows. The truth tables for the conjunction and the disjunction have two component statements, and each has four rows. The truth table in **Example 8(a)** has three component statements and eight rows.

Summarizing these in **Table 6** (seen in the margin) reveals a pattern encountered earlier. Inductive reasoning leads us to the conjecture that if a logical statement is composed of n component statements, it will have 2^n rows. This can be proved using more advanced concepts. ∎

Table 6

Number of Statements	Number of Rows
1	$2 = 2^1$
2	$4 = 2^2$
3	$8 = 2^3$

The result of **Example 9** is reminiscent of the formula for the number of subsets of a set having n elements.

Number of Rows in a Truth Table

A logical statement having n component statements will have 2^n rows in its truth table.

Alternative Method for Constructing Truth Tables

After making a reasonable number of truth tables, some people prefer the shortcut method shown in **Example 10,** which repeats **Examples 6 and 8.**

EXAMPLE 10 Constructing Truth Tables

Construct the truth table for each compound statement.

(a) $(\sim p \wedge q) \vee \sim q$ **(b)** $(\sim p \wedge r) \vee (\sim q \wedge \sim p)$

SOLUTION

(a) Start by inserting truth values for $\sim p$ and for q. Then, use the *and* truth table to obtain the truth values for $\sim p \wedge q$.

p	q	$(\sim p$	$\wedge$	$q)$	$\vee$	$\sim q$
T	T	F		T		
T	F	F		F		
F	T	T		T		
F	F	T		F		

p	q	$(\sim p$	$\wedge$	$q)$	$\vee$	$\sim q$
T	T	F	F	T		
T	F	F	F	F		
F	T	T	T	T		
F	F	T	F	F		

Now disregard the two preliminary columns of truth values for $\sim p$ and for q, and insert truth values for $\sim q$. Finally, use the *or* truth table.

p	q	$(\sim p \wedge q)$	$\vee$	$\sim q$
T	T	F		F
T	F	F		T
F	T	T		F
F	F	F		T

p	q	$(\sim p \wedge q)$	$\vee$	$\sim q$
T	T	F	F	F
T	F	F	T	T
F	T	T	T	F
F	F	F	T	T

These steps can be summarized as follows.

p	q	$(\sim p$	$\wedge$	$q)$	$\vee$	$\sim q$
T	T	F	F	T	F	F
T	F	F	F	F	T	T
F	T	T	T	T	T	F
F	F	T	F	F	T	T
		①	②	①	④	③

The circled numbers indicate the order in which the various columns of the truth table were found.

(b) Work as follows.

p	q	r	$(\sim p$	$\wedge$	$r)$	$\vee$	$(\sim q$	$\wedge$	$\sim p)$
T	T	T	F	F	T	F	F	F	F
T	T	F	F	F	F	F	F	F	F
T	F	T	F	F	T	F	T	F	F
T	F	F	F	F	F	F	T	F	F
F	T	T	T	T	T	T	F	F	T
F	T	F	T	F	F	F	F	F	T
F	F	T	T	T	T	T	T	T	T
F	F	F	T	F	F	T	T	T	T
			①	②	①	⑤	③	④	③

The circled numbers indicate the order.

Equivalent Statements and De Morgan's Laws

Two statements are **equivalent** if they have the same truth value in *every* possible situation. The columns of the two truth tables that were the last to be completed will be the same for equivalent statements.

EXAMPLE 11 Deciding Whether Two Statements Are Equivalent

Are the following two statements equivalent?

$$\sim p \wedge \sim q \quad \text{and} \quad \sim(p \vee q)$$

SOLUTION

Construct a truth table for each statement.

p	q	$\sim p \wedge \sim q$
T	T	F
T	F	F
F	T	F
F	F	T

p	q	$\sim(p \vee q)$
T	T	F
T	F	F
F	T	F
F	F	T

Because the truth values are the same in all cases, as shown in the columns in color, the statements $\sim p \wedge \sim q$ and $\sim(p \vee q)$ are equivalent. Equivalence is written with a three-bar symbol, $\equiv$.

$$\sim p \wedge \sim q \equiv \sim(p \vee q)$$

In the same way, the statements $\sim p \vee \sim q$ and $\sim(p \wedge q)$ are equivalent. We call these equivalences *De Morgan's laws.*

De Morgan's Laws for Logical Statements

For any statements p and q, the following equivalences are valid.

$$\sim(\boldsymbol{p} \vee \boldsymbol{q}) \equiv \sim \boldsymbol{p} \wedge \sim \boldsymbol{q} \quad \text{and} \quad \sim(\boldsymbol{p} \wedge \boldsymbol{q}) \equiv \sim \boldsymbol{p} \vee \sim \boldsymbol{q}$$

De Morgan's laws can be used to find the negations of certain compound statements.

EXAMPLE 12 Applying De Morgan's Laws

Find a negation of each statement by applying De Morgan's laws.

(a) I got an A or I got a B. **(b)** She won't try and he will succeed.

(c) $\sim p \vee (q \wedge \sim p)$

SOLUTION

(a) If p represents "I got an A" and q represents "I got a B," then the compound statement is symbolized $p \vee q$. The negation of $p \vee q$ is $\sim(p \vee q)$. By one of De Morgan's laws, this is equivalent to

$$\sim p \wedge \sim q,$$

or, in words, **I didn't get an A and I didn't get a B.**

This negation is reasonable—the original statement says that I got either an A or a B. The negation says that I didn't get *either* grade.

(b) From one of De Morgan's laws, $\sim(p \wedge q) \equiv \sim p \vee \sim q$, so the negation becomes

She will try or he won't succeed.

(c) Negate both component statements and change $\vee$ to $\wedge$.

$$\sim[\sim p \vee (q \wedge \sim p)] \equiv p \wedge \sim(q \wedge \sim p)$$

Now apply De Morgan's law again.

$$p \wedge \sim(q \wedge \sim p) \equiv p \wedge (\sim q \vee \sim(\sim p))$$
$$\equiv p \wedge (\sim q \vee p)$$

A truth table will show that the statements

$\sim p \vee (q \wedge \sim p)$ and $p \wedge (\sim q \vee p)$ are negations of each other. ∎

2 EXERCISES

Use the concepts introduced in this section to answer Exercises 1–6.

1. If q is false, what must be the truth value of the statement $(p \wedge \sim q) \wedge q$?

2. If q is true, what must be the truth value of the statement $q \vee (q \wedge \sim p)$?

3. If the statement $p \wedge q$ is true, and p is true, then q must be ________.

4. If the statement $p \vee q$ is false, and p is false, then q must be ________.

5. If $\sim(p \vee q)$ is true, what must be the truth values of the component statements?

6. If $\sim(p \wedge q)$ is false, what must be the truth values of the component statements?

Let p represent a false statement and let q represent a true statement. Find the truth value of the given compound statement.

7. $\sim p$

8. $\sim q$

9. $p \vee q$

10. $p \wedge q$

11. $p \vee \sim q$

12. $\sim p \wedge q$

13. $\sim p \vee \sim q$

14. $p \wedge \sim q$

15. $\sim(p \wedge \sim q)$

16. $\sim(\sim p \vee \sim q)$

17. $\sim[\sim p \wedge (\sim q \vee p)]$

18. $\sim[(\sim p \wedge \sim q) \vee \sim q]$

19. Is the statement $6 \geq 2$ a conjunction or a disjunction? Why?

20. Why is the statement $8 \geq 3$ true? Why is $5 \geq 5$ true?

Let p represent a true statement, and q and r represent false statements. Find the truth value of the given compound statement.

21. $(p \wedge r) \vee \sim q$

22. $(q \vee \sim r) \wedge p$

23. $p \wedge (q \vee r)$

24. $(\sim p \wedge q) \vee \sim r$

25. $\sim(p \wedge q) \wedge (r \vee \sim q)$

26. $(\sim r \wedge \sim q) \vee (\sim r \wedge q)$

27. $\sim[(\sim p \wedge q) \vee r]$

28. $\sim[r \vee (\sim q \wedge \sim p)]$

29. $\sim[\sim q \vee (r \wedge \sim p)]$

30. What is the only possible case in which the statement $(p \wedge \sim q) \wedge \sim r$ is true?

Let p represent the statement $16 < 8$, let q represent the statement $5 \ngtr 4$, and let r represent the statement $17 \leq 17$. Find the truth value of the given compound statement.

31. $p \wedge r$

32. $p \vee \sim q$

33. $\sim q \vee \sim r$

34. $\sim p \wedge \sim r$

35. $(p \wedge q) \vee r$

36. $\sim p \vee (\sim r \vee \sim q)$

37. $(\sim r \wedge q) \vee \sim p$

38. $\sim(p \vee \sim q) \vee \sim r$

Give the number of rows in the truth table for each compound statement.

39. $p \vee \sim r$

40. $p \wedge (r \wedge \sim s)$

41. $(\sim p \wedge q) \vee (\sim r \vee \sim s) \wedge r$

42. $[(p \vee q) \wedge (r \wedge s)] \wedge (t \vee \sim p)$

43. $[(\sim p \wedge \sim q) \wedge (\sim r \wedge s \wedge \sim t)] \wedge (\sim u \vee \sim v)$

44. $[(\sim p \wedge \sim q) \vee (\sim r \vee \sim s)] \vee [(\sim m \wedge \sim n) \wedge (u \wedge \sim v)]$

45. If the truth table for a certain compound statement has 128 rows, how many distinct component statements does it have?

46. Is it possible for the truth table of a compound statement to have exactly 54 rows? Why or why not?

Construct a truth table for each compound statement.

47. $\sim p \wedge q$

48. $\sim p \vee \sim q$

49. $\sim(p \wedge q)$

50. $p \vee \sim q$

51. $(q \vee \sim p) \vee \sim q$

52. $(p \wedge \sim q) \wedge p$

53. $\sim q \wedge (\sim p \vee q)$

54. $\sim p \vee (\sim q \wedge \sim p)$

55. $(p \vee \sim q) \wedge (p \wedge q)$

56. $(\sim p \wedge \sim q) \vee (\sim p \vee q)$

57. $(\sim p \wedge q) \wedge r$

58. $r \vee (p \wedge \sim q)$

59. $(\sim p \wedge \sim q) \vee (\sim r \vee \sim p)$

60. $(\sim r \vee \sim p) \wedge (\sim p \vee \sim q)$

61. $\sim(\sim p \wedge \sim q) \vee (\sim r \vee \sim s)$

62. $(\sim r \vee s) \wedge (\sim p \wedge q)$

Use one of De Morgan's laws to write the negation of each statement.

63. You can pay me now or you can pay me later.

64. I am not going or she is going.

65. It is summer and there is no snow.

66. $\frac{1}{2}$ is a positive number and -9 is less than zero.

67. I said yes but she said no.

68. Dan La Chapelle tried to sell the software, but he was unable to do so.

69. $6 - 1 = 5$ and $9 + 13 \neq 7$

70. $8 < 10$ or $5 \neq 2$

71. Prancer or Vixen will lead Santa's reindeer sleigh next Christmas.

72. The lawyer and the client appeared in court.

Identify each statement as true *or* false.

73. For every real number x, $x < 14$ or $x > 6$.

74. For every real number x, $x > 9$ or $x < 9$.

75. There exists an integer n such that $n > 0$ and $n < 0$.

76. For some integer n, $n \geq 3$ and $n \leq 3$.

77. Complete the truth table for *exclusive disjunction*. The symbol $\veebar$ represents "one or the other is true, but not both."

p	q	$p \veebar q$
T	T	
T	F	
F	T	
F	F	

Exclusive disjunction

78. Attorneys sometimes use the phrase "and/or." This phrase corresponds to which usage of the word *or*: inclusive or exclusive disjunction?

Stockbyte/Thinkstock

Decide whether each compound statement is true *or* false. *Remember that* $\veebar$ *is the* exclusive disjunction of **Exercise 77.**

79. $3 + 1 = 4 \veebar 2 + 5 = 7$

80. $3 + 1 = 4 \veebar 2 + 5 = 10$

81. $3 + 1 = 6 \veebar 2 + 5 = 7$

82. $3 + 1 = 12 \veebar 2 + 5 = 10$

83. In his book *The Lady or the Tiger and Other Logic Puzzles,* Raymond Smullyan proposes the following problem. It is taken from the classic Frank Stockton short story, in which a prisoner must make a choice between two doors: behind one is a beautiful lady, and behind the other is a hungry tiger.

What if each door has a sign, and the man knows that only one sign is true?

The sign on Door 1 reads:

IN THIS ROOM THERE IS A LADY AND
IN THE OTHER ROOM THERE IS A TIGER.

The sign on Door 2 reads:

IN ONE OF THESE ROOMS THERE IS A LADY AND IN ONE OF THESE ROOMS THERE IS A TIGER.

With this information, the man is able to choose the correct door. Can you?

84. In Raymond Smullyan's books, he writes about an island in which certain inhabitants are called knights and others are called knaves. Knights always tell the truth, and knaves always lie. Every inhabitant is either a knight or a knave.

Three inhabitants—A, B, and C—were standing together in a garden. A stranger passed by and asked A, "Are you a knight or a knave?" A answered, but rather indistinctly, so the stranger could not make out what he said. The stranger then asked B, "What did A say?" B replied "A said that he is a knave." At this point, the third inhabitant, C, said, "Don't believe B; he is lying!"

The question is, what are B and C?

3 THE CONDITIONAL AND CIRCUITS

Conditionals • Negation of a Conditional • Circuits

Courtesy of John Hornsby

In his April 21, 1989, five-star review of *Field of Dreams*, the *Chicago Sun-Times* movie critic Roger Ebert gave an explanation of why the movie has become an American classic.

> *There is a speech in this movie about baseball that is so simple and true that it is heartbreaking. And the whole attitude toward the players reflects that attitude. Why do they come back from the great beyond and play in this cornfield? Not to make any kind of vast, earthshattering statement, but simply to hit a few and field a few, and remind us of a good and innocent time.*

The photo above was taken in 2007 in Dyersville, Iowa, at the actual scene of the filming. The carving "Ray Loves Annie" in the bleacher seats can be seen in a quick shot during the movie. It has weathered over time.

Conditionals

"If you build it, he will come."
—The Voice in the movie *Field of Dreams*

Ray Kinsella, an Iowa farmer in the movie *Field of Dreams*, hears a voice from the sky. No one else, including his wife Annie, can hear it. Ray interprets it as a promise that if he builds a baseball field in his cornfield, then the ghost of Shoeless Joe Jackson (a baseball star in the early days of the twentieth century) would come to play on it.

This promise came in the form of a conditional statement. A **conditional** statement is a compound statement that uses the connective *if . . . then*.

If I read for too long, *then* I get tired.
If looks could kill, *then* I would be dead.
If he doesn't get back soon, *then* you should go look for him.
} Conditional statements

In each of these conditional statements, the component coming after the word *if* gives a condition (but not necessarily the only condition) under which the statement coming after *then* will be true. For example, "If it is over 90°, then I'll go to the mountains" tells one possible condition under which I will go to the mountains—if the temperature is over 90°.

The conditional is written with an arrow, so "if p, then q" is symbolized as follows.

$$p \rightarrow q \quad \text{If } p\text{, then } q.$$

We read $p \rightarrow q$ as "**p implies q**" or "**if p, then q.**" In the conditional $p \rightarrow q$, the statement p is the **antecedent,** while q is the **consequent.**

The conditional connective may not always be explicitly stated. That is, it may be "hidden" in an everyday expression. For example, consider the following statement.

Big girls don't cry.

It can be written in *if . . . then* form as

If you're a big girl, *then* you don't cry.

As another example, consider this statement.

It is difficult to study when you are distracted.

It can be written

If you are distracted, *then* it is difficult to study.

In the quotation "If you build it, he will come" from the movie *Field of Dreams*, the word "then" is not stated but understood from the context of the statement. "You build it" is the antecedent, and "he will come" is the consequent.

The conditional truth table is a little harder to define than the tables in the previous section. To see how to define the conditional truth table, we analyze a statement made by a politician, Senator Laura Kennedy.

If I am elected, then taxes will go down.

There are four possible combinations of truth values for the two component statements. Let p represent "I am elected," and let q represent "Taxes will go down."

$\sqrt[3]{250}$ $90°$ $(0, -3)$
θ $45.5 \div 2^{-1}$ ∞
$x = (4+8)-3$ $|a|$
$y = -x + 2$ $\frac{1}{4}$
10^2 $\geq$ $f(x) =$

The importance of **symbols** was emphasized by the American philosopher-logician **Charles Sanders Peirce** (1839–1914), who asserted the nature of humans as symbol-using or sign-using organisms. Symbolic notation is half of mathematics, Bertrand Russell once said.

As we analyze the four possibilities, it is helpful to think in terms of the following: "Did Senator Laura Kennedy lie?" If she lied, then the conditional statement is considered false. If she did not lie, then the conditional statement is considered true.

Possibility	Elected?	Taxes Go Down?	
1	Yes	Yes	p is T, q is T.
2	Yes	No	p is T, q is F.
3	No	Yes	p is F, q is T.
4	No	No	p is F, q is F.

The four possibilities are as follows.

1. In the first case assume that the senator was elected and taxes did go down (p is T, q is T). The senator told the truth, so place T in the first row of the truth table. (We do not claim that taxes went down *because* she was elected. It is possible that she had nothing to do with it at all.)
2. In the second case assume that the senator was elected and taxes did not go down (p is T, q is F). Then the senator did not tell the truth (that is, she lied). So we put F in the second row of the truth table.
3. In the third case assume that the senator was defeated, but taxes went down anyway (p is F, q is T). The senator did not lie. She only promised a tax reduction if she were elected. She said nothing about what would happen if she were not elected. In fact, her campaign promise gives no information about what would happen if she lost. Because we cannot say that the senator lied, place T in the third row of the truth table. (See the margin note.)
4. In the last case assume that the senator was defeated and taxes did not go down (p is F, q is F). We cannot blame her, because she only promised to reduce taxes if elected. Thus, T goes in the last row of the truth table.

You Lie! (or Do You?) Granted, the T for Case 3 is less obvious than the F for Case 2. However, the laws of symbolic logic permit only one of two truth values. Since no lie can be established in Case 3, we give the senator the benefit of the doubt. Likewise, *any* conditional statement is declared to be true whenever its antecedent is false.

The completed truth table for the conditional is defined as follows.

Truth Table for the Conditional If p, then q

If p, then q

p	q	$p \rightarrow q$
T	T	T
T	F	F
F	T	T
F	F	T

The use of the conditional connective in no way implies a cause-and-effect relationship. Any two statements may have an arrow placed between them to create a compound statement. Consider this example.

If I pass mathematics, then the sun will rise the next day.

It is true, because the consequent is true. (See the special characteristics following **Example 1** on the next page.) There is, however, no cause-and-effect connection between my passing mathematics and the rising of the sun. The sun will rise no matter what grade I get.

EXAMPLE 1 Finding the Truth Value of a Conditional

Given that p, q, and r are all false, find the truth value of the statement.

$$(p \rightarrow \sim q) \rightarrow (\sim r \rightarrow q)$$

SOLUTION

Using the short-cut method explained in **Example 3** of the previous section, we can replace p, q, and r with F (since each is false) and proceed as before, using the negation and conditional truth tables as necessary.

$$(p \rightarrow \sim q) \quad \rightarrow \quad (\sim r \rightarrow q)$$
$$(\text{F} \rightarrow \sim\text{F}) \quad \rightarrow \quad (\sim\text{F} \rightarrow \text{F})$$
$$(\text{F} \rightarrow \text{T}) \quad \rightarrow \quad (\text{T} \rightarrow \text{F}) \qquad \text{Use the negation truth table.}$$
$$\text{T} \quad \rightarrow \quad \text{F} \qquad \text{Use the conditional truth table.}$$
$$\text{F}$$

The statement $(p \rightarrow \sim q) \rightarrow (\sim r \rightarrow q)$ is false when p, q, and r are all false.

```
PROGRAM:SIGN
:Input A
:If A>0
:Then
:Disp "POSITIVE"
:
:
```

```
PROGRAM:SIGN
:
:Else
:Disp "NOT POSITIVE"
:End
:
```

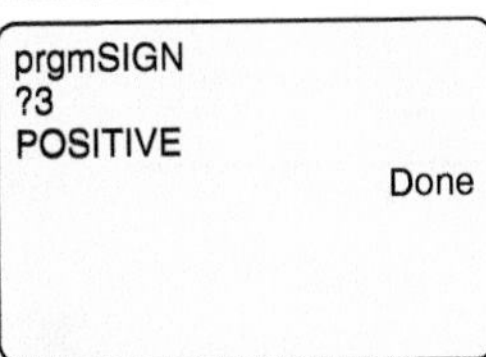

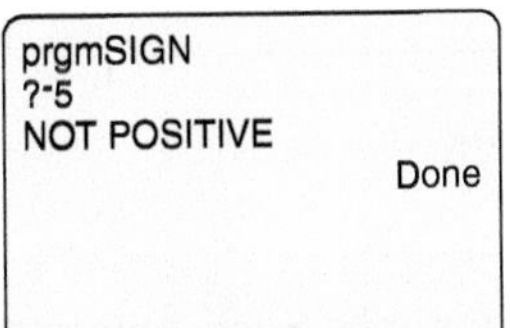

Conditional statements are useful in writing programs. The short program in the first two screens determines whether a number is positive. Notice the lines that begin with *If* and *Then.*

Special Characteristics of Conditional Statements

1. $p \rightarrow q$ is false only when the antecedent is *true* and the consequent is *false.*
2. If the antecedent is *false*, then $p \rightarrow q$ is automatically *true.*
3. If the consequent is *true*, then $p \rightarrow q$ is automatically *true.*

EXAMPLE 2 Determining Whether a Conditional Is True or False

Write *true* or *false* for each statement. Here T represents a true statement, and F represents a false statement.

(a) $\text{T} \rightarrow (7 = 3)$ **(b)** $(8 < 2) \rightarrow \text{F}$ **(c)** $(4 \neq 3 + 1) \rightarrow \text{T}$

SOLUTION

(a) Because the antecedent is true, while the consequent, $7 = 3$, is false, the given statement is false by the first point mentioned above.

(b) The antecedent is false, so the given statement is true by the second observation.

(c) The consequent is true, making the statement true by the third characteristic of conditional statements.

EXAMPLE 3 Constructing Truth Tables

Construct a truth table for each statement.

(a) $(\sim p \rightarrow \sim q) \rightarrow (\sim p \wedge q)$ **(b)** $(p \rightarrow q) \rightarrow (\sim p \vee q)$

SOLUTION

(a) Insert the truth values of $\sim p$ and $\sim q$. Find the truth values of $\sim p \rightarrow \sim q$.

p	q	$\sim p$	$\sim q$	$\sim p \rightarrow \sim q$
T	T	F	F	T
T	F	F	T	T
F	T	T	F	F
F	F	T	T	T

Next use $\sim p$ and q to find the truth values of $\sim p \wedge q$.

p	q	$\sim p$	$\sim q$	$\sim p \rightarrow \sim q$	$\sim p \wedge q$
T	T	F	F	T	F
T	F	F	T	T	F
F	T	T	F	F	T
F	F	T	T	T	F

Now find the truth values of $(\sim p \rightarrow \sim q) \rightarrow (\sim p \wedge q)$.

p	q	$\sim p$	$\sim q$	$\sim p \rightarrow \sim q$	$\sim p \wedge q$	$(\sim p \rightarrow \sim q) \rightarrow (\sim p \wedge q)$
T	T	F	F	T	F	F
T	F	F	T	T	F	F
F	T	T	F	F	T	T
F	F	T	T	T	F	F

(b) For $(p \rightarrow q) \rightarrow (\sim p \vee q)$, go through steps similar to the ones above.

p	q	$p \rightarrow q$	$\sim p$	$\sim p \vee q$	$(p \rightarrow q) \rightarrow (\sim p \vee q)$
T	T	T	F	T	T
T	F	F	F	F	T
F	T	T	T	T	T
F	F	T	T	T	T

In the 1959 Disney short film *Donald in Mathmagicland,* Donald Duck, dressed as Alice from Lewis Carroll's *Through the Looking Glass,* is attacked by a "none-too-friendly group of chess pieces." Logic and **chess** have been paired for centuries. Most scholars agree that chess dates back at least 1500 years, coming from Northern India and Afghanistan following trade routes through Persia.

Good chess players rely on memory, imagination, determination, and inspiration. They are pattern thinkers that use long-established sets of consequences and probabilities.

In the end, logic does not necessarily dictate the final outcome of any chess game, for if it did, humans would not stand a chance when playing faceless, number-crunching computers.

Sources: www.imdb.com, Walter A. Smart.

As the truth table in **Example 3(b)** shows, the statement

$$(p \rightarrow q) \rightarrow (\sim p \vee q)$$

is always true, no matter what the truth values of the components. Such a statement is called a **tautology.** Several other examples of tautologies (as can be checked by forming truth tables) are

$$p \vee \sim p, \quad p \rightarrow p, \quad \text{and} \quad (\sim p \vee \sim q) \rightarrow \sim(p \wedge q). \quad \text{Tautologies}$$

The truth tables in **Example 3** also could have been found by the alternative method shown in **Section 2.**

Negation of a Conditional

Suppose that someone makes the following conditional statement.

"If it rains, then I take my umbrella."

When will the person have lied to you? The only case in which you would have been misled is when it rains *and* the person does *not* take the umbrella. Letting p represent "it rains" and q represent "I take my umbrella," you might suspect that the symbolic statement

$$p \wedge \sim q$$

is a candidate for the negation of $p \rightarrow q$. This would imply that

$$\sim(p \rightarrow q) \equiv p \wedge \sim q.$$

This is indeed the case, as the following truth table indicates.

p	q	$p \rightarrow q$	$\sim(p \rightarrow q)$	$\sim q$	$p \wedge \sim q$
T	T	T	F	F	F
T	F	F	T	T	T
F	T	T	F	F	F
F	F	T	F	T	F

$\equiv$

Negation of $p \rightarrow q$

The negation of $p \rightarrow q$ is $p \wedge \sim q$.

Because

$$\sim(p \rightarrow q) \equiv p \wedge \sim q,$$

by negating each expression we have

$$\sim[\sim(p \rightarrow q)] \equiv \sim(p \wedge \sim q).$$

The left side of the above equivalence is $p \rightarrow q$, and one of De Morgan's laws can be applied to the right side.

$$p \rightarrow q \equiv \sim p \vee \sim(\sim q)$$
$$p \rightarrow q \equiv \sim p \vee q$$

This final row indicates that a conditional may be written as a disjunction.

Writing a Conditional as a Disjunction

$p \rightarrow q$ is equivalent to $\sim p \vee q$.

EXAMPLE 4 Determining Negations

Determine the negation of each statement.

(a) If you build it, he will come. **(b)** All dogs have fleas.

Do not try to negate a conditional with another conditional.

SOLUTION

(a) If b represents "you build it" and q represents "he will come," then the given statement can be symbolized by $b \rightarrow q$. The negation of $b \rightarrow q$, as shown earlier, is $b \wedge \sim q$, so the negation of the statement is

You build it and he will not come.

(b) First, we must restate the given statement in *if . . . then* form.

If it is a dog, then it has fleas.

Based on our earlier discussion, the negation is

It is a dog and it does not have fleas. ∎∎∎

As seen in **Example 4,** the negation of a conditional statement is written as a conjunction.

EXAMPLE 5 Determining Statements Equivalent to Conditionals

Write each conditional as an equivalent statement without using *if . . . then.*

(a) If the Indians win the pennant, then Johnny will go to the World Series.

(b) If it's Borden's, it's got to be good.

SOLUTION

(a) Because the conditional $p \rightarrow q$ is equivalent to $\sim p \vee q$, let p represent "The Indians win the pennant" and q represent "Johnny will go to the World Series." Restate the conditional as

The Indians do not win the pennant or Johnny will go to the World Series.

(b) If p represents "it's Borden's" and if q represents "it's got to be good," the conditional may be restated as

It's not Borden's or it's got to be good. ■■■

Circuits

Figure 1

One of the first nonmathematical applications of symbolic logic was seen in the master's thesis of Claude Shannon in 1937. Shannon showed how logic could be used to design electrical circuits. His work was immediately used by computer designers. Then in the developmental stage, computers could be simplified and built for less money using the ideas of Shannon.

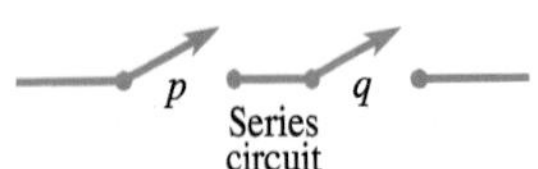

Figure 2

To see how Shannon's ideas work, look at the electrical switch shown in **Figure 1.** We assume that current will flow through this switch when it is closed and not when it is open.

Figure 2 shows two switches connected in *series.* In such a circuit, current will flow only when both switches are closed. Note how closely a series circuit corresponds to the conjunction $p \wedge q$. We know that $p \wedge q$ is true only when both p and q are true.

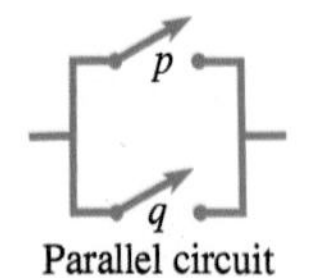

Figure 3

A circuit corresponding to the disjunction $p \vee q$ can be found by drawing a *parallel* circuit, as in **Figure 3.** Here, current flows if either p *or* q is closed or if both p *and* q are closed.

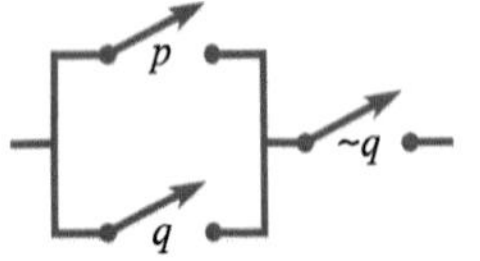

Figure 4

The circuit in **Figure 4** corresponds to the statement $(p \vee q) \wedge \sim q$, which is a compound statement involving both a conjunction and a disjunction.

Simplifying an electrical circuit depends on the idea of equivalent statements from **Section 2.** Recall that two statements are equivalent if they have the same truth table final column. The symbol $\equiv$ is used to indicate that the two statements are equivalent. Some equivalent statements are shown in the following box.

Equivalent Statements Used to Simplify Circuits

$$p \vee (q \wedge r) \equiv (p \vee q) \wedge (p \vee r) \qquad p \vee p \equiv p$$
$$p \wedge (q \vee r) \equiv (p \wedge q) \vee (p \wedge r) \qquad p \wedge p \equiv p$$
$$p \rightarrow q \equiv \sim q \rightarrow \sim p \qquad \sim(p \wedge q) \equiv \sim p \vee \sim q$$
$$p \rightarrow q \equiv \sim p \vee q \qquad \sim(p \vee q) \equiv \sim p \wedge \sim q$$

If T represents any true statement and F represents any false statement, then

$$p \vee \mathbf{T} \equiv \mathbf{T} \qquad p \vee \sim p \equiv \mathbf{T}$$
$$p \wedge \mathbf{F} \equiv \mathbf{F} \qquad p \wedge \sim p \equiv \mathbf{F}.$$

Circuits can be used as models of compound statements, with a closed switch corresponding to T, while an open switch corresponds to F.

EXAMPLE 6 Simplifying a Circuit

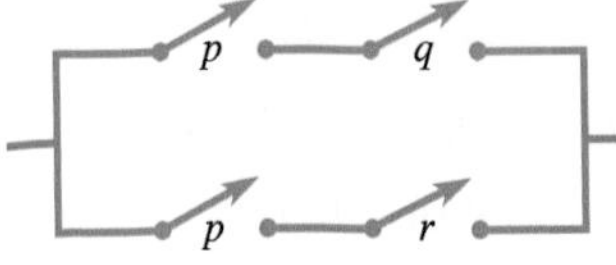

Figure 5

Simplify the circuit of **Figure 5.**

SOLUTION

At the top of **Figure 5,** p and q are connected in series, and at the bottom, p and r are connected in series. These are interpreted as the compound statements $p \wedge q$ and $p \wedge r$, respectively. These two conjunctions are connected in parallel, as indicated by the figure treated as a whole.

Write the disjunction of the two conjunctions.

$$(p \wedge q) \vee (p \wedge r)$$

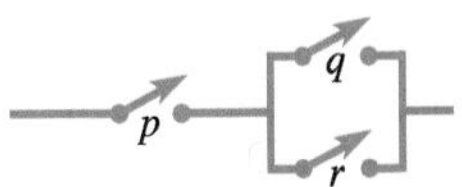

Figure 6

(Think of the two switches labeled "p" as being controlled by the same lever.) By one of the pairs of equivalent statements in the preceding box,

$$(p \wedge q) \vee (p \wedge r) \equiv p \wedge (q \vee r),$$

which has the circuit of **Figure 6.** This circuit is logically equivalent to the one in **Figure 5,** and yet it contains only three switches instead of four—which might well lead to a large savings in manufacturing costs.

EXAMPLE 7 Drawing a Circuit for a Conditional Statement

Draw a circuit for $p \rightarrow (q \wedge \sim r)$.

SOLUTION

From the list of equivalent statements in the box, $p \rightarrow q$ is equivalent to $\sim p \vee q$. This equivalence gives $p \rightarrow (q \wedge \sim r) \equiv \sim p \vee (q \wedge \sim r)$, which has the circuit diagram in **Figure 7.**

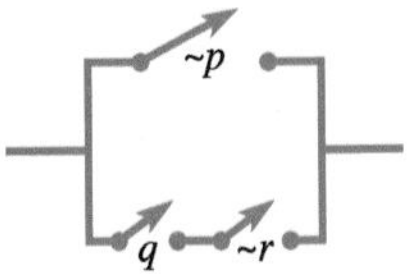

Figure 7

3 EXERCISES

Rewrite each statement using the if . . . then *connective. Rearrange the wording or add words as necessary.*

1. You can believe it if you see it on the Internet.

2. It must be alive if it is breathing.

3. Every integer divisible by 10 is divisible by 5.

4. All perfect square integers have units digit 0, 1, 4, 5, 6, or 9.

5. All Marines love boot camp.

6. Every picture tells a story.

7. No pandas live in Idaho.

iStockphoto/Thinkstock

8. No guinea pigs are scholars.

BananaStock/Thinkstock

9. An opium eater cannot have self-command.

10. Running Bear loves Little White Dove.

Decide whether each statement is true *or* false.

11. If the antecedent of a conditional statement is false, the conditional statement is true.

12. If the consequent of a conditional statement is true, the conditional statement is true.

13. If q is true, then $(p \wedge q) \rightarrow q$ is true.

14. If p is true, then $\sim p \rightarrow (q \vee r)$ is true.

15. The negation of "If pigs fly, I'll believe it" is "If pigs don't fly, I won't believe it."

16. The statements "If it flies, then it's a bird" and "It does not fly or it's a bird" are logically equivalent.

17. Given that $\sim p$ is true and q is false, the conditional $p \rightarrow q$ is true.

18. Given that $\sim p$ is false and q is false, the conditional $p \rightarrow q$ is true.

19. Explain why the statement "If $3 = 5$, then $4 = 6$" is true.

20. In a few sentences, explain how to determine the truth value of a conditional statement.

Tell whether each conditional is true (T) *or* false (F).

21. $\text{T} \rightarrow (7 < 3)$

22. $\text{F} \rightarrow (4 \neq 8)$

23. $\text{F} \rightarrow (5 \neq 5)$

24. $(8 \geq 8) \rightarrow \text{F}$

25. $(5^2 \neq 25) \rightarrow (8 - 8 = 16)$

26. $(5 = 12 - 7) \rightarrow (9 > 0)$

Let s represent "She has a bird for a pet," *let p represent* "he trains dogs," *and let m represent* "they raise alpacas." *Express each compound statement in words.*

27. $\sim m \rightarrow p$

28. $p \rightarrow \sim m$

29. $s \rightarrow (m \wedge p)$

30. $(s \wedge p) \rightarrow m$

31. $\sim p \rightarrow (\sim m \vee s)$

32. $(\sim s \vee \sim m) \rightarrow \sim p$

Let b represent "I ride my bike," *let s represent* "it snows," *and let p represent* "the play is cancelled." *Write each compound statement in symbols.*

33. If I ride my bike, then the play is cancelled.

34. If it snows, then I ride my bike.

35. If the play is cancelled, then it does not snow.

36. If I do not ride my bike, then it does not snow.

37. The play is cancelled, and if it snows then I do not ride my bike.

38. I ride my bike, or if the play is cancelled then it snows.

39. It snows if the play is cancelled.

40. I'll ride my bike if it doesn't snow.

Find the truth value of each statement. Assume that p and r are false, and q is true.

41. $\sim r \rightarrow q$

42. $\sim p \rightarrow \sim r$

43. $q \rightarrow p$

44. $\sim r \rightarrow p$

45. $p \rightarrow q$

46. $\sim q \rightarrow r$

47. $\sim p \rightarrow (q \wedge r)$

48. $(\sim r \vee p) \rightarrow p$

49. $\sim q \rightarrow (p \wedge r)$

50. $(\sim p \wedge \sim q) \rightarrow (p \wedge \sim r)$

51. $(p \rightarrow \sim q) \rightarrow (\sim p \wedge \sim r)$

52. $(p \rightarrow \sim q) \wedge (p \rightarrow r)$

53. Explain why, if we know that p is true, we also know that

$$[r \vee (p \vee s)] \rightarrow (p \vee q)$$

is true, even if we are not given the truth values of q, r, and s.

54. Construct a true statement involving a conditional, a conjunction, a disjunction, and a negation (not necessarily in that order), that consists of component statements p, q, and r, with all of these component statements false.

Construct a truth table for each statement. Identify any tautologies.

55. $\sim q \rightarrow p$

56. $p \rightarrow \sim q$

57. $(\sim p \rightarrow q) \rightarrow p$

58. $(\sim q \rightarrow \sim p) \rightarrow \sim q$

59. $(p \vee q) \rightarrow (q \vee p)$

60. $(p \wedge q) \rightarrow (p \vee q)$

61. $(\sim p \rightarrow \sim q) \rightarrow (p \wedge q)$

62. $r \rightarrow (p \wedge \sim q)$

63. $[(r \vee p) \wedge \sim q] \rightarrow p$

64. $[(r \wedge p) \wedge (p \wedge q)] \rightarrow p$

65. $(\sim r \rightarrow s) \vee (p \rightarrow \sim q)$

66. $(\sim p \wedge \sim q) \rightarrow (s \rightarrow r)$

67. What is the minimum number of Fs that must appear in the final column of a truth table for us to be assured that the statement is not a tautology?

68. If all truth values in the final column of a truth table are F, how can we easily transform the statement into a tautology?

Write the negation of each statement. Remember that the negation of $p \rightarrow q$ *is* $p \wedge \sim q$.

69. If that is an authentic Rolex watch, I'll be surprised.

Strelnikova Tetiana/Shutterstock

70. If Minnie Ripperton reaches that note, she will shatter glass.

Michael Ochs Archives/Getty Images

71. If the English measures are not converted to metric measures, then the spacecraft will crash on the surface of Saturn.

72. If you say "I do," then you'll be happy for the rest of your life.

73. "If you want to be happy for the rest of your life, never make a pretty woman your wife." *Jimmy Soul*

74. "If loving you is wrong, I don't want to be right." *Luther Ingram*

Write each statement as an equivalent statement that does not use the if . . . then *connective. Remember that*

$$p \rightarrow q \quad \text{is equivalent to} \quad \sim p \vee q.$$

75. If you give your plants tender, loving care, they flourish.

76. If the check is in the mail, I will buy you lunch.

77. If she doesn't, he will.

78. If I say "black," she says "white."

79. All residents of Pensacola are residents of Florida.

80. All women were once girls.

Use truth tables to decide which of the pairs of statements are equivalent.

81. $p \rightarrow q$; $\sim p \vee q$

82. $\sim(p \rightarrow q)$; $p \wedge \sim q$

83. $p \rightarrow q$; $\sim q \rightarrow \sim p$

84. $q \rightarrow p$; $\sim p \rightarrow \sim q$

85. $p \wedge \sim q$; $\sim q \rightarrow \sim p$

86. $p \rightarrow q$; $q \rightarrow p$

87. $p \rightarrow \sim q$; $\sim p \vee \sim q$

88. $\sim p \wedge q$; $\sim p \rightarrow q$

89. $q \rightarrow \sim p$; $p \rightarrow \sim q$

90. $\sim p \rightarrow q$; $p \vee q$

Write a logical statement representing each of the following circuits. Simplify each circuit when possible.

91.

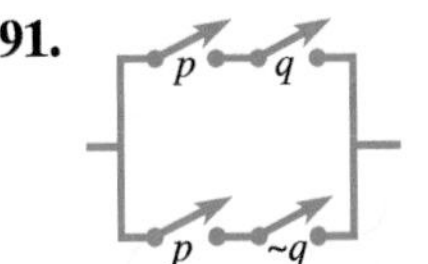

92.

93.

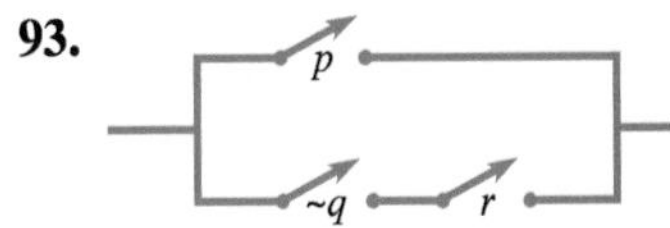

94.

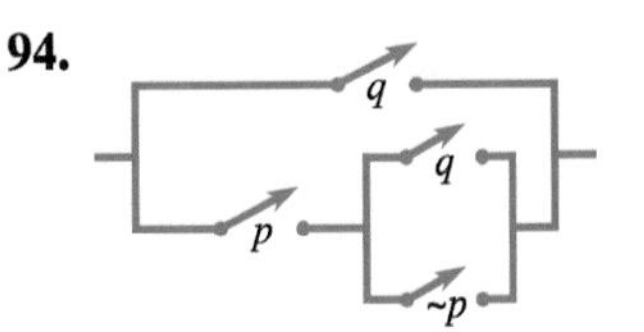

95.

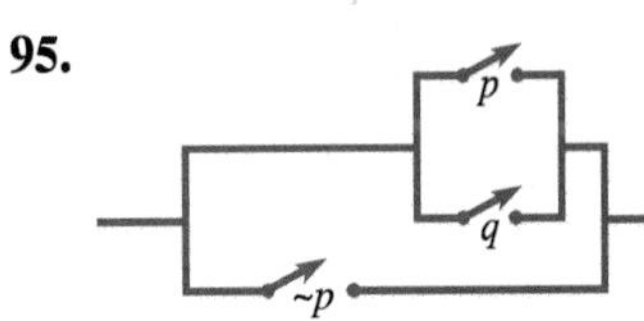

96.

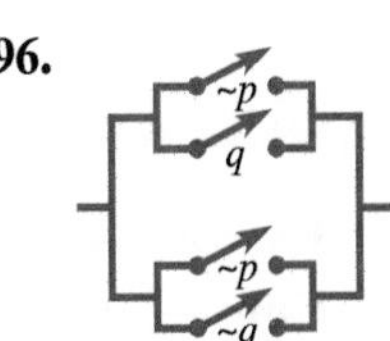

Draw circuits representing the following statements as they are given. Simplify if possible.

97. $p \wedge (q \vee \sim p)$

98. $(\sim p \wedge \sim q) \wedge \sim r$

99. $(p \vee q) \wedge (\sim p \wedge \sim q)$

100. $(\sim q \wedge \sim p) \vee (\sim p \vee q)$

101. $[(p \vee q) \wedge r] \wedge \sim p$

102. $[(\sim p \wedge \sim r) \vee \sim q] \wedge (\sim p \wedge r)$

103. $\sim q \rightarrow (\sim p \rightarrow q)$

104. $\sim p \rightarrow (\sim p \vee \sim q)$

105. Refer to **Figures 5 and 6** in **Example 6.** Suppose the cost of the use of one switch for an hour is \$0.06. By using the circuit in **Figure 6** rather than the circuit in **Figure 5,** what is the savings for a year of 365 days, assuming that the circuit is in continuous use?

106. Explain why the circuit shown will always have exactly one open switch. What does this circuit simplify to?

4 THE CONDITIONAL AND RELATED STATEMENTS

Converse, Inverse, and Contrapositive • Alternative Forms of "If p, then q" • Biconditionals • Summary of Truth Tables

Interfoto/Alamy

Alfred North Whitehead (1861–1947) and Bertrand Russell worked together on *Principia Mathematica*. During that time, Whitehead was teaching mathematics at Cambridge University and had written *Universal Algebra*. In 1910 he went to the University of London, exploring not only the philosophical basis of science but also the "aims of education" (as he called one of his books). It was as a philosopher that he was invited to Harvard University in 1924. Whitehead died at the age of 86 in Cambridge, Massachusetts.

Converse, Inverse, and Contrapositive

Many mathematical properties and theorems are stated in *if . . . then* form. Any conditional statement $p \to q$ is made up of an antecedent p and a consequent q. If they are interchanged, negated, or both, a new conditional statement is formed. Suppose that we begin with a conditional statement.

If you stay, then I go. Conditional Statement

By interchanging the antecedent ("you stay") and the consequent ("I go"), we obtain a new conditional statement.

If I go, then you stay. Converse

This new conditional is called the **converse** of the given conditional statement.

By negating both the antecedent and the consequent, we obtain the **inverse** of the given conditional statement.

If you do not stay, then I do not go. Inverse

If the antecedent and the consequent are both interchanged *and* negated, the **contrapositive** of the given conditional statement is formed.

If I do not go, then you do not stay. Contrapositive

These three related statements for the conditional $p \to q$ are summarized below. (***The inverse is the contrapositive of the converse.***)

Related Conditional Statements

Conditional Statement	$p \to q$	(If p, then q.)
Converse	$q \to p$	(If q, then p.)
Inverse	$\sim p \to \sim q$	(If not p, then not q.)
Contrapositive	$\sim q \to \sim p$	(If not q, then not p.)

EXAMPLE 1 Determining Related Conditional Statements

Determine each of the following, given the conditional statement

If I live in Orlando, then I live in Florida.

(a) the converse **(b)** the inverse **(c)** the contrapositive

SOLUTION

(a) Let p represent "I live in Orlando" and q represent "I live in Florida." Then the given statement may be written $p \to q$. The converse, $q \to p$, is

If I live in Florida, then I live in Orlando.

Notice that for this statement, the converse is not necessarily true, even though the given statement is true.

(b) The inverse of $p \to q$ is $\sim p \to \sim q$. Thus, the inverse is

If I don't live in Orlando, then I don't live in Florida.

Again, this is not necessarily true.

Pictorial Press Ltd./Alamy

Bertrand Russell (1872–1970) was a student of Whitehead's before they wrote the *Principia*. Like his teacher, Russell turned toward philosophy. His works include a critique of Leibniz, analyses of mind and of matter, and a history of Western thought.

Russell became a public figure because of his involvement in social issues. Deeply aware of human loneliness, he was "passionately desirous of finding ways of diminishing this tragic isolation." During World War I he was an antiwar crusader, and he was imprisoned briefly. Again in the 1960s he championed peace. He wrote many books on social issues, winning the Nobel Prize for Literature in 1950.

(c) The contrapositive, $\sim q \rightarrow \sim p$, is

If I don't live in Florida, then I don't live in Orlando.

The contrapositive, like the given conditional statement, is true. ∎∎∎

Example 1 shows that the converse and inverse of a true statement need not be true. They *can* be true, but they need not be. The relationships between the related conditionals are shown in the truth table that follows.

Equivalent (Conditional and Contrapositive)
Equivalent (Converse and Inverse)

		Conditional	Converse	Inverse	Contrapositive
p	q	$p \rightarrow q$	$q \rightarrow p$	$\sim p \rightarrow \sim q$	$\sim q \rightarrow \sim p$
T	T	T	T	T	T
T	F	F	T	T	F
F	T	T	F	F	T
F	F	T	T	T	T

As this truth table shows,

1. ***A conditional statement and its contrapositive always have the same truth values,*** making it possible to replace any statement with its contrapositive without affecting the logical meaning.
2. ***The converse and inverse always have the same truth values.***

Equivalences

A conditional statement and its contrapositive are equivalent. Also, the converse and the inverse are equivalent.

EXAMPLE 2 Determining Related Conditional Statements

For the conditional statement $\sim p \rightarrow q$, write each of the following.

(a) the converse **(b)** the inverse **(c)** the contrapositive

SOLUTION

(a) The converse of $\sim p \rightarrow q$ is $q \rightarrow \sim p$.

(b) The inverse is $\sim(\sim p) \rightarrow \sim q$, which simplifies to $p \rightarrow \sim q$.

(c) The contrapositive is $\sim q \rightarrow \sim(\sim p)$, which simplifies to $\sim q \rightarrow p$. ∎∎∎

Alternative Forms of "If *p*, then *q*"

The conditional statement "if *p*, then *q*" can be stated in several other ways in English. Consider this statement.

If you go to the outlet mall, then you will find a place to park.

It can also be written as follows.

Going to the outlet mall is *sufficient* for finding a place to park.

According to this statement, going to the outlet mall is enough to guarantee finding a place to park. Going to other places, such as schools or office buildings, *might* also guarantee a place to park, but at least we *know* that going to the outlet mall does. Thus, $p \rightarrow q$ can be written "*p* is sufficient for *q*." Knowing that *p* has occurred is sufficient to guarantee that *q* will also occur.

On the other hand, consider this statement, which has a different meaning.

Having the set on is necessary for watching television. (*)

Here, we are saying that one condition that is necessary for watching television is that the set be turned on. This may not be enough. The set might be broken, for example. The statement labeled (*) could be written as

If you watch television, then the set was turned on.

As this example suggests, $p \rightarrow q$ is the same as "q is necessary for p." In other words, if q doesn't happen, then neither will p. Notice how this idea is closely related to the idea of equivalence between a conditional statement and its contrapositive.

Common Translations of $p \rightarrow q$

The conditional $p \rightarrow q$ can be translated in any of the following ways, none of which depends on the truth or falsity of $p \rightarrow q$.

If *p*, then *q*.	***p* is sufficient for *q*.**
If *p*, *q*.	***q* is necessary for *p*.**
***p* implies *q*.**	**All *p* are *q*.**
***p* only if *q*.**	***q* if *p*.**

Example: If you live in Dubuque, then you live in Iowa. Statement

You live in Iowa if you live in Dubuque.
You live in Dubuque only if you live in Iowa.
Living in Iowa is necessary for living in Dubuque.
Living in Dubuque is sufficient for living in Iowa.
All residents of Dubuque are residents of Iowa.
Being a resident of Dubuque implies residency in Iowa.

} Common translations

EXAMPLE 3 Rewording Conditional Statements

Write each statement in the form "if p, then q."

(a) You'll be sorry if I go. **(b)** Today is Tuesday only if yesterday was Monday.

(c) All nurses wear white shoes.

SOLUTION

(a) If I go, then you'll be sorry.

(b) If today is Tuesday, then yesterday was Monday.

(c) If you are a nurse, then you wear white shoes. ■■■

EXAMPLE 4 Translating from Words to Symbols

Let p represent "A triangle is equilateral," and let q represent "A triangle has three sides of equal length." Write each of the following in symbols.

(a) A triangle is equilateral if it has three sides of equal length.

(b) A triangle is equilateral only if it has three sides of equal length.

SOLUTION

(a) $q \rightarrow p$ **(b)** $p \rightarrow q$ ■■■

Library of Congress Prints and Photographs Division (LC-USZ62-10191)

Principia Mathematica, the title chosen by Whitehead and Russell, was a deliberate reference to *Philosophiae naturalis principia mathematica,* or "mathematical principles of the philosophy of nature," Isaac Newton's epochal work of 1687. Newton's *Principia* pictured a kind of "clockwork universe" that ran via his Law of Gravitation. Newton independently invented the calculus, unaware that Leibniz had published his own formulation of it earlier.

Biconditionals

The compound statement ***p* *if and only if* *q*** (often abbreviated ***p* *iff* *q***) is called a **biconditional.** It is symbolized $\boldsymbol{p \leftrightarrow q}$, and is interpreted as the conjunction of the two conditionals $p \rightarrow q$ and $q \rightarrow p$. Using symbols, this conjunction is written $(q \rightarrow p) \wedge (p \rightarrow q)$ so that, by definition,

$$\boldsymbol{p \leftrightarrow q \equiv (q \rightarrow p) \wedge (p \rightarrow q).}$$ Biconditional

The truth table for the biconditional $p \leftrightarrow q$ can be determined using this definition.

Truth Table for the Biconditional *p* if and only if *q*

p* if and only if *q

p	q	$p \leftrightarrow q$
T	T	T
T	F	F
F	T	F
F	F	T

A biconditional is true when both component statements have the same truth value. It is false when they have different truth values.

EXAMPLE 5 Determining Whether Biconditionals Are True or False

Determine whether each biconditional statement is *true* or *false*.

(a) $6 + 8 = 14$ if and only if $11 + 5 = 16$

(b) $6 = 5$ if and only if $12 \neq 12$

(c) $5 + 2 = 10$ if and only if $17 + 19 = 36$

SOLUTION

(a) Both $6 + 8 = 14$ and $11 + 5 = 16$ are true. By the truth table for the biconditional, this biconditional is true.

(b) Both component statements are false, so by the last line of the truth table for the biconditional, this biconditional statement is true.

(c) Because the first component $(5 + 2 = 10)$ is false, and the second is true, this biconditional statement is false. ∎

Summary of Truth Tables

Truth tables have been derived for several important types of compound statements.

Summary of Basic Truth Tables

1. $\sim p$, the **negation** of p, has truth value opposite that of p.
2. $p \wedge q$, the **conjunction,** is true only when both p and q are true.
3. $p \vee q$, the **disjunction,** is false only when both p and q are false.
4. $p \rightarrow q$, the **conditional,** is false only when p is true and q is false.
5. $p \leftrightarrow q$, the **biconditional,** is true only when both p and q have the same truth value.

4 EXERCISES

For each given conditional statement (or statement that can be written as a conditional), write **(a)** *the converse,* **(b)** *the inverse, and* **(c)** *the contrapositive in* if . . . then *form. In some of the exercises, it may be helpful to first restate the given statement in* if . . . then *form.*

1. If beauty were a minute, then you would be an hour.

2. If you lead, then I will follow.

3. If it ain't broke, don't fix it.

4. If I had a nickel for each time that happened, I would be rich.

5. Walking in front of a moving car is dangerous to your health.

6. Milk contains calcium.

7. Birds of a feather flock together.

8. A rolling stone gathers no moss.

9. If you build it, he will come.

10. Where there's smoke, there's fire.

11. $p \rightarrow \sim q$

12. $\sim p \rightarrow q$

13. $\sim p \rightarrow \sim q$

14. $\sim q \rightarrow \sim p$

15. $p \rightarrow (q \vee r)$ (*Hint:* Use one of De Morgan's laws as necessary.)

16. $(r \vee \sim q) \rightarrow p$ (*Hint:* Use one of De Morgan's laws as necessary.)

17. Discuss the equivalences that exist among a given conditional statement, its converse, its inverse, and its contrapositive.

18. State the contrapositive of "If the square of a natural number is even, then the natural number is even." The two statements must have the same truth value. Use several examples and inductive reasoning to decide whether both are true or both are false.

*Write each statement in the form "*if *p*, then *q*."

19. If it is muddy, I'll wear my galoshes.

20. If I finish studying, I'll go to the party.

21. "19 is positive" implies that 19 + 1 is positive.

22. "Today is Wednesday" implies that yesterday was Tuesday.

23. All integers are rational numbers.

24. All whole numbers are integers.

25. Doing logic puzzles is sufficient for driving me crazy.

26. Being in Kalamazoo is sufficient for being in Michigan.

27. A day's growth of beard is necessary for Jeff Marsalis to shave.

28. Being an environmentalist is necessary for being elected.

29. I can go from Boardwalk to Baltic Avenue only if I pass GO.

30. The principal will hire more teachers only if the school board approves.

31. No whole numbers are not integers.

32. No integers are irrational numbers.

33. The Nationals will win the pennant when their pitching improves.

34. Sarah will be a liberal when pigs fly.

35. A rectangle is a parallelogram with a right angle.

36. A parallelogram is a four-sided figure with opposite sides parallel.

37. A triangle with two perpendicular sides is a right triangle.

38. A square is a rectangle with two adjacent sides equal.

39. The square of a two-digit number whose units digit is 5 will end in 25.

40. An integer whose units digit is 0 or 5 is divisible by 5.

41. One of the following statements is not equivalent to all the others. Which one is it?

A. *r* only if *s*. **B.** *r* implies *s*.

C. If *r*, then *s*. **D.** *r* is necessary for *s*.

42. Many students have difficulty interpreting *necessary* and *sufficient*. Use the statement "Being in Vancouver is sufficient for being in North America" to explain why "*p* is sufficient for *q*" translates as "if *p*, then *q*."

43. Use the statement "To be an integer, it is necessary that a number be rational" to explain why "*p* is necessary for *q*" translates as "if *q*, then *p*."

44. Explain why the statement "A week has eight days if and only if October has forty days" is true.

Identify each statement as true *or* false.

45. $6 = 9 - 3$ if and only if $8 + 2 = 10$.

46. $3 + 1 \neq 7$ if and only if $8 \neq 8$.

47. $8 + 7 \neq 15$ if and only if $3 \times 5 \neq 8$.

48. $6 \times 2 = 18$ if and only if $9 + 7 \neq 16$.

49. George H. W. Bush was president if and only if George W. Bush was not president.

50. Burger King sells Big Macs if and only if Apple manufactures Ipods.

Two statements that can both be true about the same object are **consistent.** *For example,* "It is green" *and* "It weighs 60 pounds" *are consistent statements. Statements that cannot both be true about the same object are called* **contrary.** "It is a Nissan" *and* "It is a Mazda" *are contrary. In Exercises 51–56, label each pair of statements as either* contrary *or* consistent.

51. Michael Jackson is alive. Michael Jackson is dead.

52. Barack Obama is a Democrat. Barack Obama is a Republican.

53. That animal has four legs. That same animal is a cat.

54. That book is nonfiction. That book costs more than \$150.

55. This number is a whole number. This same number is irrational.

56. This number is positive. This same number is a natural number.

57. This number is an integer. This same number is a rational number.

58. This number is a whole number. This same number is a negative number.

59. Make up two statements that are consistent.

60. Make up two statements that are contrary.

5 ANALYZING ARGUMENTS WITH EULER DIAGRAMS

Logical Arguments • Arguments with Universal Quantifiers • Arguments with Existential Quantifiers

Library of Congress Prints and Photographs Division (LC-USZ62-48329)

Leonhard Euler (1707–1783) won the Academy prize and edged out du Châtelet and Voltaire. That was a minor achievement, as was the invention of "Euler circles" (which antedated Venn diagrams). Euler was the most prolific mathematician of his generation despite blindness that forced him to dictate from memory.

Logical Arguments

With inductive reasoning we observe patterns to solve problems. Now we study how deductive reasoning may be used to determine whether logical arguments are valid or invalid.

A logical argument is made up of **premises** (assumptions, laws, rules, widely held ideas, or observations) and a **conclusion.** Recall that *deductive* reasoning involves drawing specific conclusions from given general premises. When reasoning from the premises of an argument to obtain a conclusion, we want the argument to be valid.

Valid and Invalid Arguments

An argument is **valid** if the fact that all the premises are true forces the conclusion to be true. An argument that is not valid is **invalid.** It is called a **fallacy.**

"Valid" and "true" do not have the same meaning—an argument can be valid even though the conclusion is false. **(See Example 4.)**

Arguments with Universal Quantifiers

Several techniques can be used to check whether an argument is valid. One such technique is based on **Euler diagrams.**

Leonhard Euler (pronounced "Oiler") was one of the greatest mathematicians who ever lived. He is immortalized in mathematics history with the important irrational number e, named in his honor. This number appears throughout mathematics.

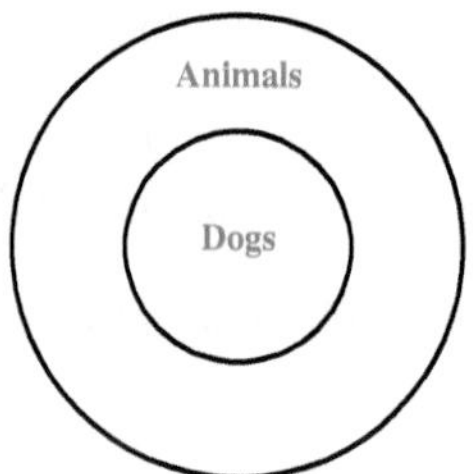

Figure 8

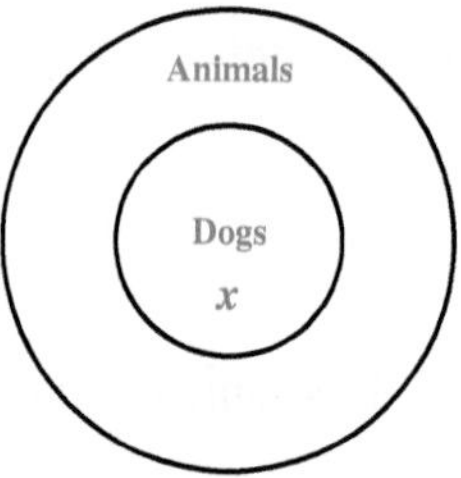

x represents Dotty.

Figure 9

EXAMPLE 1 Using an Euler Diagram to Determine Validity

Is the following argument valid?

All dogs are animals.
Dotty is a dog.
―――――――――――
Dotty is an animal.

SOLUTION

To begin, draw regions to represent the first premise. Because all dogs are animals, the region for "dogs" goes inside the region for "animals," as in **Figure 8.**

The second premise, "Dotty is a dog," suggests that "Dotty" would go inside the region representing "dogs." Let x represent "Dotty." **Figure 9** shows that "Dotty" is also inside the region for "animals." If both premises are true, the conclusion that Dotty is an animal must be true also. The argument is valid. ■■■

EXAMPLE 2 Using an Euler Diagram to Determine Validity

Is the following argument valid?

All rainy days are cloudy.
Today is not cloudy.
―――――――――――
Today is not rainy.

SOLUTION

In **Figure 10,** the region for "rainy days" is drawn entirely inside the region for "cloudy days." Since "Today is *not* cloudy," place an x for "today" *outside* the region for "cloudy days." See **Figure 11.** Placing the x outside the region for "cloudy days" forces it also to be outside the region for "rainy days." Thus, if the two premises are true, then it is also true that today is not rainy. The argument is valid.

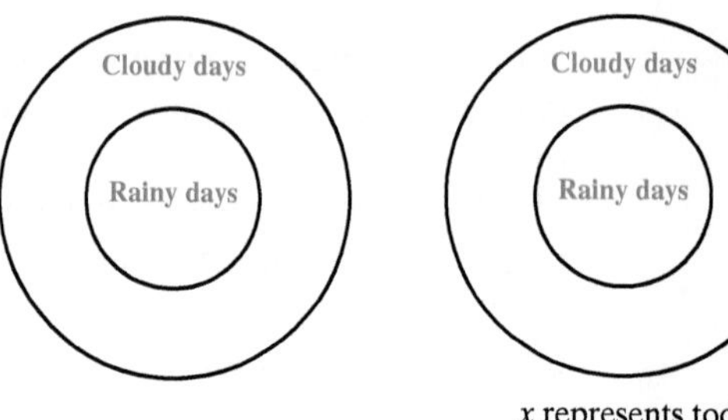

x represents today.

Figure 10 Figure 11

■■■

EXAMPLE 3 Using an Euler Diagram to Determine Validity

Is the following argument valid?

All magnolia trees have green leaves.
That plant has green leaves.
―――――――――――
That plant is a magnolia tree.

SOLUTION

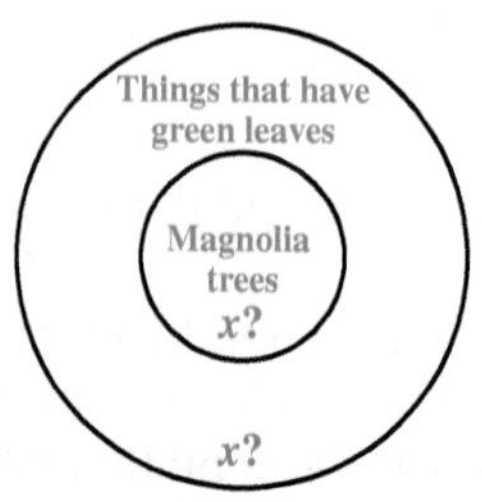

Figure 12

The region for "magnolia trees" goes entirely inside the region for "things that have green leaves." See **Figure 12.** The x that represents "that plant" must go inside the region for "things that have green leaves," but can go either inside or outside the region for "magnolia trees." Even if the premises are true, we are not forced to accept the conclusion as true. This argument is invalid. It is a fallacy. ■■■

EXAMPLE 4 Using an Euler Diagram to Determine Validity

Is the following argument valid?

All expensive things are desirable.
All desirable things make you feel good.
All things that make you feel good make you live longer.
———
All expensive things make you live longer.

SOLUTION

A diagram for the argument is given in **Figure 13.**

If each premise is true, then the conclusion must be true because the region for "expensive things" lies completely within the region for "things that make you live longer." Thus, the argument is valid. (This argument is an example of the fact that a *valid* argument need *not* have a true conclusion.)

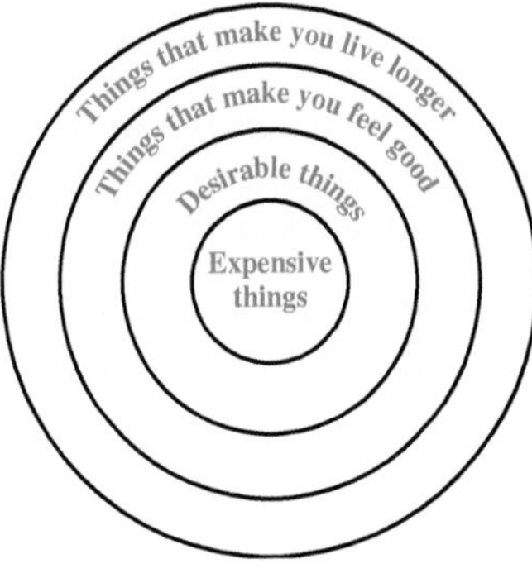

Figure 13

People who go to the beach for Spring Break
Students

Figure 14

Arguments with Existential Quantifiers

EXAMPLE 5 Using an Euler Diagram to Determine Validity

Is the following argument valid?

Some students go to the beach for Spring Break.
I am a student.
———
I go to the beach for Spring Break.

SOLUTION

The first premise is sketched in **Figure 14,** where some (but not necessarily *all*) students go to the beach. There are two possibilities for *I*, as shown in **Figure 15.** One possibility is that *I* go to the beach. The other is that *I* don't. Since the truth of the premises does not force the conclusion to be true, the argument is invalid.

Figure 15

For Further Thought

Discussions in everyday conversation, politics, and advertising provide a nearly endless stream of examples of **fallacies**—arguments exhibiting illogical reasoning. There are many general forms of fallacies, and we now present descriptions and examples of some of the more common ones. (Much of this list is adapted from the excellent web page Mission: Critical, A Project of the Institute of Teaching and Learning, San Jose State University, www.sjsu.edu/depts/itl/graphics.)

1. **Circular Reasoning** (also called *Begging the Question*) In circular reasoning, the person making the argument assumes to be true what he is trying to prove.

   Husband: What makes you say that this dress makes you look fat?

   Wife: Because it does.

   Here the wife makes her case by stating what she wants to prove.

2. **False Dilemma** (also called the *Either-Or Fallacy,* or *the Black and White Fallacy*) Presenting two options with the assumption that they are contradictions (that is, the truth of one implies the falsity of the other) when in fact they are not, is the basis of a common fallacy.

   Politician: America: Love it or leave it.

   This argument implies only two choices. It is possible that someone may love America and yet leave, while someone else may not love America and yet stay.

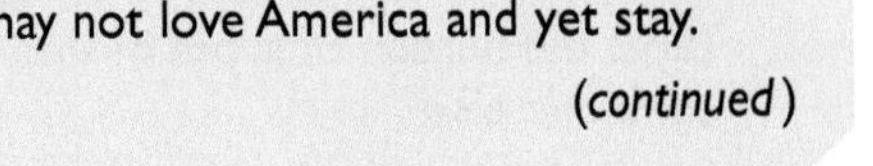
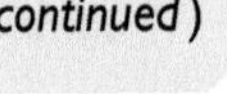

(*continued*)

For Further Thought (*cont.*)

3. **Loaded Question and Complex Claims** This fallacy involves one person asking a question or making a statement that is constructed in such a way as to obtain an answer in which the responder agrees to something with which he does not actually agree.

   Teenager Beth to her father: I hope you enjoyed embarrassing me in front of my friends.

   If Beth gets the expected response "No, I didn't enjoy it," the answer allows Beth to interpret that while her father didn't enjoy it, he did indeed embarrass her.

4. ***Post Hoc* Reasoning** An argument that is based on the false belief that if event A preceded event B, then A must have caused B is called *post hoc* reasoning.

   Johnny: I wore my Hawaiian shirt while watching all three playoff games, and my team won all three games. So I am going to wear that shirt every time I watch them.

   The fact that Johnny put the same shirt on before each game has nothing to do with the outcomes of the games.

5. **Red Herring** (also called *Smoke Screen,* or *Wild Goose Chase)* This fallacy involves introducing an irrelevant topic to divert attention away from the original topic, allowing the person making the argument to seemingly prevail.

   (From the movie *Field of Dreams,* in a scene where Annie and Beulah are arguing at a town meeting about the banning of books)

   Beulah: I say smut and filth like this has no place in our schools. . . . The so-called novels of Terence Mann endorse promiscuity, godlessness, the mongrelization of the races, and disrespect to high-ranking officers of the United States army. And that is why school boards across the country have been banning his books since 1969.
   Annie: Excuse me, madam. Terence Mann was a warm and gentle voice of reason in a time of great madness. He coined the phrase "Make love, not war." . . . He was talking about peace, and love, and understanding . . .
   Beulah: Oh yeah, well your husband plowed under his corn and built a baseball field . . . the weirdo. . . .
   Annie: Now there's an intelligent response.

   While most of the people in the audience agreed that Annie's husband Ray was doing strange things, those things had nothing to do with banning books.

6. **Shifting the Burden of Proof** A person making a claim usually is required to support that claim. In this fallacy, if the claim is difficult to support, that person turns the burden of proof of that claim over to someone else.

   Employee: You accuse me of embezzling money? That's ridiculous.
   Employer: Well, until you can prove otherwise, you will just have to accept it as true.

   If money has been disappearing, it is up to the employer to prove that this employee is guilty. The burden of proof is on the employer, but he is insinuating that the employee must prove that he is not the one taking the money.

7. **Straw Man** This fallacy involves creating a false image (like a scarecrow, or straw man) of someone else's position in an argument.

Steve Liss/Time & Life Images/Getty Images

   Dan Quayle: I have as much experience in the Congress as Jack Kennedy did when he sought the presidency.
   Lloyd Bentsen: Senator, I served with Jack Kennedy. I knew Jack Kennedy. Jack Kennedy was a friend of mine. And Senator, you're no Jack Kennedy.
   Dan Quayle: That was really uncalled for, Senator.
   Lloyd Bentsen: You're the one that was making the comparison, Senator.

   While this was the defining moment of the 1988 vice-presidential debate, Bentsen expertly used the straw man fallacy. Quayle did not compare himself or his accomplishments to those of Kennedy, but merely stated that he had spent as much time in Congress as Kennedy had when the latter ran for president.

For Group or Individual Investigation

Use the Internet to investigate the following additional logical fallacies.

Appeal to Authority	Appeal to Common Belief	Common Practice
Two Wrongs	Indirect Consequences	Wishful Thinking
Appeal to Fear	Appeal to Loyalty	Appeal to Pity
Appeal to Prejudice	Appeal to Spite	Appeal to Vanity
Guilt by Association	Slippery Slope	Hasty Generalization

5 EXERCISES

Decide whether each argument is valid *or* invalid.

1. All amusement parks have thrill rides.
Universal Orlando is an amusement park.
―――
Universal Orlando has thrill rides.

2. All disc jockeys play music.
Phlash Phelps is a disc jockey.
―――
Phlash Phelps plays music.

3. All politicians lie, cheat, and steal.
That man lies, cheats, and steals.
―――
That man is a politician.

4. All Southerners speak with an accent.
Bill Leonard speaks with an accent.
―――
Bill Leonard is a Southerner.

5. All dogs love to bury bones.
Puddles does not love to bury bones.
―――
Puddles is not a dog.

6. All vice-presidents use cell phones.
Bob DeBiasio does not use a cell phone.
―――
Bob DeBiasio is not a vice-president.

7. All residents of Minnesota know how to live in freezing temperatures.
Jessica Rockswold knows how to live in freezing temperatures.
―――
Jessica Rockswold lives in Minnesota.

8. All people who apply for a loan must pay for a title search.
Kurt Massey paid for a title search.
―――
Kurt Massey applied for a loan.

9. Some dinosaurs were plant eaters.
Danny was a plant eater.
―――
Danny was a dinosaur.

10. Some philosophers are absent minded.
Nicole Mallon is a philosopher.
―――
Nicole Mallon is absent minded.

11. Some nurses wear blue uniforms.
Dee Boyle is a nurse.
―――
Dee Boyle wears a blue uniform.

12. Some trucks have sound systems.
Some trucks have gun racks.
―――
Some trucks with sound systems have gun racks.

13. Refer to **Example 3.** If the second premise and the conclusion were interchanged, would the argument then be valid?

14. Refer to **Example 4.** Give a different conclusion than the one given there so that the argument is still valid.

Construct a valid argument based on the Euler diagram shown.

15. **16.**

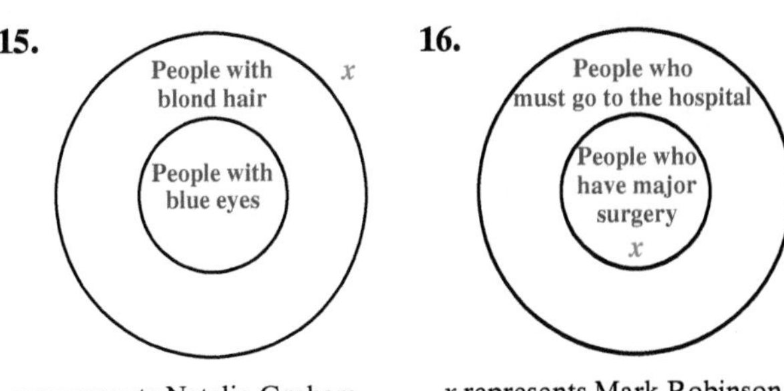

x represents Natalie Graham *x* represents Mark Robinson

As mentioned in the text, an argument can have a true conclusion yet be invalid. In these exercises, each argument has a true conclusion. Identify each argument as valid *or* invalid.

17. All birds fly.
All planes fly.
―――
A bird is not a plane.

18. All cars have tires.
All tires are rubber.
―――
All cars have rubber.

19. All chickens have beaks.
All hens are chickens.
―――
All hens have beaks.

20. All chickens have beaks.
All birds have beaks.
―――
All chickens are birds.

21. Little Rock is northeast of Texarkana.
Little Rock is northeast of Austin.
―――
Texarkana is northeast of Austin.

22. Veracruz is south of Tampico.
Tampico is south of Monterrey.
―――
Veracruz is south of Monterrey.

23. No whole numbers are negative.
−3 is negative.
―――
−3 is not a whole number.

24. A scalene triangle has a longest side.
A scalene triangle has a largest angle.
―――
The largest angle in a scalene triangle is opposite the longest side.

In Exercises 25–30, the premises marked A, B, *and* C *are followed by several possible conclusions. Take each conclusion in turn, and check whether the resulting argument is* valid *or* invalid.

A. *All people who drive contribute to air pollution.*

B. *All people who contribute to air pollution make life a little worse.*

C. *Some people who live in a suburb make life a little worse.*

25. Some people who live in a suburb contribute to air pollution.

26. Some people who live in a suburb drive.

27. Suburban residents never drive.

28. Some people who contribute to air pollution live in a suburb.

29. Some people who make life a little worse live in a suburb.

30. All people who drive make life a little worse.

EXTENSION Logic Problems and Sudoku

How to Solve Logic Problems • How to Solve Sudoku

Dell Magazines/Penny Publications

Logic problems, which are based on deductive reasoning, appear in periodicals such as *Original Logic Problems, World-Class Logic Problems,* and *England's Best Logic Problems* (all PennyPress), and *Logic Puzzles* (Dell). The following explanation on solving such problems appeared in the February 2010 issue of *Original Logic Problems.*

How to Solve Logic Problems Solving logic problems is entertaining and challenging. All the information you need to solve a logic problem is given in the introduction and clues, and in illustrations, when provided. If you've never solved a logic problem before, our sample should help you get started. Fill in the Sample Solving Chart as you follow our explanation. We use a "•" to signify "Yes" and an "X" to signify "No."

Sample Logic Problem
Five couples were married last week, each on a different weekday. From the information provided, determine the woman (one is Cathy) and man (one is Paul) who make up each couple, as well as the day on which each couple was married.

1. Anne was married on Monday, but not to Wally.
2. Stan's wedding was on Wednesday. Rob was married on Friday, but not to Ida.
3. Vern (who married Fran) was married the day after Eve.

Sample Solving Chart:

	PAUL	ROB	STAN	VERN	WALLY	MONDAY	TUESDAY	WEDNESDAY	THURSDAY	FRIDAY
ANNE										
CATHY										
EVE										
FRAN										
IDA										
MONDAY										
TUESDAY										
WEDNESDAY										
THURSDAY										
FRIDAY										

1

	PAUL	ROB	STAN	VERN	WALLY	MONDAY	TUESDAY	WEDNESDAY	THURSDAY	FRIDAY
ANNE		X	X		X	•	X	X	X	X
CATHY						X				
EVE						X				
FRAN						X				
IDA		X				X				X
MONDAY		X	X							
TUESDAY		X	X							
WEDNESDAY	X	X	•	X	X					
THURSDAY		X	X							
FRIDAY	X	•	X	X	X					

Explanation

Anne was married Mon. (1), so put a "•" at the intersection of Anne and Mon. Put "X"s in all the other days in Anne's row and all the other names in the Mon. column. (Whenever you establish a relationship, as we did here, be sure to place "X"s at the intersections of all relationships that become impossible as a result.) Anne wasn't married to Wally (1), so put an "X" at the intersection of Anne and Wally. Stan's wedding was Wed. (2), so put a "•" at the intersection of Stan and Wed. (Don't forget the "X"s.) Stan didn't marry Anne, who was married Mon., so put an "X" at the intersection of Anne and Stan. Rob was married Fri., but not to Ida (2), so put a "•" at the intersection of Rob and Fri., and "X"s at the intersections of Rob and Ida and Ida and Fri. Rob also didn't marry Anne, who was married Mon., so put an "X" at the intersection of Anne and Rob. Now your chart should look like **chart 1.**

Vern married Fran (3), so put a "•" at the intersection of Vern and Fran. This leaves Anne's only possible husband as Paul, so put a "•" at the intersection of Anne and Paul and Paul and Mon. Vern and Fran's wedding was the day after Eve's (3), which wasn't Mon. [Anne], so Vern's wasn't Tue. It must have been Thu. [see chart], so Eve's was Wed. (3). Put "•"s at the intersections of Vern and Thu., Fran and Thu., and Eve and Wed. Now your chart should look like **chart 2.**

2	PAUL	ROB	STAN	VERN	WALLY	MONDAY	TUESDAY	WEDNESDAY	THURSDAY	FRIDAY
ANNE	•	X	X	X	X	•	X	X	X	X
CATHY	X			X		X		X	X	
EVE	X			X		X	X	•	X	X
FRAN	X	X	X	•	X	X	X	X	•	X
IDA	X	X		X		X		X	X	X
MONDAY	•	X	X	X	X					
TUESDAY	X	X	X	X						
WEDNESDAY	X	X	•	X	X					
THURSDAY	X	X	X	•	X					
FRIDAY	X	•	X	X	X					

3	PAUL	ROB	STAN	VERN	WALLY	MONDAY	TUESDAY	WEDNESDAY	THURSDAY	FRIDAY
ANNE	•	X	X	X	X	•	X	X	X	X
CATHY	X	•	X	X	X	X	X	X	X	•
EVE	X	X	•	X	X	X	X	•	X	X
FRAN	X	X	X	•	X	X	X	X	•	X
IDA	X	X	X	X	•	X	•	X	X	X
MONDAY	•	X	X	X	X					
TUESDAY	X	X	X	X	•					
WEDNESDAY	X	X	•	X	X					
THURSDAY	X	X	X	•	X					
FRIDAY	X	•	X	X	X					

The chart shows that Cathy was married Fri., Ida was married Tue., and Wally was married Tue. Ida married Wally, and Cathy's wedding was Fri., so she married Rob. After this information is filled in, Eve could only have married Stan. You've completed the puzzle, and your chart should now look like **chart 3.**

In summary: Anne and Paul, Mon.; Cathy and Rob, Fri.; Eve and Stan, Wed.; Fran and Vern, Thu.; Ida and Wally, Tue.

In some problems, it may be necessary to make a logical guess based on facts you've established. When you do, always look for clues or other facts that disprove it. If you find that your guess is incorrect, eliminate it as a possibility.

Dell Magazines/Penny Publications

How to Solve Sudoku Sudoku is a simple game that has gained great popularity in the United States during the past few years. It is believed that the game originated as Number Place in the United States over 25 years ago, but gained in popularity only after it became a sensation in Japan, where it was renamed Sudoku, meaning "single number." (*Source: Sudoku #13*, 2005, Platinum Magazine Group.)

There is only one rule in Sudoku: **"Fill in the grid so that every row, every column, and every 3 × 3 box contains the digits 1 through 9."** This involves scanning the given digits, marking up the grid, and analyzing. Here is a sample Sudoku.

		7	3	2				
8	4		1				9	
						8	2	1
		9		8	7			5
2	8		4		1		6	3
1			5	6		9		
5	3	8						9
	9				2		1	4
				7	5	6		

Given Form

9	1	7	3	2	8	4	5	6
8	4	2	1	5	6	3	9	7
6	5	3	7	4	9	8	2	1
3	6	9	2	8	7	1	4	5
2	8	5	4	9	1	7	6	3
1	7	4	5	6	3	9	8	2
5	3	8	6	1	4	2	7	9
7	9	6	8	3	2	5	1	4
4	2	1	9	7	5	6	3	8

Solved Form

You can find Sudoku puzzles and solving strategies online at www.sudoku.org.uk and at www.pennydellsudokusolver.com.

EXTENSION EXERCISES

Follow the guidelines to solve each logic problem, which appeared in the February 2010 issue of Original Logic Problems, *published by PennyPress.*

1. ***Breath Taking*** As part of a weekly tradition, Drew and four of his friends met for lunch at Aristotle's Grill. Each person enjoyed a different lunch special, but when it came time for the post-meal conversation, the five quickly realized that they were all in need of a mint or two. Luckily, each person had a container of mints on his or her person. No two friends had the same brand of mint (one is Inti-mints), and no two friends had mints with the same flavor. A few seconds later they were all ready to talk, but they agreed that next week, they'll be a little more careful about what they order for lunch! From the information provided, can you determine the meal enjoyed by each friend, as well as the brand and flavor of mint each person used afterward?

		MEAL					BRAND					FLAVOR				
		BUFFALO CHICKEN	FRENCH ONION SOUP	GARLIC SHRIMP	SPANAKOPITA	TUNA-SALAD SANDWICH	DELTOIDS	FRESH AIR	INTI-MINTS	LIPLICKERS	TKO	CINNAMON	ORANGE	SPEARMINT	VANILLA	WINTERGREEN
FRIEND	DREW															
	ILSE															
	NASH															
	UMA															
	XERXES															
FLAVOR	CINNAMON															
	ORANGE															
	SPEARMINT															
	VANILLA															
	WINTERGREEN															
BRAND	DELTOIDS															
	FRESH AIR															
	INTI-MINTS															
	LIPLICKERS															
	TKO															

(a) The friend who had garlic shrimp ate a couple of orange-flavored mints (which weren't Fresh Air mints). The person who ordered the spanakopita isn't the one who had wintergreen-flavored TKO mints.

(b) The friend who ate French onion soup followed it with a few Liplickers mints. Nash (who didn't have the spearmint-flavored mints) didn't order garlic shrimp.

(c) Neither Nash nor Xerxes is the one who ate a tuna-salad sandwich. The friend who had a buffalo-chicken sandwich isn't the one who freshened his or her breath with spearmint-flavored mints.

(d) One friend had a couple of cinnamon-flavored Deltoids mints. The Liplickers mints were vanilla-flavored.

(e) Ilse (who ate a buffalo-chicken sandwich) didn't have wintergreen-flavored mints. Neither Uma nor Xerxes is the friend who had a couple of Fresh Air mints.

2. ***Kings of Hearts*** Although the exact origins of the holiday are murky, the tradition of Valentine's Day probably harkens back to the Middle Ages, when it was better known as the feast of Saint Valentine. Couples exchanged gifts on this February holiday even back then, and no one gave more expensive and elaborate valentines than the royalty of that time. One Valentine's Day, each of four kings, each whom ruled a different small kingdom, gave his queen a different valuable gift. It just goes to show that love (or at least the idea of it) stands the test of time! From the information provided, can you determine the king and queen of each kingdom, as well as the gift each king gave his wife for the feast of Saint Valentine?

(a) King Jacobus didn't give his queen a platinum crown.

(b) Neither the jeweled scepter nor the platinum crown was the gift given to Queen Meyla (who was married to either King Kevrick or King Vermond).

(c) Queen Dejah (who was married to either King Fedris or King Jacobus) wasn't the ruler of Undervale.

(d) King Kevrick wasn't the ruler of the Dalelands.

(e) Neither the platinum crown nor the set of velvet robes was the gift given by King Vermond.

(f) The queen of Undervale (who was married to either King Fedris or King Jacobus) was given a golden throne by her husband.

(g) Queen Tilnara wasn't given a jeweled scepter by her husband. Queen Aasta ruled Hightop.

		QUEEN				KINGDOM				GIFT			
		AASTA	DEJAH	MEYLA	TILNARA	DALELANDS	HIGHTOP	SHADOW COAST	UNDERVALE	GOLDEN THRONE	JEWELED SCEPTER	PLATINUM CROWN	VELVET ROBES
KING	FEDRIS												
	JACOBUS												
	KEVRICK												
	VERMOND												
GIFT	GOLDEN THRONE												
	JEWELED SCEPTER												
	PLATINUM CROWN												
	VELVET ROBES												
KINGDOM	DALELANDS												
	HIGHTOP												
	SHADOW COAST												
	UNDERVALE												

3. ***New Year's Revelations*** Lucy and four of her friends met at the Golden Panda for dinner one evening in January. Much to their surprise, they had wandered in to the restaurant during a celebration of the Chinese New Year. Luckily for the five, this meant a discount on their meals and a free session with the mysterious medium Madame Wau Pei. The five friends had their fortunes told, one at a time. Each person told the mystic the date and year of his or her birth and learned that, according to Chinese astrology, each friend's birth year is designated by a different animal. Also, each of the five was told that he or she has a different lucky element. Before leaving the restaurant, the five friends compared their predictions, noticing that all of them had a long journey in their future—the trip back home! From the information provided, determine the order in which the five friends had their fortunes told, the year in which each person was born, and each person's lucky element.

(a) Toni was the third person to get her fortune told. The person whose lucky element is wood was the last person to see the fortune-teller.

(b) Earl (whose lucky element is fire) had his fortune told immediately before the person who was born in the Year of the Rooster. The fourth person to visit the fortune-teller was born in the Year of the Dragon.

(c) The person born in the Year of the Ox had his or her fortune told at some point before the one whose lucky element is metal. Ivana was born in the Year of the Horse.

(d) The person whose lucky element is water (who was born in the Year of the Cow) wasn't the first person to have his or her fortune told.

(e) The person whose lucky element is earth had his or her fortune told exactly two after Philip.

		FRIEND					YEAR					ELEMENT				
		EARL	IVANA	LUCY	PHILIP	TONI	COW	DRAGON	HORSE	OX	ROOSTER	EARTH	FIRE	METAL	WATER	WOOD
ORDER	FIRST															
	SECOND															
	THIRD															
	FOURTH															
	FIFTH															
ELEMENT	EARTH															
	FIRE															
	METAL															
	WATER															
	WOOD															
YEAR	COW															
	DRAGON															
	HORSE															
	OX															
	ROOSTER															

4. ***Barn Again*** For as long as I can remember, I've dreamed of owning my own bed-and-breakfast, and it looks like my dream is about to come true! We'd like our inn to be distinctive, so my husband and I have decided to purchase a barn and convert it into unique living quarters. We viewed five barns recently, each of which had once served a different purpose. My husband and I visited each barn with a different contractor, each of whom gave us a different estimate ($50,000, $60,000, $70,000, $80,000, or $100,000) for the conversion. Each barn has a different feature that makes it appealing (one has a functioning hoist), but we still haven't decided which one to buy—we're starting to go a little haywire! From the information provided, determine the contractor who visited each barn with us and the special feature of each structure, as well as the estimate given for the renovation of each barn.

(a) The apple barn (which has distinctive octagonal windows) will cost exactly $20,000 less to convert than the barn we visited with a Bill's Building representative. The estimate for renovating the hay barn is higher than the estimate for converting the potato barn.

(b) The barn we visited with the person from AB Contracting (which isn't the barn that has fabulous heavy beams) will cost more to renovate than the barn we viewed with the contractor from Pine Valley but exactly $10,000 less to convert than the horse barn.

(c) The estimates for converting the apple barn and the barn with lovely board-and-batten siding are the lowest and highest estimates, in some order.

(d) The barn we visited with the contractor from Dekker Ltd. will cost exactly $20,000 more to renovate than the barn with insulation worth preserving.

(e) The old dairy barn will cost more to renovate than the one we visited with the representative from Vander Estates.

		BARN					FEATURE					ESTIMATE				
		APPLE	DAIRY	HAY	HORSE	POTATO	BEAMS	HOIST	INSULATION	SIDING	WINDOWS	$50,000	$60,000	$70,000	$80,000	$100,000
CONTRACTOR	AB CONTRACTING															
	BILL'S BUILDING															
	DEKKER LTD.															
	PINE VALLEY															
	VANDER ESTATES															
ESTIMATE	$50,000															
	$60,000															
	$70,000															
	$80,000															
	$100,000															
FEATURE	BEAMS															
	HOIST															
	INSULATION															
	SIDING															
	WINDOWS															

Solve each Sudoku, which appeared in Dell Original Sudoku, *March 2010, Penny Publications. (They are categorized according to difficulty level.)*

5. ***Easy***

	4		1	6	8			5
		9		5			2	8
	6		9					4
		4	7		9			
	3	8		4		2	9	
			2		3	8		
2					1		6	
9	7			2		5		
4			6	9	5		7	

6. ***Easy***

2		3			8	1	4	
	7		6	2	4			
	8			3				7
8	4	7	2				6	
			8		6			
	1				9	4	8	2
7				6			2	
			9	5	7		1	
	6	9	3			5		4

7. ***Medium***

8	3		6					1
	1			4			5	6
		6			8			
		7	1				3	8
		1		2		4		
5	4				6	1		
			5			7		
9	8			7			1	
6					1		2	3

8. ***Medium***

			4	5		6		
4	5					3		9
	6	1			3			8
5	8				1		6	
		9		3		2		
	4		9				1	7
8			1			7	3	
1		5					9	2
		6		7	2			

9. ***Hard***

	1			2				4
4		9			1		7	
		8				9		
	3		6				2	
7				3				9
	9				8	5		
		2				4		
	8		2			6		5
9				8			3	

10. ***Hard***

	2			9		6	7	
	5	6						
			6		4			5
	6	9						1
			3	6	9			
8						9	4	
1			4		7			
						4	2	
	4	8		2			3	

6 ANALYZING ARGUMENTS WITH TRUTH TABLES

Truth Tables (Two Premises) • Valid and Invalid Argument Forms • Truth Tables (More Than Two Premises) • Arguments of Lewis Carroll

Notro Films/Bocaboca Producciones/The Kobal Collection

In the 2007 Spanish film ***La Habitacion de Fermat (Fermat's Room)***, four mathematicians are invited to dinner, only to discover that the room in which they are meeting is designed to eventually crush them as walls creep in closer and closer. The only way for them to delay the inevitable is to answer enigmas, questions, puzzles, problems, and riddles that they are receiving on a cell phone.

One of the enigmas deals with a hermetically sealed room that contains a single light bulb. There are three switches outside the room, and only one of the switches controls the bulb. You are allowed to push any or all of the buttons as many times as you wish before you enter the room, but once you enter you cannot return to the switches outside. How can you determine which one controls the bulb? (The answer is on **the next page**.)

Truth Tables (Two Premises)

In **Section 5** we used Euler diagrams to test the validity of arguments. While Euler diagrams often work well for simple arguments, difficulties can develop with more complex ones, because Euler diagrams require a sketch showing every possible case. In complex arguments, it is hard to be sure that all cases have been considered.

In deciding whether to use Euler diagrams to test the validity of an argument, look for quantifiers such as "all," "some," or "no." These words often indicate arguments best tested by Euler diagrams. If these words are absent, it may be better to use truth tables to test the validity of an argument.

As an example of this method, consider the following argument:

If the floor is dirty, then I must mop it.
The floor is dirty.
―――――――――――――
I must mop it.

To test the validity of this argument, we begin by identifying the *component* statements found in the argument. They are "the floor is dirty" and "I must mop it." We assign the letters p and q to represent these statements:

p represents "the floor is dirty";
q represents "I must mop it."

Now we write the two premises and the conclusion in symbols.

Premise 1: $p \rightarrow q$
Premise 2: p
―――――――――
Conclusion: q

To decide if this argument is valid, we must determine whether the conjunction of both premises implies the conclusion for all possible cases of truth values for p and q. Therefore, write the conjunction of the premises as the antecedent of a conditional statement, and the conclusion as the consequent.

$$[(p \rightarrow q) \quad \wedge \quad p] \quad \rightarrow \quad q$$

$(p \rightarrow q)$ ↑ premise; $\wedge$ ↑ and; p ↑ premise; $\rightarrow$ ↑ implies; q ↑ conclusion

Finally, construct the truth table for this conditional statement, as shown below.

p	q	$p \rightarrow q$	$(p \rightarrow q) \wedge p$	$[(p \rightarrow q) \wedge p] \rightarrow q$
T	T	T	T	T
T	F	F	F	T
F	T	T	F	T
F	F	T	F	T

Because the final column, shown in color, indicates that the conditional statement that represents the argument is true for all possible truth values of p and q, the statement is a tautology. Thus, the argument is valid.

Answer to the Light Bulb question.

Label the switches 1, 2, and 3. Turn switch 1 on and leave it on for several minutes. Then turn switch 1 off, turn switch 2 on, and then immediately enter the room. If the bulb is on, then you know that switch 2 controls it. If the bulb is off, touch it to see if it is still warm. If it is, then switch 1 controls it. If the bulb is not warm, then switch 3 controls it.

The pattern of the argument in the floor-mopping example

$$\begin{array}{l} p \to q \\ \underline{p \quad\quad} \\ q \end{array}$$

is called **modus ponens,** or the *law of detachment.*

To test the validity of an argument using a truth table, follow the steps in the box.

Testing the Validity of an Argument with a Truth Table

Step 1 Assign a letter to represent each component statement in the argument.

Step 2 Express each premise and the conclusion symbolically.

Step 3 Form the symbolic statement of the entire argument by writing the *conjunction* of *all* the premises as the antecedent of a conditional statement, and the conclusion of the argument as the consequent.

Step 4 Complete the truth table for the conditional statement formed in Step 3. If it is a tautology, then the argument is valid; otherwise, it is invalid.

EXAMPLE 1 Using a Truth Table to Determine Validity

Determine whether the argument is *valid* or *invalid.*

If my check arrives in time, I'll register for the fall semester.
I've registered for the fall semester.
____
My check arrived in time.

SOLUTION

Let p represent "my check arrives (arrived) in time" and let q represent "I'll register (I've registered) for the fall semester." The argument can be written as follows.

$$\begin{array}{l} p \to q \\ \underline{q \quad\quad} \\ p \end{array}$$

To test for validity, construct a truth table for the statement $[(p \to q) \wedge q] \to p$.

p	q	$p \to q$	$(p \to q) \wedge q$	$[(p \to q) \wedge q] \to p$
T	T	T	T	T
T	F	F	F	T
F	T	T	T	F
F	F	T	F	T

The third row of the final column of the truth table shows F, and this is enough to conclude that the argument is invalid.

If a conditional and its converse were logically equivalent, then an argument of the type found in **Example 1** would be valid. Because a conditional and its converse are *not* equivalent, the argument is an example of what is sometimes called the **fallacy of the converse.**

EXAMPLE 2 Using a Truth Table to Determine Validity

Determine whether the argument is *valid* or *invalid.*

If a man could be in two places at one time, I'd be with you.
I am not with you.
____
A man can't be in two places at one time.

SOLUTION

If p represents "a man could be in two places at one time" and q represents "I'd be with you," the argument is written as follows.

$$\begin{array}{l} p \rightarrow q \\ \underline{\sim q} \\ \sim p \end{array}$$

The symbolic statement of the entire argument is as follows.

$$[(p \rightarrow q) \wedge \sim q] \rightarrow \sim p$$

The truth table for this argument indicates a tautology, and the argument is valid.

p	q	$p \rightarrow q$	$\sim q$	$(p \rightarrow q) \wedge \sim q$	$\sim p$	$[(p \rightarrow q) \wedge \sim q] \rightarrow \sim p$
T	T	T	F	F	F	T
T	F	F	T	F	F	T
F	T	T	F	F	T	T
F	F	T	T	T	T	T

The pattern of reasoning of this example is called **modus tollens,** or the *law of contraposition,* or *indirect reasoning.* ■■■

With reasoning similar to that used to name the fallacy of the converse, the fallacy

$$\begin{array}{l} p \rightarrow q \\ \underline{\sim p} \\ \sim q \end{array}$$

is called the **fallacy of the inverse.** An example of such a fallacy is "If it rains, I get wet. It doesn't rain. Therefore, I don't get wet."

EXAMPLE 3 Using a Truth Table to Determine Validity

Determine whether the argument is *valid* or *invalid.*

I'll buy a car or I'll take a vacation.
I won't buy a car.
———————————
I'll take a vacation.

SOLUTION

If p represents "I'll buy a car" and q represents "I'll take a vacation," the argument is symbolized as follows.

$$\begin{array}{l} p \vee q \\ \underline{\sim p} \\ q \end{array}$$

We must set up a truth table for the statement $[(p \vee q) \wedge \sim p] \rightarrow q$.

p	q	$p \vee q$	$\sim p$	$(p \vee q) \wedge \sim p$	$[(p \vee q) \wedge \sim p] \rightarrow q$
T	T	T	F	F	T
T	F	T	F	F	T
F	T	T	T	T	T
F	F	F	T	F	T

The statement is a tautology and the argument is valid. Any argument of this form is valid by the law of **disjunctive syllogism.** ■■■

EXAMPLE 4 Using a Truth Table to Determine Validity

Determine whether the argument is *valid* or *invalid*.

If it squeaks, then I use WD-40.
If I use WD-40, then I must go to the hardware store.
———
If it squeaks, then I must go to the hardware store.

SOLUTION

Let p represent "it squeaks," let q represent "I use WD-40," and let r represent "I must go to the hardware store." The argument takes on the following general form.

$$\begin{array}{l} p \rightarrow q \\ \underline{q \rightarrow r} \\ p \rightarrow r \end{array}$$

Make a truth table for this statement, which requires eight rows.

$$[(p \rightarrow q) \wedge (q \rightarrow r)] \rightarrow (p \rightarrow r)$$

p	q	r	$p \rightarrow q$	$q \rightarrow r$	$p \rightarrow r$	$(p \rightarrow q) \wedge (q \rightarrow r)$	$[(p \rightarrow q) \wedge (q \rightarrow r)] \rightarrow (p \rightarrow r)$
T	T	T	T	T	T	T	T
T	T	F	T	F	F	F	T
T	F	T	F	T	T	F	T
T	F	F	F	T	F	F	T
F	T	T	T	T	T	T	T
F	T	F	T	F	T	F	T
F	F	T	T	T	T	T	T
F	F	F	T	T	T	T	T

This argument is valid because the final statement is a tautology. This pattern of argument is called **reasoning by transitivity,** or the *law of hypothetical syllogism.* ■■■

Mary Evans/Python Pictures/Ronald Grant/Everett Collection

In a scene near the beginning of the 1974 film *Monty Python and the Holy Grail,* an amazing application of **poor logic** leads to the apparent demise of a supposed witch. Some peasants have forced a young woman to wear a nose made of wood. The convoluted argument they make is this: Witches and wood are both burned, and because witches are made of wood, and wood floats, and ducks also float, if she weighs the same as a duck, then she is made of wood and, therefore, is a witch!

Valid and Invalid Argument Forms

A summary of the valid and invalid forms of argument presented so far in this section follows.

Valid Argument Forms

Modus Ponens	Modus Tollens	Disjunctive Syllogism	Reasoning by Transitivity
$p \rightarrow q$	$p \rightarrow q$	$p \vee q$	$p \rightarrow q$
$\underline{p}$	$\underline{\sim q}$	$\underline{\sim p}$	$\underline{q \rightarrow r}$
q	$\sim p$	q	$p \rightarrow r$

Invalid Argument Forms (Fallacies)

Fallacy of the Converse	Fallacy of the Inverse
$p \rightarrow q$	$p \rightarrow q$
$\underline{q}$	$\underline{\sim p}$
p	$\sim q$

Truth Tables (More Than Two Premises)

When an argument contains more than two premises, it is necessary to determine the truth values of the conjunction of *all* of them. ***If at least one premise in a conjunction of several premises is false, then the entire conjunction is false.***

EXAMPLE 5 Using a Truth Table to Determine Validity

Determine whether the argument is *valid* or *invalid*.

If Eddie goes to town, then Mabel stays at home. If Mabel does not stay at home, then Rita will cook. Rita will not cook. Therefore, Eddie does not go to town.

SOLUTION

In an argument written in this manner, the premises are given first, and the conclusion is the statement that follows the word "Therefore." Let p represent "Eddie goes to town," let q represent "Mabel stays at home," and let r represent "Rita will cook."

$$\begin{array}{l} p \rightarrow q \\ \sim q \rightarrow r \\ \underline{\sim r \quad\quad} \\ \sim p \end{array}$$

To test validity, set up a truth table for this statement.

$$[(p \rightarrow q) \wedge (\sim q \rightarrow r) \wedge \sim r] \rightarrow \sim p$$

p	q	r	$p \rightarrow q$	$\sim q$	$\sim q \rightarrow r$	$\sim r$	$(p \rightarrow q) \wedge (\sim q \rightarrow r) \wedge \sim r$	$\sim p$	$[(p \rightarrow q) \wedge (\sim q \rightarrow r) \wedge \sim r] \rightarrow \sim p$
T	T	T	T	F	T	F	F	F	T
T	T	F	T	F	T	T	T	F	F
T	F	T	F	T	T	F	F	F	T
T	F	F	F	T	F	T	F	F	T
F	T	T	T	F	T	F	F	T	T
F	T	F	T	F	T	T	T	T	T
F	F	T	T	T	T	F	F	T	T
F	F	F	T	T	F	T	F	T	T

Because the final column does not contain all Ts, the statement is not a tautology. The argument is invalid. ■■■

Arguments of Lewis Carroll

Consider the following verse, which has been around for many years.

For want of a nail, the shoe was lost. For want of a shoe, the horse was lost. For want of a horse, the rider was lost. For want of a rider, the battle was lost. For want of a battle, the war was lost.

Therefore, for want of a nail, the war was lost.

Each line of the verse may be written as an *if . . . then* statement. For example, the first line may be restated as "if a nail is lost, then the shoe is lost." The conclusion, "for want of a nail, the war was lost," follows from the premises, because repeated use of the law of transitivity applies. Arguments such as the one used by Lewis Carroll in the next example often take on a similar form.

Wonderstock/Alamy

Alice in the Forest of Forgetfulness
When Alice entered the Forest of Forgetfulness, she often forgot what day of the week it was. She encountered a Lion and a Unicorn, two strange creatures. The Lion lies on Mondays, Tuesdays, and Wednesdays and tells the truth on the other days of the week. The Unicorn, on the other hand, lies on Thursdays, Fridays, and Saturdays, but tells the truth on the other days of the week.

One day Alice met the Lion and the Unicorn resting under a tree. They made the following statements:

Lion: Yesterday was one of my lying days.
Unicorn: Yesterday was one of my lying days, too.

From these two statements, Alice was able to deduce the day of the week. What day was it? (Turn the page to see the answer.)

(Adapted from a problem in Raymond Smullyan's *What Is the Name of This Book?*)

EXAMPLE 6 Supplying a Conclusion to Assure Validity

Supply a conclusion that yields a valid argument for the following premises.

Babies are illogical.
Nobody is despised who can manage a crocodile.
Illogical persons are despised.

SOLUTION

First, write each premise in the form *if . . . then. . . .*

If you are a baby, then you are illogical.
If you can manage a crocodile, then you are not despised.
If you are illogical, then you are despised.

Let p be "you are a baby," let q be "you are logical," let r be "you can manage a crocodile," and let s be "you are despised." The statements can be written symbolically.

$$p \rightarrow \sim q$$
$$r \rightarrow \sim s$$
$$\sim q \rightarrow s$$

Begin with any letter that appears only once. Here p appears only once. Using the contrapositive of $r \rightarrow \sim s$, which is $s \rightarrow \sim r$, rearrange the statements as follows.

$$p \rightarrow \sim q$$
$$\sim q \rightarrow s$$
$$s \rightarrow \sim r$$

From the three statements, repeated use of reasoning by transitivity gives the conclusion

$p \rightarrow \sim r$, which leads to a valid argument.

In words, the conclusion is "If you are a baby, then you cannot manage a crocodile," or, as Lewis Carroll would have written it, "Babies cannot manage crocodiles."

6 EXERCISES

Each argument is either valid by one of the forms of valid arguments discussed in this section, or it is a fallacy by one of the forms of invalid arguments discussed. (See the summary boxes.) Decide whether the argument is valid *or a* fallacy, *and give the form that applies.*

1. If James Taylor comes to town, then I will go to the concert.
If I go to the concert, then I'll call in sick for work.
―――
If James Taylor comes to town, then I'll call in sick for work.

2. If you use binoculars, then you get a glimpse of the space shuttle.
If you get a glimpse of the space shuttle, then you'll be amazed.
―――
If you use binoculars, then you'll be amazed.

3. If Julie Nhem works hard enough, she will get a promotion.
Julie Nhem works hard enough.
―――
She gets a promotion.

4. If Andrew Noble sells his quota, he'll get a bonus.
Andrew Noble sells his quota.
―――
He gets a bonus.

5. If he doesn't have to get up at 3:00 A.M., he's ecstatic.
He's ecstatic.
―――
He doesn't have to get up at 3:00 A.M.

6. If she buys another pair of shoes, her closet will overflow.
Her closet will overflow.
―――
She buys another pair of shoes.

7. If Mariano Rivera pitches, the Yankees win.
The Yankees do not win.
Mariano Rivera does not pitch.

8. If Nelson Dida plays, the opponent gets shut out.
The opponent does not get shut out.
Nelson Dida does not play.

9. "If we evolved a race of Isaac Newtons, that would not be progress." (quote from Aldous Huxley)
We have not evolved a race of Isaac Newtons.
That is progress.

10. "If I have seen farther than others, it is because I stood on the shoulders of giants." (quote from Sir Isaac Newton)
I have not seen farther than others.
I have not stood on the shoulders of giants.

11. She uses e-commerce or she pays by credit card.
She does not pay by credit card.
She uses e-commerce.

12. Mia kicks or Drew passes.
Drew does not pass.
Mia kicks.

Use a truth table to determine whether the argument is valid *or* invalid.

13. $$\begin{array}{l} p \vee q \\ \underline{p \quad\quad} \\ \sim q \end{array}$$

14. $$\begin{array}{l} p \wedge \sim q \\ \underline{p \quad\quad} \\ \sim q \end{array}$$

15. $$\begin{array}{l} \sim p \rightarrow \sim q \\ \underline{q \quad\quad\quad} \\ p \end{array}$$

16. $$\begin{array}{l} p \vee \sim q \\ \underline{p \quad\quad} \\ \sim q \end{array}$$

17. $$\begin{array}{l} p \rightarrow q \\ \underline{q \rightarrow p} \\ p \wedge q \end{array}$$

18. $$\begin{array}{l} \sim p \rightarrow q \\ \underline{p \quad\quad} \\ \sim q \end{array}$$

19. $$\begin{array}{l} p \rightarrow \sim q \\ \underline{q \quad\quad} \\ \sim p \end{array}$$

20. $$\begin{array}{l} p \rightarrow \sim q \\ \underline{\sim p \quad\quad} \\ \sim q \end{array}$$

21. $$\begin{array}{l} (p \wedge q) \vee (p \vee q) \\ \underline{q \quad\quad\quad\quad\quad\quad} \\ p \end{array}$$

22. $$\begin{array}{l} (p \rightarrow q) \wedge (q \rightarrow p) \\ \underline{p \quad\quad\quad\quad\quad\quad} \\ p \vee q \end{array}$$

23. $$\begin{array}{l} (\sim p \vee q) \wedge (\sim p \rightarrow q) \\ \underline{p \quad\quad\quad\quad\quad\quad} \\ \sim q \end{array}$$

24. $$\begin{array}{l} (r \wedge p) \rightarrow (r \vee q) \\ \underline{q \wedge p \quad\quad\quad\quad} \\ r \vee p \end{array}$$

25. $$\begin{array}{l} (\sim p \wedge r) \rightarrow (p \vee q) \\ \underline{\sim r \rightarrow p \quad\quad\quad} \\ q \rightarrow r \end{array}$$

26. $$\begin{array}{l} (p \rightarrow \sim q) \vee (q \rightarrow \sim r) \\ \underline{p \vee \sim r \quad\quad\quad\quad} \\ r \rightarrow p \end{array}$$

27. Earlier we showed how to analyze arguments using Euler diagrams. Refer to **Example 4** in this section, restate each premise and the conclusion using a quantifier, and then draw an Euler diagram to illustrate the relationship.

28. Explain in a few sentences how to determine the statement for which a truth table will be constructed so that the arguments that follow in **Exercises 29–38** can be analyzed for validity.

Determine whether each argument is valid *or* invalid.

29. Joey loves to watch movies. If Terry likes to jog, then Joey does not love to watch movies. If Terry does not like to jog, then Carrie drives a school bus. Therefore, Carrie drives a school bus.

30. If Hurricane Gustave hit that grove of trees, then the trees are devastated. People plant trees when disasters strike and the trees are not devastated. Therefore, if people plant trees when disasters strike, then Hurricane Gustave did not hit that grove of trees.

Shutterstock

31. If the social networking craze continues, then downloading music will remain popular. American Girl dolls are favorites or downloading music will remain popular. American Girl dolls are not favorites. Therefore, the social networking craze does not continue.

32. Carrie Underwood sings or Joe Jonas is not a teen idol. If Joe Jonas is not a teen idol, then Jennifer Hudson does not win a Grammy. Jennifer Hudson wins a Grammy. Therefore, Carrie Underwood does not sing.

33. The Dolphins will be in the playoffs if and only if Chad leads the league in passing. Tony coaches the Dolphins or Chad leads the league in passing. Tony does not coach the Dolphins. Therefore, the Dolphins will not be in the playoffs.

34. If I've got you under my skin, then you are deep in the heart of me. If you are deep in the heart of me, then you are not really a part of me. You are deep in the heart of me or you are really a part of me. Therefore, if I've got you under my skin, then you are really a part of me.

35. If Dr. Hardy is a department chairman, then he lives in Atlanta. He lives in Atlanta and his first name is Larry. Therefore, if his first name is not Larry, then he is not a department chairman.

36. If I were your woman and you were my man, then I'd never stop loving you. I've stopped loving you. Therefore, I am not your woman or you are not my man.

37. All men are created equal. All people who are created equal are women. Therefore, all men are women.

38. All men are mortal. Socrates is a man. Therefore, Socrates is mortal.

39. Suppose that you ask a stranger for the time and you get the following response:

> "If I tell you the time, then we'll start chatting. If we start chatting, then you'll want to meet me at a truck stop. If we meet at a truck stop, then we'll discuss my family. If we discuss my family, then you'll find out that my daughter is available for marriage. If you find out that she is available for marriage, then you'll want to marry her. If you want to marry her, then my life will be miserable since I don't want my daughter married to some fool who can't afford a $10 watch."

Use reasoning by transitivity to draw a valid conclusion.

40. Molly Riggs made the following observation: "If I want to determine whether an argument leading to the statement

$$[(p \rightarrow q) \wedge \sim q] \rightarrow \sim p$$

is valid, I only need to consider the lines of the truth table which lead to T for the column headed $(p \rightarrow q) \wedge \sim q$." Molly was very perceptive. Can you explain why her observation was correct?

In the arguments used by Lewis Carroll, it is helpful to restate a premise in if . . . then *form in order to more easily identify a valid conclusion. The following premises come from Lewis Carroll. Write each premise in* if . . . then *form.*

41. All my poultry are ducks.

42. None of your sons can do logic.

43. Guinea pigs are hopelessly ignorant of music.

44. No teetotalers are pawnbrokers.

45. No teachable kitten has green eyes.

46. Opium-eaters have no self-command.

47. I have not filed any of them that I can read.

48. All of them written on blue paper are filed.

Exercises 49–54 involve premises from Lewis Carroll. Write each premise in symbols, and then in the final part, give a conclusion that yields a valid argument.

49. Let p be "it is a duck," q be "it is my poultry," r be "one is an officer," and s be "one is willing to waltz."

(a) No ducks are willing to waltz.

(b) No officers ever decline to waltz.

(c) All my poultry are ducks.

(d) Give a conclusion that yields a valid argument.

Shutterstock

50. Let p be "one is able to do logic," q be "one is fit to serve on a jury," r be "one is sane," and s be "he is your son."

(a) Everyone who is sane can do logic.

(b) No lunatics are fit to serve on a jury.

(c) None of your sons can do logic.

(d) Give a conclusion that yields a valid argument.

51. Let p be "one is honest," q be "one is a pawnbroker," r be "one is a promise-breaker," s be "one is trustworthy," t be "one is very communicative," and u be "one is a wine-drinker."

(a) Promise-breakers are untrustworthy.

(b) Wine-drinkers are very communicative.

(c) A person who keeps a promise is honest.

(d) No teetotalers are pawnbrokers. (*Hint:* Assume "teetotaler" is the opposite of "wine-drinker.")

(e) One can always trust a very communicative person.

(f) Give a conclusion that yields a valid argument.

52. Let p be "it is a guinea pig," q be "it is hopelessly ignorant of music," r be "it keeps silent while the *Moonlight Sonata* is being played," and s be "it appreciates Beethoven."

(a) Nobody who really appreciates Beethoven fails to keep silent while the *Moonlight Sonata* is being played.

(b) Guinea pigs are hopelessly ignorant of music.

(c) No one who is hopelessly ignorant of music ever keeps silent while the *Moonlight Sonata* is being played.

(d) Give a conclusion that yields a valid argument.

53. Let p be "it begins with 'Dear Sir'," q be "it is crossed," r be "it is dated," s be "it is filed," t be "it is in black ink," u be "it is in the third person," v be "I can read it," w be "it is on blue paper," x be "it is on one sheet," and y be "it is written by Brown."

(a) All the dated letters are written on blue paper.

(b) None of them are in black ink, except those that are written in the third person.

(c) I have not filed any of them that I can read.

(d) None of them that are written on one sheet are undated.

(e) All of them that are not crossed are in black ink.

(f) All of them written by Brown begin with "Dear Sir."

(g) All of them written on blue paper are filed.

(h) None of them written on more than one sheet are crossed.

(i) None of them that begin with "Dear Sir" are written in the third person.

(j) Give a conclusion that yields a valid argument.

54. Let p be "he is going to a party," q be "he brushes his hair," r be "he has self-command," s be "he looks fascinating," t be "he is an opium-eater," u be "he is tidy," and v be "he wears white kid gloves."

(a) No one who is going to a party ever fails to brush his hair.

(b) No one looks fascinating if he is untidy.

(c) Opium-eaters have no self-command.

(d) Everyone who has brushed his hair looks fascinating.

(e) No one wears white kid gloves unless he is going to a party. (*Hint:* "a unless b" $\equiv \sim b \rightarrow a$.)

(f) A man is always untidy if he has no self-command.

(g) Give a conclusion that yields a valid argument.

Answer to Alice in the Forest of Forgetfulness:

The only days the Lion can say, "I lied yesterday" are Mondays and Thursdays. The only days the Unicorn can say "I lied yesterday" are Thursdays and Sundays. Therefore the only day they can both say that is Thursday.

COLLABORATIVE INVESTIGATION

Logic Problems and Sudoku Revisited

Logic problems and Sudoku were first discussed in the **Extension.** The problems here require more time and reasoning skills than the ones appearing in the **Extension.** They are taken from *Original Logic Problems*, February 2010, and *Dell Original Sudoku*, March 2010.

The class may wish to divide up into groups and see which group can solve these problems fastest.

EXERCISES

Note: Answers to these Collaborative Investigation Exercises are given at the end of this chapter.

1. ***Out to Launch*** The National Space Association has scheduled five rockets for launch early next year. Each rocket (including the *Penchant*) will take off in a different month (January through May) on a different date (the 1st through the 5th). Each rocket will launch from a different site (including the San Simeon Launch Center) and engage in a different mission. For fans of the space program, next year will be a real blast! From the information provided, determine the month and date of the launch of the rocket from each launch site, as well as each rocket's mission.

		DATE					LAUNCH SITE					ROCKET					MISSION				
		1ST	2ND	3RD	4TH	5TH	CAPE CARNIVAL	EDDINGS A. F. B.	SAN SIMEON L. C.	VANDYKE FACILITY	WILLARD ISLAND	BRAVURA	FALCONER	LIBERTY	PENCHANT	TWILIGHT	INVESTIGATE	LAND ON MOON	MEASURE	REPAIR SATELLITE	TEST PROPULSION
MONTH	JANUARY																				
	FEBRUARY																				
	MARCH																				
	APRIL																				
	MAY																				
MISSION	INVESTIGATE																				
	LAND ON MOON																				
	MEASURE																				
	REPAIR																				
	TEST																				
ROCKET	BRAVURA																				
	FALCONER																				
	LIBERTY																				
	PENCHANT																				
	TWILIGHT																				
LAUNCH SITE	CAPE CARNIVAL																				
	EDDINGS AIR																				
	SAN SIMEON																				
	VANDYKE																				
	WILLARD ISLAND																				

(a) The date of the May launch is numbered exactly two lower than the date of the Willard Island launch. None of the rockets will launch on February 1. The mission to test a new propulsion system won't be launching in January.

(b) The *Liberty* and the rocket that will blast off in April will launch from Cape Carnival and Willard Island in some order. Neither the rocket on a mission to measure magnetic fields (which won't launch on the 1st of a month) nor the Willard Island rocket will blast off on the 3rd of a month.

(c) The *Bravura* will launch the month after the rocket that will blast off on the 4th of a month (which will launch later than the rocket that will land on the moon). The *Liberty* won't blast off on the 2nd of a month.

(d) The rocket that will launch from Cape Carnival won't be testing a new propulsion system. The *Twilight*'s mission (which isn't the mission to repair a satellite) won't begin on the 5th of a month.

(e) The rocket on a mission to investigate strange radiation will launch at some point earlier in the year than the *Liberty* (which won't be repairing a satellite) but at some point later in the year than the vessel that will blast off from the Vandyke Facility.

(f) The rocket that will blast off from Eddings Air Force Base will launch on a lower-numbered date than the one that will launch in March (which won't be testing a new propulsion system), which will blast off on a lower-numbered date than the *Falconer*.

2. *Super Challenger Puzzle* To solve the following Super Challenger puzzle, place a number into every box so that each row across, each column down, each small 16-box square (there are 16 of these), and each of the two diagonals contains each number from 1 to 16. No number may appear more than once in any one row or column, in either diagonal, or within any small 16-box square.

○	10		4		6	14		16			8				○
	○	7		8		9		2	11	5		16		○	6
13	8	○	14				7		15	3			○	12	
		2	○	5		12	15	6				○	4	7	8
	13		10	○			3	1		8	○				
		16	2		○	15	4		5	○	11	1	3		
1			12		8	○			○			9		10	13
	14			13	9		○	○	2	15	10		6		11
4		5		14	12	3	○	○		2	15			1	
15	16		9			○			○	13		14			4
		10	6	9	○	4		11	1	○		3	5		
				○	1		16	5			○	2		11	
10	9	14	○				12	15	13		3	○	11		
	2	○			11	5		7				10	○	3	16
16	○		13		7	1	6		10		2		14	○	
○				10			9		4	16		6		2	○

CHAPTER TEST

Write a negation for each statement.

1. $6 - 3 = 3$

2. All men are created equal.

3. Some members of the class went on the field trip.

4. If that's the way you feel, then I will accept it.

5. She applied and got a student loan.

Let p represent "You will love me" *and let q represent* "I will love you." *Write each statement in symbols.*

6. If you won't love me, then I will love you.

7. I will love you if you will love me.

8. I won't love you if and only if you won't love me.

Using the same statements as for Exercises 6–8, write each of the following in words.

9. $\sim p \wedge q$

10. $\sim(p \vee \sim q)$

In each of the following, assume that p is true and that q and r are false. Find the truth value of each statement.

11. $\sim q \wedge \sim r$

12. $r \vee (p \wedge \sim q)$

13. $r \rightarrow (s \vee r)$ (The truth value of the statement s is unknown.)

14. $p \leftrightarrow (p \rightarrow q)$

15. Explain in your own words why, if p is a statement, the biconditional $p \leftrightarrow \sim p$ must be false.

16. State the necessary conditions for each of the following.

(a) a conditional statement to be false

(b) a conjunction to be true

(c) a disjunction to be false

Construct a truth table for each of the following.

17. $p \wedge (\sim p \vee q)$

18. $\sim(p \wedge q) \rightarrow (\sim p \vee \sim q)$

Decide whether each statement is true *or* false.

19. Some negative integers are whole numbers.

20. All irrational numbers are real numbers.

Write each conditional statement in if . . . then *form.*

21. All integers are rational numbers.

22. Being a rhombus is sufficient for a polygon to be a quadrilateral.

23. Being divisible by 2 is necessary for a number to be divisible by 4.

24. She digs dinosaur bones only if she is a paleontologist.

For each statement, write **(a)** *the converse,* **(b)** *the inverse, and* **(c)** *the contrapositive.*

25. If a picture paints a thousand words, the graph will help me understand it.

26. $\sim p \rightarrow (q \wedge r)$ (Use one of De Morgan's laws as necessary.)

27. Use an Euler diagram to determine whether the argument is *valid* or *invalid.*

All members of that athletic club save money.
Don O'Neal is a member of that athletic club.
―――――――――――――――
Don O'Neal saves money.

28. Match each argument in parts (a)–(d) in the next column with the law that justifies its validity, or the fallacy of which it is an example, in choices A–F.

A. Modus ponens
B. Modus tollens
C. Reasoning by transitivity
D. Disjunctive syllogism
E. Fallacy of the converse
F. Fallacy of the inverse

(a) If he eats liver, then he'll eat anything.
He eats liver.
―――――――――――――――
He'll eat anything.

(b) If you use your seat belt, you will be safer.
You don't use your seat belt.
―――――――――――――――
You won't be safer.

(c) If I hear *Mr. Bojangles*, I think of her.
If I think of her, I smile.
―――――――――――――――
If I hear *Mr. Bojangles*, I smile.

(d) She sings or she dances.
She does not sing.
―――――――――――――――
She dances.

Use a truth table to determine whether each argument is valid *or* invalid.

29. If I write a check, it will bounce. If the bank guarantees it, then it does not bounce. The bank guarantees it. Therefore, I don't write a check.

30. $\sim p \rightarrow \sim q$
$q \rightarrow p$
―――
$p \vee q$

ANSWERS TO SELECTED EXERCISES

1 Exercises

1. statement **3.** not a statement **5.** statement **7.** statement **9.** statement **11.** not a statement **13.** statement **15.** compound **17.** not compound **19.** not compound **21.** compound **23.** Her aunt's name is not Hermione. **25.** At least one dog does not have its day. **27.** No book is longer than this book. **29.** At least one computer repairman can play blackjack. **31.** Someone does not love somebody sometime. **33.** $x \leq 12$ **35.** $x < 5$ **37.** Answers will vary. **39.** She does not have green eyes. **41.** She has green eyes and he is 60 years old. **43.** She does not have green eyes or he is 60 years old. **45.** She does not have green eyes or he is not 60 years old. **47.** It is not the case that she does not have green eyes and he is 60 years old. **49.** $p \wedge \sim q$ **51.** $\sim p \vee q$ **53.** $\sim(p \vee q)$ or, equivalently, $\sim p \wedge \sim q$ **55.** Answers will vary. **57.** C **59.** A, B **61.** A, C **63.** B **65.** true **67.** true **69.** true **71.** true **73.** false **75.** Answers will vary. **77.** Every person here has done that at one time or another.

2 Exercises

1. false **3.** true **5.** They must both be false. **7.** T **9.** T **11.** F **13.** T **15.** T **17.** T **19.** It is a disjunction, because it means "$6 > 2$ or $6 = 2$." **21.** T **23.** F **25.** T **27.** T **29.** F **31.** F **33.** T **35.** T **37.** T **39.** 4 **41.** 16 **43.** 128 **45.** seven **47.** FFTF

49. FTTT **51.** TTTT **53.** FFFT **55.** TFFF **57.** FFFFTFFF **59.** FTFTTTTT **61.** TTTTTTTTTTTTFTTT **63.** You can't pay me now and you can't pay me later. **65.** It is not summer or there is snow. **67.** I did not say yes or she did not say no. **69.** $6 - 1 \neq 5$ or $9 + 13 = 7$ **71.** Neither Prancer nor Vixen will lead Santa's reindeer sleigh next Christmas.

73. T **75.** F **77.**

p	q	$p \veebar q$
T	T	F
T	F	T
F	T	T
F	F	F

79. F **81.** T **83.** The lady is behind Door 2. *Reasoning*: Suppose that the sign on Door 1 is true. Then the sign on Door 2 would also be true, but this is impossible. So the sign on Door 2 must be true, and the sign on Door 1 must be false. Because the sign on Door 1 says the lady is in Room 1, and this is false, the lady must be behind Door 2.

3 Exercises

1. If you see it on the Internet, then you can believe it. **3.** If an integer is divisible by 10, then it is divisible by 5. **5.** If the soldier is a marine, then the soldier loves boot camp. **7.** If it is a panda, then it does not live in Idaho. **9.** If it is an opium-eater, then it has no self-command. **11.** true **13.** true **15.** false **17.** true **19.** Answers will vary. **21.** F **23.** T **25.** T **27.** If they do not raise alpacas, then he trains dogs. **29.** If she has a bird for a pet, then they raise alpacas and he trains dogs. **31.** If he does not train dogs, then they do not raise alpacas or she has a bird for a pet. **33.** $b \to p$ **35.** $p \to \sim s$ **37.** $p \wedge (s \to \sim b)$ **39.** $p \to s$ **41.** T **43.** F **45.** T **47.** F **49.** T **51.** T **53.** Answers will vary. **55.** TTTF **57.** TTFT **59.** TTTT; tautology **61.** TFTF **63.** TTTTTTFT **65.** TTTFTTTTTTTTTTTT **67.** one **69.** That is an authentic Rolex watch and I am not surprised. **71.** The English measures are not converted to metric measures and the spacecraft does not crash on the surface of Saturn. **73.** You want to be happy for the rest of your life and you make a pretty woman your wife. **75.** You do not give your plants tender, loving care or they flourish. **77.** She does or he will. **79.** The person is not a resident of Pensacola or is a resident of Florida. **81.** equivalent **83.** equivalent **85.** not equivalent **87.** equivalent **89.** equivalent **91.** $(p \wedge q) \vee (p \wedge \sim q)$; The statement simplifies to p. **93.** $p \vee (\sim q \wedge r)$ **95.** $\sim p \vee (p \vee q)$; The statement simplifies to T.

97. The statement simplifies to $p \wedge q$.

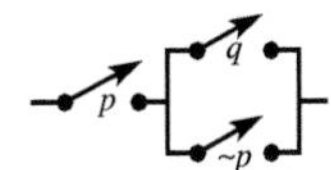

99. The statement simplifies to F.

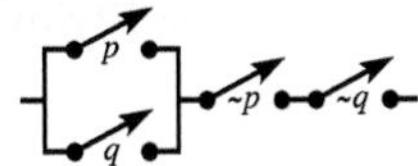

101. The statement simplifies to $(r \wedge \sim p) \wedge q$.

103. The statement simplifies to $p \vee q$.

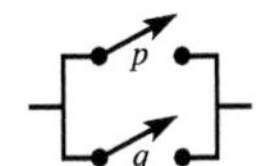

105. $525.60

4 Exercises

1. **(a)** If you were an hour, then beauty would be a minute. **(b)** If beauty were not a minute, then you would not be an hour. **(c)** If you were not an hour, then beauty would not be a minute. **3.** **(a)** If you don't fix it, then it ain't broke. **(b)** If it's broke, then fix it. **(c)** If you fix it, then it's broke. **5.** **(a)** If it is dangerous to your health, then you walk in front of a moving car. **(b)** If you do not walk in front of a moving car, then it is not dangerous to your health. **(c)** If it is not dangerous to your health, then you do not walk in front of a moving car. **7.** **(a)** If they flock together, then they are birds of a feather. **(b)** If they are not birds of a feather, then they do not flock together. **(c)** If they do not flock together, then they are not birds of a feather. **9.** **(a)** If he comes, then you built it. **(b)** If you don't build it, then he won't come. **(c)** If he doesn't come, then you didn't build it. **11.** **(a)** $\sim q \to p$ **(b)** $\sim p \to q$ **(c)** $q \to \sim p$ **13.** **(a)** $\sim q \to \sim p$ **(b)** $p \to q$ **(c)** $q \to p$ **15.** **(a)** $(q \vee r) \to p$ **(b)** $\sim p \to (\sim q \wedge \sim r)$ **(c)** $(\sim q \wedge \sim r) \to \sim p$ **17.** Answers will vary. **19.** If it is muddy, then I'll wear my galoshes. **21.** If 19 is positive, then $19 + 1$ is positive. **23.** If a number is an integer, then it is a rational number. **25.** If I do logic puzzles, then I am driven crazy. **27.** If Jeff Marsalis is to shave, then he must have a day's growth of beard. **29.** If I go from Boardwalk to Baltic Avenue, then I pass GO. **31.** If a number is a whole number, then it is an integer. **33.** If their pitching improves, then the Nationals will win the pennant. **35.** If the figure is a rectangle, then it is a parallelogram with a right angle. **37.** If a triangle has two perpendicular sides, then it is a right triangle. **39.** If a two-digit number whose units digit is 5 is squared, then the square will end in 25. **41.** D **43.** Answers will vary. **45.** true **47.** false

49. false **51.** contrary **53.** consistent **55.** contrary **57.** consistent **59.** Answers will vary. One example is: That man is Otis Taylor. That man sells books.

5 Exercises

1. valid **3.** invalid **5.** valid **7.** invalid **9.** invalid
11. invalid **13.** yes
15. All people with blue eyes have blond hair.
Natalie Graham does not have blond hair.
———————————————
Natalie Graham does not have blue eyes.
17. invalid **19.** valid **21.** invalid **23.** valid
25. invalid **27.** invalid **29.** valid

Extension Exercises

1. Drew, spanakopita, Fresh Air, spearmint; Ilse, buffalo-chicken sandwich, Deltoids, cinnamon; Nash, French onion soup, Liplickers, vanilla; Uma, tuna-salad sandwich, TKO, wintergreen; Xerxes, garlic shrimp, Inti-mints, orange **3.** 1st, Earl, Ox, fire; 2nd, Philip, Rooster, metal; 3rd, Toni, Cow, water; 4th, Lucy, Dragon, earth; 5th, Ivana, Horse, wood

5.

7	4	2	1	6	8	9	3	5
3	1	9	4	5	7	6	2	8
8	6	5	9	3	2	7	1	4
6	2	4	7	8	9	1	5	3
1	3	8	5	4	6	2	9	7
5	9	7	2	1	3	8	4	6
2	5	3	8	7	1	4	6	9
9	7	6	3	2	4	5	8	1
4	8	1	6	9	5	3	7	2

7.

8	3	9	6	5	7	2	4	1
7	1	2	9	4	3	8	5	6
4	5	6	2	1	8	3	7	9
2	6	7	1	9	4	5	3	8
3	9	1	8	2	5	4	6	7
5	4	8	7	3	6	1	9	2
1	2	3	5	6	9	7	8	4
9	8	4	3	7	2	6	1	5
6	7	5	4	8	1	9	2	3

9.

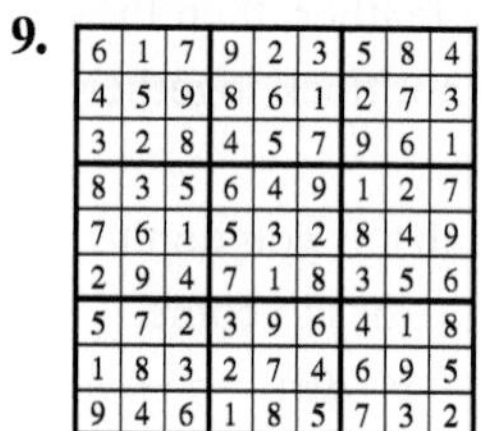

6	1	7	9	2	3	5	8	4
4	5	9	8	6	1	2	7	3
3	2	8	4	5	7	9	6	1
8	3	5	6	4	9	1	2	7
7	6	1	5	3	2	8	4	9
2	9	4	7	1	8	3	5	6
5	7	2	3	9	6	4	1	8
1	8	3	2	7	4	6	9	5
9	4	6	1	8	5	7	3	2

6 Exercises

1. valid by reasoning by transitivity **3.** valid by modus ponens **5.** fallacy by fallacy of the converse **7.** valid by modus tollens **9.** fallacy by fallacy of the inverse
11. valid by disjunctive syllogism **13.** invalid **15.** valid
17. invalid **19.** valid **21.** invalid **23.** invalid
25. invalid
27. Every time something squeaks, I use WD-40.
Every time I use WD-40, I go to the hardware store.
———————————————
Every time something squeaks, I go to the hardware store.

29. valid **31.** invalid **33.** invalid **35.** valid
37. valid **39.** If I tell you the time, then my life will be miserable. **41.** If it is my poultry, then it is a duck.
43. If it is a guinea pig, then it is hopelessly ignorant of music. **45.** If it is a teachable kitten, then it does not have green eyes. **47.** If I can read it, then I have not filed it. **49. (a)** $p \to \sim s$ **(b)** $r \to s$ **(c)** $q \to p$
(d) None of my poultry are officers. **51. (a)** $r \to \sim s$
(b) $u \to t$ **(c)** $\sim r \to p$ **(d)** $\sim u \to \sim q$ **(e)** $t \to s$
(f) All pawnbrokers are honest. **53. (a)** $r \to w$
(b) $\sim u \to \sim t$ **(c)** $v \to \sim s$ **(d)** $x \to r$ **(e)** $\sim q \to t$
(f) $y \to p$ **(g)** $w \to s$ **(h)** $\sim x \to \sim q$ **(i)** $p \to \sim u$
(j) I can't read any of Brown's letters.

Collaborative Investigation

1. Jan. 1, Vandyke Facility, *Penchant*, repair satellite; Feb. 5, San Simeon Launch Center, *Falconer*, investigate radiation; Mar. 3, Cape Carnival, *Liberty*, land on moon; Apr. 4, Willard Island, *Twilight*, test propulsion; May 2, Eddings Air Force Base, *Bravura*, measure magnetic fields

2.

5	10	11	4	1	6	14	2	16	7	12	8	15	9	13	3
12	15	7	3	8	4	9	13	2	11	5	1	16	10	14	6
13	8	6	14	11	16	10	7	9	15	3	4	5	1	12	2
9	1	2	16	5	3	12	15	6	14	10	13	11	4	7	8
11	13	9	10	2	14	16	3	1	12	8	6	7	15	4	5
7	6	16	2	12	10	15	4	13	5	9	11	1	3	8	14
1	4	15	12	6	8	11	5	3	16	7	14	9	2	10	13
3	14	8	5	13	9	7	1	4	2	15	10	12	6	16	11
4	7	5	11	14	12	3	10	8	6	2	15	13	16	1	9
15	16	1	9	7	5	2	11	10	3	13	12	14	8	6	4
2	12	10	6	9	13	4	8	11	1	14	16	3	5	15	7
14	3	13	8	15	1	6	16	5	9	4	7	2	12	11	10
10	9	14	7	16	2	8	12	15	13	6	3	4	11	5	1
6	2	12	15	4	11	5	14	7	8	1	9	10	13	3	16
16	5	4	13	3	7	1	6	12	10	11	2	8	14	9	15
8	11	3	1	10	15	13	9	14	4	16	5	6	7	2	12

Chapter Test

1. $6 - 3 \neq 3$ **2.** Some men are not created equal.
3. No members of the class went on the field trip.
4. That's the way you feel and I won't accept it.

5. She did not apply or did not get a student loan. **6.** $\sim p \rightarrow q$ **7.** $p \rightarrow q$ **8.** $\sim q \leftrightarrow \sim p$ **9.** You won't love me and I will love you. **10.** It is not the case that you will love me or I will not love you. (Equivalently: You won't love me and I will love you.) **11.** T **12.** T **13.** T **14.** F **15.** Answers will vary. **16. (a)** The antecedent must be true and the consequent must be false. **(b)** Both component statements must be true. **(c)** Both component statements must be false. **17.** TFFF **18.** TTTT (tautology) **19.** false **20.** true

Wording may vary in the answers for Exercises 21–25.

21. If the number is an integer, then it is a rational number. **22.** If a polygon is a rhombus, then it is a quadrilateral. **23.** If a number is divisible by 4, then it is divisible by 2. **24.** If she digs dinosaur bones, then she is a paleontologist. **25. (a)** If the graph helps me understand it, then a picture paints a thousand words. **(b)** If a picture doesn't paint a thousand words, then the graph won't help me understand it. **(c)** If the graph doesn't help me understand it, then a picture doesn't paint a thousand words. **26. (a)** $(q \wedge r) \rightarrow \sim p$ **(b)** $p \rightarrow (\sim q \vee \sim r)$ **(c)** $(\sim q \vee \sim r) \rightarrow p$ **27.** valid **28. (a)** A **(b)** F **(c)** C **(d)** D **29.** valid **30.** invalid

Introduction to Logic

1 Exercises

1. "February 2, 2009, was a Monday" is a declarative sentence that is true and, therefore, is considered a statement.

3. "Listen my children and you shall hear of the midnight ride of Paul Revere" is not a declarative sentence and does not have the property of being true or false. Hence, it is not considered a statement.

5. "$5 + 9 \neq 14$ and $4 - 1 = 12$" is a declarative sentence that is false and, therefore, is considered a statement.

7. "Some numbers are positive" is a declarative sentence that is true and, therefore, is a statement.

9. "Accidents are the main cause of deaths of children under the age of 7" is a declarative sentence that has the property of being true or false and, therefore, is considered to be a statement.

11. "Where are you going tomorrow?" is a question, not a declarative sentence and, therefore, is not considered a statement.

13. "Kevin 'Catfish' McCarthy once took a prolonged continuous shower for 340 hours, 40 minutes" is a declarative sentence that has the property of being either true or false and, therefore, is considered to be a statement.

15. "I read the Detroit Free Press, and I read the Sacramento Bee" is a compound statement because it consists of two simple statements combined by the connective "and."

17. "Tomorrow is Saturday" is a simple statement because only one assertion is being made.

19. "Jay Beckenstein's wife loves Ben and Jerry's ice cream" is not compound because only one assertion is being made.

21. "If Lorri Morgan sells her quota, then Michelle Cook will be happy" is a compound statement because it consists of two simple statements combined by the connective "if...then."

23. The negation of "Her aunt's name is Hermione" is "Her aunt's name is not Hermione."

25. A negation of "Every dog has its day" is "At least one dog does not have its day."

27. A negation of "Some books are longer than this book" is "No book is longer than this book."

29. A negation of "No computer repairman can play blackjack" is "At least one computer repairman can play blackjack."

31. A negation of "Everybody loves somebody sometime" is "Someone does not love somebody sometime."

33. A negation of "$x > 12$" (without using a slash sign) would be "$x \leq 12$."

35. A negation for "$x \geq 5$" would be "$x < 5$."

37. Writing exercise; answers will vary.

Let p represent the statement "She has green eyes," and let q represent "He is 60 years old." Translate each symbolic compound statement into words.

39. A translation for "$\sim p$" is "She does not have green eyes."

41. A translation for "$p \wedge q$" is "She has green eyes and he is 60 years old."

43. A translation for "$\sim p \vee q$" is "She does not have green eyes or he is 60 years old."

45. A translation for "$\sim p \vee \sim q$" is "She does not have green eyes or he is not 60 years old."

47. A translation for "$\sim(\sim p \wedge q)$" is "It is not the case that she does not have green eyes and he is 60 years old."

49. "Chris collects DVDs and Josh is not an art major" may be symbolized as $p \wedge \sim q$.

51. "Chris does not collect DVDs or Josh is an art major" may be symbolized as $\sim p \vee q$.

53. "Neither Chris collects DVDs nor Josh is an art major" may be symbolized as $\sim(p \vee q)$ or equivalently, $\sim p \wedge \sim q$.

55. Writing exercise; answers will vary.

Refer to the sketches labeled A, B, and C in the text, and identify the sketch (or sketches) that is (are) satisfied by the given statement involving a quantifier.

57. The condition that "all pictures have frames" is satisfied by group C.

59. The condition that "At least one picture does not have a frame" is met by groups A and B.

61. The condition that "At least one picture has a frame" is satisfied by groups A and C.

63. The condition that "all pictures do not have frames" is satisfied by group B. Observe that this statement is equivalent to "No pictures have a frame."

65. Since all whole numbers are integers, the statement "Every whole number is an integer" is true.

67. Since $\frac{1}{2}$ is a rational number but not an integer, the statement "There exists a rational number that is not an integer" is true.

69. Since rational numbers are real numbers, the statement "All rational numbers are real numbers" is true.

71. Since $\frac{1}{2}$ is a rational number but not an integer, the statement "Some rational numbers are not integers" is true.

73. The number 0 is a whole number but not positive. Thus, the statement "Each whole number is a positive number" is false.

75. Writing exercise; answers will vary.

77. We might write the statement "There is no one here who has not done that at one time or another" using the word "every" as "Every person here has done that at one time or another."

2 Exercises

1. If q is false, then $(p \wedge \sim q) \wedge q$ must be false, since both conjuncts (parts of the conjunction) must be true for the compound statement to be true.

3. If $p \wedge q$ is true, and p is true, then q must also be true in order for the conjunctive statement to be true. Observe that both conjuncts must be true for a conjunctive statement to be true.

5. If $\sim(p \vee q)$ is true, both components (disjuncts) must be false. Thus, the disjunction itself is false making its negation true.

In exercises 7–17, p represents a false statement and q represents a true statement.

7. Since p = F, $\sim p = \sim$F = T. That is, replace p by F and determine the truth of ~F.

9. Since p is false and q is true, we may consider the "or" statement as
F $\vee$ T
T,
by logical definition of an "or" statement. That is $p \vee q$ is true.

11. With the given truth values for p and q, we may consider $p \vee \sim q$ as
F $\vee$ ~T
F $\vee$ F
F,
by the logical definition of "$\vee$."

13. With the given truth values for p and q, we may consider $\sim p \vee \sim q$ as
~F $\vee$ ~T
T $\vee$ F
T.
Thus, the compound statement is true.

15. Replacing p and q with the given truth values, we have
~(F $\wedge$ ~T)
~(F $\wedge$ F)
~F
T.
Thus, the compound statement $\sim(p \wedge \sim q)$ is true.

17. Replacing p and q with the given truth values, we have
$\sim[\sim F \wedge (\sim T \vee F)]$
$\sim[T \wedge (F \vee F)]$
$\sim[T \wedge F]$
$\sim F$
T.
Thus, the compound statement $\sim[\sim p \wedge (\sim q \vee p)]$ is true.

19. The statement $6 \geq 2$ is a disjunction since it means "6 > 2" or "6 = 2."

In exercises 21–27, p represents a true statement, and q and r represent false statements.

21. Replacing p, q and r with the given truth values, we have
$(T \wedge F) \vee \sim F$
$F \vee T$
T.
Thus, the compound statement $(p \wedge r) \vee \sim q$ is true.

23. Replacing p, q and r with the given truth values, we have
$T \wedge (F \vee F)$
$T \wedge F$
F.
Thus, the compound statement $p \wedge (q \vee r)$ is false.

25. Replacing p, q and r with the given truth values, we have
$\sim(T \wedge F) \wedge (F \vee \sim F)$
$\sim F \wedge (F \vee T)$
$T \wedge T$
T.
Thus, the compound statement $\sim(p \wedge q) \wedge (r \vee \sim q)$ is true.

27. Replacing p, q and r with the given truth values, we have
$\sim[(\sim T \wedge F) \vee F]$
$\sim[(F \wedge F) \vee F]$
$\sim[F \vee F]$
$\sim F$
T.
Thus, the compound statement $\sim[(\sim p \wedge q) \vee r]$ is true.

29. Replacing p, q and r with the given truth values, we have
$\sim[\sim q \vee (r \wedge \sim p)]$
$\sim[\sim F \vee (F \wedge \sim T)]$
$\sim[T \vee F]$
$\sim T$
F.
Thus, the compound statement $\sim[\sim q \vee (r \wedge \sim p)]$ is false.

Let p represent the statement "16 < 8," which is false, let q represent "5 ≯ 4," which is false and let r represent "17 ≤ 17," which is true.
[E.g. p = F, q = F and r = T.]

31. Replacing p and r with the given truth values, we have
$F \wedge T$
F.
The compound statement $p \wedge r$ is false.

33. Replacing q adn r with the observed truth values, we have
$\sim F \vee \sim T$
$T \vee F$
T.
The compound statement $\sim q \vee \sim r$ is true.

35. Replacing p, q and r with the observed truth values, we have
$(F \wedge F) \vee T$
$F \vee T$
T.
The compound statement $(p \wedge q) \vee r$ is true.

37. Replacing p, q and r with the observed truth values, we have
$(\sim T \wedge F) \vee \sim F$
$(F \wedge F) \vee T$
$F \vee T$
T.
The compound statement $(\sim r \wedge q) \vee \sim p$ is true.

39. Since there are two simple statements (p and r), we have $2^2 = 4$ combinations of truth values, or rows in the truth table, to examine.

41. Since there are four simple statements (p, q, r, and s), we have $2^4 = 16$ combinations of truth values, or rows in the truth table, to examine.

43. Since there are seven simple statements (p, q, r, s, t, u, and v), we have $2^7 = 128$ combinations of truth values, or rows in the truth table, to examine.

45. If the truth table for a certain compound statement has 128 rows, then there must be seven distinct component statements ($2^7 = 128$).

47. $\sim p \wedge q$

p	q	$\sim p$	$\sim p \wedge q$
T	T	F	F
T	F	F	F
F	T	T	T
F	F	T	F

49. $\sim(p \wedge q)$

p	q	$p \wedge q$	$\sim(p \wedge q)$
T	T	T	F
T	F	F	T
F	T	F	T
F	F	F	T

51. $(q \vee \sim p) \vee \sim q$

p	q	$\sim p$	$\sim q$	$(q \vee \sim p)$	$(q \vee \sim p) \vee \sim q$
T	T	F	F	T	T
T	F	F	T	F	T
F	T	T	F	T	T
F	F	T	T	T	T

53. $\sim q \wedge (\sim p \vee q)$

p	q	$\sim q$	$\wedge$	$(\sim p$	$\vee$	$q)$
T	T	F	F	F	T	T
T	F	T	F	F	F	F
F	T	F	F	T	T	T
F	F	T	T	T	T	F
		1	3	1	2	1

55. $(p \vee \sim q) \wedge (p \wedge q)$

p	q	$(p$	$\vee$	$\sim q)$	$\wedge$	$(p$	$\wedge$	$q)$
T	T	T	T	F	T	T	T	T
T	F	T	T	T	F	T	F	F
F	T	F	F	F	F	F	F	T
F	F	F	T	T	F	F	F	F
		1	2	1	3	1	2	1

57. $(\sim p \wedge q) \wedge r$

p	q	r	$(\sim p$	$\wedge$	$q)$	$\wedge$	r
T	T	T	F	F	T	F	T
T	T	F	F	F	T	F	F
T	F	T	F	F	F	F	T
T	F	F	F	F	F	F	F
F	T	T	T	T	T	T	T
F	T	F	T	T	T	F	F
F	F	T	T	F	F	F	T
F	F	F	T	F	F	F	F
			1	2	1	3	1

59. $(\sim p \wedge \sim q) \vee (\sim r \vee \sim p)$

p	q	r	$(\sim p$	$\wedge$	$\sim q)$	$\vee$	$(\sim r$	$\vee$	$\sim p)$
T	T	T	F	F	F	F	F	F	F
T	T	F	F	F	F	T	T	T	F
T	F	T	F	F	T	F	F	F	F
T	F	F	F	F	T	T	T	T	F
F	T	T	T	F	F	T	F	T	T
F	T	F	T	F	F	T	T	T	T
F	F	T	T	T	T	T	F	T	T
F	F	F	T	T	T	T	T	T	T
			1	2	1	3	1	2	1

61. $\sim(\sim p \wedge \sim q) \vee (\sim r \vee \sim s)$

p	q	r	s	$\sim$	$(\sim p$	$\wedge$	$\sim q)$	$\vee$	$(\sim r$	$\vee$	$\sim s)$
T	T	T	T	T	F	F	F	T	F	F	F
T	T	T	F	T	F	F	F	T	F	T	T
T	T	F	T	T	F	F	F	T	T	T	F
T	T	F	F	T	F	F	F	T	T	T	T
T	F	T	T	T	F	F	T	T	F	F	F
T	F	T	F	T	F	F	T	T	F	T	T
T	F	F	T	T	F	F	T	T	T	T	F
T	F	F	F	T	F	F	T	T	T	T	T
F	T	T	T	T	T	F	F	T	F	F	F
F	T	T	F	T	T	F	F	T	F	T	T
F	T	F	T	T	T	F	F	T	T	T	F
F	T	F	F	T	T	F	F	T	T	T	T
F	F	T	T	F	T	T	T	F	F	F	F
F	F	T	F	F	T	T	T	T	F	T	T
F	F	F	T	F	T	T	T	T	T	T	F
F	F	F	F	F	T	T	T	T	T	T	T
				3	1	2	1	4	2	3	2

63. "You can pay me now or you can pay me later" has the symbolic form $(p \vee q)$. The negation, $\sim(p \vee q)$, is equivalent, by one of De Morgan's laws, to $(\sim p \wedge \sim q)$. The corresponding word statement is "You can't pay me now and you can't pay me later."

65. "It is summer and there is no snow" has the symbolic form $p \wedge \sim q$. The negation, $\sim(p \wedge \sim q)$, is equivalent by De Morgan's to $\sim p \vee q$. The word translation for the negation is "It is not summer or there is snow."

67. "I said yes but she said no" is of the form $p \wedge q$. The negation, $\sim(p \wedge q)$, is equivalent, by De Morgan's, to $\sim p \vee \sim q$. The word translation for the negation is "I did not say yes or she did not say no." (Note: The connective "but" is equivalent to that of "and.")

69. "$6 - 1 = 5$ and $9 + 3 \neq 7$" is of the form
$p \wedge \sim q$. The negation, $\sim(p \wedge \sim q)$, is equivalent, by De Morgan's, to $\sim p \vee q$. The translation for the negation is "$6 - 1 \neq 5$ or
$9 + 3 = 7$."

71. "Prancer or Vixen will lead Santa's sleigh next Christmas" is of the form $p \vee q$. The negation, $\sim(p \vee q)$, is equivalent, by De Morgan's, to $\sim p \wedge \sim q$. A translation for the negation is "Neither Prancer nor Vixen will lead Santa's sleigh next Christmas."

73. "For every real number x, $x < 14$ or $x > 6$" is true since for any real number at least one of the component statements is true.

75. "There exists an integer n such that $n > 0$ and $n < 0$" is false since any integer which is true for one of the component statements will be false for the other.

77. $p \veebar q$

p	q	$p \veebar q$
T	T	F
T	F	T
F	T	T
F	F	F

Observe that it is only the first line in the truth table that changes for "exclusive disjunction" since the component statements cannot both be true at the same time.

79. "$3 + 1 = 4 \veebar 2 + 5 = 7$" is false since both component statements are true.

81. "$3 + 1 = 6 \veebar 2 + 5 = 7$" is true since the first component statement is false and the second is true.

83. The lady is behind Door 2. *Reasoning:* Suppose that the sign on Door 1 is true. Then the sign on Door 2 would also be true, but this is impossible. So the sign on door 2 must be true, and the sign on door 1 must be false. Because the sign on Door 1 says the lady is in Room 1 and this is false, the lady must be behind Door 2.

3 Exercises

1. The statement "You can believe it if you see it on the Internet" becomes "If you see it on the Internet, then you can believe it."

3. The statement "Every integer divisible by 10 is divisible by 5" becomes "If an integer is divisible by 10, then it is divisible by 5."

5. The statement "All marines love boot camp" becomes "If the soldier is a marine, then the soldier loves boot camp."

7. The statement "No pandas live in Idaho" becomes "If it is a panda, then it does not live in Idaho."

9. The statement "An opium-eater cannot have self-command" becomes "If it is an opium eater, then it has no self-command."

11. The statement "If the antecedent of a conditional statement is false, the conditional statement is true" is true, since a false antecedent will always yield a true conditional statement.

13. The statement "If q is true, then $(p \wedge q) \rightarrow q$ is true" is true, since with a true consequent the conditional statement is always true (even though the antecedent may be false).

15. The negation of "If pigs fly, I'll believe it" is "If pigs don't fly, I won't believe it." This statement is false. The negation is "Pigs fly and I don't believe it."

17. "Given that $\sim p$ is true and q is false, the conditional $p \rightarrow q$ is true" is a true statement since the antecedent, p, must be false.

19. Writing exercise; answers will vary.

21. "$T \rightarrow (7 < 3)$" is a false statement, since the antecedent is true and the consequent is false.

23. "$F \rightarrow (5 \neq 5)$" is a true statement, since a false antecedent always yields a true conditional statement.

25. "$(5^2 \neq 25) \rightarrow (9 > 0)$" is a true statement, since a false antecedent always yields a true conditional statement.

Let s represent the statement "She has a bird for a pet," let p represent the statement "he trains dogs," and let m represent "they raise alpacas."

27. "$\sim m \rightarrow p$" expressed in words, becomes "If they do not raise alpacas, then he trains dogs."

29. "$s \rightarrow (m \wedge p)$" expressed in words, becomes "If she has a bird for a pet, then they raise alpacas and he trains dogs."

31. "$\sim p \rightarrow (\sim m \vee s)$" expressed in words, becomes "If he does not train dogs, then they do not raise alpacas or she has a bird for a pet."

Let b represent the statement "I ride my bike," let s represent the statement "it snows" and let p represent "the play is canceled."

33. The statement "If I ride my bike, then the play is canceled," can be symbolized as "$b \rightarrow p$."

35. The statement "If the play is canceled, then it does not snow" can be symbolized as "$p \rightarrow \sim s$."

37. The statement "The play is canceled, and if it snows then I do not ride my bike" can be symbolized as "$p \wedge (s \to \sim b)$."

39. The statement "It snows if the play is canceled" can be symbolized as "$p \to s$."

Assume that p and r are false, and q is true.

41. Replacing r and q with the given truth values, we have
~F → T
T → T
T.
Thus, the compound statement $\sim r \to q$ is true.

43. Replacing p and q with the given truth values, we have
T → F
F.
Thus, the compound statement $q \to p$ is false.

45. Replacing p and q with the given truth values, we have
F → T
T.
Thus, the compound statement $p \to q$ is true.

47. Replacing p, r and q with the given truth values, we have
~F → (T ∧ F)
T → F
F.
Thus, the compound statement $\sim p \to (q \wedge r)$ is false.

49. Replacing p, r and q with the given truth values, we have
~T → (F ∧ F)
F → F
T.
Thus, the compound statement $\sim q \to (p \wedge r)$ is true.

51. Replacing p, r and q with the given truth values, we have
(F → ~T) → (~F ∧ ~F)
(F → F) → (T ∧ T)
T → T
T.
Thus, the compound statement $(p \to \sim q) \to (\sim p \wedge \sim r)$ is true.

53. Writing exercise; answers will vary.

55. $\sim q \to p$

p	q	$\sim q$	$\to$	p
T	T	F	T	T
T	F	T	T	T
F	T	F	T	F
F	F	T	F	F
		1	2	1

57. $(\sim p \to q) \to p$

p	q	$(\sim p$	$\to$	$q)$	$\to$	p
T	T	F	T	T	T	T
T	F	F	T	F	T	T
F	T	T	T	T	F	F
F	F	T	F	F	T	F
		1	2	1	3	2

59. $(p \vee q) \to (q \vee p)$

p	q	$(p$	$\vee$	$q)$	$\to$	$(q$	$\vee$	$p)$
T	T	T	T	T	T	T	T	T
T	F	T	T	F	T	F	T	T
F	T	F	T	T	T	T	T	F
F	F	F	F	F	T	F	F	F
		1	2	1	3	1	2	1

Since this statement is always true (column 3), it is a tautology.

61. $(\sim p \to \sim q) \to (p \wedge q)$

p	q	$(\sim p$	$\to$	$\sim q)$	$\to$	$(p$	$\wedge$	$q)$
T	T	F	T	F	T	T	T	T
T	F	F	T	T	F	T	F	F
F	T	T	F	F	T	F	F	T
F	F	T	T	T	F	F	F	F
		1	2	1	3	1	2	1

63. $[(r \vee p) \wedge \sim q] \rightarrow p$

p	q	r	$[(r$	$\vee$	$p)$	$\wedge$	$\sim q]$	$\rightarrow$	p
T	T	T	T	T	T	F	F	T	T
T	T	F	F	T	T	F	F	T	T
T	F	T	T	T	T	T	T	T	T
T	F	F	F	T	T	T	T	T	T
F	T	T	T	T	F	F	F	T	F
F	T	F	F	F	F	F	F	T	F
F	F	T	T	T	F	T	T	F	F
F	F	F	F	F	F	F	T	T	F
			1	2	1	3	2	4	3

65. $(\sim r \rightarrow s) \vee (p \rightarrow \sim q)$

p	q	r	s	$(\sim r$	$\rightarrow$	$s)$	$\vee$	$(p$	$\rightarrow$	$\sim q)$
T	T	T	T	F	T	T	T	T	F	F
T	T	T	F	F	T	F	T	T	F	F
T	T	F	T	T	T	T	T	T	F	F
T	T	F	F	T	F	F	F	T	F	F
T	F	T	T	F	T	T	T	T	T	T
T	F	T	F	F	T	F	T	T	T	T
T	F	F	T	T	T	T	T	T	T	T
T	F	F	F	T	F	F	T	T	T	T
F	T	T	T	F	T	T	T	F	T	F
F	T	T	F	F	T	F	T	F	T	F
F	T	F	T	T	T	T	T	F	T	F
F	T	F	F	T	F	F	T	F	T	F
F	F	T	T	F	T	T	T	F	T	T
F	F	T	F	F	T	F	T	F	T	T
F	F	F	T	T	T	T	T	F	T	T
F	F	F	F	T	F	F	T	F	T	T
				1	2	1	3	1	2	1

67. The statement is not a tautology if only one F appears in the final column of a truth table, since a tautology requires all T's in the final column.

69. The negation of "If that is an authentic Rolex watch, I'll be surprised" is "That is an authentic Rolex watch and I am not surprised."

71. The negation of "If the English measures are not converted to metric measures, then the spacecraft will crash on the surface of Saturn" is "The English measures are not converted to metric measures and the spacecraft does not crash on the surface of Saturn."

73. The negation of "If you want to be happy for the rest of your life, never make a pretty woman your wife" is "You want to be happy for the rest of your life and make a pretty woman your wife."

75. An equivalent statement to "If you give your plants tender, loving care, they will flourish" is "You do not give your plants tender, loving care or they flourish."

77. An equivalent statement to "If she doesn't, he will" is "She does or he will."

79. An equivalent conditional statement to "All residents of Pensacola are residents of Florida" is "If you are a resident of Pensacola, then you are a resident of Florida." An equivalent statement would be "The person is not a resident of Pensacola or is a resident of Florida."

81. The statements $p \to q$ and $\sim p \vee q$ are equivalent if they have the same truth tables.

p	q	p	$\to$	q	$\sim p$	$\vee$	q
T	T	T	T	T	F	T	T
T	F	T	F	F	F	F	F
F	T	F	T	T	T	T	T
F	F	F	T	F	T	T	F
		1	2	1	1	2	1

Since the truth values in the final columns for each statement are the same, the statements are equivalent.

83.

p	q	p	$\to$	q	$\sim q$	$\to$	$\sim p$
T	T	T	T	T	F	T	F
T	F	T	F	F	T	F	F
F	T	F	T	T	F	T	T
F	F	F	T	F	T	T	T
		1	2	1	1	2	1

Since the truth values in the final columns for each statement are the same, the statements are equivalent.

85.

p	q	p	$\wedge$	$\sim q$	$\sim q$	$\to$	$\sim p$
T	T	T	F	F	F	T	F
T	F	T	T	T	T	F	F
F	T	F	F	F	F	T	T
F	F	F	F	T	T	T	T
		1	2	1	1	2	1

Since the truth values in the final columns for each statement are not the same, the statements are not equivalent. Observe that since they have opposite truth values, each statement is the negation of the other.

87.

p	q	p	$\to$	$\sim q$	$\sim p$	$\vee$	$\sim q$
T	T	T	F	F	F	F	F
T	F	T	T	T	F	T	T
F	T	F	T	F	T	T	F
F	F	F	T	T	T	T	T
		1	2	1	1	2	1

Since the truth values in the final columns for each statement are the same, the statements are equivalent.

89.

p	q	q	$\to$	$\sim p$	p	$\to$	$\sim q$
T	T	T	F	F	T	F	F
T	F	F	T	F	T	T	T
F	T	T	T	T	F	T	F
F	F	F	T	T	F	T	T
		1	3	2	1	3	2

Since the truth values in the final columns for each statement are the same, the statements are equivalent.

91. In the diagram, two series circuits are shown, which correspond to $p \wedge q$ and $p \wedge \sim q$. These circuits, in turn, form a parallel circuit. Thus, the logical statement is $(p \wedge q) \vee (p \wedge \sim q)$.
One pair of equivalent statements listed in the text includes
$(p \wedge q) \vee (p \wedge \sim q) \equiv p \wedge (q \vee \sim q)$.
Since $(q \vee \sim q)$ is always true, $p \wedge (q \vee \sim q)$ simplifies to $p \wedge \mathrm{T} \equiv p$.

93. In the diagram, a series circuit is shown, which corresponds to $\sim q \wedge r$. This circuit, in turn, forms a parallel circuit with p. Thus, the logical statement is $p \vee (\sim q \wedge r)$.

95. In the diagram, a parallel circuit corresponds to $p \vee q$. This circuit is parallel to $\sim p$. Thus, the total circuit corresponds to the logical statement $\sim p \vee (p \vee q)$.
This statement in turn, is equivalent to
$(\sim p \vee p) \vee (\sim p \vee q)$.
Since $\sim p \vee p$ is always true, we have
$\mathrm{T} \vee (\sim p \vee q)$; T.

97. The logical statement, $p \wedge (q \vee \sim p)$, can be represented by the following circuit.

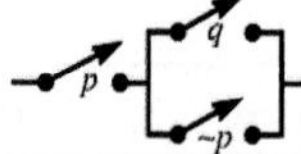

The statement, $p \wedge (q \vee \sim p)$, simplifies to $p \wedge q$ as follows:

$$\begin{aligned} p \wedge (q \vee \sim p) &\equiv (p \wedge q) \vee (p \wedge \sim p) \\ &\equiv (p \wedge q) \vee \text{F} \\ &\equiv p \wedge q. \end{aligned}$$

99. The logical statement, $(p \vee q) \wedge (\sim p \wedge \sim q)$, can be represented by the following circuit.

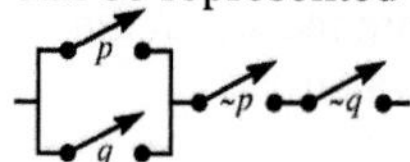

The statement, $(p \vee q) \wedge (\sim p \wedge \sim q)$, simplifies to F as follows:

$$\begin{aligned} &(p \vee q) \wedge (\sim p \wedge \sim q) \\ &\equiv [p \wedge (\sim p \wedge \sim q)] \vee [q \wedge (\sim p \wedge \sim q)] \\ &\equiv [p \wedge \sim p \wedge \sim q] \vee [q \wedge \sim q \wedge \sim p] \\ &\equiv [\text{F} \wedge \sim q] \vee [\text{F} \wedge \sim p] \\ &\equiv \text{F} \vee \text{F} \\ &\equiv \text{F}. \end{aligned}$$

101. The logical statement, $[(p \vee q) \wedge r] \wedge \sim p$, can be represented by the following circuit.

The statement, $[(p \vee q) \wedge r] \wedge \sim p$, simplifies to $(r \wedge \sim p) \wedge q$ as follows:

$$\begin{aligned} &[(p \vee q) \wedge r] \wedge \sim p \\ &\equiv [(p \wedge r) \vee (q \wedge r)] \wedge \sim p \\ &\equiv [(p \wedge r) \wedge \sim p] \vee [(q \wedge r) \wedge \sim p] \\ &\equiv [p \wedge r \wedge \sim p] \vee [(q \wedge r) \wedge \sim p] \\ &\equiv [(p \wedge \sim p) \wedge r] \vee [(r \wedge \sim p) \wedge q] \\ &\equiv (\text{F} \wedge r) \vee [(r \wedge \sim p) \wedge q] \\ &\equiv \text{F} \vee [(r \wedge \sim p) \wedge q] \\ &\equiv (r \wedge \sim p) \wedge q \text{ or } q \wedge (r \wedge \sim p). \end{aligned}$$

103. The logical statement, $\sim q \to (\sim p \to q)$, can be represented by the following circuit.

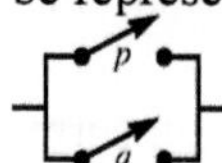

The statement, $\sim q \to (\sim p \to q)$, simplifies to $p \sim q$ as follows:

$$\begin{aligned} \sim q \to (\sim p \to q) &\equiv \sim q \to (p \vee q) \\ &\equiv q \vee (p \vee q) \\ &\equiv q \vee p \vee q \\ &\equiv p \vee q \vee q \\ &\equiv p \vee (q \vee q) \\ &\equiv p \vee q. \end{aligned}$$

105. Referring to Figures 5 and 6 of Example 6 in the text:

Cost per year of the circuit in Figure 5
= number of switches × \$.06 × 24 hr × 365 days
= (4) × (.06) × 24 × 365
= \$2102.40.

Cost per year of the circuit in Figure 6
= number of switches × \$.06 × 24 hr × 365 days
= (3) × (.06) × 24 × 365
= \$1576.80.

Thus, the savings is \$2102.40 – \$1576.80 = \$525.60.

4 Exercises

For each given conditional statement (symbolically as $p \to q$), write (a) the converse ($q \to p$), (b) the inverse ($\sim p \to \sim q$), and (c) the contrapositive ($\sim q \to \sim p$) in if...then forms. Wording may vary in the answers to Exercises 1–9.

1. The conditional statement: If beauty were a minute, then you would be an hour.

(a) *Converse*: If you were an hour, then beauty would be a minute.

(b) *Inverse*: If beauty were not a minute, then you would not be an hour.

(c) *Contrapositive*: If you were not an hour, then beauty would not be a minute.

3. The conditional statement: If it ain't broke, don't fix it.

(a) *Converse*: If you don't fix it, then it ain't broke.

(b) *Inverse*: If it's broke, then fix it.

(c) *Contrapositive*: If you fix it, then it's broke.

It is helpful to restate the conditional statement in an "if...then" form for the exercises 5–8 and 10.

5. The conditional statement: If you walk in front of a moving car, then it is dangerous to your health.

(a) *Converse*: If it is dangerous to your health, then you walk in front of a moving car.

(b) *Inverse*: If you do not walk in front of a moving car, then it is not dangerous to your health.

(c) *Contrapositive*: If it is not dangerous to your health, then you do not walk in front of a moving car.

7. The conditional statement: If they are birds of a feather, then they flock together.

(a) *Converse*: If they flock together, then they are birds of a feather.

(b) *Inverse*: If they are not birds of a feather, then they do not flock together.

(c) *Contrapositive*: If they do not flock together, then they are not birds of a feather.

9. The conditional statement: If you build it, then he will come.

(a) *Converse*: If he comes, then you built it.

(b) *Inverse*: If you don't build it, then he won't come.

(c) *Contrapositive*: If he doesn't come, then you didn't build it.

11. The conditional statement: $p \rightarrow {\sim}q$.

(a) *Converse*: ${\sim}q \rightarrow p$

(b) *Inverse*: ${\sim}p \rightarrow q$.

(c) *Contrapositive*: $q \rightarrow {\sim}p$.

13. The conditional statement: ${\sim}p \rightarrow {\sim}q$.

(a) *Converse*: ${\sim}q \rightarrow {\sim}p$.

(b) *Inverse*: $p \rightarrow q$.

(c) *Contrapositive*: $q \rightarrow p$.

15. The conditional statement: $p \rightarrow (q \vee r)$.

(a) *Converse*: $(q \vee r) \rightarrow p$.

(b) *Inverse*: ${\sim}p \rightarrow {\sim}(q \vee r)$ or ${\sim}p \rightarrow ({\sim}q \wedge {\sim}r)$.

(c) *Contrapositive*: $({\sim}q \wedge {\sim}r) \rightarrow {\sim}p$.

17. Writing exercise, answers will vary.

Writing the statements, Exercises 19–39, in the form "if p, then q" we arrive at the following results.

19. The statement "If it is muddy, I'll wear my galoshes" becomes "If it is muddy, then I'll wear my galoshes."

21. The statement "'19 is positive' implies that 19 + 1 is positive" becomes "If 19 is positive, then 19 + 1 is positive."

23. The statement "All integers are rational numbers" becomes "If a number is an integer, then it is a rational number."

25. The statement "Doing logic puzzles is sufficient for driving me crazy" becomes "If I do logic puzzles, then I am driven crazy."

27. "A day's growth of beard is necessary for Jeff Marsalis to shave" becomes "If Jeff Marsalis is to shave, then he must have a day's growth of beard."

29. The statement "I can go from Boardwalk to Baltic Avenue only if I pass GO" becomes "If I go from Boardwalk to Baltic, then I pass GO."

31. The statement "No whole numbers are not integers" becomes "If a number is a whole number, then it is an integer."

33. The statement "The Nationals will win the pennant when their pitching improves" becomes "If their pitching improves, then the Nationals will win the pennant."

35. The statement "A rectangle is a parallelogram with a right angle" becomes "If the figure is a rectangle, then it is a parallelogram with a right angle."

37. The statement "A triangle with two perpendicular sides is a right triangle" becomes "If a triangle has two perpendicular sides, then it is a right triangle."

39. The statement "The square of a two-digit number whose units digit is 5 will end in 25" becomes "If a two-digit number whose units digit is 5 is squared, then it will end in 25."

41. Option D is the answer since "*r* is necessary for *s*" represents the converse, $s \rightarrow r$, of all of the other statements.

43. Writing exercise; answers will vary.

45. The statement "$6 = 9 - 3$ if and only if $8 + 2 = 10$" is true, since this is a biconditional composed of two true statements.

47. The statement "$8 + 7 \neq 15$ if and only if $3 \times 5 \neq 8$" is false, since this is a biconditional consisting of a false and a true statement.

49. The statement "George H.W. Bush was president if and only if George W. Bush was not president" is false, since this is a biconditional consisting of a true and a false statement.

51. The statements "Michael Jackson is alive" and "Michael Jackson is dead" are contrary, since both cannot be true at the same time.

53. The statements "That animal has four legs" and "That same animal is a cat" are consistent, since both statements can be true.

55. The statements "This number is a whole number" and "This number is irrational" are contrary, since both cannot be true at the same time.

57. The statements "This number is an integer" and "This same number is a rational number" are consistent, since both statements can be true.

59. Answers will vary. One example is: That man is Otis Taylor; that man sells books.

5 Exercises

1. Draw an Euler diagram where the region representing "amusement parks" must be inside the region representing "locations that have thrill rides" so that the first premise is true.

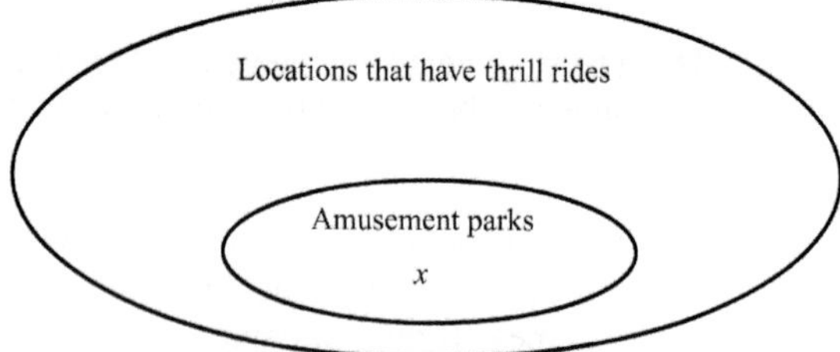

x represents *Universal Orlando*

Let x represent the amusement park "*Universal Orlando*." By the second premise, x must lie in the "amusement parks" region. Since this forces the conclusion to be true, the argument is valid.

3. Draw an Euler diagram where the region representing "politicians" must be inside the region representing "those who lie, cheat, and steal" so that the first premise is true.

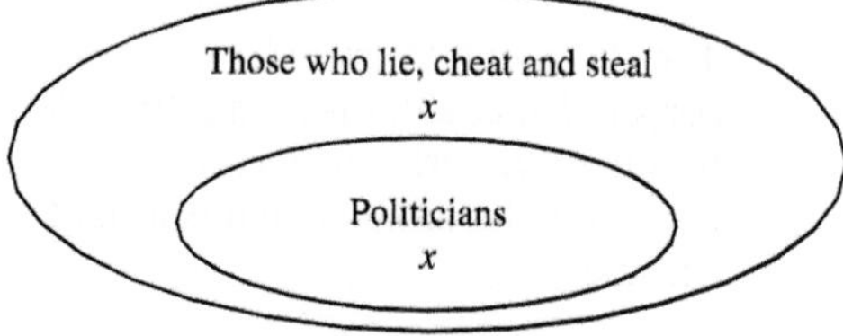

x represents that man

Let x represent "that man." By the second premise, x must lie in the "those who lie, cheat and steal" region. Thus, he could be inside or outside the inner region. Since this allows for a false conclusion (he doesn't have to be in the "politicians" region for both premises to be true), the argument is invalid.

5. Draw an Euler diagram where the region representing "dogs" must be inside the region representing "creatures that love to bury bones" so that the first premise is true.

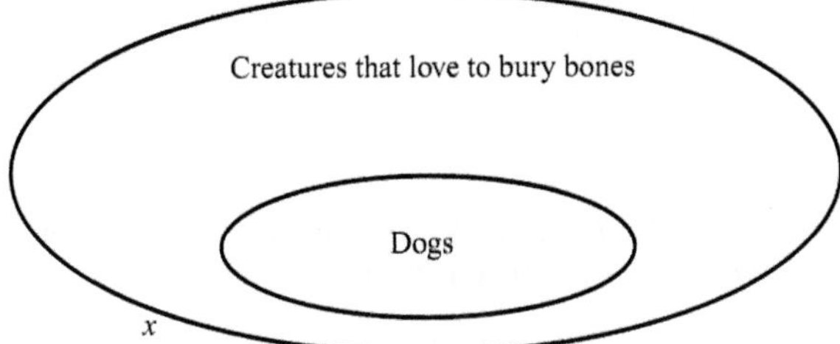

x represents Puddles

Let x represent "Puddles." By the second premise, x must lie outside the region representing "creatures that love to bury bones." Since this forces the conclusion to be true, the argument is valid.

7. Draw an Euler diagram where the region representing "residents of Minnesota" must be inside the region representing "those who know how to live in freezing temperatures" so that the first premise is true.

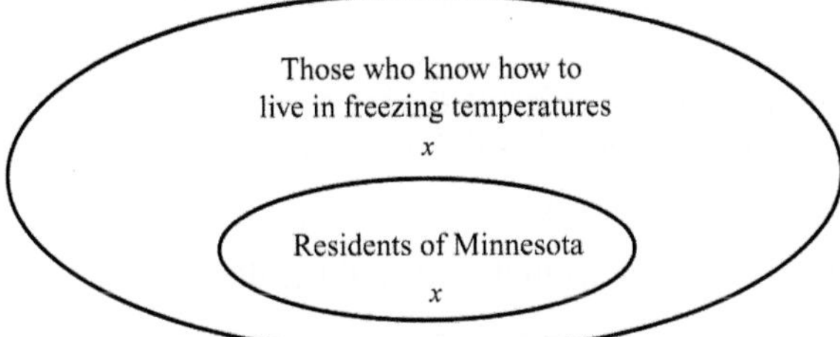

x represents Jessica Rockswold

Let x represent "Jessica Rockswold." By the second premise, x must lie in the "those who know how to live in freezing temperatures" region. Thus, she could be inside or outside the inner region. Since this allows for a false conclusion (she doesn't have to be in the "residents of Minnesota" region for both premises to be true), the argument is invalid.

9. Draw an Euler diagram where the region representing "dinosaurs" intersects the region representing "plant-eaters." This keeps the first premise true.

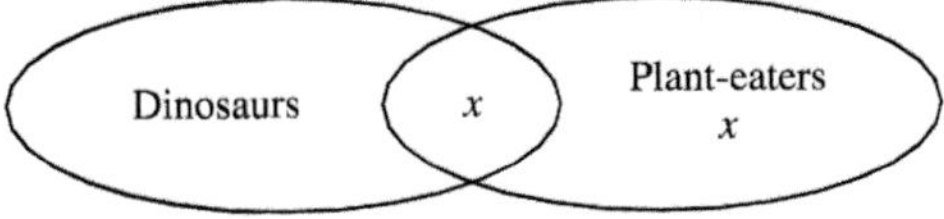

x represents Danny

Let x represent "Danny." By the second premise, x must lie in the region representing "plant-eaters." Thus, he could be inside or outside the region "dinosaurs." Since this allows for a false conclusion, the argument is invalid.

11. Draw an Euler diagram where the region representing "nurses" intersects the region representing "those who wear blue uniforms." This keeps the first premise true.

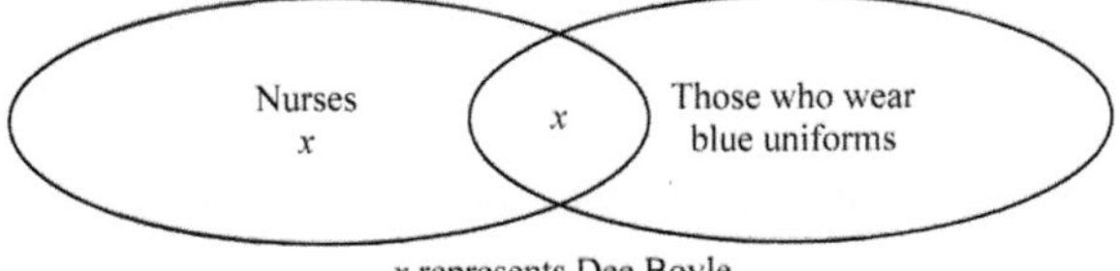

x represents Dee Boyle

Let x represent "Dee Boyle." By the second premise, x must lie in the region representing "nurses." Thus, she could be inside or outside the region "those who wear blue uniforms." Since this allows for a false conclusion, the argument is invalid.

13. Interchanging the second premise and the conclusion of Example 3 (in the text) yields the following argument,

All magnolia trees have green leaves.
That plant is a magnolia tree.
That plant has green leaves.

Draw an Euler diagram where the region representing "Magnolia trees" must be inside the region representing "Things that have green leaves" so that the first premise is true.

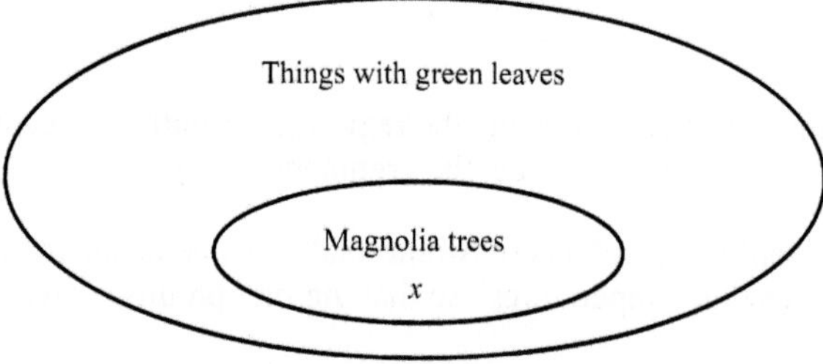

x represents that plant

Let *x* represent "That plant." By the second premise, *x* must lie inside the region representing "Magnolia trees." Since this forces the conclusion to be true, the argument is valid, which makes the answer to the question yes.

15. The following is a valid argument which can be constructed from the given Euler diagram.

All people with blue eyes have blond hair.
Natalie Graham does not have blond hair.
Natalie Graham does not have blue eyes.

17. The following represents one way to diagram the premises so that they are true; however, the argument is invalid since, according to the diagram, all birds are planes, which is false even though the stated conclusion is true.

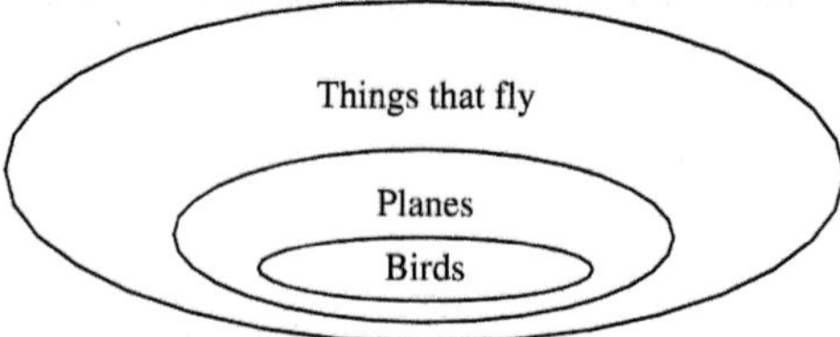

19. The following Euler diagram yields true premises. It also forces the conclusion to be true.

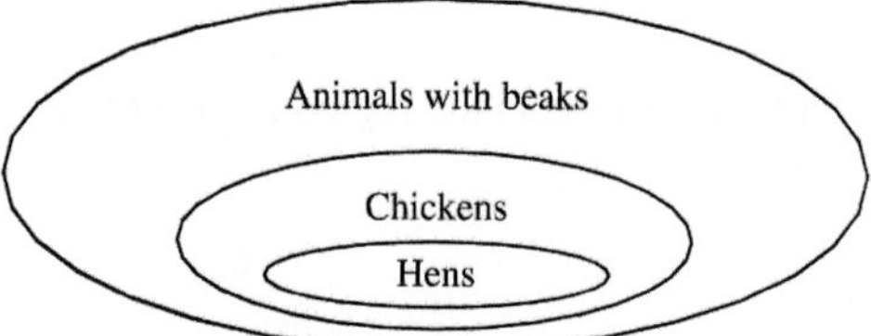

Thus, the argument is valid. Observe that the diagram is the only way to show true premises.

21. The following Euler diagram represents true premises.

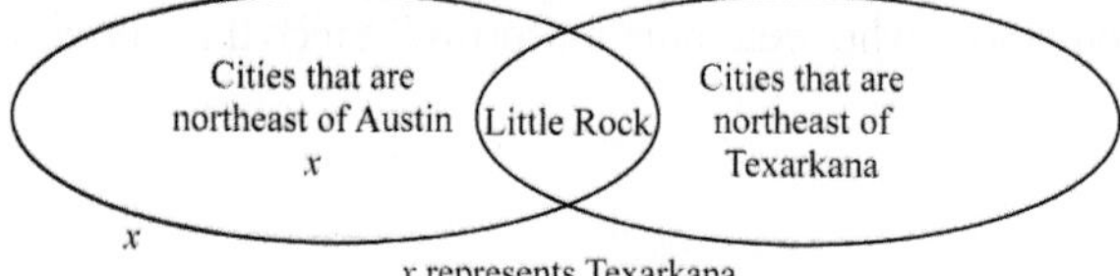

x represents Texarkana

But *x* can reside inside or outside of the "Cities that are northeast of Austin" diagram. In the one case (*x* inside) the conclusion is true. In the other case (*x* outside) the conclusion is false. Since true premises must always give a true conclusion, the argument is invalid.

23. The following Euler diagram represents the two premises as being true and we are forced into a true conclusion.

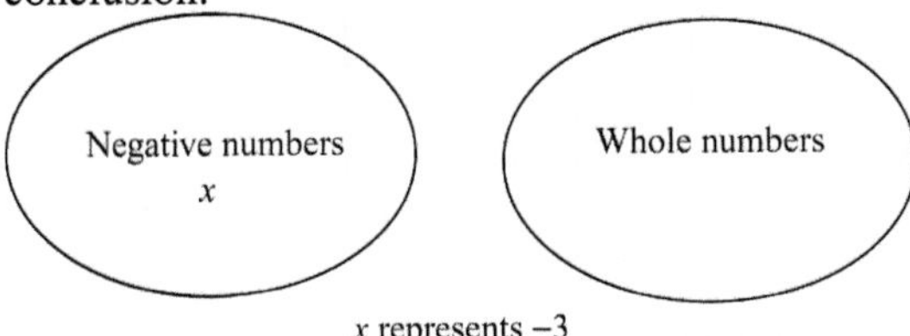

Thus, the argument is valid.

The premises marked A, B, and C are followed by several possible conclusions (Exercises 25–29). Take each conclusion in turn, and check whether the resulting argument is valid or invalid.

A. All people who drive contribute to air pollution.

B. All people who contribute to air pollution make life a little worse.

C. Some people who live in a suburb make life a little worse.

Diagram the three premises to be true.

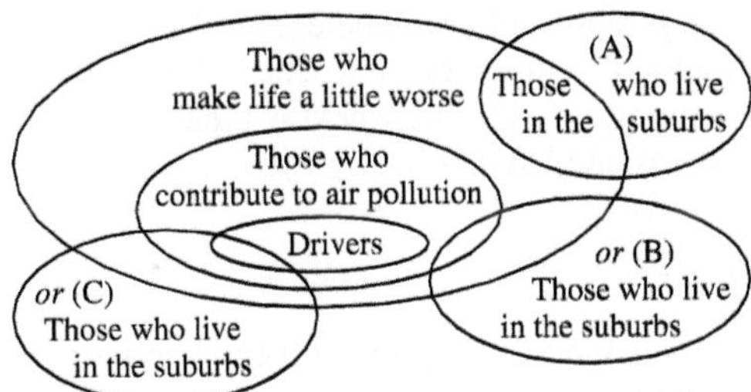

25. We are not forced into the conclusion, "Some people who live in a suburb contribute to air pollution" since option (*A*) represents true premises and a false conclusion. Thus, the argument is invalid.

27. We are not forced into the conclusion, "Suburban residents never drive" since diagram (C) represents true premises where this conclusion is false. Thus, the argument is invalid.

29. The conclusion, "Some people who make life a little worse live in a suburb" yields a valid argument since all three options (*A–C*) represent true premises and force this conclusion to be true.

EXTENSION: LOGIC PROBLEMS AND SUDOKU

1. Because the orange mints are not Fresh Air mints, they must be Inti-Mints. Then the Fresh Air mints are spearmint. The person who ate the tuna-salad sandwich brought the wintergreen TKO mints. Neither Uma nor Xerxes had the Fresh Air mints, so neither of them had the spanakopita. And Nash didn't have the spearmint mints, so he didn't have spanakopita either. So Nash must have had the French onion soup, and the vanilla Liplickers. Drew must have had the spanakopita, so he also had the Fresh Air spearmint mints. Xerxes must have had the garlic shrimp, followed by orange Inti-mints. Uma had the tuna-salad sandwich, followed by wintergreen TKO mints. Ilse had the buffalo-chicken sandwich and the cinnamon Deltoids. Here are the final combinations:
Drew, spanakopita, Fresh Air, spearmint;
Ilse, buffalo-chicken sandwich, Deltoids, cinnamon;
Nash, French onion soup, Liplickers, vanilla;
Uma, tuna-salad sandwich, TKO, wintergreen;
Xerxes, garlic shrimp, Inti-mints, orange

3. Toni's lucky element is not wood. Earl was not the fifth person and not born in the Year of the Rooster. The person born in the Year of the Ox was not fifth either. The third person was not born in the Year of the Horse because Ivana was not the third person. the person whose element is earth was not first or second. Toni was not born in the Year of the Dragon. The fourth person's element is not water. Philip must have been either first or second and his lucky element is not earth. The first person's element is not metal, so the first person's element must be fire. This person was not born in the Year of the Dragon, so the person whose element is earth was born in the Year of the Dragon, and that is the fourth person. Then Philip is the second person. The person born in the Year of the Ox had his or her fortune told before the person whose element is metal, so this person was not third. Therefore the third person was born in the Year of the Cow, and this person's element is water so the second person's element is metal. Now the first person must have been born in the Year of the Ox. Ivana was born in the Year of the Horse, so she must have been fifth. Then Lucy's element is earth, and she was the fourth person and born in the Year of the Dragon. That means Earl was first and born in the Year of the Fox, Philip was born in the Year of the Rooster, and Toni's element was water.
Here are the final combinations:
1st, Earl, Ox, fire; 2nd, Philip, Rooster, metal; 3rd, Toni, Cow, water; 4th, Lucy, Dragon, earth; 5th, Ivana, Horse, wood

5.

7	4	2	1	6	8	9	3	5
3	1	9	4	5	7	6	2	8
8	6	5	9	3	2	7	1	4
6	2	4	7	8	9	1	5	3
1	3	8	5	4	6	2	9	7
5	9	7	2	1	3	8	4	6
2	5	3	8	7	1	4	6	9
9	7	6	3	2	4	5	8	1
4	8	1	6	9	5	3	7	2

7.

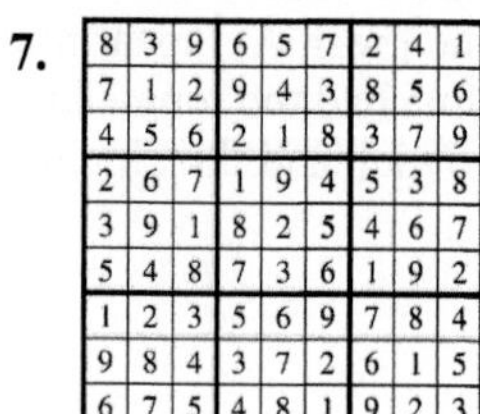

8	3	9	6	5	7	2	4	1
7	1	2	9	4	3	8	5	6
4	5	6	2	1	8	3	7	9
2	6	7	1	9	4	5	3	8
3	9	1	8	2	5	4	6	7
5	4	8	7	3	6	1	9	2
1	2	3	5	6	9	7	8	4
9	8	4	3	7	2	6	1	5
6	7	5	4	8	1	9	2	3

9.

6	1	7	9	2	3	5	8	4
4	5	9	8	6	1	2	7	3
3	2	8	4	5	7	9	6	1
8	3	5	6	4	9	1	2	7
7	6	1	5	3	2	8	4	9
2	9	4	7	1	8	3	5	6
5	7	2	3	9	6	4	1	8
1	8	3	2	7	4	6	9	5
9	4	6	1	8	5	7	3	2

6 Exercises

1. Let p represent "James Taylor comes to town," q represent "I will go to the concert," and r represent "I'll call in sick for work." The argument is then represented symbolically by:
$p \to q$
$\underline{q \to r}$
$p \to r.$
This is the valid argument form "reasoning by transitivity."

3. Let p represent "Julie Nhem works hard enough" and q represent "she will get a promotion." The argument is then represented symbolically by:
$p \to q$
$\underline{p \quad\quad}$
$q.$
This is the valid argument form "modus ponens."

5. Let p represent "He doesn't have to get up at 3:00 A.M." and q represent "he is ecstatic." The argument is then represented symbolically by:
$p \to q$
$\underline{q \quad\quad}$
$p.$
Since this is the form "fallacy of the converse," it is invalid and considered a fallacy.

7. Let p represent "Mariano Rivera pitches" and q represent "the Yankees win." The argument is then represented symbolically by:
$p \to q$
$\underline{\sim q \quad\quad}$
$\sim p.$
This is the valid argument form "modus tollens."

9. Let p represent "we evolved a race of Isaac Newtons" and q represent "that would not be progress." The argument is then represented symbolically by:

$p \rightarrow q$
$\underline{\sim p \quad}$
$\sim q$.
Note: that since we let q represent "that would not be progress," then $\sim q$ represents "that is progress." Since this is the form "fallacy of the inverse," it is invalid and considered a fallacy.

11. Let p represent "She uses e-commerce" and q represent "she pays by credit card." The argument is then represented symbolically by:
$p \lor q$ (or $q \lor p$)
$\underline{\sim q \quad}$
p.
Since this is the form "disjunctive syllogism," it is a valid argument.

To show validity for the arguments in the following exercises, we must show that the conjunction of the premises implies the conclusion. That is, the conditional statement $[P_1 \land P_2 \land \ldots \land P_n] \rightarrow C$ must be a tautology. For exercises 13 and 14 we will use the standard (long format) to develop the corresponding truth tables. For the remainder of the exercises we will use the alternate (short format) to create the truth tables.

13. Form the conditional statement
$[(p \lor q) \land p] \rightarrow \sim q$
from the argument. Complete a truth table.

p	q	$p \lor q$	$(p \lor q) \land p$	$\sim q$	$[(p \lor q) \land p] \rightarrow \sim q$
T	T	T	T	F	F
T	F	T	T	T	T
F	T	T	F	F	T
F	F	F	F	T	T

Since the conditional, formed by the conjunction of premises implying the conclusion, is not a tautology, the argument is invalid.

15. Form the conditional statement
$[(\sim p \rightarrow \sim q) \land q] \rightarrow p$
from the argument. Complete a truth table.

p	q	$[(\sim p$	$\rightarrow$	$\sim q)$	$\land$	$q]$	$\rightarrow$	p
T	T	F	T	F	T	T	T	T
T	F	F	T	T	F	F	T	T
F	T	T	F	F	F	T	T	F
F	F	T	T	T	F	F	T	F
		1	2	1	3	2	4	3

Since the conditional, formed by the conjunction of premises implying the conclusion, is a tautology, the argument is valid.

17. Form the conditional statement
$[(p \to q) \wedge (q \to p)] \to (p \wedge q)$
from the argument. Complete a truth table.

p	q	$[(p \to q)$	$\wedge$	$(q \to p)]$	$\to$	$(p \wedge q)$
T	T	T	T	T	T	T
T	F	F	F	T	T	F
F	T	T	F	F	T	F
F	F	T	T	T	F	F
		1	3	2	4	3

Since the conditional,, formed by the conjunction of premises implying the conclusion, is not a tautology, the argument is <u>invalid</u>.

19. Form the conditional statement
$[(p \to {\sim}q) \wedge q] \to {\sim}p$
from the argument. Complete a truth table.

p	q	$[(p$	$\to$	${\sim}q)$	$\wedge$	$q]$	$\to$	${\sim}p$
T	T	T	F	F	F	T	T	F
T	F	T	T	T	F	F	T	F
F	T	F	T	F	T	T	T	T
F	F	F	T	T	F	F	T	T
		1	2	1	3	2	4	3

Since the conditional, formed by the conjunction of premises implying the conclusion, is a tautology, the argument is <u>valid</u>.

21. Form the conditional statement $\{[(p \wedge q) \vee (p \vee q)] \wedge q\} \to {\sim}q$ from the argument. Complete a truth table.

p	q	$\{[(p$	$\wedge$	$q)$	$\vee$	$(p$	$\vee$	$q)$	$\wedge$	$q\}$	$\to$	${\sim}q$
T	T	T	T	T	T	T	T	T	T	T	F	F
T	F	T	F	F	T	T	T	F	F	F	T	T
F	T	F	F	T	T	F	T	T	T	T	F	F
F	F	F	F	F	F	F	F	F	F	F	T	T
		1	2	1	3	1	2	1	4		5	

Since the conditional formed by the conjunction of premises implying the conclusion, is not a tautology, the argument is <u>invalid</u>.

23. Form the conditional statement
$[(\sim p \lor q) \land (\sim p \to q) \land p] \to \sim q$
from the argument. Complete a truth table.

p	q	$[(\sim p$	$\lor$	$q)$	$\land$	$(\sim p$	$\to$	$q)]$	$\land$	$p]$	$\to$	$\sim q$
T	T	F	T	T	T	F	T	T	T	T	F	F
T	F	F	F	F	F	F	T	F	F	T	T	T
F	T	T	T	T	T	T	T	T	F	F	T	F
F	F	T	T	F	F	T	F	F	F	F	T	T
		1	2	1	3		2		4	3	5	4

Since the conditional, formed by the conjunction of premises implying the conclusion, is not a tautology, the argument is <u>invalid</u>.

25. Form the conditional statement
$\{[(\sim p \land r) \to (p \lor q)] \land (\sim r \to p)\} \to (q \to r)$
from the argument.

p	q	r	$\{[(\sim p$	$\land$	$r)$	$\to$	$(p \lor q)]$	$\land$	$(\sim r$	$\to$	$p)\}$	$\to$	$(q \to r)$
T	T	T	F	F	T	T	T	T	F	T	T	T	T
T	T	F	F	F	F	T	T	T	T	T	T	F	F
T	F	T	F	F	T	T	T	T	F	T	T	T	T
T	F	F	F	F	F	T	T	T	T	T	T	T	T
F	T	T	T	T	T	T	T	T	F	T	F	T	T
F	T	F	T	F	F	T	T	F	T	F	F	T	F
F	F	T	T	T	T	F	F	F	F	T	F	T	T
F	F	F	T	F	F	T	F	F	T	F	F	T	T
			1	2	1	3	2	4	2	3	2	5	4

The F in the final column 5 shows us that the statement is not a tautology and hence, the argument is <u>invalid</u>.

27. Every time something squeaks, I use WD-40.
<u>Every time I use WD-40, I must go to the hardware store.</u>
Every time something squeaks, I go to the hardware store.

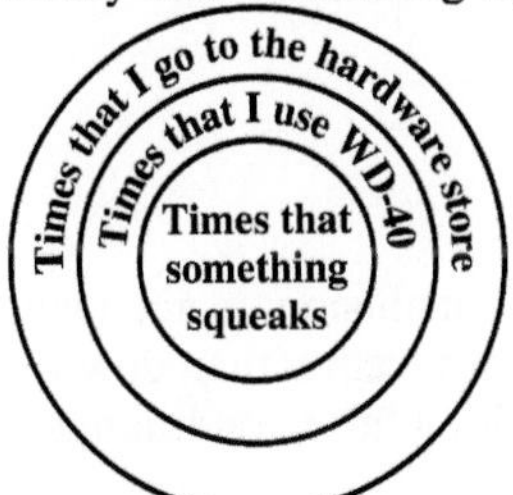

29. Let p represent "Joey loves to watch movies," q represent "Terry likes to jog," and r represent "Carrie drives a school bus." The argument is then represented symbolically by:
p
$q \to \sim p$
$\underline{\sim q \to r}$
$r.$
Construct the truth table for $[p \land (q \to \sim p) \land (\sim q \to r)] \to r$.

p	q	r	$[p$	$\wedge$	$(q$	$\to$	$\sim p)$	$\wedge$	$(\sim q$	$\to$	$r)]$	$\to$	r
T	T	T	T	F	T	F	F	F	F	T	T	T	T
T	T	F	T	F	T	F	F	F	F	T	F	T	F
T	F	T	T	T	F	T	F	T	T	T	T	T	T
T	F	F	T	T	F	T	F	F	T	F	F	T	F
F	T	T	F	F	T	T	T	F	F	T	T	T	T
F	T	F	F	F	T	T	T	F	F	T	F	T	F
F	F	T	F	F	F	T	T	F	T	T	T	T	T
F	F	F	F	F	F	T	T	F	T	F	F	T	F
			2	3	1	2	1	4	2	3	2	5	4

Since the conditional, formed by the conjunction of premises implying the conclusion, is a tautology, the argument is valid.

31. Let p represent "the social networking craze continues," q represent "downloading music will remain popular," and r represent "American girl dolls are favorites." The argument is then represented symbolically by:

$p \to q$
$r \vee q$
$\underline{\sim r \quad}$
$\sim p.$

Construct the truth table for $[(p \to q) \wedge (r \vee q) \wedge (\sim r)] \to \sim p$. (Note: we do not have to complete a column under each simple statement p, q, and r, as we did in exercises above, since it is easy to compare the appropriate index columns to create the truth value for each connective.)

p	q	r	$[(p \to q)$	$\wedge$	$(r \vee q)$	$\wedge$	$(\sim r)]$	$\to$	$\sim p$
T	T	T	T	T	T	F	F	T	F
T	T	F	T	T	T	T	T	F	F
T	F	T	F	F	T	F	F	T	F
T	F	F	F	F	F	F	T	T	F
F	T	T	T	T	T	F	F	T	T
F	T	F	T	T	T	T	T	T	T
F	F	T	T	T	T	F	F	T	T
F	F	F	T	F	F	F	T	T	T
			1	2	1	3	2	4	3

Since the conditional, formed by the conjunction of premises implying the conclusion, is not a tautology, the argument is invalid. Note: If you are completing the truth table along rows (rather than down columns), you could stop after completing the second row, knowing that with a false conditional, the statement will not be a tautology.

33. Let p represent "The Dolphins will be in the playoffs," q represent "Chad leads the league in passing," and r represent "Tony coaches the Dolphins." The argument is then represented symbolically by

$p \leftrightarrow q$
$r \vee q$
$\underline{\sim r \quad}$
$\sim p.$

Construct the truth table for $[(p \leftrightarrow q) \wedge (r \vee q) \wedge (\sim r)] \to \sim p$.

p	q	r	$[(p \leftrightarrow q)$	$\wedge$	$(r \vee q)$	$\wedge$	$(\sim r)]$	$\rightarrow$	$\sim p$
T	T	T	T	T	T	F	F	T	F
T	T	F	T	T	T	T	T	F	F
T	F	T	F	F	T	F	F	T	F
T	F	F	F	F	F	F	T	T	F
F	T	T	F	F	T	F	F	T	T
F	T	F	F	F	T	F	T	T	T
F	F	T	T	T	T	F	F	T	T
F	F	F	T	F	F	F	T	T	T
			1	2	1	3	2	4	3

Since the conditional, formed by the conjunction of premises implying the conclusion, is not a tautology, the argument is invalid. (Note: If you are completing the truth table along rows, rather than down columns, you could stop after completing the second row, knowing that with a false conditional, the statement will not be a tautology.

35. Let p represent "Dr. Hardy is a department chairman," q represent "he lives in Atlanta," and r represent "his first name is Larry." The argument is then represented symbolically by

$p \rightarrow q$
$\underline{q \wedge r}$
$\sim r \rightarrow \sim p.$

Construct the truth table for $[(p \rightarrow q) \wedge (q \wedge r)] \rightarrow (\sim r \rightarrow \sim p)$.

p	q	r	$[(p \rightarrow q)$	$\wedge$	$(q \wedge r)]$	$\rightarrow$	$(\sim r$	$\rightarrow$	$\sim p)$
T	T	T	T	T	T	T	F	T	F
T	T	F	T	F	F	T	T	F	F
T	F	T	F	F	F	T	F	T	F
T	F	F	F	F	F	T	T	F	F
F	T	T	T	T	T	T	F	T	T
F	T	F	T	F	F	T	T	T	T
F	F	T	T	F	F	T	F	T	T
F	F	F	T	F	F	T	T	T	T
			1	2	1	3	1	2	1

Since the conditional, formed by the conjunction of premises implying the conclusion, is a tautology, the argument is valid.

The following exercises involve Quantified arguments and can be analyzed, as such, by Euler diagrams. However, the quantified statements can be represented as conditional statements as well. This allows us to use a truth table–or recognize a valid argument form–to analyze the validity of the argument.

37. Let p represent "you are a man," q represent "you are created equal," and r represent "you are a woman." The argument is then represented symbolically by:

$p \rightarrow q$
$\underline{q \rightarrow r}$
$p \rightarrow r.$

This is a "reasoning by Transitivity" argument form and, hence, is valid.

39. We apply reasoning by repeated transitivity to the six premises. A conclusion from this reasoning, which makes the argument valid, is reached by linking the first antecedent to the last consequent. This conclusion is "If I tell you the time, then my life will be miserable."

Answers in Exercises 39–46 may be replaced by their contrapositives.

41. The statement "all my poultry are ducks" becomes "if it is my poultry, then it is a duck."

43. The statement "guinea pigs are hopelessly ignorant of music" becomes "if it is a guinea pig, then it is hopelessly ignorant of music."

45. The statement "no teachable kitten has green eyes" becomes "if it is a teachable kitten, then it does not have green eyes."

47. The statement "I have not filed any of them that I can read" becomes "if I can read it, then I have not filed it."

49. (a) "No ducks are willing to waltz" becomes "if it is a duck, then it is not willing to waltz" or $p \to \sim s$.

(b) "No officers ever decline to waltz" becomes "if one is an officer, then one is willing to waltz" or $r \to s$.

(c) "All my poultry are ducks" becomes "if it is my poultry, then it is a duck" or $q \to p$.

(d) The three symbolic premises are

$p \to \sim s$
$r \to s$
$q \to p$.

Begin with q, which only appears once. Replacing $r \to s$ with its contrapositive, $\sim s \to \sim r$, rearrange the three premises.

$q \to p$
$p \to \sim s$
$\sim s \to \sim r$

By repeated use of reasoning by transitivity, the conclusion which provides a valid argument is $q \to \sim r$. In words, "if it is my poultry, then it is not an officer," or "none of my poultry are officers."

51. (a) "Promise-breakers are untrustworthy" becomes "if one is a promise-breaker, then one is not trustworthy" or $r \to \sim s$.

(b) "Wine-drinkers are very communicative" becomes "if one is a wine-drinker, then one is very communicative" or $u \to t$.

(c) "A person who keeps a promise is honest" becomes "if one is not a promise-breaker, then one is honest" or $\sim r \to p$.

(d) "No teetotalers are pawnbrokers" becomes "if one is not a wine-drinker, then one is not a pawnbroker" or $\sim u \to \sim q$.

(e) "One can always trust a very communicative person" becomes "if one is very communicative, then one is trustworthy" or $t \to s$.

(f) The symbolic premise statements are

$r \to \sim s$
$u \to t$
$\sim r \to p$
$\sim u \to \sim q$
$t \to s$.

Begin with q, which only appears once. Using the contrapositive of $\sim u \to \sim q$, $(q \to u)$, and $r \to \sim s$, $(s \to \sim r)$, rearrange the five premises as follows:

$q \to u$
$u \to t$
$t \to s$
$s \to \sim r$
$\sim r \to p$.

By repeated use of reasoning by transitivity, the conclusion which provides a valid argument is $q \to p$. In words, this conclusion can be stated as "if one is a pawnbroker, then one is honest," or "all pawnbrokers are honest."

53. Begin by changing each quantified premise to a conditional statement.

(a) The statement "all the dated letters in this room are written on blue paper" becomes "if it is dated, then it is on blue paper" or $r \to w$.

(b) The statement "none of them are in black ink, except those that are written in the third person" becomes "if it is not in the third person, then it is not in black ink" or $\sim u \rightarrow \sim t$.

(c) The statement "I have not filed any of them that I can read" becomes "if I can read it, then it is not filed" or $v \rightarrow \sim s$.

(d) The statement "none of them that are written on one sheet are undated" becomes "if it is on one sheet, then it is dated" or $x \rightarrow r$.

(e) The statement "all of them that are not crossed are in black ink" becomes "if it is not crossed, then it is in black ink" or $\sim q \rightarrow t$.

(f) The statement "all of them written by Brown begin with 'Dear Sir'" becomes "if it is written by Brown, then it begins with 'Dear Sir'" or $y \rightarrow p$.

(g) The statement "all of them written on blue paper are filed" becomes "if it is on blue paper, then it is filed" or $w \rightarrow s$.

(h) The statement "none of them written on more than one sheet are crossed" becomes "if it is not on more than one sheet, then it is not crossed" or $\sim x \rightarrow \sim q$.

(i) The statement "none of them that begin with 'Dear Sir' are written in the third person" becomes "if it begins with 'Dear Sir,' then it is not written in the third person" or $p \rightarrow \sim u$.

(j) The symbolic premise statements are
(a) $r \rightarrow w$
(b) $\sim u \rightarrow \sim t$
(c) $v \rightarrow \sim s$
(d) $x \rightarrow r$
(e) $\sim q \rightarrow t$
(f) $y \rightarrow p$
(g) $w \rightarrow s$
(h) $\sim x \rightarrow \sim q$
(i) $p \rightarrow \sim u$.
Begin with y, which appears only once. Using contrapositives of $v \rightarrow \sim s$ ($s \rightarrow \sim v$), $\sim q \rightarrow t$ ($\sim t \rightarrow q$), and $\sim x \rightarrow \sim q$ ($q \rightarrow x$), rearrange the nine statements.
$y \rightarrow p$
$p \rightarrow \sim u$
$\sim u \rightarrow \sim t$
$\sim t \rightarrow q$
$q \rightarrow x$
$x \rightarrow r$
$r \rightarrow w$
$w \rightarrow s$
$s \rightarrow \sim v$.
By repeated use of reasoning by transitivity, the conclusion that makes the argument valid is $y \rightarrow \sim v$.
In words, the conclusion can be stated as "if it is written by Brown, then I can't read it," or equivalently "I can't read any of Brown's letters."

Chapter Test

1. The negation of "$6 - 3 = 3$" is "$6 - 3 \neq 3$."

2. The negation of "all men are created equal" is "some men are not created equal."

3. The negation of "some members of the class went on the field trip" is "no members of the class went on the field trip." An equivalent answer would be "all members of the class did not go on the field trip."

4. The negation of "if that's the way you feel, then I will accept it" is "that's the way you feel and I won't accept it." Remember that $\sim(p \rightarrow q) \equiv (p \wedge \sim q)$.

5. The negation of "she applied and got a student loan" is "she did not apply or did not get a student loan." Remember that $\sim(p \wedge q) \equiv (\sim p \vee \sim q)$.

Let p represent "you will love me" and let q represent "I will love you."

6. The symbolic form of "If you won't love me, then I will love you" is "$\sim p \rightarrow q$."

7. The symbolic form of "I will love you if you will love me." is "$p \rightarrow q$."

8. The symbolic form of "I won't love you if and only if you won't love me" is "$\sim q \leftrightarrow \sim p$."

9. Writing the symbolic form "$\sim p \wedge q$" in words, we get "you won't love me and I will love you."

10. Writing the symbolic form "$\sim(p \vee \sim q)$" in words, we get "it is not the case that you will love me or I won't love you" (or equivalently, by De Morgan's, "you won't love me and I will love you").

Assume that p is true and that q and r are false for Exercises 11–14.

11. Replacing q and r with the given truth values, we have
$\sim F \wedge \sim F$
$T \wedge T$
T.
The compound statement $\sim q \wedge \sim r$ is true.

12. Replacing p, q and r with the given truth values, we have
$F \vee (T \wedge \sim F)$
$F \vee (T \wedge T)$
$F \vee T$
T.
The compound statement $r \vee (p \wedge \sim q)$ is true.

13. Replacing r with the given truth value (s not known), we have
$F \to (s \vee F)$
$F \to$ not known
T.
The compound statement $r \to (s \vee r)$ is true.

14. Replacing p and q with the given truth values, we have
$T \leftrightarrow (T \to F)$
$T \leftrightarrow (F)$
F.
The compound statement $p \leftrightarrow (p \to q)$ is false.

15. Writing exercise; answers will vary.

16. The necessary condition for

(a) a conditional statement to be false is that the antecedent must be true and the consequent must be false.

(b) a conjunction to be true is that both component statements true.

(c) a disjunction to be false is that both component statements must be false.

17.

p	q	p	$\wedge$	$(\sim p$	$\vee$	$q)$
T	T	T	T	F	T	T
T	F	T	F	F	F	F
F	T	F	F	T	T	T
F	F	F	F	T	T	F
		2	3	1	2	1

18.

p	q	$\sim$	$(p \wedge q)$	$\to$	$(\sim p$	$\vee$	$\sim q)$
T	T	F	T	T	F	F	F
T	F	T	F	T	F	T	T
F	T	T	F	T	T	T	F
F	F	T	F	T	T	T	T
		2	1	3	1	2	1

Since the last completed column (3) is all true, the conditional is a tautology.

19. The statement "some negative integers are whole numbers" is false, since all whole numbers are non-negative.

20. The statement "all irrational numbers are real numbers" is true, because the real numbers are made up of both the rational and irrational numbers.

The wording may vary in the answer in Exercises 21–26.

21. "All integers are rational numbers" can be stated as "if the number is an integer, then it is a rational number."

22. "Being a rhombus is sufficient for a polygon to be a quadrilateral" can be stated as "if a polygon is a rhombus, then it is a quadrilateral."

23. "Being divisible by 2 is necessary for a number to be divisible by 4" can be stated as "if a number is divisible by 4, then it is divisible by 2." Remember that the "necessary" part of the statement becomes the consequent.

24. "She digs dinosaur bones only if she is a paleontologist" can be stated as "if she digs dinosaur bones, then she is a paleontologist." Remember that the "only if" part of the statement becomes the consequent.

25. The conditional statement: If a picture paints a thousand words, then the graph will help me understand it.

(a) *Converse*: If the graph will help me understand it, then a picture paints a thousand words.

(b) *Inverse*: If a picture doesn't paint a thousand words, then the graph won't help me understand it.

(c) *Contrapositive*: If the graph doesn't help me understand it, then a picture doesn't paint a thousand words.

26. The conditional statement: $\sim p \rightarrow (q \wedge r)$.

(a) Converse: $(q \wedge r) \rightarrow \sim p$.

(b) Inverse: $p \rightarrow \sim(q \wedge r)$, or $p \rightarrow (\sim q \vee \sim r)$.

(c) Contrapositive: $\sim(q \wedge r) \rightarrow p$, or $(\sim q \vee \sim r) \rightarrow p$.

27. Complete an Euler diagram as:

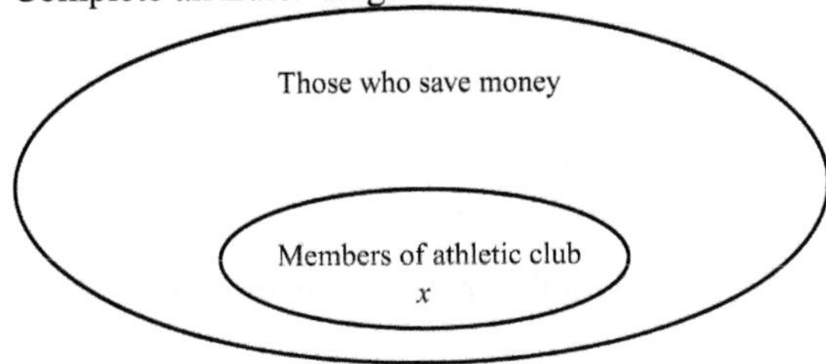

x represents Don O'Neal

Since, when the premises are diagrammed as being true, and we are forced into a true conclusion, the argument is valid.

28. **(a)** Let p represent "he eats liver" and q represent "he will eat anything." The argument is then represented symbolically by:

$p \rightarrow q$
$\underline{p\quad}$
q.

This is the valid argument form "modus ponens," hence the answer is A.

(b) Let p represent "you use your seat belt" and q represent "you will be safer." The argument is then represented symbolically by:

$p \rightarrow q$
$\underline{\sim p\quad}$
$\sim q$.

The answer is F, a fallacy of the inverse.

(c) Let p represent "I hear *Mr. Bojangles*," q represent "I think of her," and r represent "I smile." The argument is then represented symbolically by:

$p \rightarrow q$
$\underline{q \rightarrow r}$
$p \rightarrow r$.

This is the valid argument form "reasoning by transitivity," hence the answer is C.

(d) Let p represent "she sings" and q represent "she dances."
The argument is then represented symbolically by:

$p \vee q$
$\underline{\sim p\quad}$
q.

This is the valid argument form "disjunctive syllogism," hence the answer is D.

29. Let p represent "I write a check," q represent "it will bounce," and "the bank guarantees it." The argument is then represented symbolically by:

$p \to q$
$r \to \sim q$
$\underline{r\quad}$
$\sim p.$

Construct the truth table for $\{[(p \to q) \wedge (r \to \sim q)] \wedge r\} \to (\sim p)$.

p	q	r	$\{[(p \to q)$	$\wedge$	$(r$	$\to$	$\sim q)]$	$\wedge$	$r\}$	$\to$	$(\sim p)$
T	T	T	T	F	T	F	F	F	T	T	F
T	T	F	T	T	F	T	F	F	F	T	F
T	F	T	F	F	T	T	T	F	T	T	F
T	F	F	F	F	F	T	T	F	F	T	F
F	T	T	T	F	T	F	F	F	T	T	T
F	T	F	T	T	F	T	F	F	F	T	T
F	F	T	T	T	T	T	T	T	T	T	T
F	F	F	T	T	F	T	T	F	F	T	T
			2	3	1	2	1	4	3	5	4

Since the conditional, formed by the conjunction of premises implying the conclusion, is a tautology, the argument is <u>valid</u>.

30. Construct the truth table for $[(\sim p \to \sim q) \wedge (q \to p)] \to (p \sim q)$.

p	q	$[(\sim p$	$\to$	$\sim q)$	$\wedge$	$(q$	$\to$	$p)]$	$\to$	$(p$	$\vee$	$q)$
T	T	F	T	F	T	T	T	T	T	T	T	T
T	F	F	T	T	T	F	T	T	T	T	T	F
F	T	T	F	F	F	T	F	F	T	F	T	T
F	F	T	T	T	T	F	T	F	F	F	F	F
		1	2	1	3	1	2	1	4	2	3	2

Since the conditional, formed by the conjunction of premises implying the conclusion, is not a tautology, the argument is <u>invalid</u>.

COUNTING METHODS

February 7, 2010, Miami, FL. Super Bowl XLIV pits the National Football Conference (NFC) New Orleans Saints against the American Football Conference (AFC) Indianapolis Colts. The Saints, led by quarterback Drew Brees (the game's MVP), eventually win an exciting game 31 to 17.

Before the game starts, the coin toss by Emmitt Smith, under the watchful eye of referee Scott Green, is called "heads" by the visiting Saints and comes up heads.

ANNOUNCER: "Can you believe this? (For) thirteen straight years the NFC has won the toss. The odds of any one side winning thirteen straight coin tosses is about 8100 to 1."

Was the announcer correct? The methods of this chapter enable us to count those odds exactly.

1 COUNTING BY SYSTEMATIC LISTING

Counting • One-Part Tasks • Product Tables for Two-Part Tasks • Tree Diagrams for Multiple-Part Tasks • Other Systematic Listing Methods

Simon James/Alamy

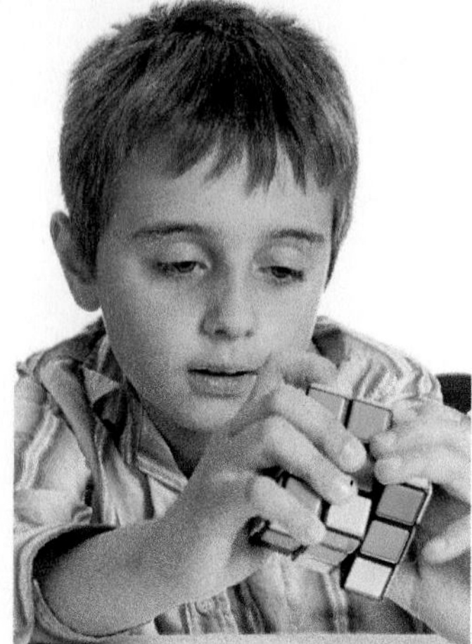

Counting methods can be used to find the number of moves required to solve a Rubik's Cube. The scrambled cube must be modified so that each face is a solid color. Rubik's royalties from sales of the cube in Western countries made him Hungary's richest man.

Although the craze over the cube of the early 1980s has waned, certain groups have remained intensely interested in not only solving the scrambled cube, but doing so as fast as possible. And the 30-year search for an exact number of moves (called face turns) that is guaranteed to suffice in all cases while no smaller number will suffice finally ended in July of 2010. That number is now known to be 20.

Even so, it is not yet known if an "efficient" algorithm exists for finding an actual solution in every case. So the cube still conceals mysteries for computer scientists to pursue.

Today, the cube's popularity is rivaled, among many people, by Sudoku puzzles.

Counting

In this chapter, "counting" means finding the number of objects, of some certain type, that exist. Among many possible reasons to ask and answer such a question, a major one is to be able to calculate the likelihood that some event may occur, that is the *probability* of the event.

The methods of counting presented in this section involve listing the possible results for a given task. This approach is practical only for fairly short lists. When listing possible results, it is extremely important to use a *systematic* approach, so that no possibilities are missed.

One-Part Tasks

The results for simple, one-part tasks can often be listed easily. For the task of tossing a single fair coin, for example, the list is *heads, tails,* with two possible results. If the task is to roll a single fair die (a cube with faces numbered 1 through 6), the different results are 1, 2, 3, 4, 5, 6, a total of six possibilities.

EXAMPLE 1 Selecting a Club President

Consider a club N with five members:

$$N = \{\text{Alan, Bill, Cathy, David, Evelyn}\}, \quad \text{abbreviated as} \quad N = \{A, B, C, D, E\}.$$

In how many ways can this group select a president (assuming all members are eligible)?

SOLUTION

The task in this case is to select one of the five members as president. There are five possible results:

$$A,\ B,\ C,\ D, \text{ and } E.$$

Product Tables for Two-Part Tasks

EXAMPLE 2 Building Numbers from a Set of Digits

Determine the number of two-digit numbers that can be written using only the digits 1, 2, and 3.

SOLUTION

This task consists of two parts:

1. Choose a first digit. **2.** Choose a second digit.

The results for a two-part task can be pictured in a **product table** such as **Table 1**. From the table we obtain our list of possible results:

$$11,\ 12,\ 13,\ 21,\ 22,\ 23,\ 31,\ 32,\ 33.$$

There are nine possibilities.

Table 1

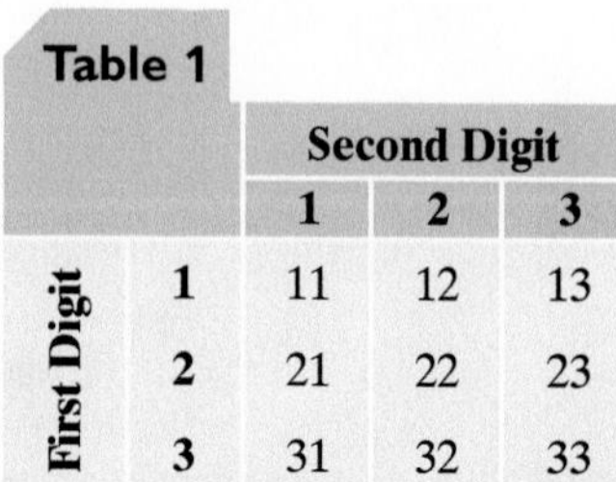

		Second Digit		
		1	2	3
First Digit	1	11	12	13
	2	21	22	23
	3	31	32	33

EXAMPLE 3 Rolling a Pair of Dice

Determine the number of different possible results when two ordinary dice are rolled.

SOLUTION

Assume the dice are easily distinguishable. Perhaps one is red and the other green. Then the task consists of two parts:

1. Roll the red die. **2.** Roll the green die.

The product table in **Table 2** shows that there are thirty-six possible results.

Table 2 Rolling Two Fair Dice

		Green Die					
		1	**2**	**3**	**4**	**5**	**6**
Red Die	**1**	(1, 1)	(1, 2)	(1, 3)	(1, 4)	(1, 5)	(1, 6)
	2	(2, 1)	(2, 2)	(2, 3)	(2, 4)	(2, 5)	(2, 6)
	3	(3, 1)	(3, 2)	(3, 3)	(3, 4)	(3, 5)	(3, 6)
	4	(4, 1)	(4, 2)	(4, 3)	(4, 4)	(4, 5)	(4, 6)
	5	(5, 1)	(5, 2)	(5, 3)	(5, 4)	(5, 5)	(5, 6)
	6	(6, 1)	(6, 2)	(6, 3)	(6, 4)	(6, 5)	(6, 6)

You will want to refer to* Table 2 *when various dice-rolling problems occur in the remainder of this chapter and the next.

EXAMPLE 4 Electing Two Club Officers

Find the number of ways that club N of **Example 1** can elect both a president and a secretary. Assume that all members are eligible, but that no one can hold both offices.

SOLUTION

Again, the required task has two parts:

1. Determine the president. **2.** Determine the secretary.

Constructing **Table 3** gives us the possibilities (where, for example, AB denotes president A and secretary B, while BA denotes president B and secretary A).

Table 3 Electing Two Officers

		Secretary				
		A	B	C	D	E
President	A		AB	AC	AD	AE
	B	BA		BC	BD	BE
	C	CA	CB		CD	CE
	D	DA	DB	DC		DE
	E	EA	EB	EC	ED	

Notice that certain entries (down the main diagonal, from upper left to lower right) are omitted from the table, since the cases AA, BB, and so on would imply one person holding both offices. Altogether, there are twenty possibilities.

Trustees of The British Museum/Art Resource, New York

Bone dice were unearthed in the remains of a Roman garrison, Vindolanda, near the border between England and Scotland. Life on the Roman frontier was occupied with gaming as well as fighting. Some of the Roman dice were loaded in favor of 6 and 1.

Life on the American frontier was reflected in cattle brands that were devised to keep alive the memories of hardships, feuds, and romances. A rancher named Ellis from Paradise Valley in Arizona designed his cattle brand in the shape of a pair of dice. You can guess that the pips were 6 and 1.

EXAMPLE 5 Selecting Committees for a Club

Find the number of ways that club N can appoint a committee of two members to represent them at an association conference.

SOLUTION

The required task again has two parts. In fact, we can refer to **Table 3** again, but this time, the order of the two letters (people) in a given pair really makes no difference. For example, BD and DB are the same committee. (In **Example 4,** BD and DB were different results since the two people would be holding different offices.)

In the case of committees, we can eliminate not only the main diagonal entries but also all entries below the main diagonal. The resulting list contains ten possibilities:

$$AB, \quad AC, \quad AD, \quad AE, \quad BC, \quad BD, \quad BE, \quad CD, \quad CE, \quad DE.$$

Tree Diagrams for Multiple-Part Tasks

PROBLEM-SOLVING HINT A task that has more than two parts is not easy to analyze with a product table. Another helpful device is the **tree diagram.**

EXAMPLE 6 Building Numbers from a Set of Digits

Find the number of three-digit numbers that can be written using only the digits 1, 2, and 3, assuming that **(a)** repeated digits are allowed and **(b)** repeated digits are not allowed.

SOLUTION

(a) The task of constructing such a number has three parts:

1. Select the first digit. **2.** Select the second digit. **3.** Select the third digit.

As we move from left to right through the tree diagram in **Figure 1**, the tree branches at the first-stage to all possibilities for the first digit. Then each first-stage branch again branches, or splits, at the second stage, to all possibilities for the second digit. Finally, the third-stage branching shows the third-digit possibilities. The list of possible results (twenty-seven of them) is shown in **Figure 1**.

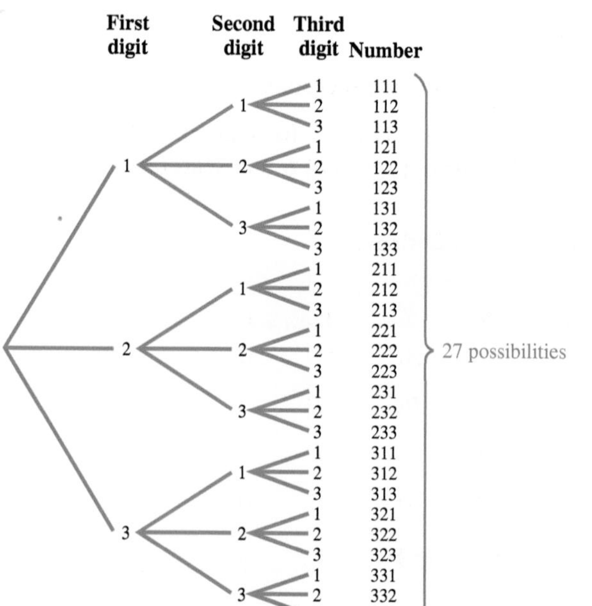

Tree diagram for three-digit numbers using digits 1, 2, and 3

Figure 1

(b) For the case of nonrepeating digits, we could construct a whole new tree diagram, as in **Figure 2**, or we could simply go down the list of numbers from the first tree diagram and strike out any that contain repeated digits. In either case we obtain only six possibilities.

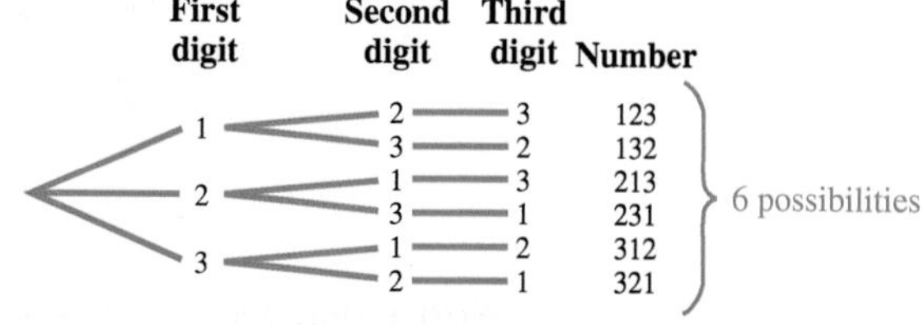

Tree diagram for nonrepeating three-digit numbers using digits 1, 2, and 3

Figure 2

Notice the distinction between parts (a) and (b) of **Example 6.** There are twenty-seven possibilities when "repetitions (of digits) are allowed," but only six possibilities when "repetitions are not allowed."

Here is another way to phrase the problem of **Example 6:**

> A three-digit number is to be determined by placing three slips of paper (marked 1, 2, and 3) into a hat and drawing out three slips in succession. Find the number of possible results if the drawing is done **(a)** *with replacement* and **(b)** *without replacement.*

Drawing "with replacement" means drawing a slip, recording its digit, and replacing the slip into the hat so that it is again available for subsequent draws.

> ***Drawing "with replacement" has the effect of "allowing repetitions," while drawing "without replacement" has the effect of "not allowing repetitions."***

The words "repetitions" and "replacement" are important in the statement of a problem. In **Example 2,** since no restrictions were stated, we assumed that *repetitions* (of digits) *were allowed,* or equivalently that digits were to be selected *with replacement.*

EXAMPLE 7 Selecting Switch Settings on a Printer

Pamela DeMar's computer printer allows for optional settings with a panel of four on-off switches in a row. How many different settings can she select if no two adjacent switches can both be off?

SOLUTION

This situation is typical of user-selectable options on various devices, including computer equipment, garage door openers, and other appliances. In **Figure 3**, we denote "on" and "off" with 1 and 0, respectively. The number of possible settings is eight.

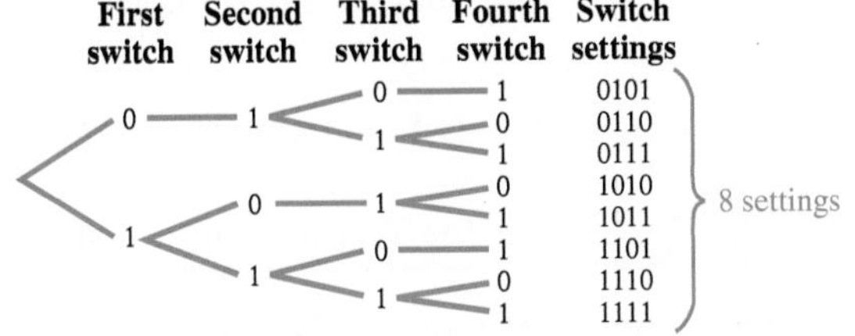

Tree diagram for printer settings

Figure 3

Notice that each time a switch is indicated as off (0), the next switch can only be on (1). This is to satisfy the restriction that no two adjacent switches can both be off.

EXAMPLE 8 Seating Attendees at a Concert

Arne, Bobbette, Chuck, and Deirdre have tickets for four reserved seats in a row at a concert. In how many different ways can they seat themselves so that Arne and Bobbette will sit next to each other?

SOLUTION

Here we have a four-part task:

Assign people to the first, second, third, and fourth seats.

The tree diagram in **Figure 4** on the next page avoids repetitions, because no person can occupy more than one seat. Also, once A or B appears in the tree, the other one *must* occur at the next stage. (Why is this?) No splitting occurs from stage three to stage four because by that time there is only one person left unassigned. The right column in the figure shows the twelve possible seating arrangements.

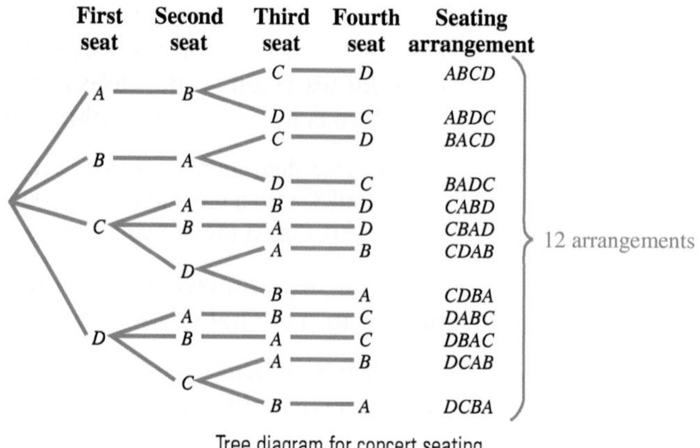

Tree diagram for concert seating

Figure 4

Although we have applied tree diagrams only to tasks with three or more parts, they can also be used for two-part or even simple, one-part tasks. Product tables, on the other hand, are practical only for two-part tasks.

Other Systematic Listing Methods

There are additional systematic ways to produce complete listings of possible results besides product tables and tree diagrams.

In **Example 4,** where we used a product table (**Table 3**) to list all possible president-secretary pairs for the club $N = \{A, B, C, D, E\}$, we could have systematically constructed the same list using a sort of alphabetical or left-to-right approach.

First, consider the results where A is president. Any of the remaining members (B, C, D, or E) could then be secretary. That gives us the pairs AB, AC, AD, and AE. Next, assume B is president. The secretary could then be A, C, D, or E. We get the pairs BA, BC, BD, and BE. Continuing in order, we get the complete list just as in **Example 4:**

$$AB, \ AC, \ AD, \ AE, \ BA, \ BC, \ BD, \ BE, \ CA, \ CB,$$
$$CD, \ CE, \ DA, \ DB, \ DC, \ DE, \ EA, \ EB, \ EC, \ ED.$$

EXAMPLE 9 Counting Triangles in a Figure

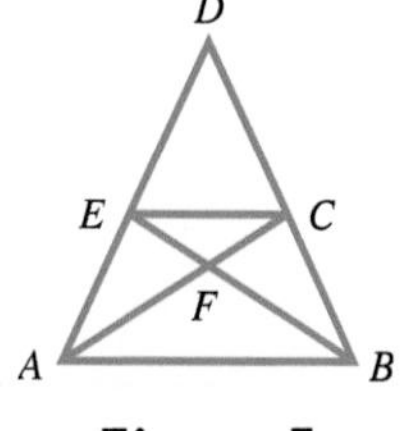

Figure 5

How many different triangles (of any size) can be traced in **Figure 5**?

SOLUTION

One systematic approach is to label points as shown, begin with A, and proceed in alphabetical order to write all three-letter combinations, then cross out the ones that are not triangles in the figure.

ABC, *ABD*, *ABE*, *ABF*, *ACD*, *ACE*, ~~*ACF*~~, ~~*ADE*~~, ~~*ADF*~~, *AEF*,
~~*BCD*~~, *BCE*, *BCF*, *BDE*, ~~*BDF*~~, ~~*BEF*~~, *CDE*, ~~*CDF*~~, *CEF*, ~~*DEF*~~

Finally, there are twelve different triangles in the figure. Why are ACB and CBF (and many others) not included in the list?

Another method might be first to identify the triangles consisting of a single region each: DEC, ECF, AEF, BCF, ABF. Then list those consisting of two regions each: AEC, BEC, ABE, ABC; and those with three regions each: ACD, BED. There are no triangles with four regions, but there is one with five: ABD. The total is again twelve. Can you think of other systematic ways of getting the same list?

Notice that in the first method shown in **Example 9,** the labeled points were considered in alphabetical order. In the second method, the single-region triangles were listed by using a top-to-bottom and left-to-right order. Using a definite system helps to ensure that we get a complete list.

1 EXERCISES

Electing Officers of a Club *Refer to* **Examples 1 and 4,** *involving the club*

$$N = \{\text{Alan, Bill, Cathy, David, Evelyn}\}.$$

Assuming all members are eligible, but that no one can hold more than one office, list and count the different ways the club could elect each group of officers.

1. a president and a treasurer

2. a president and a treasurer if the president must be a female

3. a president and a treasurer if the two officers must be the same sex

4. a president, a secretary, and a treasurer, if the president and treasurer must be women

5. a president, a secretary, and a treasurer, if the president must be a man and the other two must be women

6. a president, a secretary, and a treasurer, if all three officers must be men

Appointing Committees *List and count the ways club N could appoint a committee of three members under each condition.*

7. There are no restrictions.

8. The committee must include more men than women.

Refer to **Table 2** *(the product table for rolling two dice). Of the 36 possibilities, determine the number for which the sum (for both dice) is the following.*

9. 2 **10.** 3 **11.** 4

12. 5 **13.** 6 **14.** 7

15. 8 **16.** 9 **17.** 10

18. 11 **19.** 12 **20.** odd

21. even

22. from 6 through 8 inclusive

23. between 6 and 10

24. less than 5

25. Construct a product table showing all possible two-digit numbers using digits from the set

$$\{2, 3, 5, 7\}.$$

Of the sixteen numbers in the product table for Exercise 25, list the ones that belong to each category.

26. even numbers

27. numbers with repeating digits

28. multiples of 3

29. prime numbers

30. Construct a tree diagram showing all possible results when three fair coins are tossed. Then list the ways of getting each result.

(a) at least two heads

(b) more than two heads

(c) no more than two heads

(d) fewer than two heads

31. Extend the tree diagram of **Exercise 30** for four fair coins. Then list the ways of getting each result.

(a) more than three tails

(b) fewer than three tails

(c) at least three tails

(d) no more than three tails

Determine the number of triangles (of any size) in each figure.

32.

33.

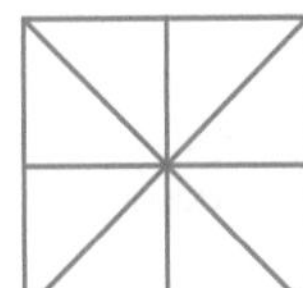

34.

35.

Determine the number of squares (of any size) in each figure.

36.

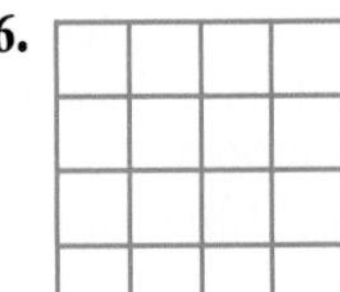

37.

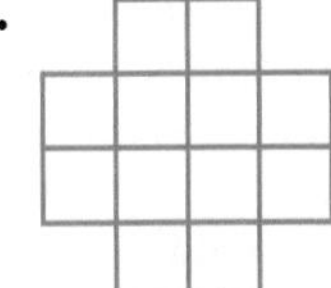

38.

39.

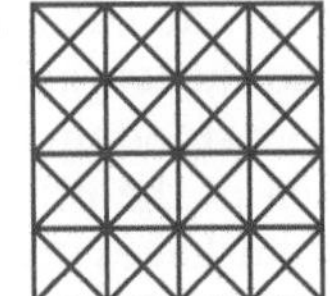

Consider only the smallest individual cubes and assume solid stacks (no gaps). Determine the number of cubes in each stack that are not visible from the perspective shown.

40. **41.**

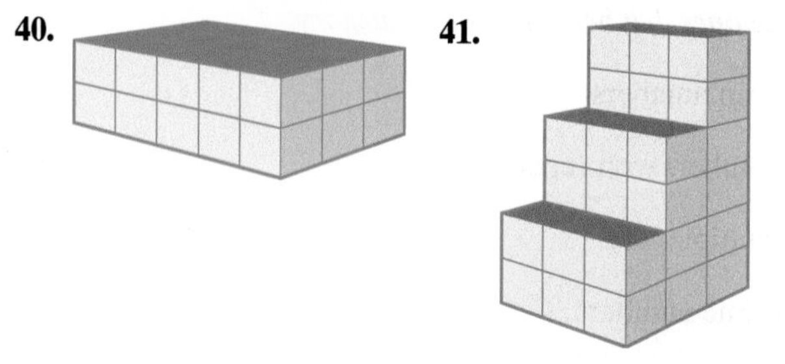

42. **43.**

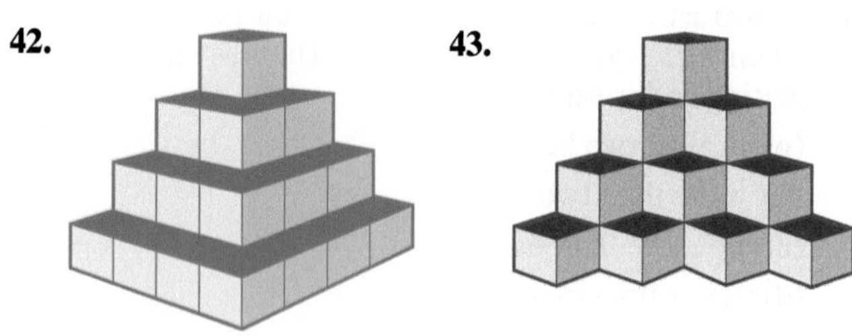

44. In the plane figure illustrated here, only movement that tends downward is allowed. Find the total number of paths from A to B.

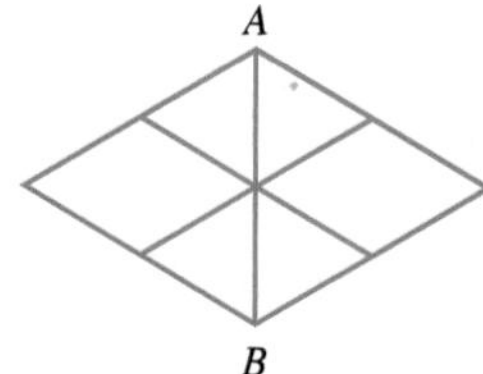

45. Find the number of paths from A to B in the figure illustrated here if the directions on various segments are restricted as shown.

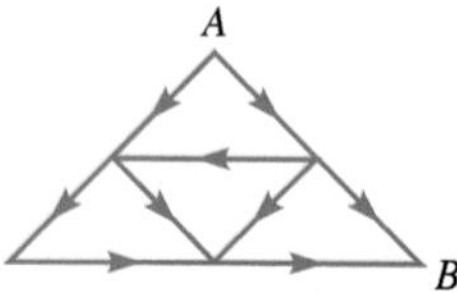

In each of Exercises 46–48, determine the number of different ways the given number can be written as the sum of two primes.

46. 30 **47.** 40 **48.** 95

49. ***Rolling Unusual Dice*** An unusual die has the numbers 2, 2, 3, 3, 5, and 8 on its six faces. Two of these dice are rolled, and the two numbers on the top faces are added. How many different sums are possible? (*Mathematics Teacher* calendar problem)

50. ***Shaking Hands in a Group*** A group of six strangers sat in a circle, and each one got acquainted only with the person to the left and the person to the right. Then all six people stood up and each one shook hands (once) with each of the others who was still a stranger. How many handshakes occurred?

51. ***Number of Games in a Chess Tournament*** Fifty people enter a single-elimination chess tournament. (If you lose one game, you're out.) Assuming no ties occur, what is the number of games required to determine the tournament champion?

52. ***Sums of Digits*** How many positive integers less than 100 have the sum of their digits equal to a perfect square?

53. ***Sums of Digits*** How many three-digit numbers have the sum of their digits equal to 22?

54. ***Integers Containing the Digit 2*** How many integers between 100 and 400 contain the digit 2?

55. ***Filling an Order*** A customer ordered fifteen Zingers. Zingers are placed in packages of four, three, or one. In how many different ways can this order be filled? (*Mathematics Teacher* calendar problem)

56. ***Selecting Dinner Items*** Michael Bailey and friends are dining at the Clam Shell Restaurant this evening, where a complete dinner consists of three items:

(1) soup (clam chowder or minestrone) or salad (fresh spinach or shrimp),

(2) sourdough rolls or bran muffin, and

(3) entree (lasagna, lobster, or roast turkey).

Michael selects his meal subject to the following restrictions. He cannot stomach more than one kind of seafood at a sitting. Also, whenever he tastes minestrone, he cannot resist having lasagna as well. Use a tree diagram to determine the number of different choices Michael has.

Setting Options on a Computer Printer *For Exercises 57–59, refer to* ***Example 7****. How many different settings could Pamela choose in each case?*

57. No restrictions apply to adjacent switches.

58. No two adjacent switches can be off *and* no two adjacent switches can be on.

59. There are five switches rather than four, and no two adjacent switches can be on.

60. ***Building Numbers from Sets of Digits*** Determine the number of odd, nonrepeating three-digit numbers that can be written using only the digits 0, 1, 2, and 3.

61. ***Lattice Points on a Line Segment*** A line segment joins the points

$$(8, 12) \quad \text{and} \quad (53, 234)$$

in the Cartesian plane. Including its endpoints, how many lattice points does this line segment contain? (A *lattice point* is a point with integer coordinates.)

62. ***Lengths of Segments Joining Lattice Points*** In the pattern that follows, dots are one unit apart horizontally and vertically. If a segment can join any two dots, how many segments can be drawn with each length?

(a) 1 **(b)** 2 **(c)** 3 **(d)** 4 **(e)** 5

• • • • •
• • • • •
• • • • •
• • • • •
• • • • •

63. ***Counting Matchsticks in a Grid*** Uniform-length matchsticks are used to build a rectangular grid as shown here. If the grid is 12 matchsticks high and 25 matchsticks wide, how many matchsticks are used?

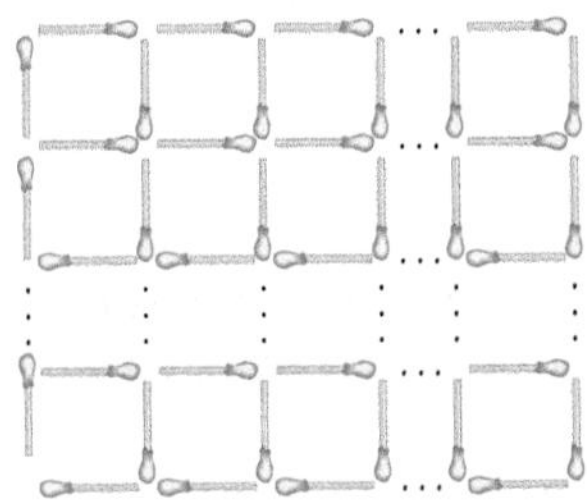

64. ***Patterns in Floor Tiling*** A square floor is to be tiled with square tiles as shown at the top of the next column, with blue tiles on the main diagonals and red tiles everywhere else. (In all cases, both blue and red tiles must be used and the two diagonals must have a common blue tile at the center of the floor.)

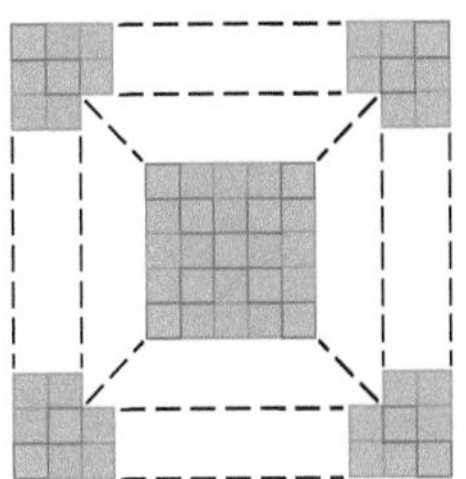

(a) If 81 blue tiles will be used, how many red tiles will be needed?

(b) For what numbers in place of 81 would this problem still be solvable?

(c) Find an expression in k giving the number of red tiles required in general.

65. ***Shaking Hands in a Group*** Chris Heister and his son were among four father-and-son pairs who gathered to trade baseball cards. As each person arrived, he shook hands with anyone he had not known previously. Each person ended up making a different number of new acquaintances (0–6), except Chris and his son, who each met the same number of people. How many hands did Chris shake?

In Exercises 66 and 67, restate the given counting problem in two ways, first **(a)** *using the word* repetition, *and then* **(b)** *using the word* replacement.

66. Example 2

67. Example 4

2 USING THE FUNDAMENTAL COUNTING PRINCIPLE

Uniformity and the Fundamental Counting Principle • Factorials • Arrangements of Objects

Uniformity and the Fundamental Counting Principle

In **Section 1,** we obtained complete lists of all possible results for various tasks. However, if the total number of possibilities is all we need to know, then an actual listing usually is unnecessary and often is difficult or tedious to obtain, especially when the list is long.

Figure 6 repeats **Figure 2** of **Section 1** (for **Example 6(b)**), which shows all possible nonrepeating three-digit numbers using only the digits 1, 2, and 3.

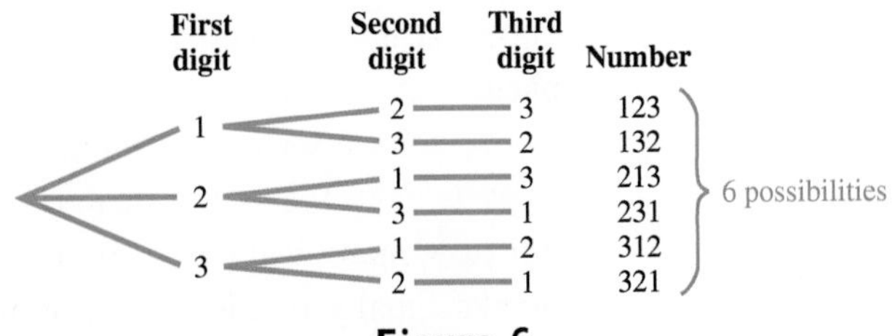

Figure 6

The tree diagram in **Figure 6** is "uniform" in the sense that a given part of the task can be done in the same number of ways no matter which choices were selected for previous parts. For example, there are always two choices for the second digit. (If the first digit is 1, the second can be 2 or 3. If the first is 2, the second can be 1 or 3. If the first is 3, the second can be 1 or 2.)

Example 6(a) of **Section 1** addressed the same basic situation:

Find the number of three-digit numbers that can be written using the digits 1, 2, and 3.

In that case repetitions were allowed. With repetitions allowed, there were many more possibilities (27 rather than 6—see **Figure 1** of **Section 1**). But the uniformity criterion mentioned above still applied. No matter what the first digit is, there are three choices for the second (1, 2, 3). And no matter what the first and second digits are, there are three choices for the third. This uniformity criterion can be stated in general as follows.

Uniformity Criterion for Multiple-Part Tasks

A multiple-part task is said to satisfy the **uniformity criterion** if the number of choices for any particular part is the same *no matter which choices were selected for previous parts.*

The uniformity criterion is not always satisfied. Refer to **Example 7** (and **Figure 3**) of **Section 1.** After the first switch (two possibilities), other switches had either one or two possible settings depending on how previous switches were set. (This "nonuniformity" arose, in that case, from the requirement that no two adjacent switches could both be off.)

In the many cases where uniformity does hold, we can avoid having to construct a tree diagram by using the **fundamental counting principle,** stated as follows.

Fundamental Counting Principle

When a task consists of k separate parts and satisfies the uniformity criterion, if the first part can be done in n_1 ways, the second part can then be done in n_2 ways, and so on through the kth part, which can be done in n_k ways, then the total number of ways to complete the task is given by the product

$$n_1 \cdot n_2 \cdot n_3 \cdot \ldots \cdot n_k.$$

PROBLEM-SOLVING HINT A problem-solving strategy suggested was: "*If a formula applies, use it.*" The fundamental counting principle provides a formula that applies to a variety of problems. The trick is to visualize the "task" at hand as being accomplished in a sequence of two or more separate parts.

A helpful technique when applying the fundamental counting principle is to write out all the separate parts of the task, with a blank for each one. Reason out how many ways each part can be done, and enter these numbers in the blanks. Finally, multiply these numbers together.

Interfoto/Alamy

Richard Dedekind (1831–1916) studied at the University of Göttingen, where he was Gauss's last student. His work was not recognized during his lifetime, but his treatment of the infinite and of what constitutes a real number are influential even today.

While on vacation in Switzerland, Dedekind met Georg Cantor. Dedekind was interested in Cantor's work on infinite sets. Perhaps because both were working in new and unusual fields of mathematics, such as number theory, and because neither received the professional attention he deserved during his lifetime, the two struck up a lasting friendship.

EXAMPLE 1 Counting the Two-Digit Numbers

How many two-digit numbers are there in our (base-ten) system of counting numbers? (**While 40 is a two-digit number, 04 is not.**)

SOLUTION

Our "task" here is to select, or construct, a two-digit number. Set up the work as follows.

Part of task	**Select first digit**	**Select second digit**
Number of ways	____	____

There are nine choices for the first digit (1 through 9). Since there were no stated or implied restrictions, we assume that repetition of digits is allowed. Therefore, no matter which nonzero digit is used as the first digit, all nine choices are available for the second digit. Also, unlike the first digit, the second digit may be zero, so we have ten choices for the second digit. We can now fill in the blanks and multiply.

Part of task	**Select first digit**		**Select second digit**	
Number of ways	9	·	10	= 90

There are 90 two-digit numbers. (As a check, notice that they are the numbers from 10 through 99, a total of $99 - 10 + 1 = 90$.) ■■■

EXAMPLE 2 Building Two-Digit Numbers with Restrictions

Find the number of two-digit numbers that do not contain repeated digits.

SOLUTION

The basic task is again to select a two-digit number, and there are two parts:

1. Select the first digit. **2.** Select the second digit.

But a new restriction applies—no repetition of digits. There are nine choices for the first digit (1 through 9). Then nine choices remain for the second digit, since one nonzero digit has been used and cannot be repeated, but zero is now available. The total number is $9 \cdot 9 = 81$. ■■■

EXAMPLE 3 Electing Club Officers with Restrictions

In how many ways can Club N of the previous section elect a president and a secretary if no one may hold more than one office and the secretary must be a man?

SOLUTION

Recall that $N = \{A, B, C, D, E\} = \{\text{Alan, Bill, Cathy, David, Evelyn}\}$. Considering president first, there are five choices (no restrictions). But now we have a problem with finding the number of choices for secretary. If a woman was selected president (C or E), there are three choices for secretary (A, B, and D). If a man was selected president, only two choices (the other two men) remain for secretary. ***In other words, the uniformity criterion is not met and our attempt to apply the fundamental counting principle has failed.***

All is not lost, however. To find the total number of ways, we can consider secretary first. There are three choices (A, B, and D). Now, no matter which man was chosen secretary, both of the other men, and both women, are available for president (four choices in every case). In this order, we satisfy the uniformity criterion and can use the fundamental counting principle. The total number of ways to elect a president and a secretary is $3 \cdot 4 = 12$. ■■■

> **PROBLEM-SOLVING HINT** **Example 3** suggests a useful problem-solving strategy: Whenever one or more parts of a task have special restrictions, try considering that part (or those parts) before other parts.

EXAMPLE 4 Counting Three-Digit Numbers with Restrictions

How many nonrepeating odd three-digit counting numbers are there?

SOLUTION

The most restricted digit is the third, since it must be odd. There are five choices (1, 3, 5, 7, and 9). Next, consider the first digit. It can be any nonzero digit except the one already chosen as the third digit. There are eight choices. Finally, the second digit can be any digit (including 0) except for the two (nonzero) digits already used. There are eight choices.

Part of task	**Select third digit**		**Select first digit**		**Select second digit**	
Number of ways	5	·	8	·	8	= 320

There are 320 nonrepeating odd three-digit counting numbers. ∎

EXAMPLE 5 Counting License Plates

In some states, auto license plates have contained three letters followed by three digits. How many such licenses are possible?

Preamble (1987), Mike Wilkins. Painted metal on vinyl and wood. 96 × 96 in. Smithsonian American Art Museum, Washington, DC/Art Resource, New York

SOLUTION

The basic task is to design a license plate with three letters followed by three digits. There are six component parts to this task. Since there are no restrictions on letters or digits, the fundamental counting principle gives

$$26 \cdot 26 \cdot 26 \cdot 10 \cdot 10 \cdot 10 = 26^3 \cdot 10^3 = 17{,}576{,}000 \text{ possible licenses.}$$

(In practice, a few of the possible sequences of letters are considered undesirable and are not used.) ∎

Julie Jacobson/AP Images

Answer to the Chapter Opener Question The Super Bowl announcer was pretty close. Since each coin must fall in one of two ways (heads or tails), the 13 consecutive NFC wins was just one of

$$2^{13} = 8192 \text{ possibilities.}$$

EXAMPLE 6 Building Numbers with Specified Digits

A four-digit number is to be constructed using only the digits 1, 2, and 3.

(a) How many such numbers are possible?

(b) How many of these numbers are odd and less than 2000?

SOLUTION

(a) To construct such a number, we must select four digits, in succession, from the given set of three digits, where the selection is done with replacement (since repetition of digits is apparently allowed). The number of possibilities is

$$3 \cdot 3 \cdot 3 \cdot 3 = 3^4 = 81 \quad \text{Fundamental counting principle}$$

(b) The number is less than 2000 only if the first digit is 1 (just one choice) and is odd only if the fourth digit is 1 or 3 (two choices). The second and third digits are unrestricted (three choices for each). The answer is

$$1 \cdot 3 \cdot 3 \cdot 2 = 18.$$

As a check, can you list the eighteen possibilities? ■■■

PROBLEM-SOLVING HINT A counting problem may sometimes prove to be essentially the same, or at least fit the same pattern, as another problem already solved.

Ocean/Corbis

EXAMPLE 7 Distributing Golf Clubs

Vern has four antique wood head golf clubs that he wants to give to his three sons, Mark, Chris, and Scott.

(a) How many ways can the clubs be distributed?

(b) How many choices are there if the power driver must go to Mark and the number 3 wood must go to either Chris or Scott?

SOLUTION

(a) The task is to distribute four clubs among three sons. Consider the clubs in succession, and, for each one, ask how many sons could receive it. In effect, we must select four sons, in succession, from the list Mark, Chris, Scott, selecting with replacement. Compare this with **Example 6(a),** in which we selected four digits, in succession, from the digits 1, 2, and 3, selecting with replacement. In this case, we are selecting sons rather than digits, but the pattern is the same and the numbers are the same. Again our answer is

$$3^4 = 81.$$

(b) Just as in **Example 6(b),** one part of the task is now restricted to a single choice and another part is restricted to two choices. As in that example, the number of possibilities is

$$1 \cdot 3 \cdot 3 \cdot 2 = 18.$$

■■■

EXAMPLE 8 Seating Attendees at a Concert

Rework **Example 8** of **Section 1,** this time using the fundamental counting principle.

SOLUTION

Recall that Arne, Bobbette, Chuck, and Deirdre (A, B, C, and D) are to seat themselves in four adjacent seats (say 1, 2, 3, and 4) so that A and B are side-by-side. One approach to accomplish this task is to make three successive decisions as follows.

1	2	3	4
X	X	_	_
_	X	X	_
_	_	X	X

Seats available to A and B

1. Which pair of seats should A and B occupy? There are *three* choices (1 and 2, 2 and 3, 3 and 4, as illustrated in the margin).
2. Which order should A and B take? There are *two* choices (A left of B, or B left of A).
3. Which order should C and D take? There are *two* choices (C left of D, or D left of C, not necessarily right next to each other).

(Why did we not ask which two seats C and D should occupy?) The fundamental counting principle now gives the total number of choices:

$$3 \cdot 2 \cdot 2 = 12 \quad \text{Same result as in } \textbf{Section 1}$$

Factorials

Short Table of Factorials Factorial values increase rapidly. The value of 100! is a number with 158 digits.

$0! = 1$
$1! = 1$
$2! = 2$
$3! = 6$
$4! = 24$
$5! = 120$
$6! = 720$
$7! = 5040$
$8! = 40,320$
$9! = 362,880$
$10! = 3,628,800$

This section began with a discussion of nonrepeating three-digit numbers using digits 1, 2, and 3. The number of possibilities was

$$3 \cdot 2 \cdot 1 = 6. \quad \text{Fundamental counting principle}$$

That product can also be thought of as the total number of distinct *arrangements* of the three digits 1, 2, and 3.

Similarly, the number of distinct arrangements of four objects, say A, B, C, and D, is

$$4 \cdot 3 \cdot 2 \cdot 1 = 24. \quad \text{Fundamental counting principle}$$

Since this type of product occurs so commonly in applications, we give it a special name and symbol as follows. For any counting number n, the product of *all* counting numbers from n down through 1 is called ***n* factorial,** and is denoted ***n*!**.

Factorial Formula

For any counting number n, the quantity ***n* factorial** is given as follows.

$$\boldsymbol{n! = n(n-1)(n-2)\ldots 2 \cdot 1}$$

The first few factorial values are easily found by simple multiplication, but they rapidly become very large. The use of a calculator is advised in most cases.

PROBLEM-SOLVING HINT Sometimes expressions involving factorials can be evaluated easily by observing that, in general, $n! = n(n-1)!$, $n! = n(n-1)(n-2)!$, and so on. For example,

$$8! = 8 \cdot 7!, \quad 12! = 12 \cdot 11 \cdot 10 \cdot 9!, \quad \text{and so on.}$$

This pattern is especially helpful in evaluating quotients of factorials, such as

$$\frac{10!}{8!} = \frac{10 \cdot 9 \cdot 8!}{8!} = 10 \cdot 9 = 90.$$

EXAMPLE 9 Evaluating Expressions Containing Factorials

Evaluate each expression.

(a) $3!$ **(b)** $6!$ **(c)** $(6-3)!$ **(d)** $6! - 3!$

(e) $\frac{6!}{3!}$ **(f)** $\left(\frac{6}{3}\right)!$ **(g)** $15!$ **(h)** $100!$

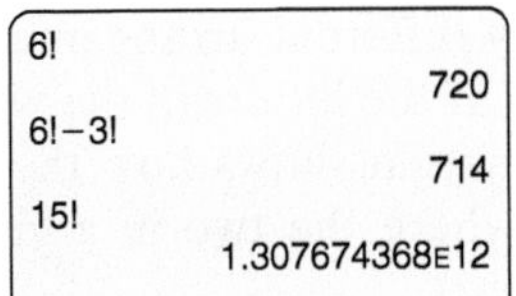

The results of **Example 9(b), (d), and (g)** are illustrated in this calculator screen.

SOLUTION

(a) $3! = 3 \cdot 2 \cdot 1 = 6$

(b) $6! = 6 \cdot 5 \cdot 4 \cdot 3 \cdot 2 \cdot 1 = 720$

(c) $(6-3)! = 3! = 6$

(d) $6! - 3! = 720 - 6 = 714$

(e) $\frac{6!}{3!} = \frac{6 \cdot 5 \cdot 4 \cdot 3!}{3!} = 6 \cdot 5 \cdot 4 = 120$ Note application of the Problem-Solving Hint.

(f) $\left(\frac{6}{3}\right)! = 2! = 2 \cdot 1 = 2$

(g) $15! = 1.307674368000 \times 10^{12}$ ← Done on a calculator

(h) $100! = 9.332621544 \times 10^{157}$ ← Too large for most calculators

Notice the distinction between parts (c) and (d) and between parts (e) and (f).

So that factorials will be defined for all whole numbers, including zero, we define 0! as follows.

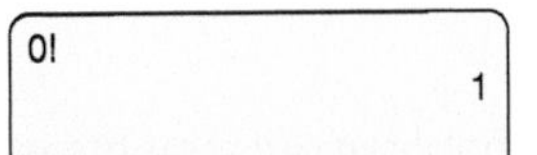

The definition $0! = 1$ is illustrated here.

Definition of Zero Factorial

$$0! = 1$$

(We will see later that this special definition makes other results easier to state.)

Arrangements of Objects

When finding the total number of ways to *arrange* a given number of distinct objects, we can use a factorial. The fundamental counting principle would do, but factorials provide a shortcut.

Arrangements of *n* Distinct Objects

The total number of different ways to arrange n distinct objects is $\boldsymbol{n!}$.

EXAMPLE 10 Arranging Essays

Michelle Cook has seven essays to include in her English 1A folder. In how many different orders can she arrange them?

SOLUTION

The number of ways to arrange seven distinct objects is $7! = 5040$.

EXAMPLE 11 Arranging Preschoolers

Tricia Caruso is taking thirteen preschoolers to the park. How many ways can the children line up, in single file, to board the van?

SOLUTION

Thirteen children can be arranged in $13! = 6{,}227{,}020{,}800$ different ways. ■■■

D_1AD_2
D_2AD_1

D_1D_2A
D_2D_1A

AD_1D_2
AD_2D_1

In counting arrangements of objects that contain look-alikes, the normal factorial formula must be modified to find the number of truly different arrangements. For example, the number of distinguishable arrangements of the letters of the word DAD is not $3! = 6$ but rather $\frac{3!}{2!} = 3$. The listing in the margin shows how the six total arrangements consist of just three groups of two, where the two in a given group look alike.

Arrangements of *n* Objects Containing Look-Alikes

The number of **distinguishable arrangements** of n objects, where one or more subsets consist of look-alikes (say n_1 are of one kind, n_2 are of another kind, . . . , and n_k are of yet another kind), is given by

$$\frac{n!}{n_1!n_2!\ldots n_k!}.$$

EXAMPLE 12 Counting Distinguishable Arrangements

Determine the number of distinguishable arrangements of the letters in each word.

(a) ATTRACT **(b)** NIGGLING

SOLUTION

(a) For the letters of ATTRACT, the number of distinguishable arrangements is

7 letters total ⟶ (numerator)
3 T's, 2 A's ⟶ (denominator)

$$\frac{7!}{3!\,2!} = 420.$$

(b) For the letters of NIGGLING, the number of distinguishable arrangements is

8 letters total ⟶ (numerator)
2 N's, 2 I's, 3 G's ⟶ (denominator)

$$\frac{8!}{2!\,2!\,3!} = 1680.$$ ■■■

For Further Thought

Stirling's Approximation for *n*!

Although all factorial values are counting numbers, they can be approximated using **Stirling's formula,**

$$n! \approx \sqrt{2\pi n} \cdot n^n \cdot e^{-n},$$

which involves two famous irrational numbers, π and e. For example, while the exact value of 5! is $5 \cdot 4 \cdot 3 \cdot 2 \cdot 1 = 120$, the corresponding approximation is

$$5! \approx \sqrt{2\pi \cdot 5} \cdot 5^5 \cdot e^{-5} \approx 118.019168,$$

which is off by less than 2, an error of only 1.65%.

For Group or Individual Investigation

Use a calculator to fill in all values in the table on the next page. The column values are defined as follows.

$C = n!$	(exact value, by calculator)
$S \approx n!$	(Stirling's approximation, by calculator)
$D =$ Difference	$(C - S)$
$P =$ Percentage difference	$\left(\frac{D}{C} \cdot 100\%\right)$

n	C	S	D	P
1				
2				
3				
4				
5				
6				
7				
8				
9				
10				

Try to obtain percentage differences accurate to two decimal places.

Based on your calculations, answer each question.

1. In general, is Stirling's approximation too low or too high?
2. Observe the values in the table as n grows larger.
   (a) Do the differences (D) get larger or smaller?
   (b) Do the percentage differences (P) get larger or smaller?
   (c) Does Stirling's formula become more accurate or less accurate?

2 EXERCISES

1. Explain the fundamental counting principle in your own words.

2. Describe how factorials can be used in counting problems.

For Exercises 3–6, n and m are counting numbers. Do the following: **(a)** *Tell whether the given statement is true in general, and* **(b)** *explain your answer, using specific examples.*

3. $(n + m)! = n! + m!$ **4.** $(n \cdot m)! = n! \cdot m!$

5. $(n - m)! = n! - m!$ **6.** $n! = n(n - 1)!$

Evaluate each expression without using a calculator.

7. $4!$ **8.** $6!$ **9.** $\frac{9!}{7!}$

10. $\frac{16!}{14!}$ **11.** $\frac{5!}{(5-2)!}$ **12.** $\frac{6!}{(6-3)!}$

13. $\frac{8!}{6!(8-6)!}$ **14.** $\frac{10!}{4!(10-4)!}$

15. $\frac{n!}{(n-r)!}$, where $n = 7$ and $r = 4$

16. $\frac{n!}{r!(n-r)!}$, where $n = 12$ and $r = 4$

Evaluate each expression using a calculator.

17. $10!$ **18.** $14!$ **19.** $\frac{12!}{5!}$

20. $\frac{13!}{(13-6)!}$ **21.** $\frac{20!}{10! \cdot 10!}$ **22.** $\frac{19!}{9! \cdot 10!}$

23. $\frac{n!}{(n-r)!}$, where $n = 17$ and $r = 8$

24. $\frac{n!}{r!(n-r)!}$, where $n = 24$ and $r = 18$

Arranging Letters *Find the number of distinguishable arrangements of the letters of each word.*

25. GOOGOL **26.** HEEBIE-JEEBIES

Settings on a Switch Panel *A panel containing three on–off switches in a row is to be set.*

27. Assuming no restrictions on individual switches, use the fundamental counting principle to find the total number of possible panel settings.

28. Assuming no restrictions, construct a tree diagram to list all the possible panel settings of **Exercise 27.**

29. Now assume that no two adjacent switches can both be off. Explain why the fundamental counting principle does not apply.

30. Construct a tree diagram to list all possible panel settings under the restriction of **Exercise 29.**

31. ***Rolling Dice*** **Table 2** in the previous section shows that there are 36 possible outcomes when two fair dice are rolled. How many would there be if three fair dice were rolled?

StillFX/Shutterstock

32. ***Counting Five-Digit Numbers*** How many five-digit numbers are there in our system of counting numbers?

33. ***Bowling*** After rolling the first ball of a frame in a game of 10-pin bowling, how many different pin configurations can remain (assuming all configurations are physically possible)? (*Mathematics Teacher* calendar problem)

Exercises from the *Mathematics Teacher* monthly calendar appear on the following pages of the text. These are reprinted with permission from *Mathematics Teacher*, copyright © 1980–2010 by the National Council of Teachers of Mathematics. All Rights Reserved

34. ***Bowling*** Answer the question of **Exercise 33** assuming that pins 1, 2, and 3 were knocked down on the first roll.

Matching Club Members with Tasks *Recall the club*

$$N = \{\text{Alan, Bill, Cathy, David, Evelyn}\}.$$

In how many ways could they do each of the following?

35. line up all five members for a photograph

36. schedule one member to work in the office on each of five different days, assuming members may work more than one day

37. select a male and a female to decorate for a party

38. select two members, one to open their next meeting and another to close it, given that Bill will not be present

Building Numbers with Specified Digits *In Exercises 39–42, counting numbers are to be formed using only the digits 3, 4, and 5. Determine the number of different possibilities for each type of number described.*

39. two-digit numbers

40. odd three-digit numbers

41. four-digit numbers with one pair of adjacent 4s and no other repeated digits (*Hint:* You may want to split the task of designing such a number into three parts, such as *(1)* position the pair of 4s, *(2)* position the 3, and *(3)* position the 5.)

42. five-digit numbers beginning and ending with 3 and with unlimited repetitions allowed

Selecting Dinner Items *The Gourmet de Coeur Restaurant offers five choices in the soup and salad category (two soups and three salads), two choices in the bread category, and four choices in the entree category. Find the number of dinners available in each case.*

43. One item is to be included from each of the three categories.

44. Only salad and entree are to be included.

Selecting Answers on a Test *Determine the number of possible ways to mark your answer sheet (with an answer for each question) for each test.*

45. a six-question true-or-false test

46. a ten-question multiple-choice test with five answer choices for each question

Selecting a College Class Schedule *Jessica Elbern's class schedule for next semester must consist of exactly one class from each of the four categories shown in the table at the top of the next column.*

For each situation in Exercises 47–52, use the table to determine the number of different sets of classes Jessica can take.

Category	Choices	Number of Choices
Economics	Free Markets Controlled Markets	2
Mathematics	History of Mathematics College Algebra Finite Mathematics	3
Education	Classroom Technology Group Dynamics Language Supervision Parent/Teacher Relations	4
Sociology	Social Problems Sociology of the Middle East Aging in America Minorities in America Women in American Culture	5

47. All classes shown are available.

48. She is not eligible for Free Markets or for Group Dynamics.

49. All sections of Minorities in America and Women in American Culture already are filled.

50. She does not have the prerequisites for Controlled Markets, College Algebra, or Language Supervision.

51. Funding has been withdrawn for three of the Education courses and for two of the Sociology courses.

52. She must complete Finite Mathematics and Social Problems next semester to fulfill her degree requirements.

53. ***Selecting Clothing*** Don Beville took two pairs of shoes, four pairs of pants, and six shirts on a trip. If all items are compatible, how many different outfits can he wear?

54. ***Selecting Music Equipment*** A music equipment outlet stocks ten different guitars, three guitar cases, six amplifiers, and five effects processors, with all items mutually compatible and all suitable for beginners. How many different complete setups could Lionel choose to start his musical career?

55. ***Counting ZIP Codes*** Tonya's ZIP code is 85726. How many ZIP codes altogether could be formed, each one using those same five digits?

56. ***Listing Phone Numbers*** John Cross keeps the phone numbers for his seven closest friends (three men and four women) in his digital phone memory. (Refer to **Example 8**.) How many ways can he list them if

(a) men are listed before women?

(b) men are all listed together?

(c) no two men are listed next to each other?

57. ***Counting Telephone Area Codes*** Until 1995, the rules for three-digit area codes in the United States were as follows:

- The first digit could not be 0 or 1.
- The second digit had to be 0 or 1.
- The third digit had no such restrictions.

In 1995, the restriction on the second digit of area codes was removed. How many area codes are currently possible? (*Mathematics Teacher* calendar problem)

Seating Arrangements at a Theater *In Exercises 58–61, Arne, Bobbette, Chuck, Deirdre, Ed, and Fran have reserved six seats in a row at the theater, starting at an aisle seat. (Refer to* ***Example 8****.)*

58. In how many ways can they arrange themselves? (*Hint:* Divide the task into the series of six parts shown below, performed in order.)

(a) If A is seated first, how many seats are available for him?

(b) Now, how many are available for B?

(c) Now, how many for C?

(d) Now, how many for D?

(e) Now, how many for E?

(f) Now, how many for F?

Now multiply together your six answers above.

59. In how many ways can they arrange themselves so that Arne and Bobbette will be next to each other?

Anthony Ladd/iStockphoto

1	2	3	4	5	6
X	X	_	_	_	_
_	X	X	_	_	_
_	_	X	X	_	_
_	_	_	X	X	_
_	_	_	_	X	X

Seats available to A and B

(*Hint:* Answer these questions, in order.)

(a) How many pairs of adjacent seats can A and B occupy?

(b) Now, given the two seats for A and B, in how many orders can they be seated?

(c) Now, how many seats are available for C?

(d) Now, how many for D?

(e) Now, how many for E?

(f) Now, how many for F?

Now multiply your six answers above.

60. In how many ways can they arrange themselves if the men and women are to alternate seats and a man must sit on the aisle? (*Hint:* Answer the questions at the top of the next column, in order.)

(a) How many choices are there for the person to occupy the first seat, next to the aisle? (It must be a man.)

(b) Now, how many choices of people may occupy the second seat from the aisle? (It must be a woman.)

(c) Now, how many for the third seat? (one of the remaining men)

(d) Now, how many for the fourth seat? (a woman)

(e) Now, how many for the fifth seat? (a man)

(f) Now, how many for the sixth seat? (a woman)

Now multiply your six answers above.

61. In how many ways can they arrange themselves if the men and women are to alternate with either a man or a woman on the aisle? (*Hint:* Answer these questions.)

(a) How many choices of people are there for the aisle seat?

(b) Now, how many are there for the second seat? (This person may not be of the same sex as the person on the aisle.)

(c) Now, how many choices are there for the third seat?

(d) Now, how many for the fourth seat?

(e) Now, how many for the fifth seat?

(f) Now, how many for the sixth seat?

Now multiply your six answers above.

62. Try working **Example 4** by considering digits in the order first, then second, then third. Explain what goes wrong.

63. Try working **Example 4** by considering digits in the order third, then second, then first. Explain what goes wrong.

64. Repeat **Example 4** but this time allow repeated digits. Does the order in which digits are considered matter in this case?

65. If all the six-digit numbers formed by using the digits 1, 2, 3, 4, 5, and 6, without repetition, are listed from least to greatest, which number will be 500th in the list? (*Mathematics Teacher* calendar problem)

66. The number $2^7 \cdot 3^4 \cdot 5 \cdot 7^2 \cdot 11^3$ is divisible by many perfect squares. How many? (*Mathematics Teacher* calendar problem)

67. How many of the anagrams [arrangements of the letters] of INDIANA are palindromes, that is arrangements that read the same forward and backward? *Hint:* One such palindrome is INADANI. (*Mathematics Teacher* calendar problem)

68. How many distinguishable rearrangements of the letters in the word CONTEST start with the two vowels? (*Mathematics Teacher* calendar problem)

3 USING PERMUTATIONS AND COMBINATIONS

Permutations • Combinations • Guidelines on Which Method to Use

Permutations

Again recall the club

$$N = \{\text{Alan, Bill, Cathy, David, Evelyn}\} = \{A, B, C, D, E\},$$

and consider two questions:

1. How many ways can all the club members arrange themselves in a row for a photograph?
2. How many ways can the club elect a president, a secretary, and a treasurer if no one can hold more than one office?

From **Section 2,** the answer to the first question above is

$$5! = 5 \cdot 4 \cdot 3 \cdot 2 \cdot 1 = 120,$$

the number of possible arrangements of 5 distinct objects. We previously answered questions like the second one by using a tree diagram, or the fundamental counting principle. The answer is

$$5 \cdot 4 \cdot 3 = 60.$$

A good way to think of this second question is:

How many arrangements are there of five things taken three at a time?

The factors begin with 5 and proceed downward, just as in a factorial product, but do not go all the way to 1. (In this example the product stops when there are three factors.)

In the context of counting problems, arrangements are called **permutations.** The number of permutations of n distinct things taken r at a time is denoted $_nP_r$.* Since the number of objects being arranged cannot exceed the total number available, we assume that $r \leq n$. Applying the fundamental counting principle gives

$$_nP_r = n(n-1)(n-2)\ldots[n-(r-1)].$$

The first factor is $n - 0$, the second is $n - 1$, the third is $n - 2$, and so on. The rth factor, the last one in the product, will be the one with $r - 1$ subtracted from n, as shown above. We can express permutations, in general, in terms of factorials, to obtain a formula as follows.

$$\begin{aligned} {}_nP_r &= n(n-1)(n-2)\ldots[n-(r-1)] \\ &= n(n-1)(n-2)\ldots(n-r+1) && \text{Simplify the last factor.} \\ &= \frac{n(n-1)(n-2)\ldots(n-r+1)(n-r)(n-r-1)\ldots2\cdot1}{(n-r)(n-r-1)\ldots2\cdot1} && \text{Multiply and divide by } (n-r)(n-r-1)\ldots2\cdot1. \\ &= \frac{n!}{(n-r)!} && \text{Definition of factorial} \end{aligned}$$

*Alternative notations are $P(n, r)$ and P^n_r.

Factorial Formula for Permutations

The number of **permutations,** or *arrangements,* of n distinct things taken r at a time, where $r \le n$, can be calculated as follows.

$$_{n}P_{r} = \frac{n!}{(n-r)!}$$

Although we sometimes refer to a symbol such as $_{4}P_{2}$ as "a permutation"(see **Examples 1 and 2**), the symbol actually represents "the number of permutations of 4 distinct things taken 2 at a time" (or "the number of size-2 arrangements that can be selected from 4 distinct things").

EXAMPLE 1 Using the Factorial Formula for Permutations

Evaluate each permutation.

(a) $_{4}P_{2}$ **(b)** $_{8}P_{5}$ **(c)** $_{5}P_{5}$

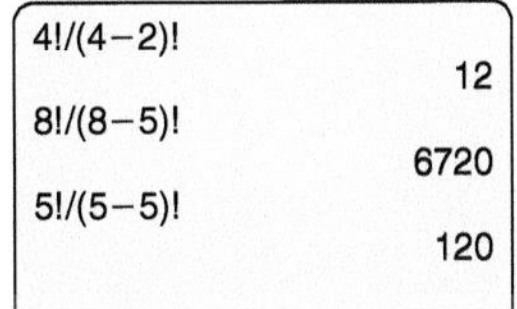

This screen uses factorials to support the results of **Example 1.**

SOLUTION

(a) $_{4}P_{2} = \frac{4!}{(4-2)!} = \frac{4!}{2!} = \frac{24}{2} = 12$

(b) $_{8}P_{5} = \frac{8!}{(8-5)!} = \frac{8!}{3!} = \frac{40{,}320}{6} = 6720$

(c) $_{5}P_{5} = \frac{5!}{(5-5)!} = \frac{5!}{0!} = \frac{120}{1} = 120$

Notice that $_{5}P_{5}$ is equal to 5!. The following is true for all whole numbers n.

$$_{n}P_{n} = n!$$

(This is the number of arrangements of n distinct objects taken all n at a time.)

Most graphing and scientific calculators allow direct calculation of permutations, in which case the factorial formula is not needed.

EXAMPLE 2 Calculating Permutations Directly

10 nPr 6
151200
20 nPr 0
1
18 nPr 12
8.892185702E12

This screen uses the permutations feature to support the results of **Example 2.**

Evaluate each permutation.

(a) $_{10}P_{6}$ **(b)** $_{28}P_{0}$ **(c)** $_{18}P_{12}$

SOLUTION

(a) $_{10}P_{6} = 151{,}200$ **(b)** $_{28}P_{0} = 1$ **(c)** $_{18}P_{12} = 8{,}892{,}185{,}702{,}400$

Concerning part (c), many calculators will not display this many digits, so you may obtain an answer such as 8.8921857×10^{12}.

PROBLEM-SOLVING HINT Permutations can be used any time we need to know the number of arrangements of r objects that can be selected from a collection of n objects. The word *arrangement* implies an ordering, so we use permutations only in cases when

1. repetitions are not allowed, and **2. order is important.**

Tim Gartside/Alamy

Change ringing, the English way of ringing church bells, combines mathematics and music. Bells are rung first in sequence, 1, 2, 3, ... Then the sequence is permuted ("changed"). On six bells, 720 different "changes" (different permutations of tone) can be rung: ${}_6P_6 = 6!$.

The church bells are swung by means of ropes attached to the wheels beside them. One ringer swings each bell, listening intently and watching the other ringers closely. If one ringer gets lost and stays lost, the rhythm of the ringing cannot be maintained; all the ringers have to stop.

A ringer can spend weeks just learning to keep a bell going and months learning to make the bell ring in exactly the right place. Errors of $\frac{1}{4}$ second mean that two bells are ringing at the same time. Even errors of $\frac{1}{10}$ second can be heard.

EXAMPLE 3 Building Numbers from a Set of Digits

How many nonrepeating three-digit numbers can be written using only the digits 3, 4, 5, 6, 7, and 8?

SOLUTION

Repetitions are not allowed since the numbers are to be "nonrepeating." (For example, 448 is not acceptable.) Also, order is important. (For example, 476 and 746 are *distinct* cases.) So we use permutations.

$${}_6P_3 = 6 \cdot 5 \cdot 4 = 120$$

EXAMPLE 4 Designing Account Numbers

Suppose certain account numbers are to consist of two letters followed by four digits and then three more letters, where repetitions of letters or digits are not allowed *within* any of the three groups, but the last group of letters may contain one or both of those used in the first group. How many such accounts are possible?

SOLUTION

The task of designing such a number consists of three parts:

1. Determine the first set of two letters.
2. Determine the set of four digits.
3. Determine the final set of three letters.

Each part requires an arrangement without repetitions, which is a permutation. Multiply together the results of the three parts.

$${}_{26}P_2 \cdot {}_{10}P_4 \cdot {}_{26}P_3 = \underbrace{650}_{\text{Part 1}} \cdot \underbrace{5040}_{\text{Part 2}} \cdot \underbrace{15{,}600}_{\text{Part 3}}$$

$$= 51{,}105{,}600{,}000$$

Combinations

We introduced permutations to evaluate the number of arrangements of n things taken r at a time, where repetitions are not allowed. The order of the items was important. Recall that club

$$N = \{\text{Alan, Bill, Cathy, David, Evelyn}\}$$

could elect three officers in ${}_5P_3 = 60$ different ways. With three-member committees, on the other hand, order is not important. The committees B, D, E and E, B, D are not different. The possible number of committees is not the number of arrangements of size 3. Rather, it is the number of *subsets* of size 3.

Recall that in the study of sets, a **set** is a collection or group of things, commonly designated using a list within braces, as we have been designating the club

$$N = \{A, B, C, D, E\}.$$

The order of listing of the members (of any set) is unimportant. For example, $\{D, B, A, E, C\}$ is the same club. A **subset** of a set is a collection of some of the members. It may be all members of the original set, or even none of them, or anywhere in between. Again, the order of listing of the members is unimportant.

In the study of counting methods, subsets are called **combinations.** The number of combinations of n things taken r at a time (that is, the number of size r subsets, given a set of size n) is written ${}_nC_r$.*

Since there are n things available and we are choosing r of them, we can read ${}_nC_r$ as "n choose r."

The size-3 committees (subsets) of the club (set) $N = \{A, B, C, D, E\}$ are:

$$\begin{array}{ccccc} \{A, B, C\}, & \{A, B, D\}, & \{A, B, E\}, & \{A, C, D\}, & \{A, C, E\}, \\ \{A, D, E\}, & \{B, C, D\}, & \{B, C, E\}, & \{B, D, E\}, & \{C, D, E\}. \end{array}$$

There are ten subsets of size 3, so ten is the number of three-member committees possible. Just as with permutations, repetitions are not allowed. For example, $\{E, E, B\}$ is not a valid three-member subset, just as EEB is not a valid three-member arrangement.

To see how to find the number of such subsets without listing them all, notice that each size-3 subset (combination) gives rise to six size-3 arrangements (permutations). For example, the single combination ADE yields these six permutations:

$$A, D, E \qquad A, E, D \qquad D, A, E \qquad D, E, A \qquad E, A, D \qquad E, D, A.$$

There must be six times as many size-3 permutations as there are size-3 combinations, or, in other words, one-sixth as many combinations as permutations.

$${}_5C_3 = \frac{{}_5P_3}{6} = \frac{60}{6} = 10$$

Again, the 6 appears in the denominator because there are six different ways to arrange a set of three things (since $3! = 3 \cdot 2 \cdot 1 = 6$). Generalizing from this example, we obtain a formula for evaluating numbers of combinations.

$${}_nC_r = \frac{{}_nP_r}{r!}$$ r things can be arranged in $r!$ ways.

$$= \frac{\frac{n!}{(n-r)!}}{r!}$$ Substitute the factorial formula for ${}_nP_r$.

$$= \frac{n!}{r!(n-r)!}$$ Simplify algebraically.

A	B	C	D	E	F
aaaaa	aaaab	aaaba.	aaabb.	aabaa.	aabab.
G	H	I	K	L	M
aabba	aabbb	abaaa.	abaab.	ababa.	ababb.
N	O	P	Q	R	S
abbaa.	abbab.	abbba.	abbbb.	baaaa.	baaab.
T	V	W	X	Y	Z
baaba.	baabb.	babaa.	babab.	babba.	babbb.

"Bilateral cipher" (above) was invented by **Francis Bacon** early in the seventeenth century to code political secrets. This binary code, *a* and *b* in combinations of five, has 32 permutations. Bacon's "biformed alphabet" (bottom four rows) uses two type fonts to conceal a message in some straight text. The decoder deciphers a string of *a*s and *b*s, groups them by fives, then deciphers letters and words. This code was applied to Shakespeare's plays in efforts to prove Bacon the rightful author.

Factorial Formula for Combinations

The number of **combinations,** or *subsets,* of n distinct things taken r at a time, where $r \le n$, can be calculated as follows.

$${}_nC_r = \frac{{}_nP_r}{r!} = \frac{n!}{r!(n-r)!}$$

In **Examples 5 and 6,** we refer to ${}_nC_r$ as "a combination" even though it actually represents "the number of combinations of n distinct things taken r at a time" (or "the number of size-r subsets that can be selected from a set of n things").

*Alternative notations are $C(n, r)$, C_r^n, and $\binom{n}{r}$.

EXAMPLE 5 Using the Factorial Formula for Combinations

Evaluate each combination.

(a) ${}_9C_7$ **(b)** ${}_{24}C_{18}$

SOLUTION

```
9!/(7!*2!)
                36
24!/(18!*6!)
            134596
```

This screen uses factorials to support the results of **Example 5.**

(a) $${}_9C_7 = \frac{9!}{7!(9-7)!} = \frac{9!}{7!2!} = \frac{362{,}880}{5040 \cdot 2} = 36$$

(b) $${}_{24}C_{18} = \frac{24!}{18!(24-18)!} = \frac{24!}{18!6!} = 134{,}596$$

EXAMPLE 6 Calculating Combinations Directly

Evaluate each combination.

(a) ${}_{14}C_6$ **(b)** ${}_{21}C_{15}$

SOLUTION

```
14 nCr 6
              3003
21 nCr 15
             54264
```

This screen uses the combinations feature to support the results of **Example 6.**

(a) ${}_{14}C_6 = 3003$ **(b)** ${}_{21}C_{15} = 54{,}264$ Use a calculator in each case.

> **PROBLEM-SOLVING HINT** Combinations have an important common property with permutations (repetitions are not allowed) and have an important distinction (order is *not* important with combinations). Combinations are applied only when
>
> **1.** repetitions are not allowed, and **2. order is *not* important.**

EXAMPLE 7 Finding the Number of Subsets

Find the number of different subsets of size 2 in the set $\{a, b, c, d\}$. List them to check the answer.

SOLUTION

A subset of size 2 must have two distinct elements, so repetitions are not allowed. And since the order in which the elements of a set are listed makes no difference, order is not important. Use the combinations formula with $n = 4$ and $r = 2$.

$${}_4C_2 = \frac{4!}{2!(4-2)!} = \frac{4!}{2!2!} = 6$$

The six subsets of size 2 are $\{a, b\}, \{a, c\}, \{a, d\}, \{b, c\}, \{b, d\}, \{c, d\}$.

EXAMPLE 8 Finding the Number of Possible Poker Hands

A common form of poker involves "hands" (sets) of five cards each, dealt from a standard deck consisting of 52 different cards. How many different 5-card hands are possible?

SOLUTION

A 5-card hand must contain five distinct cards, so repetitions are not allowed. Also, the order is not important since a given hand depends only on the cards it contains, and not on the order in which they were dealt or the order in which they are displayed or played.

Beth Anderson/Pearson

The set of 52 playing cards in the standard deck has four suits.

♠ spades ♦ diamonds
♥ hearts ♣ clubs

Ace is the unit card. Jacks, queens, and kings are "face cards." Each suit contains thirteen denominations: ace, 2, 3, . . . , 10, jack, queen, king. (In some games, ace rates above king, instead of counting as 1.)

Since order does not matter, use combinations (and a calculator).

$$_{52}C_5 = \frac{52!}{5!(52-5)!} = \frac{52!}{5!\,47!} = 2{,}598{,}960$$

EXAMPLE 9 Finding the Number of Subsets of Paintings

Keri Beers would like to buy ten different paintings but can afford only four of them. In how many ways can she make her selections?

SOLUTION

The four paintings selected must be distinct (repetitions are not allowed), and the order of the four chosen has no bearing in this case, so we use combinations.

$$_{10}C_4 = \frac{10!}{4!(10-4)!} = \frac{10!}{4!\,6!} = 210 \text{ ways}$$

Notice that, according to our formula for combinations,

$$_{10}C_6 = \frac{10!}{6!(10-6)!} = \frac{10!}{6!\,4!} = 210,$$

which is the same as $_{10}C_4$. In fact, **Exercise 62** asks you to prove the following fact, in general, for all whole numbers n and r, with $r \leq n$.

$$_nC_r = {_nC_{n-r}}$$

Guidelines on Which Method to Use

The following table summarizes the similarities and differences between permutations and combinations, as well as the appropriate formulas for calculating their values.

Permutations	**Combinations**
Number of ways of selecting r items out of n items	
Repetitions are not allowed.	
Order is important.	Order is not important.
Arrangements of n items taken r at a time	Subsets of n items taken r at a time
$_nP_r = \frac{n!}{(n-r)!}$	$_nC_r = \frac{n!}{r!(n-r)!}$
Clue words: arrangement, schedule, order	Clue words: set, group, sample, selection

In cases where r items are to be selected from n items and repetitions are allowed, it is usually best to make direct use of the fundamental counting principle.

Most, if not all, of the exercises in this section will call for permutations and/or combinations. And in the case of multiple-part tasks, the fundamental counting principle may also be required. ***In all cases, decide carefully whether order is important, since that determines whether to use permutations or combinations.***

PROBLEM-SOLVING HINT Many counting problems involve selecting some of the items from a given set of items. The particular conditions of the problem will determine which specific technique to use.

1. **If selected items can be repeated, use the fundamental counting principle.**
   Example: How many four-digit numbers are there?
   $$9 \cdot 10^3 = 9000$$
2. **If selected items cannot be repeated, and order is important, use permutations.**
   Example: How many ways can three of eight people line up at a ticket counter?
   $${}_8P_3 = \frac{8!}{(8-3)!} = 336$$
3. **If selected items cannot be repeated, and order is *not* important, use combinations.**
   Example: How many ways can a committee of three be selected from a group of twelve people?
   $${}_{12}C_3 = \frac{12!}{3!(12-3)!} = 220$$

EXAMPLE 10 Distributing Toys to Children

Igor Stepovik/Shutterstock

In how many ways can a mother distribute three different toys among her seven children if a child may receive anywhere from none to all three toys?

SOLUTION

Because a given child can be a repeat recipient, repetitions are allowed here, so we use the fundamental counting principle. Each of the three toys can go to any of the seven children. The number of possible distributions is $7 \cdot 7 \cdot 7 = 343$. ■■■

EXAMPLE 11 Selecting Committees

How many different three-member committees could club N appoint so that exactly one woman is on the committee?

SOLUTION

Recall that $N = \{\text{Alan, Bill, Cathy, David, Evelyn}\}$. Two members are women; three are men. Although the question mentioned only that the committee must include exactly one woman, to complete the committee two men must be selected as well. The task of selecting the committee members consists of two parts:

1. Choose one woman. **2.** Choose two men.

Because order is not important for committees, use combinations for the two parts. One woman can be chosen in ${}_2C_1 = \frac{2!}{1!1!} = 2$ ways, and two men can be chosen in ${}_3C_2 = \frac{3!}{2!1!} = 3$ ways. Finally, use the fundamental counting principle to obtain $2 \cdot 3 = 6$ different committees. This small number can be checked by listing.

$$\{C, A, B\},\ \{C, A, D\},\ \{C, B, D\},\ \{E, A, B\},\ \{E, A, D\},\ \{E, B, D\}$$ ■■■

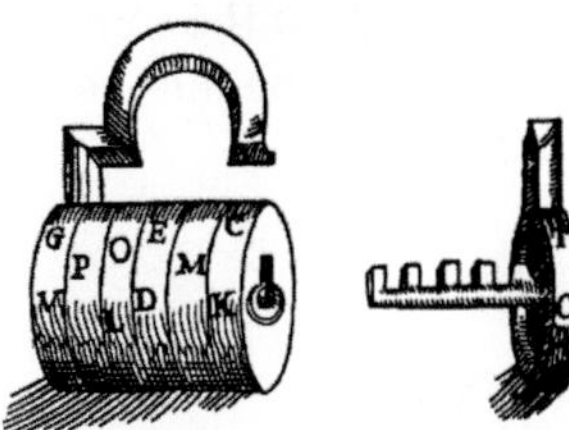

The illustration above is from the 1560s text ***Logistica,*** by the mathematician J. Buteo. Among other topics, the book discusses the number of possible throws of four dice and the number of arrangements of the cylinders of a combination lock. Note that "combination" is a misleading name for these locks since repetitions are allowed, and, also, order makes a difference.

EXAMPLE 12 Selecting Attendees for an Event

Every member of the Alpha Beta Gamma fraternity would like to attend a special event this weekend, but only ten members will be allowed to attend. How many ways could the lucky ten be selected if there are a total of forty-eight members?

SOLUTION

In this case, ten distinct men are required (repetitions are not allowed), and the order of selection makes no difference, so we use combinations.

$${}_{48}C_{10} = \frac{48!}{10!\,38!} = 6{,}540{,}715{,}896 \quad \text{Use a calculator.}$$

■■■

EXAMPLE 13 Selecting Escorts

When the ten fraternity men of **Example 12** arrive at the event, four of them are selected to escort the four homecoming queen candidates. In how many ways can this selection be made?

SOLUTION

Of the ten, four distinct men are required, and order is important here because different orders will pair the men with different women. Use permutations.

$${}_{10}P_4 = \frac{10!}{6!} = 5040 \text{ possible selections}$$

■■■

EXAMPLE 14 Dividing into Groups

In how many ways can the 9 members of a baseball lineup divide into groups of 4, 3, and 2 players?

SOLUTION

Order is not important within the groups. The players within a group are interchangeable in their order of listing. Use combinations.

First, 4 can be chosen from 9 in ${}_9C_4 = 126$ ways.
Then, 3 can be chosen from the remaining 5 in ${}_5C_3 = 10$ ways.
Then, 2 can be chosen from the remaining 2 in ${}_2C_2 = 1$ way.

The three groups also are not interchangeable. They all have different sizes. Apply the fundamental counting principle.

$${}_9C_4 \cdot {}_5C_3 \cdot {}_2C_2 = 126 \cdot 10 \cdot 1 = 1260$$

■■■

EXAMPLE 15 Dividing into Groups

In how many ways can the 9 players of **Example 14** divide into three groups of 3?

SOLUTION

After the pattern of **Example 14,** the answer may *seem* to be

$${}_9C_3 \cdot {}_6C_3 \cdot {}_3C_3 = 84 \cdot 20 \cdot 1 = 1680.$$

However, this would impose an *unwanted order,* not within the groups, but *among* the groups. Ordering the three group selections was appropriate in **Example 14,** because those three groups were distinguishable. They were all different sizes. But here, all groups are size-3.

If the players are denoted A, B, C, D, E, F, G, H, and I, then the list

(1) BIG, HEF, CAD	**(2)** BIG, CAD, HEF	**(3)** HEF, BIG, CAD
(4) HEF, CAD, BIG	**(5)** CAD, BIG, HEF	**(6)** CAD, HEF, BIG

contains six orderings of the same three groups. Since the product calculated above, from the fundamental counting principle, duplicates every set of three groups in this way, we must adjust that value by dividing by $3! = 6$ to obtain the true number of *unordered* sets of three groups. The idea is the same as when we adjust the number of arrangements—orderings—of n things taken r at a time to obtain the number of unordered sets of n things taken r at a time according to the formula

$$_nC_r = \frac{_nP_r}{r!}.$$

The number of ways 9 players can divide into three groups of 3 is

$$\frac{_9C_3 \cdot {_6C_3} \cdot {_3C_3}}{3!} = \frac{1680}{6} = 280.$$

For Further Thought

Poker Hands

In 5-card poker, played with a standard 52-card deck, 2,598,960 different hands are possible. (See **Example 8.**) The desirability of the various hands depends upon their relative chance of occurrence, which, in turn, depends on the number of different ways they can occur, as shown in **Table 4**. Note that an ace can generally be positioned either below 2 (as a 1) or above king (as a 14). This is important in counting straight flush hands and straight hands.

Table 4 Categories of Hands in 5-Card Poker

Event E	Description of Event E	Number of Outcomes Favorable to E
Royal flush	Ace, king, queen, jack, and 10, all of the same suit	4
Straight flush	5 cards of consecutive denominations, all in the same suit (excluding royal flush)	36
Four of a kind	4 cards of the same denomination, plus 1 additional card	______
Full house	3 cards of one denomination, plus 2 cards of a second denomination	3744
Flush	Any 5 cards all of the same suit (excluding royal flush and straight flush)	______
Straight	5 cards of consecutive denominations (not all the same suit)	10,200
Three of a kind	3 cards of one denomination, plus 2 cards of two additional denominations	54,912
Two pairs	2 cards of one denomination, plus 2 cards of a second denomination, plus 1 card of a third denomination	______
One pair	2 cards of one denomination, plus 3 additional cards of three different denominations	1,098,240
No pair	No two cards of the same denomination (and excluding any sort of flush or straight)	1,302,540
Total		**2,598,960**

For Group or Individual Investigation

As the table shows, a full house is a relatively rare occurrence. (Only four of a kind, straight flush, and royal flush are less likely.) To verify that there are 3744 different full house hands possible, carry out the following steps.

1. Explain why there are ${}_4C_3$ different ways to select three aces from the deck.
2. Explain why there are ${}_4C_2$ different ways to select two 8s from the deck.
3. If "aces and 8s" (three aces and two 8s) is one kind of full house, show that there are ${}_{13}P_2$ different kinds of full house altogether.
4. Multiply the expressions from Steps 1, 2, and 3 together. Explain why this product should give the total number of full house hands possible.
5. Find the three missing values in the right column of **Table 4**.
6. Verify the right column total shown in **Table 4**.

3 EXERCISES

Evaluate each expression.

1. ${}_9P_3$ **2.** ${}_{12}P_5$

3. ${}_{11}C_7$ **4.** ${}_{14}C_6$

Determine the number of permutations (arrangements) of each of the following.

5. 20 things taken 4 at a time

6. 15 things taken 5 at a time

Determine the number of combinations (subsets) of each of the following.

7. 9 things taken 4 at a time

8. 13 things taken 6 at a time

Use a calculator to evaluate each expression.

9. ${}_{22}P_9$ **10.** ${}_{32}C_{12}$

11. Is it possible to evaluate ${}_8P_{10}$? Explain.

12. Is it possible to evaluate ${}_9C_{14}$? Explain.

13. Explain how permutations and combinations differ.

14. Explain how factorials are related to permutations.

15. ***Permutations or Combinations?*** Decide whether each object is a permutation or a combination.

(a) a telephone number
(b) a Social Security number
(c) a hand of cards in poker
(d) a committee of politicians
(e) the "combination" on a student gym locker combination lock
(f) a lottery choice of six numbers where the order does not matter
(g) an automobile license plate number
(h) an internet password

Exercises 16–23 can be solved with permutations even though the problem statements will not always include a form of the word "permutation," or "arrangement," or "ordering."

16. ***Placing in a Race*** How many different ways could first-, second-, and third-place finishers occur in a race with six runners competing?

17. ***Arranging New Home Models*** Tyler Aunan, a contractor, builds homes of eight different models and presently has five lots to build on. In how many different ways can he arrange homes on these lots? Assume five different models will be built.

Racheal Grazias/Shutterstock

18. ***ATM PIN Numbers*** An automated teller machine (ATM) requires a four-digit personal identification number (PIN), using the digits 0–9. (The first digit may be 0.) How many such PINs have no repeated digits?

19. ***Electing Officers of a Club*** How many ways can president and vice president be determined in a club with twelve members?

20. ***Counting Prize Winners*** First, second, and third prizes are to be awarded to three different people. If there are ten eligible candidates, how many outcomes are possible?

21. ***Counting Prize Winners*** How many ways can a teacher give five different prizes to five of her 25 students?

22. ***Scheduling Security Team Visits*** A security team visits 12 offices each night. How many different ways can the team order its visits?

23. ***Sums of Digits*** How many counting numbers have four distinct nonzero digits such that the sum of the four digits is

(a) 10? **(b)** 11?

Exercises 24–31 can be solved with combinations even though the problem statements will not always include the word "combination" or "subset."

24. ***Sampling Cell Phones*** How many ways can a sample of five cell phones be selected from a shipment of twenty-four cell phones?

25. ***Detecting Defective Cell Phones*** If the shipment of **Exercise 24** contains six defective phones, how many of the size-five samples would not include any of the defective ones?

26. ***Committees of U.S. Senators*** How many different five-member committees could be formed from the 100 U.S. senators?

U.S. Senate

27. ***Selecting Hands of Cards*** Refer to the standard 52-card deck pictured on **page 549** and notice that the deck contains four aces, twelve face cards, thirteen hearts (all red), thirteen diamonds (all red), thirteen spades (all black), and thirteen clubs (all black). Of the 2,598,960 different five-card hands possible, decide how many would consist of the following cards.

(a) all diamonds **(b)** all black cards

(c) all aces

28. ***Selecting Lottery Entries*** In a $\frac{7}{39}$ lottery, you select seven distinct numbers from the set 1 through 39, where order makes no difference. How many different ways can you make your selection?

29. ***Arranging New Home Models*** Tyler Aunan (the contractor) is to build six homes on a block in a new subdivision, using two different models, standard and deluxe. (All standard model homes are the same and all deluxe model homes are the same.)

(a) How many different choices does Tyler have in positioning the six houses if he decides to build three standard and three deluxe models?

(b) If Tyler builds two deluxes and four standards, how many different positionings can he use?

30. ***Choosing a Monogram*** Sheryl Jett wants to name her new baby so that his monogram (first, middle, and last initials) will be distinct letters in alphabetical order and he will share her last name. How many different monograms could she select?

31. ***Number of Paths from Point to Point*** In a certain city, there are seven streets going north–south and four streets going east–west. How many street paths start at the southwest corner of the city, end at the northeast corner of the city, and have the shortest possible length? (*Mathematics Teacher* calendar problem)

For Exercises 32–60, you may use permutations, combinations, the fundamental counting principle, or other counting methods as appropriate.

32. ***Selecting Lottery Entries*** In SuperLotto Plus, a California state lottery game, you select five distinct numbers from 1 to 47, and one MEGA number from 1 to 27, hoping that your selection will match a random list selected by lottery officials.

(a) How many different sets of six numbers can you select?

(b) Paul Burke always includes his age and his wife's age as two of the first five numbers in his SuperLotto Plus selections. How many ways can he complete his list of six numbers?

RJ Lerich/Shutterstock

33. ***Drawing Cards*** How many cards must be drawn (without replacement) from a standard deck of 52 to guarantee the following?

(a) Two of the cards will be of the same suit.

(b) Three of the cards will be of the same suit.

34. ***Flush Hands in Poker*** How many different 5-card poker hands would contain only cards of a single suit?

35. ***Identification Numbers in Research*** Subject identification numbers in a certain scientific research project consist of three letters followed by three digits and then three more letters. Assume repetitions are not allowed within any of the three groups, but letters in the first group of three may occur also in the last group of three. How many distinct identification numbers are possible?

36. ***Radio Station Call Letters*** Radio stations in the United States have call letters that begin with K or W (for west or east of the Mississippi River, respectively). Some have three call letters, such as WBZ in Boston, WLS in Chicago, and KGO in San Francisco. Assuming no repetition of letters, how many three-letter sets of call letters are possible? (Count all possibilities even though, practically, some may be inappropriate.)

37. ***Radio Station Call Letters*** Most stations that were licensed after 1927 have four call letters starting with K or W, such as WXYZ in Detroit or KRLD in Dallas. Assuming no repetitions, how many four-letter sets are possible? (Count all possibilities even though, practically, some may be inappropriate.)

38. ***Scheduling Games in a Basketball League*** Each team in an eight-team basketball league is scheduled to play each other team three times. How many games will be played altogether?

39. ***Scheduling Batting Orders in Baseball*** The Coyotes, a youth league baseball team, have seven pitchers, who only pitch, and twelve other players, all of whom can play any position other than pitcher. For Saturday's game, the coach has not yet determined which nine players to use nor what the batting order will be, except that the pitcher will bat last. How many different batting orders may occur?

40. ***Ordering Performers in a Music Recital*** A music class of five girls and four boys is having a recital. If each member is to perform once, how many ways can the program be arranged in each of the following cases?

Yenwen Lu/iStockphoto

(a) All girls must perform first.

(b) A girl must perform first and a boy must perform last.

(c) Elisa and Doug will perform first and last, respectively.

(d) The entire program will alternate between girls and boys.

(e) The first, fifth, and ninth performers must be girls.

41. ***Scheduling Daily Reading*** Carole begins each day by reading from one of seven inspirational books. How many ways can she arrange her reading for one week if the selection is done

(a) with replacement? **(b)** without replacement?

42. ***Counting Card Hands*** How many of the possible 5-card hands from a standard 52-card deck would consist of the following cards?

(a) four clubs and one non-club

(b) two face cards and three non-face cards

(c) two red cards, two clubs, and a spade

43. ***Dividing People into Groups*** In how many ways could fifteen people be divided into five groups containing, respectively, one, two, three, four, and five people?

44. ***Dividing People into Groups*** In how many ways could fifteen people be divided into five groups of three people?

45. ***Dividing People into Groups*** In how many ways could eight people be divided into two groups of three people and a group of two people?

46. ***Points and Lines in a Plane*** If any two points determine a line, how many lines are determined by seven points in a plane, no three of which are collinear?

47. ***Points and Triangles in a Plane*** How many triangles are determined by twenty points in a plane, no three of which are collinear?

48. ***Counting Possibilities on a Combination Lock*** How many different three-number "combinations" are possible on a combination lock having 40 numbers on its dial? (*Hint:* "Combination" is a misleading name for these locks since repetitions are allowed and order makes a difference.)

49. ***Selecting Drivers and Passengers for a Trip*** Natalie Graham, her husband and son, and four additional friends are driving, in two vehicles, to the seashore.

(a) If all seven people can drive, how many ways can the two drivers be selected? (Everyone wants to drive the sports car, so it is important which driver gets which car.)

(b) If the sports car must be driven by Natalie, her husband, or their son, how many ways can the drivers now be determined?

(c) If the sports car will accommodate only two people, and there are no other restrictions, how many ways can both drivers and passengers be assigned to both cars?

50. ***Winning the Daily Double in Horse Racing*** You win the "daily double" by purchasing a ticket and selecting the winners of two specific races. If there are six and eight horses running in those races, respectively, how many tickets must you buy to guarantee a win?

Photos.com/Thinkstock

51. ***Winning the Trifecta in Horse Racing*** Many race tracks offer a "trifecta" race. You win by selecting the correct first-, second-, and third-place finishers. If eight horses are entered, how many tickets must you purchase to guarantee that one of them will be a trifecta winner?

52. ***Selecting Committees*** Nine people are to be distributed among three committees of two, three, and four members, and a chairperson is to be selected for each committee. How many ways can this be done? (*Hint:* Break the task into the following sequence of parts.)
    (a) Select the members of the two-person committee.
    (b) Select the members of the three-person committee.
    (c) Select the chair of the two-person committee.
    (d) Select the chair of the three-person committee.
    (e) Select the chair of the four-person committee.

53. ***Selecting Committee Members*** Repeat **Exercise 52** in case the three committees are to have three members each. (*Hint:* Use the same general sequence of task parts, but remember to adjust for *unwanted ordering* of the three committees.)

54. ***Arranging New Home Models*** (See **Exercise 29.**) Because of his good work, Tyler Aunan gets a contract to build homes on three additional blocks in the subdivision, with six homes on each block. He decides to build nine deluxe homes on these three blocks: two on the first block, three on the second, and four on the third. The remaining nine homes will be standard.
    (a) Altogether on the three-block stretch, how many different choices does Tyler have for positioning the eighteen homes? (*Hint:* Consider the three blocks separately and use the fundamental counting principle.)
    (b) How many choices would he have if he built 2, 3, and 4 deluxe models on the three different blocks as before, but not necessarily on the first, second, and third blocks in that order?

55. ***Building Numbers from Sets of Digits***
    (a) How many six-digit counting numbers use all six digits 4, 5, 6, 7, 8, and 9?
    (b) Suppose all these numbers were arranged in increasing order: 456,789; 456,798; and so on. Which number would be 364th in the list?

56. ***Arranging Five-letter Words*** The 120 permutations of AHSME are arranged in dictionary order, as if each were an ordinary five-letter word. Find the last letter of the 86th word in the list. (*Mathematics Teacher* calendar problem)

57. ***Arranging a Wedding Reception Line*** At a wedding reception, the bride and groom, and four attendants will form a reception line. How many ways can they be arranged in each of the following cases?

Photodisc/Getty Images

    (a) Any order will do.
    (b) The bride and groom must be the last two in line.
    (c) The groom must be last in line with the bride next to him.

58. ***Assigning Student Grades*** A professor teaches a class of 60 students and another class of 40 students. Five percent of the students in each class are to receive a grade of A. How many different ways can the A grades be distributed?

59. ***Sums of Digits*** How many counting numbers consist of four distinct nonzero digits such that the sum of the four digits is
    (a) 12? **(b)** 13?

60. ***Screening Computer Processors*** A computer company will screen a shipment of 30 processors by testing a random sample of five of them. How many different samples are possible?

61. Verify that ${}_{12}C_9 = {}_{12}C_3$.

62. Use the factorial formula for combinations to prove that in general,

$${}_nC_r = {}_nC_{n-r}.$$

Exercises from the *Mathematics Teacher* monthly calendar appear on the following pages of the text. These are reprinted with permission from *Mathematics Teacher*,

4 USING PASCAL'S TRIANGLE

Pascal's Triangle • Applications

Pascal's Triangle

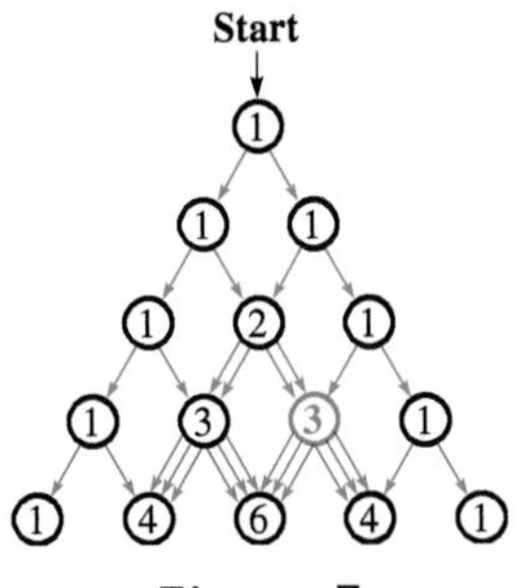

Figure 7

The triangular array in **Figure 7** represents what we can call "random walks" that begin at START and proceed downward according to the following rule:

> At each circle (branch point), a coin is tossed. If it lands heads, we go downward to the left. If it lands tails, we go downward to the right. At each point, left and right are equally likely.

In each circle we have recorded the number of different routes that could bring us to that point. For example, the colored 3 can be reached as the result of three different coin-tossing sequences:

htt, tht, and tth.

Another way to generate the same pattern of numbers is to begin with 1s down both diagonals and then fill in the interior entries by adding the two numbers just above a given position (to the left and right). For example, the colored 28 in **Table 5** is the result of adding 7 and 21 in the row above it.

Table 5 Pascal's Triangle

Row Number		Row Sum
0	1	1
1	1 1	2
2	1 2 1	4
3	1 3 3 1	8
4	1 4 6 4 1	16
5	1 5 10 10 5 1	32
6	1 6 15 20 15 6 1	64
7	1 7 21 35 35 21 7 1	128
8	1 8 28 56 70 56 28 8 1	256
9	1 9 36 84 126 126 84 36 9 1	512
10	1 10 45 120 210 252 210 120 45 10 1	1024

By continuing to add pairs of numbers, we extend the array indefinitely downward, always beginning and ending each row with 1s. (The table shows just rows 0 through 10.) This unending "triangular" array of numbers is called **Pascal's triangle,** since Blaise Pascal wrote a treatise about it in 1653. There is evidence, though, that it was known as early as around 1100 and may have been studied in China or India still earlier.

At any rate, the "triangle" possesses many interesting properties. In counting applications, the most useful property is that, in general, entry number r in row number n is equal to ${}_nC_r$—the number of *combinations* of n things taken r at a time. This correspondence is shown (through row 7) in **Table 6** on the next page.

Fourteenth-century Chinese; courtesy of author

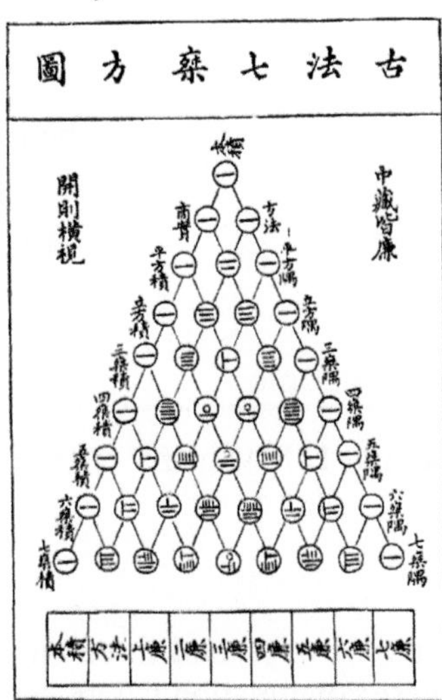

"Pascal's" triangle shown in the 1303 text ***Szu-yuen Yu-chien*** (*The Precious Mirror of the Four Elements*) by the Chinese mathematician Chu Shih-chieh.

Table 6 Combination Values in Pascal's Triangle

Row Number	
0	$_0C_0$
1	$_1C_0 \quad _1C_1$
2	$_2C_0 \quad _2C_1 \quad _2C_2$
3	$_3C_0 \quad _3C_1 \quad _3C_2 \quad _3C_3$
4	$_4C_0 \quad _4C_1 \quad _4C_2 \quad _4C_3 \quad _4C_4$
5	$_5C_0 \quad _5C_1 \quad _5C_2 \quad _5C_3 \quad _5C_4 \quad _5C_5$
6	$_6C_0 \quad _6C_1 \quad _6C_2 \quad _6C_3 \quad _6C_4 \quad _6C_5 \quad _6C_6$
7	$_7C_0 \quad _7C_1 \quad _7C_2 \quad _7C_3 \quad _7C_4 \quad _7C_5 \quad _7C_6 \quad _7C_7$
	and so on

Having a copy of Pascal's triangle handy gives us another option for evaluating combinations. Any time we need to know the number of combinations of n things taken r at a time (that is, the number of subsets of size r in a set of size n), we can simply read entry number r of row number n. ***Keep in mind that the first row shown is row number 0.*** Also, the first entry of each row can be called entry number 0. This entry gives the number of subsets of size 0 (which is always 1 since there is only one empty set).

Eighteenth-century Japanese; courtesy of author

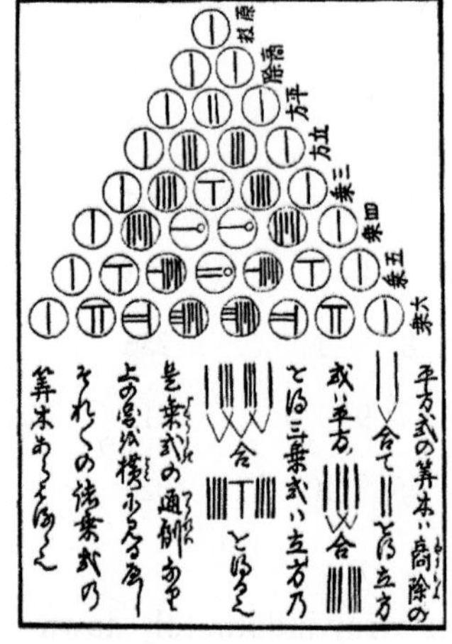

This **Japanese version** of the triangle dates from the eighteenth century. The "stick numerals" evolved from bamboo counting pieces used on a ruled board. Possibly Omar Khayyam, twelfth-century Persian mathematician and poet, may also have divined its patterns in pursuit of algebraic solutions. (The triangle lists the coefficients of the binomial expansion, explained in **For Further Thought** on **the next two pages**.)

Applications

EXAMPLE 1 Applying Pascal's Triangle to Counting People

A group of ten people includes six women and four men. If five of these people are randomly selected to fill out a questionnaire, how many different samples of five people are possible?

SOLUTION

This is simply a matter of selecting a subset of five from a set of ten (or combinations of ten things taken five at a time).

$$_{10}C_5 = 252$$ See row 10 of Pascal's triangle in **Table 5.**

EXAMPLE 2 Applying Pascal's Triangle to Counting People

Among the 252 possible samples of five people in **Example 1,** how many of them would consist of exactly two women and three men?

SOLUTION

Two women can be selected from six women in $_6C_2$ different ways, and three men can be selected from four men in $_4C_3$ different ways. These combination values can be read from Pascal's triangle. Then, since the task of obtaining two women and three men requires both individual parts, the fundamental counting principle tells us to multiply the two values.

$$_6C_2 \cdot {_4C_3} = 15 \cdot 4 = 60$$ Rows 6 and 4 of Pascal's triangle

EXAMPLE 3 Applying Pascal's Triangle to Coin Tossing

If five fair coins are tossed, in how many different ways could exactly three heads be obtained?

SOLUTION

There are various "ways" of obtaining exactly three heads because the three heads can occur on different subsets of the coins. For example, hhtht and thhth are just two of many possibilities. When such a possibility is written down, exactly three positions are occupied by an h, the other two by a t. Each distinct way of choosing three positions from a set of five positions gives a different possibility. (Once the three positions for h are determined, each of the other two positions automatically receives a t.)

So our answer is just the number of size-three subsets of a size-five set, that is, the number of combinations of five things taken three at a time.

$${}_5C_3 = 10 \quad \text{Row 5 of Pascal's triangle}$$

Notice that row 5 of Pascal's triangle also provides answers to several other questions about tossing five fair coins. They are summarized in **Table 7.**

Table 7 Tossing Five Fair Coins

Number of Heads *n*	Ways of Obtaining Exactly *n* Heads	Listing
0	${}_5C_0 = 1$	ttttt
1	${}_5C_1 = 5$	htttt, thttt, tthtt, tttht, tttth
2	${}_5C_2 = 10$	hhttt, hthtt, httht, httth, thhtt, ththt, thtth, tthht, tthth, ttthh
3	${}_5C_3 = 10$	hhhtt, hhtht, hhtth, hthht, hthth, htthh, thhht, thhth, ththh, tthhh
4	${}_5C_4 = 5$	hhhht, hhhth, hhthh, hthhh, thhhh
5	${}_5C_5 = 1$	hhhhh

To analyze the tossing of a different number of fair coins, we can simply take the pertinent numbers from a different row of Pascal's triangle. Repeated coin tossing is an example of a "binomial" experiment (because each toss has *two* possible outcomes, heads and tails).

For Further Thought

The Binomial Theorem

The combination values that comprise Pascal's triangle also arise in a totally different mathematical context. In algebra, "binomial" refers to a two-term expression such as

$$x + y, \quad \text{or} \quad a + 2b, \quad \text{or} \quad w^3 - 4.$$

The first few powers of the binomial $x + y$ are shown here.

$$(x + y)^0 = 1$$
$$(x + y)^1 = x + y$$
$$(x + y)^2 = x^2 + 2xy + y^2$$
$$(x + y)^3 = x^3 + 3x^2y + 3xy^2 + y^3$$
$$(x + y)^4 = x^4 + 4x^3y + 6x^2y^2 + 4xy^3 + y^4$$
$$(x + y)^5 = x^5 + 5x^4y + 10x^3y^2 + 10x^2y^3 + 5xy^4 + y^5$$

(continued)

For Further Thought (cont.)

The numerical coefficients of these expansions form the first six rows of Pascal's triangle. In our study of counting, we have called these numbers combinations, but in the study of algebra, they are called **binomial coefficients** and are usually denoted

$$\binom{n}{r} \quad \text{rather than} \quad {}_nC_r.$$

Generalizing the pattern of the powers shown on the preceding page yields the important result known as the **binomial theorem.**

Binomial Theorem

For any whole number n,

$$(x+y)^n = \binom{n}{0}\cdot x^n + \binom{n}{1}\cdot x^{n-1}y + \binom{n}{2}\cdot x^{n-2}y^2 + \binom{n}{3}\cdot x^{n-3}y^3 + \dots + \binom{n}{n-1}\cdot xy^{n-1} + \binom{n}{n}\cdot y^n,$$

where each binomial coefficient can be calculated by the formula

$$\binom{n}{r} = \frac{n!}{r!(n-r)!}.$$

Notice that, if $n = 0$, then the first term shown in the expansion is, at the same time, the last term, for

$$\binom{n}{0}\cdot x^n = \binom{0}{0}\cdot x^0 = \frac{0!}{0!0!}\cdot 1 = 1,$$

and $$\binom{n}{n}\cdot y^n = \binom{0}{0}\cdot y^0 = \frac{0!}{0!0!}\cdot 1 = 1.$$

EXAMPLE Applying the Binomial Theorem

Write out the binomial expansion for $(2a + 5)^4$.

SOLUTION

We take the initial coefficients from row 4 of Pascal's triangle and then simplify algebraically.

Recall that $(xy)^n = x^n \cdot y^n$.

$$\begin{aligned}(2a+5)^4 &= \binom{4}{0}\cdot(2a)^4 + \binom{4}{1}\cdot(2a)^3\cdot 5 \\ &\quad + \binom{4}{2}\cdot(2a)^2\cdot 5^2 + \binom{4}{3}\cdot(2a)\cdot 5^3 \\ &\quad + \binom{4}{4}\cdot 5^4 \\ &= 1\cdot 2^4\cdot a^4 + 4\cdot 2^3\cdot a^3\cdot 5 + 6\cdot 2^2\cdot a^2\cdot 5^2 \\ &\quad + 4\cdot 2\cdot a\cdot 5^3 + 1\cdot 5^4 \\ &= 16a^4 + 160a^3 + 600a^2 + 1000a + 625\end{aligned}$$

For Group or Individual Investigation

Write out the binomial expansion for each of the following powers.

1. $(x + y)^6$
2. $(x + y)^7$
3. $(w + 4)^5$
4. $(4x + 2y)^4$
5. $(u - v)^6$ (*Hint:* First change $u - v$ to $u + (-v)$.)
6. $(5m - 2n)^3$
7. How many terms are in the binomial expansion for $(x + y)^n$?
8. Identify the 15th term only of the expansion for $(a + b)^{18}$.

4 EXERCISES

Read each combination value directly from Pascal's triangle.

1. ${}_4C_2$ **2.** ${}_5C_3$ **3.** ${}_6C_3$ **4.** ${}_7C_5$

5. ${}_8C_5$ **6.** ${}_9C_6$ **7.** ${}_9C_2$ **8.** ${}_{10}C_7$

Selecting Committees of Congressmen *A committee of four Congressmen will be selected from a group of seven Democrats and three Republicans. Find the number of ways of obtaining each result.*

9. exactly one Democrat

10. exactly two Democrats

11. exactly three Democrats

12. exactly four Democrats

Tossing Coins *Suppose eight fair coins are tossed. Find the number of ways of obtaining each result.*

13. exactly three heads

14. exactly four heads

15. exactly five heads

16. exactly six heads

Selecting Classrooms *Diana Baniak, searching for an Ecology class, knows that it must be in one of nine classrooms. Since the professor does not allow people to enter after the class has begun, and there is very little time left, she decides to try just four of the rooms at random.*

17. How many different selections of four rooms are possible?

18. How many of the selections of **Exercise 17** will fail to locate the class?

19. How many of the selections of **Exercise 17** will succeed in locating the class?

20. What fraction of the possible selections will lead to "success"? (Give three decimal places.)

For a set of five objects, find the number of different subsets of each size. (Use row 5 of Pascal's triangle to find the answers.)

21. 0 **22.** 1

23. 2 **24.** 3

25. 4 **26.** 5

27. How many subsets (of any size) are there for a set of five elements?

28. For a given row in Pascal's triangle, let n be the row number and let s be the row sum.

(a) Write an equation relating s and n.

(b) Explain the relationship in part (a).

29. Which rows of Pascal's triangle have a single greatest entry?

30. What is the least four-digit number in Pascal's triangle? (*Mathematics Teacher* calendar problem)

Over the years, many interesting patterns have been discovered in Pascal's triangle. We explore a few of them in Exercises 31–37.*

31. Refer to **Table 5**.

(a) Choose a row whose row number is prime. Except for the 1s in this row, what is true of all the other entries?

(b) Choose a second prime row number and see if the same pattern holds.

(c) Use the usual method to construct row 11 in **Table 5**, and verify that the same pattern holds in that row.

*For example, see the article "Serendipitous Discovery of Pascal's Triangle" by Francis W. Stanley in *The Mathematics Teacher,* February 1975.

32. Name the next five numbers of the diagonal sequence in the figure. What are these numbers called?

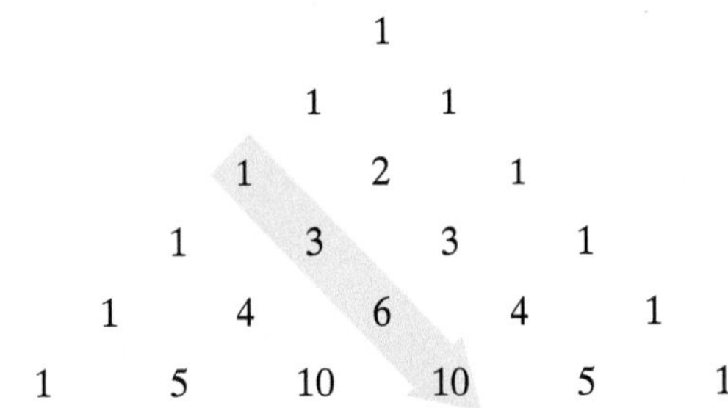

33. Complete the sequence of sums on the diagonals shown in the figure. What pattern do these sums make? What is the name of this important sequence of numbers? The presence of this sequence in the triangle apparently was not recognized by Pascal.

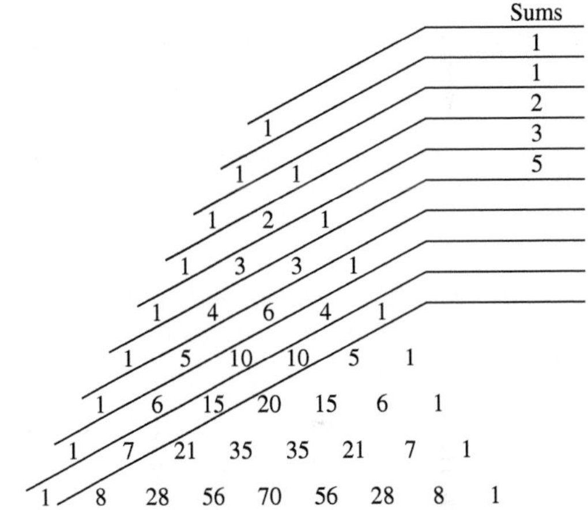

34. Construct another "triangle" by replacing every number in Pascal's triangle (rows **0** through **5**) by its remainder when divided by 2. What special property is shared by rows **2** and **4** of this new triangle?

35. What is the next row that would have the same property as rows **2** and **4** in **Exercise 34**?

36. How many even numbers are there in row **256** of Pascal's triangle? (Work **Exercises 34 and 35** first.)

37. The figure shows a portion of Pascal's triangle with several inverted triangular regions outlined. For any one of these regions, what can be said of the sum of the squares of the entries across its top row?

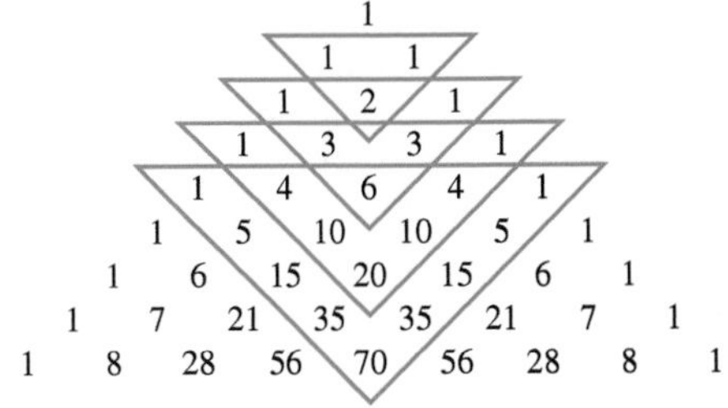

38. More than a century before Pascal's treatise on the "triangle" appeared, another work by the Italian mathematician Niccolo Tartaglia (1506–1559) came out and included the table of numbers shown here.

1	1	1	1	1	1
1	2	3	4	5	6
1	3	6	10	15	21
1	4	10	20	35	56
1	5	15	35	70	126
1	6	21	56	126	252
1	7	28	84	210	462
1	8	36	120	330	792

Explain the connection between Pascal's triangle and Tartaglia's "rectangle."

39. It was stated in the text that each interior entry in Pascal's triangle can be obtained by adding the two numbers just above it (to the left and right). This fact, known as the "Pascal identity," can be written as

$$_{n}C_{r} = {}_{n-1}C_{r-1} + {}_{n-1}C_{r}.$$

Use the factorial formula for combinations (along with some algebra) to prove the Pascal identity.

The "triangle" that Pascal studied and published in his treatise was actually more like a truncated corner of Tartaglia's rectangle, as shown here.

1	1	1	1	1	1	1	1	1	1
1	2	3	4	5	6	7	8	9	
1	3	6	10	15	21	28	36		
1	4	10	20	35	56	84			
1	5	15	35	70	126				
1	6	21	56	126					
1	7	28	84						
1	8	36							
1	9								
1									

Each number in the truncated corner of Tartaglia's rectangle can be calculated in various ways. In each of Exercises 40–43, consider the number N to be located anywhere in the array. By checking several locations in the given array, determine how N is related to the sum of all entries in the shaded cells. Describe the relationship in words.

40.

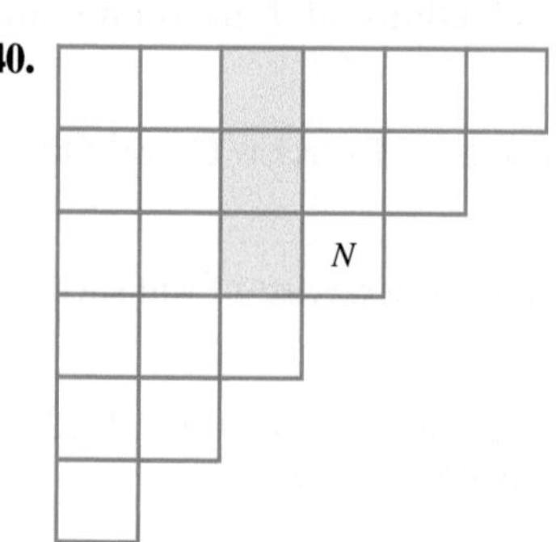

41.

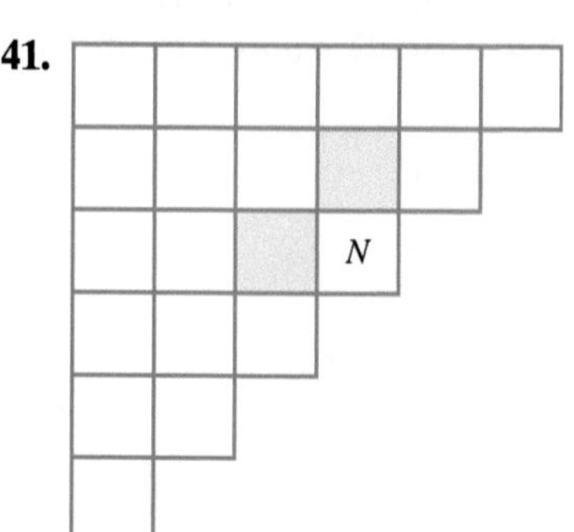

42.

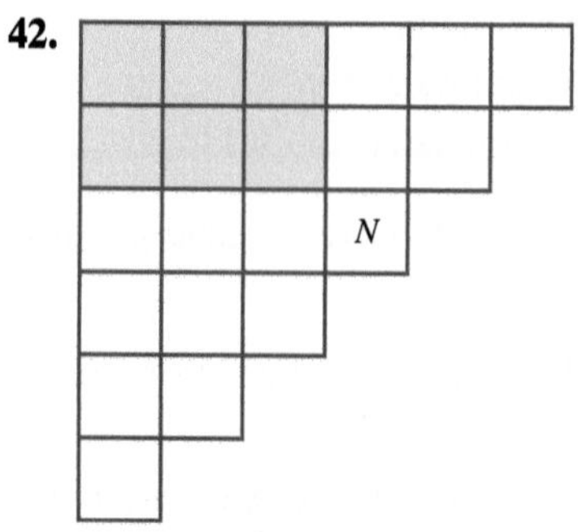

43.

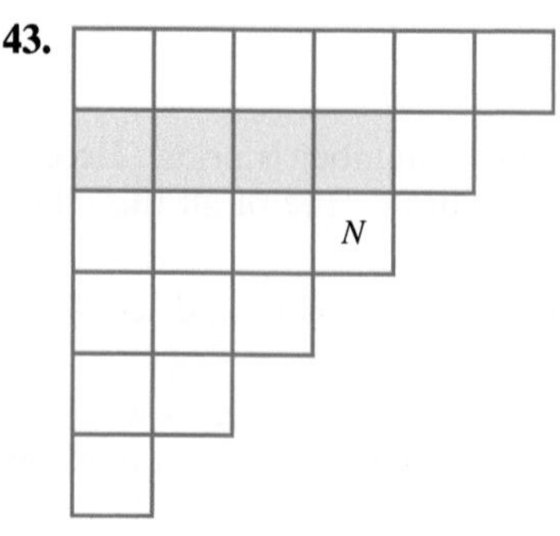

EXTENSION Magic Squares

Magic Square • Magic Sum Formula

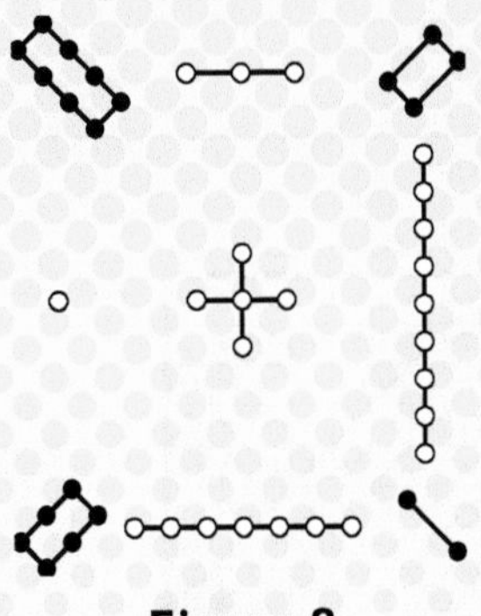

Figure 8

8	3	4
1	5	9
6	7	2

Figure 9

Magic Square The array of numbers known as Pascal's triangle has so many interesting patterns that we could almost think of it as a "magic" triangle. This **Extension** concerns another class of number arrays known as *magic squares.*

Legend has it that in about 2200 B.C. the Chinese Emperor Yu discovered on the bank of the Yellow River a tortoise whose shell bore the diagram in **Figure 8.** This so-called *lo-shu* is an early example of a **magic square.** If the numbers of dots are counted and arranged in a square fashion, the array in **Figure 9** is obtained. A magic square is a square array of numbers with the property that the sum along each row, column, and diagonal is the same. This common value is called the "magic sum." The **order** of a magic square is simply the number of rows (and columns) in the square. The magic square of **Figure 9** is an order 3 magic square.

Magic Sum Formula By using the formula for the sum of the first n terms of an arithmetic sequence, it can be shown that if a magic square of order n has entries $1, 2, 3, \ldots, n^2$, then the sum of *all entries* in the square is

$$\frac{n^2(n^2 + 1)}{2}.$$

Because there are n rows (and columns), the magic sum of the square may be found by dividing the above expression by n. This results in the following formula.

Magic Sum Formula

If a magic square of order n has entries $1, 2, 3, \ldots, n^2$, then the magic sum MS is given by the following formula.

$$\mathbf{MS} = \frac{n(n^2 + 1)}{2}$$

The magic sum of the square in **Figure 9** is

$$\text{MS} = \frac{3(3^2 + 1)}{2} = 15. \quad \text{Let } n = 3 \text{ in the formula.}$$

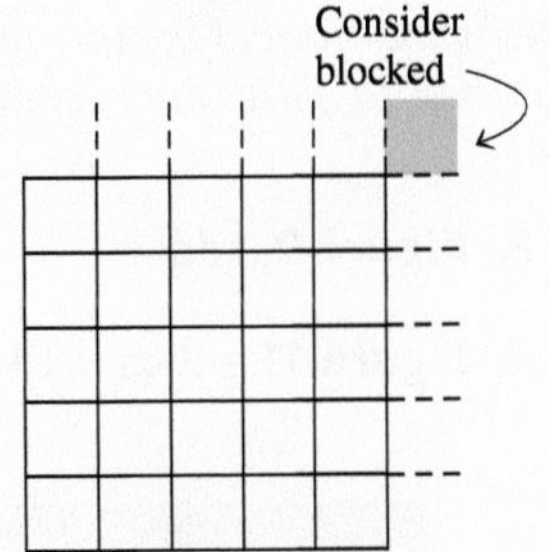

Figure 10

We can construct an odd-order magic square using the "staircase method," attributed to an early French envoy, *de la Loubere.* The method is described below for an order 5 square, with entries $1, 2, 3, \ldots, 25$.

Begin by sketching a square divided into 25 cells into which the numbers 1–25 are to be entered. Proceed as described below, referring to **Figures 10 and 11.**

Step 1 Write 1 in the middle cell of the top row.

Step 2 Always try to enter numbers in sequence in the cells by moving diagonally from lower left to upper right. There are two exceptions to this:

(a) If you go outside of the magic square, move all the way across the row or down the column to enter the number. Then proceed to move diagonally.

(b) If you run into a cell that is already occupied (that is, you are "blocked"), drop down one cell from the last entry written and enter the next number there. Then proceed to move diagonally.

Step 3 Your last entry, 25, will be in the middle cell of the bottom row.

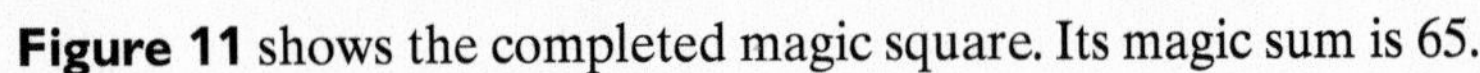

	18	25	2	9	16
17	24	1	8	15	17
23	5	7	14	16	23
4	6	13	20	22	4
10	12	19	21	3	10
11	18	25	2	9	

Figure 11

Figure 11 shows the completed magic square. Its magic sum is 65.

If magic squares catch your interest, a good source for further exploration is the website

http://mathforum.org/alejandre/magic.square.html.

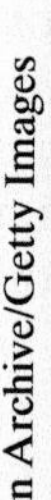
Hulton Archive/Getty Images

Benjamin Franklin admitted that he would amuse himself while in the Pennysylvania Assembly with magic squares or circles "or any thing to avoid Weariness." He wrote about the usefulness of mathematics in the *Gazette* in 1735, saying that no employment can be managed without arithmetic, no mechanical invention without geometry. He also thought that mathematical demonstrations are better than academic logic for training the mind to reason with exactness and distinguish truth from falsity even outside of mathematics.

The square shown here is one developed by Franklin. It has a sum of 2056 in each row and diagonal, and, in Franklin's words, has the additional property "that a four-square hole being cut in a piece of paper of such size as to take in and show through it just 16 of the little squares, when laid on the greater square, the sum of the 16 numbers so appearing through the hole, wherever it was placed on the greater square should likewise make 2056." He claimed that it was "the most magically magic square ever made by any magician."

You might wish to verify the following property of this magic square: The sum of any four numbers that are opposite each other and at equal distances from the center is 514 (which is one-fourth of the magic sum).

De Agostini/SuperStock

Pl. I. *A Magic Square of Squares.*

200	217	232	249	8	25	40	57	72	89	104	121	136	153	168	185
58	39	26	7	250	231	218	199	186	167	154	135	122	103	90	71
198	219	230	251	6	27	38	59	70	91	102	123	134	155	166	187
60	37	28	5	252	229	220	197	188	165	156	133	124	101	92	69
201	216	233	248	9	24	41	56	73	88	105	120	137	152	169	184
55	42	23	10	247	234	215	202	183	170	151	138	119	106	87	74
203	214	235	246	11	22	43	54	75	86	107	118	139	150	171	182
53	44	21	12	245	236	213	204	181	172	149	140	117	108	85	76
205	212	237	244	13	20	45	52	77	84	109	116	141	148	173	180
51	46	19	14	243	238	211	206	179	174	147	142	115	110	83	78
207	210	239	242	15	18	47	50	79	82	111	114	143	146	175	178
49	48	17	16	241	240	209	208	177	176	145	144	113	112	81	80
196	221	228	253	4	29	36	61	68	93	100	125	132	157	164	189
62	35	30	3	254	227	222	195	190	163	158	131	126	99	94	67
194	223	226	255	2	31	34	63	66	95	98	127	130	159	162	191
64	33	32	1	256	225	224	193	192	161	160	129	128	97	96	65

B. Franklin inv. J. Ferguson delin. J. Mynde sc.

EXTENSION EXERCISES

Given a magic square, other magic squares may be obtained by rotating the given one. For example, starting with the magic square in **Figure 9**, *a 90° rotation in a clockwise direction gives the magic square shown here.*

6	1	8
7	5	3
2	9	4

Start with **Figure 9** *and give the magic square obtained by each rotation described.*

1. 180° in a clockwise direction

2. 90° in a counterclockwise direction

Start with **Figure 11** *and give the magic square obtained by each rotation described.*

3. 90° in a clockwise direction

4. 180° in a clockwise direction

5. 90° in a counterclockwise direction

6. Try to construct an order-2 magic square containing the entries 1, 2, 3, 4. What happens?

Given a magic square, other magic squares may be obtained by adding or subtracting a constant value to or from each entry, multiplying each entry by a constant value, or dividing each entry by a nonzero constant value. In Exercises 7–10, start with the magic square whose figure number is indicated, and perform the operation described to find a new magic square. Give the new magic sum.

7. **Figure 9**, multiply by 3

8. **Figure 9**, add 7

9. **Figure 11**, divide by 2

10. **Figure 11**, subtract 10

According to a fanciful story by Charles Trigg in Mathematics Magazine *(September 1976, page 212), the Emperor Charlemagne (742–814) ordered a five-sided fort to be built at an important point in his kingdom. As good-luck charms, he had magic squares placed on all five sides of the fort. He had one restriction for these magic squares: all the numbers in them must be prime.*

Library of Congress Prints and Photographs Division (LC-USZ62-25564)

Charlemagne's magic squares are given in Exercises 11–15, with one missing entry. Find the missing entry in each square.

11.

	71	257
47	269	491
281	467	59

12.

389		227
107	269	431
311	347	149

13.

389	227	191
71	269	
347	311	149

14.

401	227	179
47	269	491
359		137

15.

401	257	149
17		521
389	281	137

16. Compare the magic sums in **Exercises 11–15.** Charlemagne had stipulated that each magic sum should be the year in which the fort was built. What was that year?

Find the missing entries in each magic square.

17.

75	68	**(a)**
(b)	72	**(c)**
71	76	**(d)**

18.

1	8	13	**(a)**
(b)	14	7	2
16	9	4	**(c)**
(d)	**(e)**	**(f)**	15

19.

3	20	**(a)**	24	11
(b)	14	1	18	10
9	21	13	**(c)**	17
16	8	25	12	**(d)**
(e)	2	**(f)**	**(g)**	**(h)**

20.

3	36	2	35	31	4
10	12	**(a)**	26	7	27
21	13	17	14	**(b)**	22
16	**(c)**	23	**(d)**	18	15
28	30	8	**(e)**	25	9
(f)	1	32	5	6	34

21. Use the "staircase method" to construct a magic square of order 7, containing the entries 1, 2, 3, . . . , 49.

The magic square shown in the photograph is from a woodcut by Albrecht Dürer entitled Melancholia.

Library of Congress Prints and Photographs Division [LC-USZ62-32058]

The two bottom center numbers give 1514, *the date of the woodcut. Refer to this magic square for Exercises 22–30.*

16	3	2	13
5	10	11	8
9	6	7	12
4	15	14	1

Dürer's Magic Square

22. What is the magic sum?

23. Verify: The sum of the entries in the four corners is equal to the magic sum.

24. Verify: The sum of the entries in any 2 by 2 square at a corner of the given magic square is equal to the magic sum.

25. Verify: The sum of the entries in the diagonals is equal to the sum of the entries not in the diagonals.

26. Verify: The sum of the squares of the entries in the diagonals is equal to the sum of the squares of the entries not in the diagonals.

27. Verify: The sum of the cubes of the entries in the diagonals is equal to the sum of the cubes of the entries not in the diagonals.

28. Verify: The sum of the squares of the entries in the top two rows is equal to the sum of the squares of the entries in the bottom two rows.

29. Verify: The sum of the squares of the entries in the first and third rows is equal to the sum of the squares of the entries in the second and fourth rows.

30. Find another interesting property of Dürer's magic square and state it.

31. A magic square of order 4 may be constructed as follows.

(1) Lightly sketch in the diagonals of the blank magic square.

(2) Beginning at the upper left, move across each row from left to right, counting the cells as you go along. If the cell is on a diagonal, count it but do not enter its number. If it is not on a diagonal, enter its number.

(3) When this is completed, reverse the procedure, beginning at the bottom right and moving across from right to left. As you count the cells, enter the number if the cell is not occupied. If it is already occupied, count it but do not enter its number.

You should obtain a magic square similar to the one given for **Exercises 22–30.** How do they differ?

With chosen values for a, b, and c, an order-3 magic square can be constructed by substituting these values in the generalized form shown here.

$a+b$	$a-b-c$	$a+c$
$a-b+c$	a	$a+b-c$
$a-c$	$a+b+c$	$a-b$

Use the given values of a, b, and c to construct an order-3 magic square, using this generalized form.

32. $a = 5, \quad b = 1, \quad c = -3$

33. $a = 16, \quad b = 2, \quad c = -6$

34. $a = 5, \quad b = 4, \quad c = -8$

35. It can be shown that if an order-n magic square has least entry k, and its entries are consecutive counting numbers, then its magic sum is given by the formula

$$\text{MS} = \frac{n(2k + n^2 - 1)}{2}.$$

Construct an order-7 magic square with least entry 10 using the staircase method. Find its magic sum.

36. Use the formula of **Exercise 35** to find the missing entries in the following order-4 magic square whose least entry is 24.

(a)	38	37	27
35	**(b)**	30	32
31	33	**(c)**	28
(d)	26	25	**(e)**

In a 1769 letter from Benjamin Franklin to a Mr. Peter Collinson, Franklin exhibited the following semimagic square of order 8. (Note: A square is semimagic if it is magic except that one or both diagonals fail to give the magic sum.)

52	61	4	13	20	29	36	45
14	3	62	51	46	35	30	19
53	60	5	12	21	28	37	44
11	6	59	54	43	38	27	22
55	58	7	10	23	26	39	42
9	8	57	56	41	40	25	24
50	63	2	15	18	31	34	47
16	1	64	49	48	33	32	17

37. What is the magic sum?

Verify the following properties of this semimagic square.

38. The sums in the first half of each row and the second half of each row are both equal to half the magic sum.

39. The four corner entries added to the four center entries is equal to the magic sum.

40. The "bent diagonals" consisting of eight entries, going up four entries from left to right and down four entries from left to right, give the magic sum. (For example, starting with 16, one bent diagonal sum is $16 + 63 + 57 + 10 + 23 + 40 + 34 + 17$.)

If we use a "knight's move" (up two, right one) from chess, a variation of the staircase method gives the magic square shown here. (When blocked, we move to the cell just below the previous entry.)

10	18	1	14	22
11	24	7	20	3
17	5	13	21	9
23	6	19	2	15
4	12	25	8	16

Use a similar process to construct an order-5 magic square, starting with 1 in the cell described.

41. fourth row, second column (up two, right one; when blocked, move to the cell just below the previous entry)

42. third row, third column (up one, right two; when blocked, move to the cell just to the left of the previous entry)

43. The integers from 1 through 27 are placed in the cells of a 3×3 cube so that the sum in all nine rows and in all nine columns is the same. Finish the solution. (*Mathematics Teacher* calendar problem)

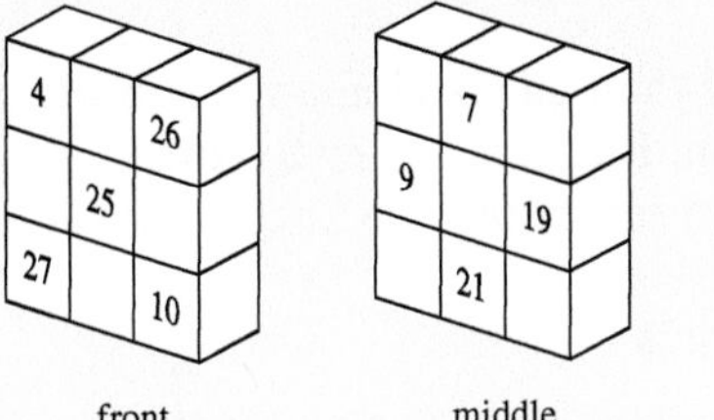

44. Consider the "magic cube" of **Exercise 43.**

(a) What is the magic sum?

(b) How many three-cell "diagonals" does the cube contain?

(c) Do the entries in all the diagonals also add to the magic sum?

(d) How many rows does the cube *really* have?

(e) Do all the additional rows also have the magic sum?

5 COUNTING PROBLEMS INVOLVING "NOT" AND "OR"

Problems Involving "Not" • Problems Involving "Or"

The counting techniques in this section, which can be thought of as *indirect techniques*, are based on some useful correspondences between set theory, logic, and arithmetic, as shown in **Table 8**.

Table 8 Set Theory/Logic/Arithmetic Correspondences

	Set Theory	Logic	Arithmetic
Operation or Connective (Symbol)	Complement (′)	Not (~)	Subtraction (−)
Operation or Connective (Symbol)	Union (∪)	Or (∨)	Addition (+)

Problems Involving "Not"

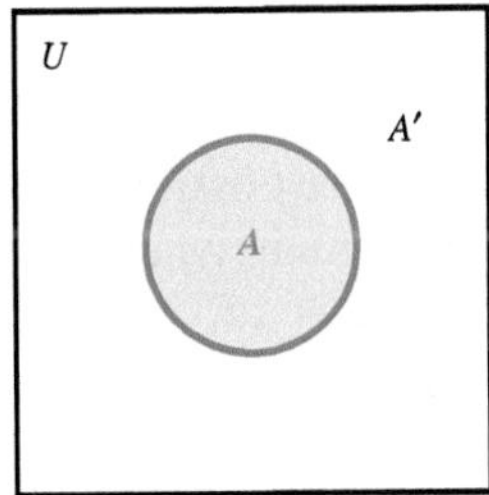

The complement of a set

Figure 12

Suppose U is the set of all possible results of some type. (The "universal set U," comprises all possibilities.) Let A be the set of all those results that satisfy a given condition. For any set S, its cardinal number is written $n(S)$, and its complement is written S'. **Figure 12** suggests that

$$n(A) + n(A') = n(U).$$

Also, $\quad n(A) = n(U) - n(A') \quad$ and $\quad n(A') = n(U) - n(A).$

We focus here on the form that expresses the following indirect counting principle (based on the complement/not/subtraction correspondence from **Table 8**).

Complements Principle of Counting

The number of ways a certain condition can be satisfied is the total number of possible results minus the number of ways the condition would **not** be satisfied. Symbolically, if A is any set within the universal set U, then

$$n(A) = n(U) - n(A').$$

EXAMPLE 1 Counting the Proper Subsets of a Set

For the set $S = \{a, b, c, d, e, f\}$, find the number of proper subsets.

SOLUTION

A proper subset of S is any subset with fewer than all six elements. Subsets of several different sizes would satisfy this condition. But, it is easier to consider the one subset that is not proper, namely S itself. From set theory, we know that set S has a total of

$$2^6 = 64 \text{ subsets.}$$

Thus, from the complements principle, the number of proper subsets is

$$64 - 1 = 63.$$

In words, the number of subsets that *are* proper is the total number of subsets minus the number of subsets that are *not* proper. ∎

Consider the tossing of three fair coins. Since each coin will land either heads (h) or tails (t), the possible results can be listed as follows.

hhh, hht, hth, thh, htt, tht, tth, ttt   Results of tossing three fair coins

(Even without the listing, we could have concluded that there would be eight possibilities. There are two possible outcomes for each coin, so the fundamental counting principle gives $2 \cdot 2 \cdot 2 = 2^3 = 8$.)

Suppose we wanted the number of ways of obtaining *at least* one head. In this case, "at least one" means one or two or three. Rather than dealing with all three cases, we can note that "at least one" is the opposite (or complement) of "fewer than one" (which is zero). Because there is only one way to get zero heads (ttt), and there are a total of eight possibilities, the complements principle gives the number of ways of getting at least one head:

$$8 - 1 = 7.$$

Indirect counting methods can often be applied to problems involving "at least," or "at most," or "less than," or "more than."

EXAMPLE 2 Counting Coin-Tossing Results

If four fair coins are tossed, in how many ways can at least one tail be obtained?

SOLUTION

By the fundamental counting principle, $2^4 = 16$ different results are possible. Exactly one of these fails to satisfy the condition of "at least one tail" (namely, no tails, or hhhh). So the answer (from the complements principle) is $16 - 1 = 15$. ∎

EXAMPLE 3 Counting Selections of Airliner Seats

Carol Britz and three friends are boarding an airliner just before departure time. There are only ten seats left, three of which are aisle seats. How many ways can the four people arrange themselves in available seats so that at least one of them sits on the aisle?

SOLUTION

The word "arrange" implies that order is important, so we shall use permutations. "At least one aisle seat" is the opposite (complement) of "no aisle seats." The total number of ways to arrange four people among ten seats is

$${}_{10}P_4 = 5040.$$

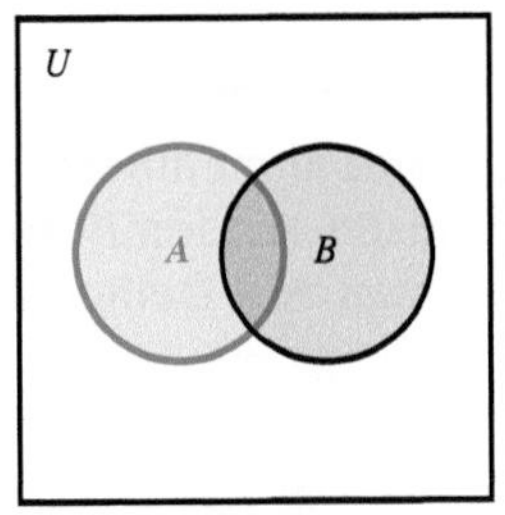

Nondisjoint sets

Figure 13

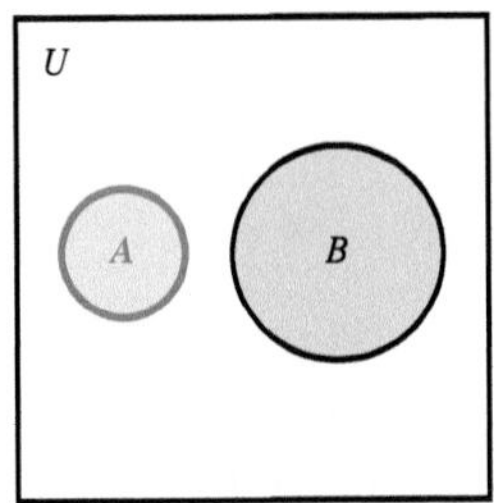

Disjoint sets

Figure 14

The number of ways to arrange four people among seven (non-aisle) seats is

$$_{7}P_{4} = 840.$$

Therefore, by the complements principle, the number of arrangements with at least one aisle seat is

$$\underset{_{10}P_4}{5040} - \underset{_{7}P_4}{840} = 4200.$$

Problems Involving "Or"

The complements principle is one way of counting indirectly. Another technique is to count the elements of a set by breaking that set into simpler component parts. If

$$S = A \cup B,$$

the cardinal number formula says to find the number of elements in S by adding the number in A to the number in B. We must then subtract the number in the intersection $A \cap B$ if A and B are not disjoint, as in **Figure 13.** But if A and B are disjoint, as in **Figure 14**, the subtraction is not necessary.

The following principle reflects the union/or/addition correspondence from **Table 8.**

Additive Principle of Counting

The number of ways that one **or** the other of two conditions could be satisfied is the number of ways one of them could be satisfied plus the number of ways the other could be satisfied minus the number of ways they could both be satisfied together.

If A and B are any two sets, then

$$n(A \cup B) = n(A) + n(B) - n(A \cap B).$$

If sets A and B are disjoint, then

$$n(A \cup B) = n(A) + n(B).$$

EXAMPLE 4 Counting Card Hands

How many five-card poker hands consist of either all clubs or all red cards?

SOLUTION

No hand that satisfies one of these conditions could also satisfy the other, so the two sets of possibilities (all clubs, all red cards) are disjoint. Therefore the second formula of the additive principle applies.

```
(10 nPr 4)-(7 nPr 4)
                4200
(13 nCr 5)+(26 nCr 5)
               67067
```

Results in **Examples 3 and 4** are supported in this screen.

$$n(\text{all clubs or all red cards}) = n(\text{all clubs}) + n(\text{all red cards})$$ Additive counting principle

$$= {_{13}C_5} + {_{26}C_5}$$ 13 clubs, 26 red cards

$$= 1287 + 65{,}780$$ Substitute values.

$$= 67{,}067$$ Add.

EXAMPLE 5 Counting Selections from a Diplomatic Delegation

Table 9 categorizes a diplomatic delegation of 18 congressional members as to political party and gender. If one of the members is chosen randomly to be spokesperson for the group, in how many ways could that person be a Democrat or a woman?

Table 9

	Men (M)	Women (W)	Totals
Republican (R)	5	3	8
Democrat (D)	4	6	10
Totals	9	9	18

SOLUTION

Since D and W are not disjoint (6 delegates are both Democrats and women), the first formula of the additive principle is required.

$$\begin{aligned} n(D \text{ or } W) &= n(D \cup W) && \text{Union/or correspondence} \\ &= n(D) + n(W) - n(D \cap W) && \text{Additive principle} \\ &= 10 + 9 - 6 && \text{Substitute values.} \\ &= 13 && \text{Add and subtract.} \end{aligned}$$

EXAMPLE 6 Counting Course Selections for a Degree Program

Chrissy Jenkins needs to take twelve more specific courses for a bachelors degree, including four in math, three in physics, three in computer science, and two in business. If five courses are randomly chosen from these twelve for next semester's program, how many of the possible selections would include at least two math courses?

SOLUTION

Of all the information given here, what is important is that there are four math courses and eight other courses to choose from, and that five of them are being selected for next semester. If T denotes the set of selections that include at least two math courses, then we can write

$$T = A \cup B \cup C$$

where A = the set of selections with exactly two math courses,

B = the set of selections with exactly three math courses,

and C = the set of selections with exactly four math courses.

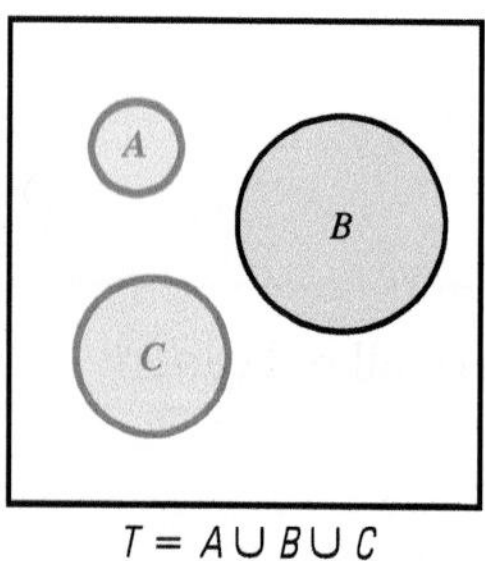

$T = A \cup B \cup C$

Figure 15

(In this case, *at least two* means exactly two **or** exactly three **or** exactly four.) The situation is illustrated in **Figure 15**. By previous methods, we know that

$$n(A) = {}_4C_2 \cdot {}_8C_3 = 6 \cdot 56 = 336,$$

$$n(B) = {}_4C_3 \cdot {}_8C_2 = 4 \cdot 28 = 112,$$

and

$$n(C) = {}_4C_4 \cdot {}_8C_1 = 1 \cdot 8 = 8,$$

so that, by the additive principle,

$$n(T) = 336 + 112 + 8 = 456.$$

EXAMPLE 7 Counting Three-Digit Numbers with Conditions

How many three-digit counting numbers are multiples of 2 or multiples of 5?

SOLUTION

A multiple of 2 must end in an even digit (0, 2, 4, 6, or 8), so there are $9 \cdot 10 \cdot 5 = 450$ three-digit multiples of 2. A multiple of 5 must end in either 0 or 5, so there are $9 \cdot 10 \cdot 2 = 180$ of those. A multiple of both 2 and 5 is a multiple of 10 and must end in 0. There are $9 \cdot 10 \cdot 1 = 90$ of those. By the additive principle there are

$$450 + 180 - 90 = 540$$

possible three-digit numbers that are multiples of 2 or multiples of 5. ∎

EXAMPLE 8 Counting Card-Drawing Results

A single card is drawn from a standard 52-card deck.

(a) In how many ways could it be a heart or a king?

(b) In how many ways could it be a club or a face card?

SOLUTION

(a) A single card can be both a heart and a king (the king of hearts), so use the first additive formula. There are thirteen hearts, four kings, and one card that is both a heart and a king.

$$13 + 4 - 1 = 16$$

(b) There are 13 clubs, 12 face cards, and 3 cards that are both clubs and face cards.

$$13 + 12 - 3 = 22$$ ∎

EXAMPLE 9 Counting Subsets of a Set with Conditions

How many subsets of a 25-element set have more than three elements?

SOLUTION

It would be a real job to count directly all subsets of size 4, 5, 6, . . . , 25. It is much easier to count those with three or fewer elements and apply the complements principle.

There is	${}_{25}C_0 = 1$	size-0 subset.
There are	${}_{25}C_1 = 25$	size-1 subsets.
There are	${}_{25}C_2 = 300$	size-2 subsets.
There are	${}_{25}C_3 = 2300$	size-3 subsets.

The total number of subsets (of all sizes, 0 through 25) is $2^{25} = 33{,}554{,}432$ (use a calculator). So the number with more than three elements must be

$$\begin{aligned} 33{,}554{,}432 - (1 + 25 + 300 + 2300) &= 33{,}554{,}432 - 2626 \\ &= 33{,}551{,}806. \end{aligned}$$ ∎

In **Example 9,** we used both the additive principle (to get the number of subsets with no more than three elements) and the complements principle.

5 EXERCISES

How many proper subsets are there of each set?

1. {A, B, C, D}

2. {u, v, w, x, y, z}

Tossing Coins *If you toss seven fair coins, in how many ways can you obtain each result?*

3. at least one head ("At least one" is the complement of "none.")

4. at least two heads ("At least two" is the complement of "zero or one.")

5. at least two tails

6. at least one of each (a head and a tail)

Rolling Dice *If you roll two fair dice (say red and green), in how many ways can you obtain each result? (Refer to* **Table 2** *in* ***Section 1.****)*

7. at least 2 on the green die

8. a sum of at least 3

9. a 4 on at least one of the dice

10. a different number on each die

Drawing Cards *If you draw a single card from a standard 52-card deck, in how many ways can you obtain each result?*

11. a card other than the ace of spades

12. a nonface card

Identifying Properties of Counting Numbers *How many two-digit counting numbers meet each requirement?*

13. not a multiple of 10

14. greater than 70 or a multiple of 10

15. ***Choosing Country Music Albums*** Jeanne Bronson's collection of ten country music albums includes *Southern Voice* by Tim McGraw. Jeanne will choose three of her albums to play on a drive to Nashville. (Assume order is not important.)

(a) How many different sets of three albums could she choose?

(b) How many of these sets would not include *Southern Voice*?

(c) How many of them would include *Southern Voice*?

16. ***Choosing Broadway Hits*** The ten longest Broadway runs include *The Phantom of the Opera* and *Les Misérables.* Four of the ten are chosen randomly. (Assume order is not important.)

(a) How many ways can the four be chosen?

(b) How many of those groups of four would include neither of the two productions mentioned?

(c) How many of them would include at least one of the two productions mentioned?

17. ***Choosing Days of the Week*** How many different ways could three distinct days of the week be chosen so that at least one of them begins with the letter S? (Assume order of selection is not important.)

18. ***Choosing School Assignments for Completion*** Diona Brown has nine major assignments to complete for school this week. Two of them involve writing essays. Diona decides to work on two of the nine assignments tonight. How many different choices of two would include at least one essay assignment? (Assume order is not important.)

Selecting Restaurants *Jason Ignacio wants to dine at four different restaurants during a summer getaway. If three of eight available restaurants serve seafood, find the number of ways that at least one of the selected restaurants will serve seafood given the following conditions.*

19. The order of selection is important.

20. The order of selection is not important.

21. ***Seating Arrangements on an Airliner*** Refer to **Example 3.** If one of the group decided at the last minute not to fly, then how many ways could the remaining three arrange themselves among the ten available seats so that at least one of them will sit on the aisle?

22. ***Identifying Properties of Counting Numbers*** Find the number of four-digit counting numbers containing at least one zero, under each of the following conditions.

(a) Repeated digits are allowed.

(b) Repeated digits are not allowed.

23. ***Counting Radio Call Letters*** Radio stations in the United States have call letters that begin with either K or W. Some have a total of three letters, and others have four letters. How many different call letter combinations are possible? Count all possibilities even though, practically, some may be inappropriate. (*Mathematics Teacher* calendar problem) (*Hint:* Do *not* apply combinations.)

24. ***Selecting Faculty Committees*** A committee of four faculty members will be selected from a department of twenty-five which includes professors Fontana and Spradley. In how many ways could the committee include at least one of these two professors?

25. ***Selecting Search and Rescue Teams*** A Civil Air Patrol unit of twelve members includes four officers. In how many ways can four members be selected for a search and rescue mission such that at least one officer is included?

26. ***Choosing Team Members*** Three students from a class of 12 will form a math contest team that must include at least 1 boy and at least 1 girl. If 160 different teams can be formed from the 12 students, which of the following can be the difference between the number of boys and the number of girls in the class?

A. 0 **B.** 2 **C.** 4 **D.** 6 **E.** 8

(*Mathematics Teacher* calendar problem)

Drawing Cards *If a single card is drawn from a standard 52-card deck, in how many ways could it be the following? (Use the additive principle.)*

27. a club or a jack

28. a face card or a black card

Counting Students Who Enjoy Music and Cinema *Of a group of* 30 *students,* 25 *enjoy music,* 22 *enjoy cinema, and* 18 *enjoy both music and cinema. How many of them enjoy the following?*

29. at least one of the two (Use the additive principle.)

30. neither of the two (complement of "at least one")

Counting Card Hands *Among the* 2,598,960 *possible 5-card poker hands from a standard 52-card deck, how many contain the following cards?*

31. at least one card that is not a heart (complement of "all hearts")

32. cards of more than one suit (complement of "all the same suit")

33. at least one face card (complement of "no face cards")

34. at least one club, but not all clubs (complement of "no clubs or all clubs")

35. ***Selecting Doughnuts*** A doughnut shop has a special on its Mix-n-Match selection, which allows customers to select three doughnuts from among the following varieties: plain, maple, frosted, chocolate, glazed, and jelly. How many different Mix-n-Match selections are possible? (*Mathematics Teacher* calendar problem)

36. ***Rolling Three Dice*** Three fair, standard six-faced dice of different colors are rolled. In how many ways can the dice be rolled such that the sum of the numbers rolled is 10? (*Mathematics Teacher* calendar problem)

The Size of Subsets of a Set *If a given set has ten elements, how many of its subsets have the given numbers of elements?*

37. at most two elements

38. at least eight elements

39. more than two elements

40. from three through seven elements

41. ***Counting License Numbers*** If license numbers consist of two letters followed by three digits, how many different licenses could be created having at least one letter or digit repeated? (*Hint:* Use the complements principle of counting.)

42. ***Drawing Cards*** If two cards are drawn from a 52-card deck without replacement (that is, the first card is not replaced in the deck before the second card is drawn), in how many different ways is it possible to obtain a king on the first draw and a heart on the second? (*Hint:* Split this event into the two disjoint components "king of hearts and then another heart" and "non-heart king and then heart." Use the fundamental counting principle on each component, then apply the additive principle.)

43. Extend the additive counting principle to three overlapping sets (as in the figure) to show that

$$n(A \cup B \cup C) = n(A) + n(B) + n(C) - n(A \cap B) - n(A \cap C) - n(B \cap C) + n(A \cap B \cap C).$$

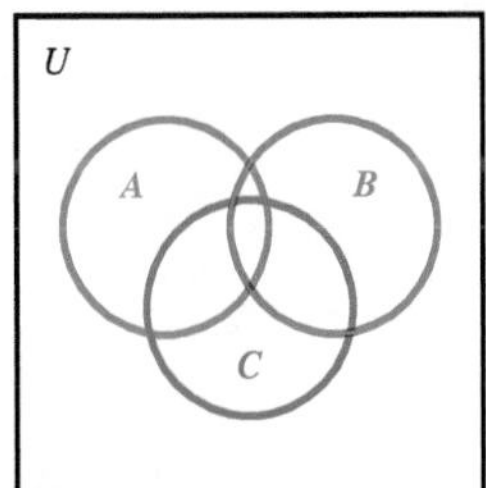

44. How many of the counting numbers 1 through 300 are *not* divisible by 2, 3, or 5? (*Hint:* Use the complements principle and the result of **Exercise 43.**)

Selecting National Monuments to Visit *Megan Lozano is planning a driving tour. While she is interested in seeing the twelve national monuments listed here, she will have to settle for seeing just three of them.*

New Mexico	Arizona	California
Gila Cliff Dwellings	Canyon de Chelly	Devils Postpile
Petroglyph	Organ Pipe Cactus	Joshua Tree
White Sands	Saguaro	Lava Beds
Aztec Ruins		Muir Woods
		Pinnacles

Caitlin Mirra/Shutterstock

In how many ways could the three monuments chosen include the following? (Assume that order of selection is not important.)

45. sites in only one state

46. at least one site not in California

47. sites in fewer than all three states

48. sites in exactly two of the three states

Counting Categories of Poker Hands **Table 4** *in this chapter (**For Further Thought** in **Section 3**) described the various kinds of hands in 5-card poker. Verify each statement in Exercises 49–52. (Explain all steps of your argument.)*

49. There are four ways to get a royal flush.

50. There are 36 ways to get a straight flush.

51. There are 10,200 ways to get a straight.

52. There are 54,912 ways to get three of a kind.

53. Explain why the complements principle of counting is called an "indirect" method.

54. Explain the difference between the two formulas of the additive principle of counting.

COLLABORATIVE INVESTIGATION

Solving a Traveling Salesman Problem

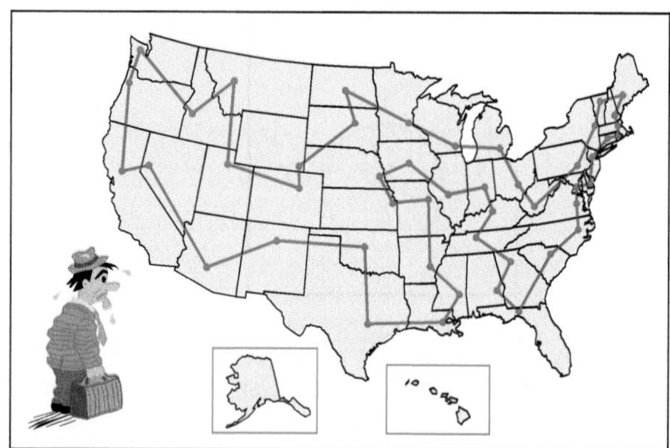

In 1985, Shen Lin came up with the route shown above for a salesman wanting to visit all capital cities in the forty-eight contiguous states, starting and ending at the same capital and traveling the shortest possible total distance. He could not prove that his 10,628-mile route was the shortest possible, but he offered $100 to anyone who could find a shorter one.

This is an example of a classic problem, the so-called **traveling salesman problem** (or **TSP**), which has many practical applications in business and industry but has baffled mathematicians for years. In the case above, there are 47! possible routes, although many of them can be quickly eliminated, leaving $\frac{24!}{3}$ possibilities to consider. This is still a 24-digit number, far too large for even state-of-the-art computers to analyze directly.

Although computer scientists have so far failed to find an "efficient algorithm" to solve the general traveling salesman problem, successes are periodically achieved for particular cases. In 2005, an optimal route was computed for a 33,810-city instance, which arose from a microchip layout problem.

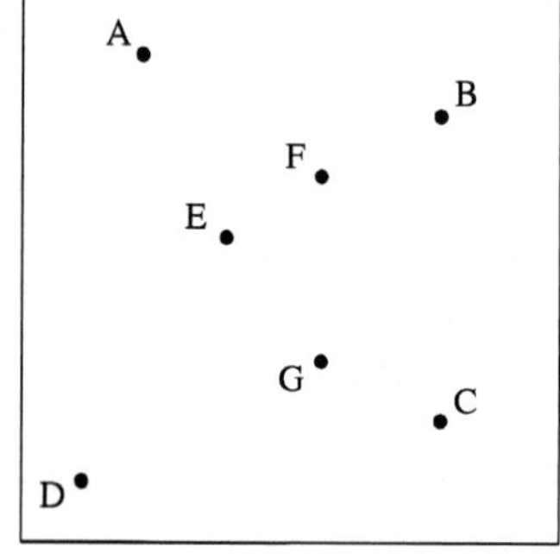

A much smaller set (of seven cities, A through G), which can be completely analyzed using a calculator, is shown here.

Notice that certain routes clearly are *not* the shortest. For example, it is apparent that the route ACEDFGBA involves too much jumping back and forth across the diagram to result in the least possible total distance. (In fact, the total distance for this route is 360 miles, considerably more than necessary.) The fifteen distances given here (in miles) between pairs of cities should be sufficient data for computing the shortest possible route.

AB = 51	AF = 36	BF = 22	CG = 22	EF = 22
AD = 71	BC = 50	BG = 45	DE = 45	EG = 28
AE = 32	BE = 45	CD = 61	DG = 45	FG = 30

Topics for Discussion

Divide the class into groups of 3 or 4 students each. Each group is to do the following.

1. Study the drawing, and make a list of all routes that you think may be the shortest.

2. For each candidate route, add the appropriate seven terms to get a total distance.

3. Arrive at a group consensus as to which route is shortest.

Now bring the whole class back together, and do the following.

1. Make a list of routes, with total distances, that the various groups thought were shortest.
2. Observe whether the different groups all agreed on which route was shortest.
3. As a class, try to achieve a consensus on the shortest route. Do you think that someone else may be able to find a shorter one?

Optimal routes joining points, computed by traveling salesman theories (see the **Collaborative Investigation**), have been used to produce a variety of art. For example, the likeness shown at the right, based on the work of Andy Warhol, consists of a route that, if printed on $8\frac{1}{2}$-by-11-inch paper, would be 45.5 feet long.

Robert Bosch

Reproduced with permission from Robert Bosch.

CHAPTER TEST

Counting Three-digit Numbers *If only digits* 0, 1, 2, 3, 4, 5, *and* 6 *may be used, find the number of possibilities in each category.*

1. three-digit numbers
2. odd three-digit numbers
3. three-digit numbers without repeated digits
4. three-digit multiples of five without repeated digits
5. ***Counting Triangles in a Figure*** Determine the number of triangles (of any size) in the figure shown here.

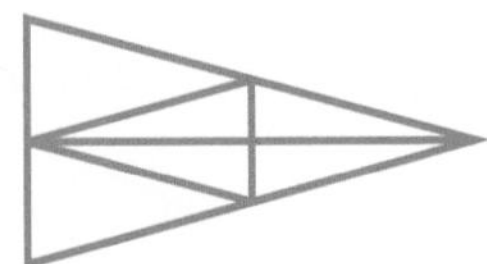

6. ***Tossing Coins*** Construct a tree diagram showing all possible results when a fair coin is tossed four times, if no two consecutive tosses can both be heads.
7. ***Sums of Digits*** How many nonrepeating four-digit numbers have the sum of their digits equal to 30?
8. ***Arranging People*** Tia, Jo, and four friends sit at a round table. How many ways can they be arranged if Tia and Jo refuse to sit next to each other? Assume that any rotation of a given arrangement, that is, when everyone moves the same number of seats in either clockwise or counterclockwise direction, is the same as the original arrangement. (*Mathematics Teacher* calendar problem)

Evaluate each expression.

9. $6!$
10. $\dfrac{8!}{6!}$
11. ${}_{12}P_3$
12. ${}_8C_5$
13. ***Building Words from Sets of Letters*** How many five-letter "words" without repeated letters are possible using the English alphabet? (Assume that any five letters make a "word.")
14. ***Building Words from Sets of Letters*** Using the Russian alphabet (which has 32 letters), and allowing repeated letters, how many five-letter "words" are possible?

Scheduling Assignments *Eileen Burke has seven homework assignments to complete. She wants to do two of them on Thursday and the other five on Saturday.*

15. In how many ways can she order Thursday's work?
16. Assuming she finishes Thursday's work successfully, in how many ways can she order Saturday's work?
17. ***Arranging Letters*** Find the number of distinguishable arrangements of the letters of the word GOOGOL.

Selecting Groups of Basketball Players *If there are ten players on a basketball team, find the number of choices the coach has in selecting each of the following.*

18. four players to carry the team equipment
19. two players for guard positions and two for forward positions

20. five starters and five subs

21. two groups of four

22. a group of three or more of the players

Choosing Switch Settings *Determine the number of possible settings for a row of five on–off switches under each condition.*

23. There are no restrictions.

24. The first and fifth switches must be on.

25. The first and fifth switches must be set the same.

26. No two adjacent switches can both be off.

27. No two adjacent switches can be set the same.

28. At least two switches must be on.

Choosing Subsets of Letters *Three distinct letters are to be chosen from the set*

$$\{A, B, C, D, E, F, G\}.$$

Determine the number of ways to obtain a subset that includes each of the following.

29. the letter B

30. both A and E

31. either A or E, but not both

32. letters to spell the word AD

33. more consonants than vowels

34. ***Number of Paths from Point to Point*** A transit bus can travel in only two directions, north and east. From its starting point on the map shown, determine how many paths exist to reach the garage. (*Mathematics Teacher* calendar problem)

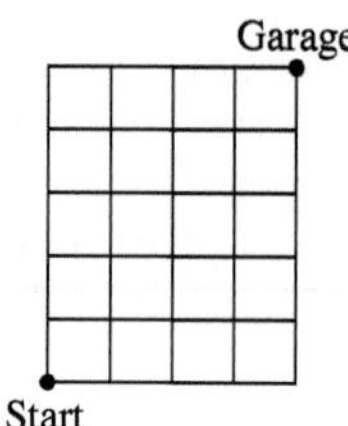

35. State the fundamental counting principle in your own words.

36. If ${}_nC_r = 495$ and ${}_nC_{r+1} = 220$, find the value of ${}_{n+1}C_{r+1}$.

37. If you write down the second entry of each row of Pascal's triangle (starting with row 1), what sequence of numbers do you obtain?

38. Explain why there are $r!$ permutations of n things taken r at a time corresponding to each combination of n things taken r at a time.

ANSWERS TO SELECTED EXERCISES

1 Exercises

1. *AB, AC, AD, AE, BA, BC, BD, BE, CA, CB, CD, CE, DA, DB, DC, DE, EA, EB, EC, ED*; 20 ways
3. *AB, AD, BA, BD, CE, DA, DB, EC*; 8 ways
5. *ACE, AEC, BCE, BEC, DCE, DEC*; 6 ways
7. *ABC, ABD, ABE, ACD, ACE, ADE, BCD, BCE, BDE, CDE*; 10 ways **9.** 1 **11.** 3 **13.** 5 **15.** 5 **17.** 3 **19.** 1 **21.** 18 **23.** 15

25.

	2	3	5	7
2	22	23	25	27
3	32	33	35	37
5	52	53	55	57
7	72	73	75	77

27. 22, 33, 55, 77 **29.** 23, 37, 53, 73 **31.** **(a)** tttt **(b)** hhhh, hhht, hhth, hhtt, hthh, htht, htth, thhh, thht, thth, tthh **(c)** httt, thtt, ttht, ttth, tttt **(d)** hhhh, hhht, hhth, hhtt, hthh, htht, htth, httt, thhh, thht, thth, thtt, tthh, ttht, ttth

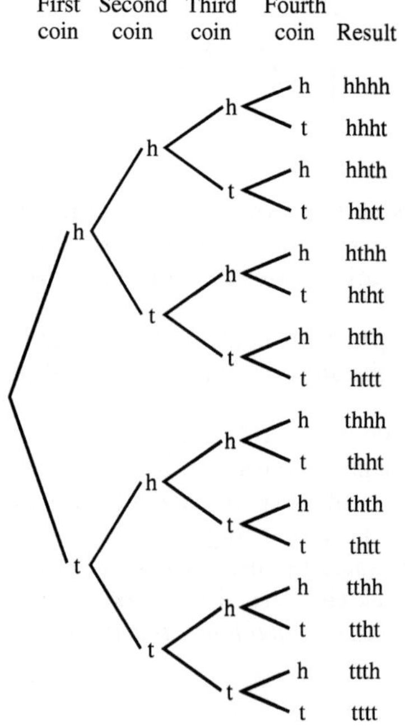

33. 16 **35.** 36 **37.** 17 **39.** 72 **41.** 12 **43.** 10 **45.** 6 **47.** 3 **49.** 9 **51.** 49 **53.** 21 **55.** 15 **57.** 16 **59.** 13 **61.** 4 **63.** 637 **65.** 3

67. **(a)** Find the number of ways to select an ordered pair of letters from the letters A, B, C, D, and E if repetition of letters is not allowed. **(b)** Find the number of ways to select an ordered pair of letters from the letters A, B, C, D, and E if the selection is done without replacement.

2 Exercises

1. Answers will vary. **3.** **(a)** no **(b)** Answers will vary. **5.** **(a)** no **(b)** Answers will vary. **7.** 24 **9.** 72 **11.** 20 **13.** 28 **15.** 840 **17.** 3,628,800 **19.** 3,991,680 **21.** 184,756 **23.** 980,179,200 **25.** 60 **27.** $2^3 = 8$ **29.** Answers will vary. **31.** $6^3 = 216$ **33.** $2^{10} = 1024$ **35.** $5! = 120$ **37.** $3 \cdot 2 = 6$ **39.** $3 \cdot 3 = 9$ **41.** $3 \cdot 2 \cdot 1 = 6$ **43.** $5 \cdot 2 \cdot 4 = 40$ **45.** $2^6 = 64$ **47.** $2 \cdot 3 \cdot 4 \cdot 5 = 120$ **49.** $2 \cdot 3 \cdot 4 \cdot 3 = 72$ **51.** $2 \cdot 3 \cdot 1 \cdot 3 = 18$ **53.** $2 \cdot 4 \cdot 6 = 48$ **55.** $5! = 120$ **57.** 800 **59.** **(a)** 5 **(b)** 2 **(c)** 4 **(d)** 3 **(e)** 2 **(f)** 1; 240 **61.** **(a)** 6 **(b)** 3 **(c)** 2 **(d)** 2 **(e)** 1 **(f)** 1; 72 **63.** Answers will vary. **65.** 516,243 **67.** 6

3 Exercises

1. 504 **3.** 330 **5.** 116,280 **7.** 126 **9.** $1.805037696 \times 10^{11}$ **11.** Answers will vary. **13.** Answers will vary. **15.** **(a)** permutation **(b)** permutation **(c)** combination **(d)** combination **(e)** permutation **(f)** combination **(g)** permutation **(h)** permutation **17.** ${}_8P_5 = 6720$ **19.** ${}_{12}P_2 = 132$ **21.** ${}_{25}P_5 = 6{,}375{,}600$ **23.** **(a)** ${}_4P_4 = 24$ **(b)** ${}_4P_4 = 24$ **25.** ${}_{18}C_5 = 8568$ **27.** **(a)** ${}_{13}C_5 = 1287$ **(b)** ${}_{26}C_5 = 65{,}780$ **(c)** 0 (impossible) **29.** **(a)** ${}_6C_3 = 20$ **(b)** ${}_6C_2 = 15$ **31.** ${}_9C_3 = 84$ **33.** **(a)** 5 **(b)** 9 **35.** ${}_{26}P_3 \cdot {}_{10}P_3 \cdot {}_{26}P_3 = 175{,}219{,}200{,}000$ **37.** $2 \cdot {}_{25}P_3 = 27{,}600$ **39.** $7 \cdot {}_{12}P_8 = 139{,}708{,}800$ **41.** **(a)** $7^7 = 823{,}543$ **(b)** $7! = 5040$ **43.** ${}_{15}C_1 \cdot {}_{14}C_2 \cdot {}_{12}C_3 \cdot {}_9C_4 \cdot {}_5C_5 = 37{,}837{,}800$ **45.** $\frac{{}_8C_3 \cdot {}_5C_3 \cdot {}_2C_2}{2!} = 280$ **47.** ${}_{20}C_3 = 1140$ **49.** **(a)** ${}_7P_2 = 42$ **(b)** $3 \cdot 6 = 18$ **(c)** ${}_7P_2 \cdot 5 = 210$ **51.** ${}_8P_3 = 336$ **53.** ${}_9C_3 \cdot {}_6C_3 \cdot {}_3C_3 \cdot 3^3 = 7560$ **55.** **(a)** $6! = 720$ **(b)** 745,896 **57.** **(a)** $6! = 720$ **(b)** $2 \cdot 4! = 48$ **(c)** $4! = 24$ **59.** **(a)** $2 \cdot 4! = 48$ **(b)** $3 \cdot 4! = 72$ **61.** Each equals 220.

4 Exercises

1. 6 **3.** 20 **5.** 56 **7.** 36 **9.** ${}_7C_1 \cdot {}_3C_3 = 7$ **11.** ${}_7C_3 \cdot {}_3C_1 = 105$ **13.** ${}_8C_3 = 56$ **15.** ${}_8C_5 = 56$ **17.** ${}_9C_4 = 126$ **19.** $1 \cdot {}_8C_3 = 56$ **21.** 1 **23.** 10 **25.** 5 **27.** 32 **29.** the even-numbered rows **31.** **(a)** All are multiples of the row number. **(b)** The same pattern holds. **(c)** The same pattern holds. **33.** . . . 8, 13, 21, 34, . . . ; A number in this sequence is the sum of the two preceding terms. This is the Fibonacci sequence. **35.** row 8 **37.** The sum of the squares of the entries across the top row equals the entry at the bottom vertex. **39.** Answers will vary.

Wording may vary for Exercises 41 and 43.

41. sum $= N$; Any entry in the array equals the sum of the two entries immediately above it and immediately to its left. **43.** sum $= N$; Any entry in the array equals the sum of the row of entries from the cell immediately above it to the left boundary of the array.

Extension Exercises

1.

2	7	6
9	5	1
4	3	8

3.

11	10	4	23	17
18	12	6	5	24
25	19	13	7	1
2	21	20	14	8
9	3	22	16	15

5.

15	16	22	3	9
8	14	20	21	2
1	7	13	19	25
24	5	6	12	18
17	23	4	10	11

7.

24	9	12
3	15	27
18	21	6

Magic sum is 45.

9.

$\frac{17}{2}$	12	$\frac{1}{2}$	4	$\frac{15}{2}$
$\frac{23}{2}$	$\frac{5}{2}$	$\frac{7}{2}$	7	8
2	3	$\frac{13}{2}$	10	11
5	6	$\frac{19}{2}$	$\frac{21}{2}$	$\frac{3}{2}$
$\frac{11}{2}$	9	$\frac{25}{2}$	1	$\frac{9}{2}$

Magic sum is $32\frac{1}{2}$.

11. 479 **13.** 467 **15.** 269 **17.** **(a)** 73 **(b)** 70 **(c)** 74 **(d)** 69 **19.** **(a)** 7 **(b)** 22 **(c)** 5 **(d)** 4 **(e)** 15 **(f)** 19 **(g)** 6 **(h)** 23

21.

30	39	48	1	10	19	28
38	47	7	9	18	27	29
46	6	8	17	26	35	37
5	14	16	25	34	36	45
13	15	24	33	42	44	4
21	23	32	41	43	3	12
22	31	40	49	2	11	20

23. Each sum is equal to 34. **25.** Each sum is equal to 68. **27.** Each sum is equal to 9248. **29.** Each sum is equal to 748.

31.

16	2	3	13
5	11	10	8
9	7	6	12
4	14	15	1

The second and third columns are interchanged.

33.

18	20	10
8	16	24
22	12	14

35.

39	48	57	10	19	28	37
47	56	16	18	27	36	38
55	15	17	26	35	44	46
14	23	25	34	43	45	54
22	24	33	42	51	53	13
30	32	41	50	52	12	21
31	40	49	58	11	20	29

Magic sum is 238.

37. 260

39. 52 + 45 + 16 + 17 + 54 + 43 + 10 + 23 = 260

41.

5	13	21	9	17
6	19	2	15	23
12	25	8	16	4
18	1	14	22	10
24	7	20	3	11

43.

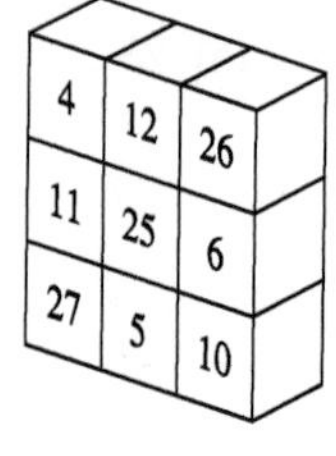

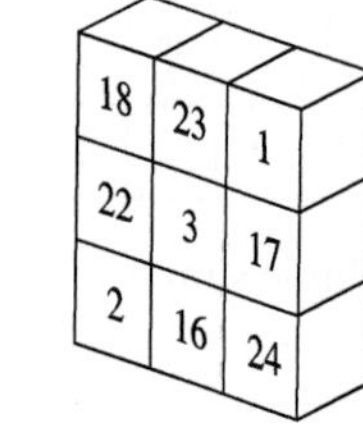

18 23 1
22 3 17
2 16 24
back

5. Exercises

1. $2^4 - 1 = 15$ **3.** $2^7 - 1 = 127$ **5.** 120
7. $36 - 6 = 30$ **9.** $6 + 6 - 1 = 11$ **11.** 51
13. $90 - 9 = 81$ **15. (a)** ${}_{10}C_3 = 120$ **(b)** ${}_9C_3 = 84$
(c) $120 - 84 = 36$ **17.** ${}_7C_3 - {}_5C_3 = 25$
19. ${}_8P_4 - {}_5P_4 = 1560$ **21.** ${}_{10}P_3 - {}_7P_3 = 510$
23. $2 \cdot 26^2 + 2 \cdot 26^3 = 36{,}504$ **25.** ${}_{12}C_4 - {}_8C_4 = 425$
27. $13 + 4 - 1 = 16$ **29.** $25 + 22 - 18 = 29$
31. $2{,}598{,}960 - {}_{13}C_5 = 2{,}597{,}673$
33. $2{,}598{,}960 - {}_{40}C_5 = 1{,}940{,}952$
35. 56 **37.** ${}_{10}C_0 + {}_{10}C_1 + {}_{10}C_2 = 56$
39. $2^{10} - 56 = 968$
41. $26^2 \cdot 10^3 - {}_{26}P_2 \cdot {}_{10}P_3 = 208{,}000$
43. Answers will vary. **45.** ${}_4C_3 + {}_3C_3 + {}_5C_3 = 15$
47. ${}_{12}C_3 - {}_4C_1 \cdot {}_3C_1 \cdot {}_5C_1 = 160$ **49.** Answers will vary.
51. Answers will vary. **53.** Answers will vary.

Chapter Test

1. $6 \cdot 7 \cdot 7 = 294$ **2.** $6 \cdot 7 \cdot 3 = 126$
3. $6 \cdot 6 \cdot 5 = 180$ **4.** $6 \cdot 5 \cdot 1 = 30$ end in 0; $5 \cdot 5 \cdot 1 = 25$ end in 5; $30 + 25 = 55$ **5.** 13

6.

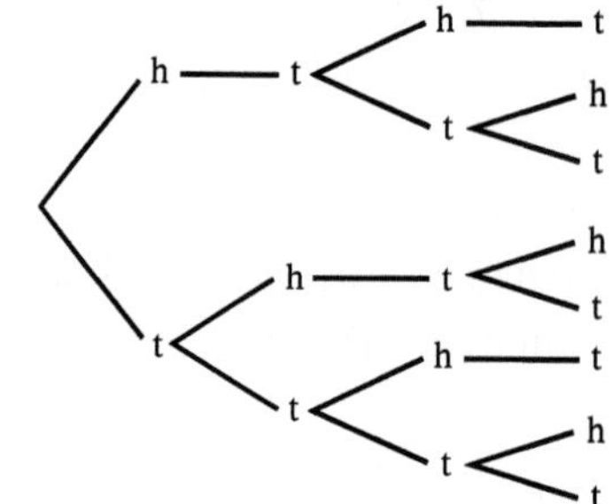

7. $4! = 24$ **8.** $3 \cdot 4! = 72$ **9.** 720
10. 56 **11.** 1320 **12.** 56 **13.** ${}_{26}P_5 = 7{,}893{,}600$
14. $32^5 = 33{,}554{,}432$ **15.** ${}_7P_2 = 42$ **16.** $5! = 120$
17. $\frac{6!}{2! \cdot 3!} = 60$ **18.** ${}_{10}C_4 = 210$ **19.** $\frac{{}_{10}C_2 \cdot {}_8C_2}{2!} = 630$
20. $\frac{{}_{10}C_5 \cdot {}_5C_5}{2!} = 126$ **21.** $\frac{{}_{10}C_4 \cdot {}_6C_4}{2!} = 1575$
22. $2^{10} - ({}_{10}C_0 + {}_{10}C_1 + {}_{10}C_2) = 968$ **23.** $2^5 = 32$
24. $2^3 = 8$ **25.** $2 \cdot 2^3 = 16$ **26.** 13 **27.** 2
28. $32 - (1 + 5) = 26$ **29.** ${}_6C_2 = 15$ **30.** ${}_5C_1 = 5$
31. $2 \cdot {}_5C_2 = 20$ **32.** ${}_5C_1 = 5$
33. ${}_5C_3 + {}_5C_2 \cdot {}_2C_1 = 30$ **34.** ${}_9C_4 = 126$
35. Answers will vary. **36.** $495 + 220 = 715$
37. the counting numbers **38.** Answers will vary.

Counting Methods

1 Exercises

In Exercises 1–7 consider the set $N = \{A, B, C, D, E\}$ for {Alan, Bill, Cathy, David, and Evelyn}. List and count the different ways of electing each of the following slates of officers.

1. A president and a treasurer
   Agreeing that the first letter represents the president and that the second represents the treasurer, we can generate systematically the following symbolic list and count the resulting possibilities: AB, AC, AD, AE; BA, BC, BD, BE; CA, CB, CD, CE; DA, DB, DC, DE; EA, EB, EC, ED. By counting, there are 20 ways to elect a president and a treasurer.

3. A president and a treasurer if the two officers must be the same sex.
   Since the men include A, B, and D, and the women are C and E, we are only interested in doubles that include combinations of just A, B, and D, or just C and E. The results are AB, AD, BA, BD, CE, DA, DB, and EC. Thus, there are
   8 ways the officers can be elected.

5. A president, a secretary, and a treasurer, if the president must be a man and the other two must be women.
   Generating a new symbolic list where the first member must be a man and the second and third, women, we get ACE, AEC, BCE, BEC, DCE, and DEC. The officers may be elected in 6 different ways.

List and count the ways club N could appoint a committee of three members under the following conditions.

7. There are no restrictions.
   One method would be to list all triples. Remembering, however, that ABC is the same committee as BAC or CAB, cross out all triples with the same three letters. We are left with: ABC, ABD, ABE, ACD, ACE, ADE, BCD, BCE, BDE, CDE. Therefore, there are 10 ways to select the 3-member committees with no restrictions.

For Exercises 9–25, refer to Table 2 (the product table for rolling two dice) in the text.

9. Only 1 member of the product table (1, 1) represents an outcome where the sum of the dice is two.

11. Only 3 members of the product table (3, 1), (2, 2), (1, 3) represent outcomes where the sum of the dice is four.

13. There are 5 members of the product table, (5, 1), (4, 2), (3, 3), (2, 4), and (1, 5), which represent outcomes where the sum is six.

15. There are 5 members of the product table, (6, 2), (5, 3), (4, 4), (3, 5), and (2, 6), which represent outcomes where the sum is 8.

17. There are only 3 members of the product table, (6, 4), (5, 5), and (4, 6), which represent outcomes where the sum of the dice is ten.

19. Only 1 member, (6, 6), of the product table yields an outcome where the sum is twelve.

21. Half of all 36 outcomes suggested by the product table should represent a sum which is even; the other half, odd. Thus, they are 18 outcomes which will be even. They are: (1, 1), (3, 1), (2, 2), (1, 3), (5, 1), (4, 2), (3, 3), (2, 4), (1, 5), (6, 2), (5, 3), (4, 4), (3, 5), (2, 6), (6, 4), (5, 5), (4, 6), (6, 6).

23. To find the sums between 6 and 10, we must count pairs in which the sum is 7, 8, or 9.
    Sum is 7: (1, 6), (2, 5), (3, 4), (4, 3), (5, 2), (6, 1)
    Sum is 8: (2, 6), (3, 5), (4, 4), (5, 3), (6, 2)
    Sum is 9: (6, 3), (5, 4), (4, 5), (3, 6)
    Since there are six pairs with a sum of 7, five pairs with a sum of 8, and 4 pairs with a sum of 9, there are $6 + 5 + 4 = 15$ pairs with a sum between 6 and 10.

25. Construct a product table showing all possible two-digit numbers using digits from the set {2, 3, 5, 7}.

	2	3	5	7
2	22	23	25	27
3	32	33	35	37
5	52	53	55	57
7	72	73	75	77

27. The following numbers in the table are numbers with repeating digits: 22, 33, 55, and 77.

29. A counting number larger than 1 is prime if it is divisible by itself and 1 only. The following numbers in the table are prime numbers: 23, 37, 53, and 73.

31. Extend the tree diagram of Exercise 30 for four fair coins. Then list the ways of getting the following results.

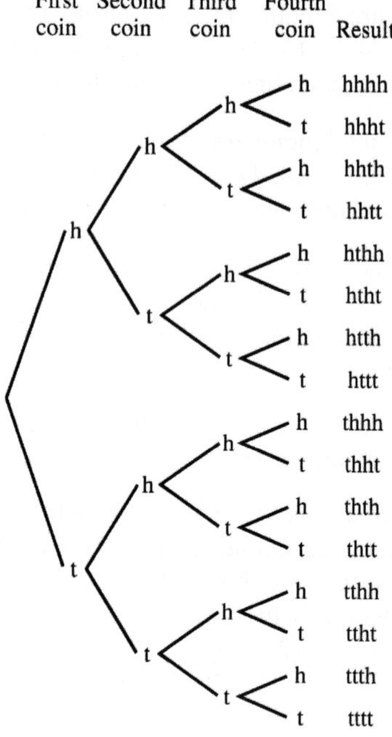

(a) More than three tails
There is only one such outcome: tttt.

(b) Fewer than three tails
List those outcomes with 0, 1 or 2 tails: hhhh, hhht, hhth, hhtt, hthh, htht, htth, thhh, thht, thth, tthh.

(c) At least three tails
List those outcomes with 3 or 4 tails: httt, thtt, ttht, ttth, tttt.

(d) No more than three tails
List those outcomes with 0, 1, 2, or 3 tails:
hhhh, hhht, hhth, hhtt, hthh, htht, htth, httt, thhh, thht, thth, thtt, tthh, ttht, ttth.

33. Begin with the largest triangles which have the long diagonals as their bases. There is 1 triangle on each side of the (2) diagonals. This gives 4 large triangles. Count the intermediate sized triangles, each with a base along the outside edge of the large square. There are 4 of these. Furthermore, each of these intermediate sized triangles contain two right triangles within. There are a total of 8 of these. Thus, the total number of triangles is $4 + 4 + 8 = 16$.

35. Begin with the larger right triangle at the center square. There are 4. Pairing two of these triangles with each other forms 4 isosceles triangles within the center box. Within each of the four right triangles in the square are two smaller right triangles for a total of 8. Associated with each exterior side of the octagon are 8 triangles, each containing two other right triangles (one of which has already been counted) for a total of 16. There are 4 more isosceles triangles which have their two equal side lengths as exterior edges of the octagon. Thus, the number of triangles contained in the figure is $4 + 4 + 8 + 16 + 4 = 36$.

37. Label the figure as shown below, so that we can refer to the small squares by number.

	1	2	
3	4	5	6
7	8	9	10
	11	12	

Find the number of squares of each size and add the results.
There are twelve 1×1 squares, which are labeled 1 through 12.
Name the 2×2 squares by listing the small squares they contain:

1, 2, 4, 5	5, 6, 9, 10
8, 9, 11, 12	3, 4, 7, 8
4, 5, 8, 9	

There are five 2×2 squares. There are no squares larger than 2×2.
Thus, there are a total of $12 + 5 = 17$ squares contained in the figure.

39. Examine carefully the figure in the text. There are sixteen 1×1 squares with horizontal bases.
There are three 2×2 squares in each of the first and second rows, the second and third rows, as well as the third and fourth rows with horizontal bases. Thus, there are a total

of nine 2 × 2 squares with horizontal bases.
There are two 3 × 3 squares with horizontal bases found in the first, second, and third rows as well as two 3 × 3 squares with horizontal base found in the second, third and fourth rows. Thus, there are a total of four 3 × 3 squares with horizontal bases.
There is one 4 × 4 square (the large square itself).
Visualize the squares along the diagonals (at a slant).
There are twenty-four 1 × 1 squares with bases along diagonals.
There are thirteen 2 × 2 squares with bases along diagonals.
There are four 3 × 3 squares with bases along diagonals.
There is only one 4 × 4 square with bases along diagonals. Add the results.

Size	Number of squares
1 × 1 (horizontal)	16
1 × 1 (slant)	24
2 × 2 (horizontal)	9
2 × 2 (slant)	13
3 × 3 (horizontal)	4
3 × 3 (slant)	4
4 × 4 (horizontal)	1
4 × 4 (horizontal)	1
	72

There are 72 squares in the figure.

41. There are 3 × 3 = 9 cubes in each of the bottom two layers. This gives a total of 18 in the bottom two layers.
There are 3 × 2 = 6 cubes in each of the middle two layers. This gives a total of 12 in the middle two layers.
There are 3 × 1 = 3 cubes in the top two layers. This gives a total of 6 in the top two layers. Altogether, there are 18 + 12 + 6 = 36 (1 × 1 × 1) cubes.
The visible cubes are:

Location	Number of cubes
Top two layers	6
Middle two layers	8
Bottom two layers	10
(exclude cubes in corners which have already been counted).	24

Thus, the number of cubes in the stack that are not visible is 36 – 24 = 12. One could ignore the top two levels since each cube is visible.

43. There are 4 cubes along each edge of the bottom layer for a total of 10 cubes. There are 3 cubes along each edge of the second layer for a total of 6 cubes. There are 2 cubes along each edge of the third layer for a total of 3 cubes. Remember not to count the back corner cube twice. The top layer cube is visible, so ignore it. Thus, there are a total of 10 + 6 + 3 = 19 (1 × 1 × 1) cubes in the bottom three layers. Of these, the following are visible.

Location	Number of cubes
Bottom layer	4
Second layer	3
Third layer	2
	9

Thus, the number of cubes in the stack that are not visible is 19 – 9 = 10.

45. Label the figure as shown below.

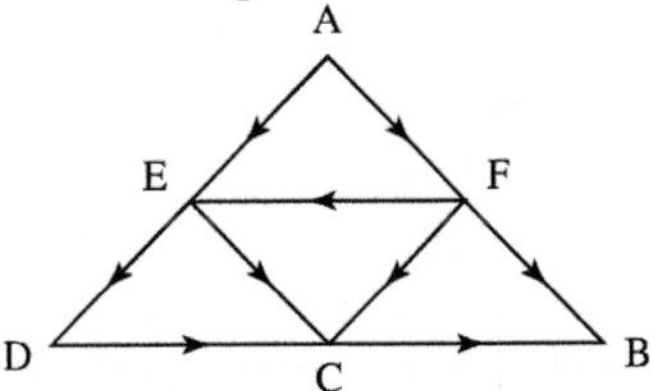

List all the paths in a systematic way. AFB, AFCB, AECB, AEDCB, AFECB, and AFEDCB represent all paths with the indicated restrictions. Thus, there are 6 paths.

47. To determine the number of ways in which 40 can be written as the sum of two primes, use trial and error in a systematic manner. Test each prime, starting with 2, as a possibility for the smaller prime.

(Since 40 – 2 = 38, and 38 is not a prime, 2 will not work.) We obtain the following list:
40 = 3 + 37
40 = 11 + 29
40 = 17 + 23.
Thus, 40 can be written as the sum of two primes in 3 different ways.

49. Make a table to determine all possible sums, then determine the number of unique sums.

	2	2	3	3	5	8
2	4	4	5	5	7	10
2	4	4	5	5	7	10
3	5	5	6	6	8	11
3	5	5	6	6	8	11
5	7	7	8	8	10	13
8	10	10	11	11	13	16

The unique sums are 4, 5, 6, 7, 8, 10, 11, 13, and 16. Thus, 9 sums are possible.

51. If there are no ties, each time a game is played, the loser is eliminated. In order to determine the champion, 49 people (all but the champion) must be eliminated. Thus, it will take 49 games to determine the champion.

53. Make a systematic list or table of all three-digit numbers that have the sum of their digits equal to 22. Notice that since the largest possible sum of two digits is 9 + 9 = 18, the smallest possible third digit in any of these number is 4.

499					
589	598				
679	688	697			
769	778	787	796		
859	868	877	886	895	
949	958	967	976	985	994

This table shows that there are 1 + 2 + 3 + 4 + 5 + 6 = 21 three-digit numbers that have the sum of their digits equal to 22.

55. The problem is essentially to find the number of ways to get a sum of 15 using the numbers 1, 3, and 4. There is one way using all 1's, and there is one way using all 3's.
There are 4 ways using 1's and 3's:
1 + 1 + 1 + 1 + 1 + 1 + 1 + 1 + 1 + 1 + 1 + 1 + 3
1 + 1 + 1 + 1 + 1 + 1 + 1 + 1 + 1 + 3 + 3
1 + 1 + 1 + 1 + 1 + 1 + 3 + 3 + 3
1 + 1 + 1 + 3 + 3 + 3 + 3
There are 3 ways using 1's and 4's:
1 + 1 + 1 + 1 + 1 + 1 + 1 + 1 + 1 + 1 + 1 + 4
1 + 1 + 1 + 1 + 1 + 1 + 1 + 4 + 4
1 + 1 + 1 + 4 + 4 + 4
There is only 1 way using 3's and 4's:
3 + 4 + 4 + 4
There are 5 ways using 1's, 3's and 4's:
1 + 1 + 1 + 1 + 1 + 1 + 1 + 1 + 3 + 4
1 + 1 + 1 + 1 + 1 + 3 + 3 + 4
1 + 1 + 3 + 3 + 3 + 4
1 + 3 + 3 + 4 + 4
1 + 1 + 1 + 1 + 3 + 4 + 4
Thus, there are 15 ways the order can be filled.

57. Draw a tree diagram showing all possible switch settings.

First Switch	Second Switch	Third Switch	Fourth Switch	Switch Settings
0	0	0	0	0000
			1	0001
		1	0	0010
			1	0011
	1	0	0	0100
			1	0101
		1	0	0110
			1	0111
1	0	0	0	1000
			1	1001
		1	0	1010
			1	1011
	1	0	0	1100
			1	1101
		1	0	1110
			1	1111

Thus, Pamela can choose 16 different switch settings.

59. There are five switches rather than four, and no two adjacent switches can be on. If no two adjacent switches can be on, the tree diagram that is constructed will not have two "1"s in succession.

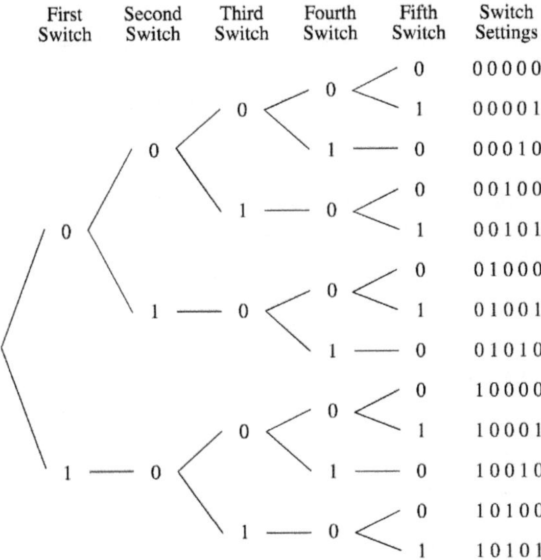

thus, Pamela can choose 13 different switch settings.

61. A line segment joins the points (8, 12) and (53, 234) in the Cartesian plane. Including its endpoints, how many lattice points does this line segment contain? (A lattice point is a point with integer coordinates.)
Any point (x, y) on the line segment, when used with either endpoint, must yield the same slope as that of the segment using both endpoints. Therefore, find the slope of the segment.

$$m = \frac{y_2 - y_1}{x_2 - x_1} = \frac{234 - 12}{53 - 8} = \frac{222}{45} = \frac{74}{15}$$

Set up the slope using the unknown point (x, y) and the known endpoint (8, 12).

$$m = \frac{y_2 - y_1}{x_2 - x_1} = \frac{y - 12}{x - 8}$$

Since the slope is the same for all points on the line segment, set these equal to each other and solve for y (in terms of x).

$$\frac{y-12}{x-8} = \frac{74}{15}$$

$$y - 12 = \frac{74}{15}(x - 8)$$

$$y = \frac{74}{15}(x - 8) + 12$$

All points on the line segment must be solutions for this equation. For the solutions to be integers (with x between 8 and 53), the denominator 15 will have to divide the value $(x - 8)$ evenly so that y remains an integer. That is, the number "$x - 8$" must be a multiple of 15 for values of x. Systematically trying integers for x from and including 8 to 53 will yield the following results. All other values for x between 8 and 53 would not.

x	$x - 8$	Divisible by 15?
8	$8 - 8 = 0$	Yes
23	$23 - 8 = 15$	Yes
38	$38 - 8 = 30$	Yes
53	$53 - 8 = 45$	Yes

Thus, including the endpoints, there are 4 lattice points.
Note that using a graphing calculator with a table feature would provide a quicker solution. Set up the function $y = \frac{74}{15}(x - 8) + 12$ in the calculator. Adjust the "table set" feature to begin at $x = 8$ with Δx set to increase by 1 and create the table (set of ordered pairs) for x and y. Scanning the table for those y-values which are whole numbers will yield the same answers as above.

63. Each row will contain 25 matchsticks. If the grid is 12 matchsticks high there will be 13 rows of matchsticks (including the top and bottom rows). Therefore, there are $13 \times 25 = 325$ matchsticks in all of the rows. Each column contains 12 matchsticks. If the grid is 25 matchsticks wide, then there will be 26 columns of matchsticks counting the first and last columns. Thus, there are $26 \times 12 = 312$ matchsticks in the columns. Altogether, the number of matchsticks are $325 + 312 = 637$.

65. There are 8 people. Let C represent Chris and 0–6 the other 7 people who meet 0–6 others respectively. One of these is Chris' son. When we find how many people Chris had to meet, we will know who his son is since the son met the same number of people as Chris. One method to solve the problem is to use sets. Each set contains the people that the designated person met.
0: { }; he met nobody.
6: {1, 2, 3, 4, 5, C}; 6 met all but 0.
1: {6}; 6 met 1 (from 6's set) so 6 is the only person in the set.
5: {2, 3, 4, 6, C}; 5 met everyone but 0 and 1.
2: {5, 6}; 5 and 6 met 2 (from their sets) so 5 and 6 are the only people 2 met.
4: {3, 5, 6, C}: 4 met everyone by 0, 1, and

2.
3: {4, 5, 6}; 4, 5, and 6 met 3 (from their sets) so 4, 5, and 6 are the only people that 3 met.
C: {4, 5, 6}; same reasoning as 3, above. Therefore, Chris met three people and shook three hands, and "3" is his son.

Wording may vary in answers for Exercise 67.

67. **(a)** Find the number of ways to select an ordered pair of letters from the set{*A*, *B*, *C*, *D*, *E*} if repetition of letters is not allowed.

(b) Find the number of ways to select an ordered pair of letters from the set {*A*, *B*, *C*, *D*, *E*} if the selection is done without replacement.

2 Exercises

1. Writing exercise; answers will vary.

3. **(a)** No, $(n+m)! \neq n! + m!$.

(b) Writing exercise; answers will vary.

5. **(a)** No, $(n-m)! \neq n! - m!$.

(b) Writing exercise; answers will vary.

Evaluate each expression without using a calculator.

7. $4! = 4 \cdot 3 \cdot 2 \cdot 1 = 24$

9. $\frac{9!}{7!} = \frac{9\cdot 8\cdot \cancel{7}\cdot \cancel{6}\cdot \cancel{5}\cdot \cancel{4}\cdot \cancel{3}\cdot \cancel{2}\cdot \cancel{1}}{\cancel{7}\cdot \cancel{6}\cdot \cancel{5}\cdot \cancel{4}\cdot \cancel{3}\cdot \cancel{2}\cdot \cancel{1}} = 72$

11. $\frac{5!}{(5-2)!} = \frac{5!}{3!} = \frac{5\cdot 4\cdot \cancel{3}\cdot \cancel{2}\cdot \cancel{1}}{\cancel{3}\cdot \cancel{2}\cdot \cancel{1}} = 20$

13. $\frac{8!}{6!(8-6)!} = \frac{8!}{6!2!}$
$= \frac{8\cdot 7\cdot \cancel{6}\cdot \cancel{5}\cdot \cancel{4}\cdot \cancel{3}\cdot \cancel{2}\cdot \cancel{1}}{\cancel{6}\cdot \cancel{5}\cdot \cancel{4}\cdot \cancel{3}\cdot 2\cdot 1\cdot \cancel{2}\cdot \cancel{1}}$
$= \frac{8\cdot 7}{2\cdot 1}$
$= \frac{56}{2}$
$= 28$

15. Evaluate $\frac{n!}{(n-r)!}$, where $n = 7$ and $r = 4$.

$\frac{7!}{(7-4)!} = \frac{7!}{3!} = \frac{7\cdot 6\cdot 5\cdot 4\cdot \cancel{3}\cdot \cancel{2}\cdot \cancel{1}}{\cancel{3}\cdot \cancel{2}\cdot \cancel{1}} = 840$

Evaluate each expression using a calculator. (Some answers may not be exact.) For Exercises 15–23, use the factorial key on a calculator, which is labeled $\boxed{x!}$ *or* $\boxed{n!}$ *or, if using a graphing calculator, find "!" in the "Math" menu.*

17. $10! = 3{,}628{,}800$

19. $\frac{12!}{5!} = 3{,}991{,}680$

21. $\frac{20!}{10!\cdot 10!} = 184{,}756$

23. Evaluate $\frac{n!}{(n-r)!}$, where $n = 17$ and $r = 8$.

$\frac{17!}{(17-8)!} = \frac{17!}{9!} = 980{,}179{,}200$

25. $\frac{6!}{2!\cdot 3!} = 60$

27. Since there are two possible outcomes for each switch (on/off), we have
$2\cdot 2\cdot 2 = 2^3 = 8$.

29. Writing exercise; answers will vary.

31. Using the fundamental counting principle, this may be considered as a three-part task.
There would be $\underline{6}\cdot\underline{6}\cdot\underline{6} = 6^3 = 216$.

33. For each of the 10 pins, there are two possibilities: either the pin is up or the pin is down. So the total number of configurations is $2^{10} = 1024$.

Recall the club
N = {*Alan, Bill, Cathy, David, Evelyn*}.

35. This is a 5-part task. Use the fundamental counting principle to count the number of ways of lining up all five members for a photograph. There would be
$\underline{5}\cdot\underline{4}\cdot\underline{3}\cdot\underline{2}\cdot\underline{1} = 120$ possibilities.
Similarly, one could use $n!$, where $n = 5$, to arrive at the total number or arrangements of a set of n objects.

37. This is a 2-part task. Since there are three males to choose from and two females to choose from, the number of possibilities is $\underline{3} \cdot \underline{2} = 6$.

In the following exercises, counting numbers are to be formed using only the digits 3, 4, and 5.

39. Choosing two-digit numbers may be considered a 2-part task. Since we can use any of the three given digits for each choice, there are $\underline{3} \cdot \underline{3} = 9$ different numbers that can be obtained.

41. Using the textbook hint, this may be considered a 3-part task. (1) Since there are only 3 positions that the two adjacent 4's can take (1st and 2nd, 2nd and 3rd, and 3rd and 4th positions), (2) two remaining positions that the 3 can take, and (3) the one last remaining digit must filled by the 5, there are $\underline{3} \cdot \underline{2} \cdot \underline{1} = 6$ different numbers that may be created.

43. Choosing from each of the three food categories is a 3-part task. There are five choices from the soup and salad category, two from the bread category, and four from the entree category. Applying the fundamental counting principle gives $5 \cdot 2 \cdot 4 = 40$ different dinners that may be selected.

45. Since there are 2 choices (T or F) for each question, we have $2^6 = 64$ possible ways.

For each situation in Exercises 47–51, use the table in the text to determine the number of different sets of classes Jessica can take.

47. All classes shown are available. Choose the number of possible courses from each category and apply the fundamental theorem: $\underline{2} \cdot \underline{3} \cdot \underline{4} \cdot \underline{5} = 120$

49. All sections of Minorities in America and Women in American Culture are filled already. The filled classes reduce the options in the Sociology category by 2. Thus, there are $\underline{2} \cdot \underline{3} \cdot \underline{4} \cdot \underline{3} = 72$ possible class schedules.

51. Funding has been withdrawn for three of the Education courses and for two of the Sociology courses. The reductions to the Education and Sociology categories leave only 1 Education course and 3 Sociology courses to choose from. Thus, there are $\underline{2} \cdot \underline{3} \cdot \underline{1} \cdot \underline{3} = 18$ possible class schedules.

53. This is a 3-part task. Applying the fundamental counting principle, there are $\underline{2} \cdot \underline{4} \cdot \underline{6} = 48$ different outfits that Don may wear.

55. The number of different ZIP codes that can be formed using all of those same five digits, 86726, would be the number of arrangements of the 5 digits. This is given by $\underline{5} \cdot \underline{4} \cdot \underline{3} \cdot \underline{2} \cdot \underline{1} = 5! = 120$.

57. There are 8 possibilities for the first digit. There are 10 possibilities for the second digit. There are 10 possibilities for the third digits. The total number of possible area codes is $8 \cdot 10 \cdot 10 = 800$.

Arne (A), Bobbette (B), Chuck (C), Deirdre (D), Ed (E), and Fran (F) have reserved six seats in a row at the theater, starting at an aisle seat.

59. Using the textbook hint, think of the problem as a six-part task, with the six parts described in (a)–(f) below.

(a) From the sketch in the textbook, we see that there are 5 pairs of adjacent seats that Arne and Bobbette can occupy.

(b) Given the two seats for A and B, they can be seated in 2 orders (A to the left of B, or B to the left of A).

(c) C may occupy any of the 4 seats which are not taken by A or B.

(d) Once A, B, and C have been seated, there are 3 remaining seats available for D.

(e) Once A, B, C, and D have been seated, there are 2 remaining seats available for E.

(f) Once all of the others have been seated, there is only 1 seat left for F.

Applying the fundamental counting principle, we conclude that the number of ways in which the six people can arrange themselves so that Aaron and Bobbette will be next to each other is $5 \cdot 2 \cdot 4 \cdot 3 \cdot 2 \cdot 1 = 240$.

61. Using the textbook hint, think of the problem as a six-part task, with the six parts described in (a)–(f) below.

(a) Any of the 6 people may sit on the aisle, so there are 6 choices.

(b) There are 3 men and 3 women. For whoever sits on the aisle, any of the 3 people of the opposite sex may occupy the second seat.

(c) For the third seat, we may choose either of the 2 remaining people of the first sex chosen.

(d) For the fourth seat, we may choose either of the 2 remaining people of the second sex chosen.

(e) For the fifth seat, there is only 1 choice, the remaining person of the first sex chosen.

(f) For the sixth seat, there is only one person left, so there is just 1 choice.

Multiplying the answers from (a)–(f), we conclude that the number of ways the people can arrange themselves if the men and women are to alternate with either a man or woman on the aisle is $6 \cdot 3 \cdot 2 \cdot 2 \cdot 1 \cdot 1 = 72.$

63. Writing exercise; answers will vary.

65. The list will begin with the smallest number possible, 123,456. The list will continue with numbers that begin with the digit 1. There will be a total of $1 \cdot 5 \cdot 4 \cdot 3 \cdot 2 \cdot 1 = 120$ numbers whose first digit is 1. Then the next numbers in the list will be the numbers beginning with the digit 2. There are 120 such numbers. Similarly, there are 120 numbers that begin with the digit 3 and 120 numbers that begin with the digit 4. The 481st number is the first number in the list that begins with the digit 5. There are $1 \cdot 1 \cdot 4 \cdot 3 \cdot 2 \cdot 1 = 24$ numbers whose first digit is 5 and whose second digit is 1, so the 500th number in the list must be of this form, since the 504th number is the number 516,432 (the largest possible number whose first digit is 5 and remaining digits are 1, 2, 3, 4, and 6). The next largest number (the 503rd number) is 516,423. The 502nd number is 516,342, the 501st number is 516,324. Finally, the 500th number is 516,243.

67. There are only 3 letters in the word INDIANA that repeat, and in a palindrome the letter D must always be the middle letter. There are 3 choices for the first letter, then 2 choices for the second letter, leaving only 1 possible letter as the third letter, for a total of $3 \cdot 2 \cdot 1 = 6$ possible palindromes.

3 Exercises

1.
$$\begin{aligned} {}_9P_3 &= \frac{9!}{(9-3)!} \\ &= \frac{9!}{6!} \\ &= \frac{9 \cdot 8 \cdot 7 \cdot 6!}{6!} \\ &= 9 \cdot 8 \cdot 7 \\ &= 504 \end{aligned}$$

3.
$$\begin{aligned} {}_{11}C_7 &= \frac{11!}{7!(11-7)!} \\ &= \frac{11!}{7!4!} \\ &= \frac{11 \cdot 10 \cdot 9 \cdot 8 \cdot 7!}{7!4 \cdot 3 \cdot 2 \cdot 1} \\ &= \frac{11 \cdot 10 \cdot 9 \cdot 8}{4 \cdot 3 \cdot 2 \cdot 1} \\ &= \frac{7920}{24} \\ &= 330 \end{aligned}$$

5. Evaluate ${}_{20}P_4$.

$$\begin{aligned} {}_{20}P_4 &= \frac{20!}{(20-4)!} \\ &= \frac{20!}{16!} \\ &= \frac{20 \cdot 19 \cdot 18 \cdot 17 \cdot 16!}{16!} \\ &= 20 \cdot 19 \cdot 18 \cdot 17 \\ &= 116,280 \end{aligned}$$

7. Evaluate ${}_9C_4$.

$$ {}_9C_4 = \frac{9!}{4!(9-4)!} = \frac{9!}{4!(5!)} = \frac{9\cdot 8\cdot 7\cdot 6\cdot 5!}{4\cdot 3\cdot 2\cdot 1\cdot 5!} = \frac{9\cdot 8\cdot 7\cdot 6}{4\cdot 3\cdot 2\cdot 1} = \frac{3024}{24} = 126 $$

Use a calculator to evaluate each expression.

9. Use the *nPr* or *P*(*n*, *r*) button on a scientific calculator in the following order: 22 [nPr] 9. Or, with a graphing calculator, find *nPr*. It is usually found in the probability menu. Insert, in the same order, 22 [nPr] 9.

$${}_{22}P_9 = 1.805037696\times 10^{11}$$

11. Writing exercise; answers will vary.

13. Writing exercise; answers will vary.

15. **(a)** Permutation, since the order of the digits is important.

(b) Permutation, since the order of the digits is important.

(c) Combination, since the order is unimportant.

(d) Combination, since the order is unimportant.

(e) Permutation, since the order of the digits is important.

(f) Combination, since the order is unimportant.

(g) Permutation, since the order of the digits is important.

(h) Permutation, since the order of the letters, digits, and symbols is important.

17. Since 5 different models will be built, items cannot be repeated. Also, order is important. Therefore, we use permutations. The number of ways in which Tyler can place the homes on the lots is given by

$${}_8P_5 = \frac{8!}{3!} = 6720.$$

19. Since no repetitions are allowed (one person will not be both) and the order of selectionis important, the number of ways to choose a president and vice president is

$${}_{12}P_3 = 12\cdot 11 = 132.$$

21. Since no repetitions are allowed and the order of selection is important, the number of ways for the teacher to give the five different prizes to her students is

$${}_{25}P_5 = 25\cdot 24\cdot 23\cdot 22\cdot 21 = 6,375,600.$$

23. **(a)** To get a sum of 10 we must use the digits {1, 2, 3, 4} since $1+2+3+4=10$. They are not repeated and order is important. Thus, there are ${}_4P_4 = 4! = 24$ such numbers.

(b) To get a sum of 11 we must use the digits {1, 2, 3, 5} since $1+2+3+5=11$. They are not repeated and order is important. Thus, there are ${}_4P_4 = 4! = 24$ such numbers.

25. Samples are subsets, so use combinations. There are $24-6=18$ non-defective players, so we are to select 5 players from a set of 18. The number of samples which contain no defective players is

$${}_{18}C_5 = \frac{18!}{5!13!} = 8568.$$

27. **(a)** Any hand represents a combination (or subset) of cards. Here we are choosing 5 cards from the 13 diamonds available. Thus, there are

$${}_{13}C_5 = \frac{13!}{5!8!} = 1287 \text{ five-card hands.}$$

(b) Since there are 26 black cards in the deck (13 spades and 13 clubs), the number of hands containing all black cards is ${}_{26}C_5 = \frac{26!}{5!21!} = 65,780.$

(c) There are only 4 aces making it impossible to draw such a hand. there are 0 ways to do so.

29. **(a)** He has 6 lots to choose from. From the six, he can choose any three to build his standard homes on. Since the standard homes are all the same, the order is not important, and we have ${}_6C_3 = 20$ possible combinations or choices. Once these have been chosen, the remaining 3 lots will contain the deluxe models.

(b) Tyler may choose the positions for the two deluxe models. Once this has been done, the four standard models must go in the four remaining positions, which can only be done in one way. The number of different positions is therefore ${}_6C_2 = \frac{6!}{2!4!} = 15.$
Notice that the result will be the same if the four standard homes are positioned first. In this case, we obtain
$${}_6C_4 = \frac{6!}{4!2!} = 15.$$

31. Assuming that the streets form a complete grid with 4 vertical lines and 7 horizontal lines, start at the bottom left corner of the grid. The shortest possible length of any path is 9 blocks long, and 3 of those must be walked to the north. Thus, there are ${}_9C_3 = 84$ different paths that may be followed to get to the northeast corner.

33. **(a)** The worst-case scenario is that the first four cards selected will be of different suits, then the 5th card chosen will be the same as one of the earlier choices. Any other scenario will require fewer cards to be drawn. Thus, there is a minimum of 5 cards to be drawn to obtain two cards of the same suit.

(b) By the 5th drawing we are guaranteed 2 cards are of the same suit. The 6th, 7th, and 8th drawings may give results that represent just 2 cards of the same suit for all 4 suits. But the 9th card must then be of one of the 4 suits, adding a 3rd card of that same suit. There must be a minimum of 9 cards drawn to guarantee three cards of the same suit.

35. For each of the first and third groups, there are ${}_{26}P_3$ possible arrangements of letters. For the second group, there are ${}_{10}P_3$ possible arrangements for the digits. Thus, by the fundamental counting principle, there are ${}_{26}P_3 \cdot {}_{10}P_3 \cdot {}_{26}P_3 = 175{,}219{,}200{,}000$ identification numbers.

37. Consider choosing the call letters for a station as a two-part task. The first part consists of choosing the first letter. Since the first letter must be K or W, this may be done in 2 ways. For the remaining three letters, we use permutations because order is important and repetition is not allowed. These three letters may be chosen from any of the 25 letters which were not used as the first letter, so the number of possibilities is ${}_{25}P_3$. Use the fundamental counting principle to combine the results from the two parts of the task. The number of possible call letters is $2 \cdot {}_{25}P_3 = 27{,}600.$

39. This is a two-part task. First choose the pitcher. This can be done in 7 ways. Now choose the players and batting order for the rest of the team. Since order is important and repetition is not allowed, use permutations. The number of choices is ${}_{12}P_8$. Use the fundamental counting principle to combine the results from the two parts of the task. The number of different batting orders is $7 \cdot {}_{12}P_8 = 139{,}708{,}800.$

41. **(a)** The number of ways she can arrange her reading with replacement is found by using the fundamental counting principle.
$7 \cdot 7 \cdot 7 \cdot 7 \cdot 7 \cdot 7 \cdot 7 = 7^7 = 823{,}543$

(b) The number of ways she can arrange her reading without replacement can be found by permutations.
${}_7P_7 = 7! = 5040$
Alternatively, one can apply the fundamental counting principle as well to get $7 \cdot 6 \cdot 5 \cdot 4 \cdot 3 \cdot 2 \cdot 1 = 7! = 5040.$

43. The number of ways each of the five groupings can be chosen is given by ${}_nC_r$ since the order in each grouping is not important. Apply the fundamental counting principle to find the total number of ways to create the 5 groupings altogether.

$_{15}C_1 \cdot {_{14}C_2} \cdot {_{12}C_3} \cdot {_9C_4} \cdot {_5C_5}$
$= 37,837,800$

45. Similar to Exercise 52, but adjusting for unwanted ordering of the three committees, the number of ways to distribute the people among the committees is

$$\frac{_8C_3 \cdot {_5C_3} \cdot {_2C_2}}{2!} = 280.$$

47. Since each group of three non collinear points determines a triangle, we are looking for the number of 3-element subsets of a set of 20 elements. Since subsets are combinations, the number of triangles determined by 20 points in a plane, no three of which are collinear, is

$$_{20}C_3 = \frac{20!}{3!17!} = 1140.$$

49. **(a)** Since any pair of the 7 people may drive and the order of selection is important, the number of choices is

$$_7P_2 = \frac{7!}{5!} = 42.$$

(b) Consider choosing the drivers as a two-part task. There are only 3 choices for the driver of the sports car. Once the driver of the first sports car has been chosen, any of the remaining 6 people can be chosen to drive the second car. By the fundamental counting principle, the number of choices for drivers is $3 \cdot 6 = 18$.

(c) Choose the drivers first. Of the two, the first could be the driver of the sports car; and the second, the driver of the other vehicle. There are $_7P_2$ choices. The second task is to pick the passenger for the sports car. There are five to choose from. By the fundamental counting principle, the total number of choices is $_7P_2 \cdot 5 = 210$.

51. The number of ways for three of the eight horses running to be 1st, 2nd, and 3rd place winners is given by $_8P_3 = 336$.
Thus, buying 336 different tickets will assure a winner.

53. Similar to Exercise 52, but adjusting for unwanted ordering of the three committees, the number of ways to distribute the people among the committees is

$$\frac{_9C_3 \cdot {_6C_3} \cdot {_3C_3}}{3!} \cdot 3^3 = 7560.$$

55. **(a)** How many numbers can be formed using all six digits 4, 5, 6, 7, 8, and 9? Since the order or arrangement of these digits is important (each being a different number), we can consider the answer to the question to be $_6P_6 = 6! = 720$ different numbers.

(b) The first number is 456,789; the second number is 456,798; the third number is 456,879 and so forth.
The number of arrangements (permutations) of the last five digits is given by 5! = 120. Thus, the 121st number is 546,789 (where we have moved to the sixth digit from right and interchanged the fifth and sixth digit—4 and 5). There are another 120 permutations (with this change on the fifth and sixth digits) bringing us to the 241st number: 645,789. In a similar manner, numbers beginning with the new first digit—6, we have another 120 permutations using the new set of numbers. For the 361st number, we change the first digit to seven, giving us 745,689. The 362nd number is 745,698. The 363rd number is 745,869 and the 364th number is 745,896.

57. **(a)** If any order will do, the number of possible arrangements is 6! = 720.

(b) If the bride and groom must be the last two in line (but in one of two possible orders) then the four attendants can be arranged in 4! ways. So the total number of arrangements is $2 \cdot 4! = 48$.

(c) If the groom must be last in line with the bride next to him, then the only people left to arrange are the four attendants, so the number of possible arrangements is 4! = 24.

59. **(a)** There are only two sets of distinct digits that add to 12. They are {1, 2, 3, 6} and {1, 2, 4, 5}. Try to find others. Therefore are 4! distinct permutations (which lead to a different counting number) for each set of digits. Thus, using the fundamental counting principle, the total number of counting numbers whose sum of digits is 12 is $2 \cdot 4! = 48$.

(b) There are only three sets of distinct digits that add to 13. They are $\{1, 2, 3, 7\}$, $\{1, 2, 4, 6\}$ and $\{1, 3, 4, 5\}$. Try to find others. There are 4! distinct permutations (which lead to a different counting number) for each set of digits. Therefore, using the fundamental counting principle, the total number of counting numbers whose sum of digits is 13 is $3 \cdot 4! = 72$.

61. $_{12}C_9 = \frac{12!}{9!(12-9)!} = \frac{12!}{9!3!} = 220$

$_{12}C_3 = \frac{12!}{3!(12-3)!} = \frac{12!}{3!9!} = 220$

Thus, $_{12}C_9 = {_{12}C_3}$.

4 Exercises

Read the following combination values directly from Pascal's triangle. For exercises 1–8, refer to Table 5 in the text.

1. To find the value of $_4C_2$ from Pascal's triangle, read entry number 2 in row 4 (remember that the top row is row "0" and that in row 4 the "1" is entry "0").
$_4C_2 = 6$

3. To find the value of $_6C_3$ from Pascal's triangle, read entry number 3 in row 6.
$_6C_3 = 20$

5. To find the value of $_8C_5$ from Pascal's triangle, read entry number 5 in row 8.
$_8C_5 = 56$

7. To find the value of $_9C_2$ from Pascal's triangle, read entry number 2 in row 9.
$_9C_2 = 36$

9. Selecting the committee is a two-part task. There are $_7C_1$ ways of choosing the one Democrat and $_3C_3$ way of choosing the remaining 3 Republicans. The combination values can be read from Pascal's triangle. By the fundamental counting principle, the total number of ways is $_7C_1 \cdot {_3C_3} = 7 \cdot 1 = 7$.

11. A committee with exactly three Democrats will consist of three Democrats and one Republican. Selecting the committee is a two-part task. There are $_7C_3$ ways of choosing three Democrats and $_3C_1$ ways to choose the one remaining Republican. Hence, there are $_7C_3 \cdot {_3C_1} = 35 \cdot 3 = 105$ ways in total.

13. There are $_8C_3 = 56$ ways to choose three different positions for heads. Using Pascal's triangle, find row 8 entry 3. Remember to count first row and first entry as 0. The remaining positions will automatically be tails.

15. There are $_8C_5 = 56$ ways to choose exactly five different positions for heads. Using Pascal's triangle, this would be found in row 8, entry 5.

17. The number of selections for four rooms is given by $_9C_4 = 126$. Using Pascal's triangle, this would be found in row 9, entry 4.

19. The number of selections that succeed in locating the class is given by total number of selections (Exercise 17) minus the number of ways which will fail to locate the classroom (Exercise 18), or
$_9C_4 - {_8C_4} = 126 - 70 = 56$ ways

21. The number of 0-element subsets for a set of five elements is entry 0 (the first entry) in row 5 of Pascal's triangle. This number is 1.

23. The number of 2-element subsets for a set of five elements is entry 2 (the third entry) in row 5 of Pascal's triangle. This number is 10.

25. The number of 4-element subsets for a set of five elements is entry 4 (the fifth entry) in row 5. This number is 5.

27. The total number of subsets is given by
$_5C_0 + {_5C_1} + {_5C_2} + {_5C_3} + {_5C_4} + {_5C_5}$
$= 1 + 5 + 10 + 10 + 5 + 1$
$= 32.$
This is the sum of elements in the fifth row of Pascal's triangle.

29. The even-numbered rows have a single entry in the middle of the row that is greater than all other entries in the row.

31. **(a)** All are multiples of the row number.

(b) The same pattern holds.

(c) Row 11:

1 11 55 165 330 462 462 330 165 55 11 1
All are multiples of 11. Thus, the same pattern holds.

33. Following the indicated sums 1, 1, 2, 3, 5, the sequence continues 8, 13, 21, 34, ...
A number in this sequence comes from the sum of the two preceding terms. This is the Fibonacci sequence.

35. Row 8 would be the next row to begin and end with 1, with all other entries 0 (each internal entry in row 8 of Pascal's triangle is even).

37. The sum of the squares of the entries across the top row equals the entry at the bottom vertex. Choose, for example, the second triangle from the bottom.

$$1^2+3^2+3^2+1^2 = 1+9+9+1 = 20 \text{ (the vertex value)}$$

39. Prove ${}_nC_r = {}_{n-1}C_{r-1} + {}_{n-1}C_r$.

$${}_{n-1}C_{r-1} + {}_{n-1}C_r$$
$$= \frac{(n-1)!}{(r-1)![(n-1)-(r-1)]!} + \frac{(n-1)!}{r![(n-1)-r]!}$$
$$= \frac{(n-1)!}{(r-1)!(n-r)!} + \frac{(n-1)!}{r!(n-r-1)!}$$
$$= \frac{n}{n} \cdot \frac{(n-1)!}{(r-1)!(n-r)!} \cdot \frac{r}{r} + \frac{n}{n} \cdot \frac{(n-1)!}{r!(n-r-1)!} \cdot \frac{(n-r)}{(n-r)}$$
$$= \frac{n! \cdot r}{n \cdot r! \cdot (n-r)!} + \frac{n! \cdot (n-r)}{n \cdot r! \cdot (n-r)!}$$
$$= \frac{n! \cdot r + n! \cdot (n-r)}{n \cdot r! \cdot (n-r)!}$$
$$= \frac{n! \cdot [r + (n-r)]}{n \cdot r! \cdot (n-r)!}$$
$$= \frac{n! \cdot \cancel{n}}{\cancel{n} \cdot r! \cdot (n-r)!}$$
$$= \frac{n!}{r!\,(n-r)!}$$
$$= {}_nC_r$$

41. The sum = N; any entry in the array equals the sum of the two entries immediately above it and immediately to its left.

43. The sum = N; any entry in the array equals the sum of the row of entries from the cell immediately above it to the left boundary of the array.

EXTENSION: MAGIC SQUARES

1. 180° in a clockwise direction
Imagine a straight line (180°) from the top left corner to the bottom right corner of the magic square in Figure 9. That moves the 8 from its original position to the bottom right corner, and the other numbers follow.

2	7	6
9	5	1
4	3	8

3. 90° in a clockwise direction
Imagine the top left corner of the box that contains the number 17 as an origin. Rotate the entire square 90° clockwise. Then the 17 will be in the top right box and the 11 will be in the top left. All the other numbers follow.

11	10	4	23	17
18	12	6	5	24
25	19	13	7	1
2	21	20	14	8
9	3	22	16	15

5. 90° in a counterclockwise direction
Use the upper right corner of the box containing 15 as the pivot point. Rotate 90° in a counterclockwise direction. Then the 9 will be in the upper right box, and 15 will be in the upper left.

15	16	22	3	9
8	14	20	21	2
1	7	13	19	25
24	5	6	12	18
17	23	4	10	11

7. Figure 9, multiply by 3

24	9	12
3	15	27
18	21	6

$$\begin{aligned} MS &= \frac{n(n^2+1)}{2}\cdot 3 \\ &= \frac{3(3^2+1)}{2}\cdot 3 \\ &= \frac{3(10)}{2}\cdot 3 \\ &= 45 \end{aligned}$$

9. Figure 11, divide by 2

$\frac{17}{2}$	12	$\frac{1}{2}$	4	$\frac{15}{2}$
$\frac{23}{2}$	$\frac{5}{2}$	$\frac{7}{2}$	7	8
2	3	$\frac{13}{2}$	10	11
5	6	$\frac{19}{2}$	$\frac{21}{2}$	$\frac{3}{2}$
$\frac{11}{2}$	9	$\frac{25}{2}$	1	$\frac{9}{2}$

$$\begin{aligned} MS &= \frac{n(n^2+1)}{2}\div 2 \\ &= \frac{5(5^2+1)}{2}\div 2 \\ &= \frac{5(26)}{2}\div 2 \\ &= \frac{65}{2} = 32\frac{1}{2} \end{aligned}$$

11. Using the third row, the magic sum is $281 + 467 + 59 = 807$.
Then $807 - (71 + 257) = 479$.
The missing entry is 479.

13. Using the first column, the magic sum is $389 + 71 + 347 = 807$.
Then, $807 - (191 + 149) = 467$.
The missing entry is 467.

15. Using the first column, the magic sum is $401 + 17 + 389 = 807$.
Then, $807 - (257 + 281) = 269$.
The missing entry is 269.

17. Using the second column, the magic sum is $68 + 72 + 76 = 216$.

(a) $216 - (75 + 68) = 73$

(b) $216 - (75 + 71) = 70$

(c) Use the answer from (b) to find $216 - (72 + 70) = 74$.

(d) $216 - (71 + 76) = 69$

19. Using the second column to obtain the magic sum, $20 + 14 + 21 + 8 + 2 = 65$.

(a) $65 - (3 + 20 + 24 + 11) = 7$

(b) $65 - (14 + 1 + 18 + 10) = 22$

(c) $65 - (9 + 21 + 13 + 17) = 5$

(d) $65 - (16 + 8 + 25 + 12) = 4$

(e) Use the first column and (b):
$65 - (3 + 9 + 16 + 22) = 15$

(f) Use the third column and (a):
$65 - (1 + 13 + 25 + 7) = 19$

(g) Use the fourth column and (c):
$65 - (24 + 18 + 12 + 5) = 6$

(h) Use the fifth column and (d):
$65 - (11 + 10 + 17 + 4) = 23$

21. Use the "staircase method" to construct a magic square of order 7, containing the entries 1, 2, 3, ...

	31	40	49	2	11	20	
30	39	48	1	10	19	28	30
38	47	7	9	18	27	29	38
46	6	8	17	26	35	37	46
5	14	16	25	34	36	45	5
13	15	24	33	42	44	4	13
21	23	32	41	43	3	12	21
22	31	40	49	2	11	20	

23. The sum of the entries in the four corners is $16 + 13 + 4 + 1 = 34$.

25. The entries in the diagonals are $16 + 10 + 7 + 1 + 13 + 11 + 6 + 4 = 68$.
The entries not in the diagonals are $3 + 2 + 5 + 8 + 9 + 12 + 15 + 14 = 68$.

27. Sum of cubes of diagonal entries:

$$\begin{aligned} &16^3 + 10^3 + 7^3 + 1^3 + 13^3 + 11^3 + 6^3 + 4^3 \\ &= 4096 + 1000 + 343 + 1 + 2197 + 1331 + 216 \\ &\quad + 64 \\ &= 9248 \end{aligned}$$

Sum of cubes of entries not in the diagonals:

$$3^2+2^3+5^3+8^3+9^3+12^3+15^3+14^3$$
$$=27+8+125+512+729+1728+3375+2744$$
$$=9248$$

29. $16^2+3^2+2^2+13^2+9^2+6^2+7^2+12^2$
$=256+9+4+169+81+36+49+144$
$=748;$

$5^2+10^2+11^2+8^2+4^2+15^2+14^2+1^2$
$=25+100+121+64+16+225+196+1$
$=748$

31.

→	2	3	→
5	→	→	8
9	→	→	12
→	14	15	→

16	2	3	13
5	11	10	8
9	7	6	12
4	14	15	1

The second and third columns are interchanged.

33. $a = 16$, $b = 2$, $c = -6$
Replace a, b, and c with these numbers to find the entries in the magic square.
$a + b = 16 + 2 = 18$
$a - b - c = 16 - 2 - (-6) = 20$
$a + c = 16 + (-6) = 10$
$a - b + c = 16 - 2 + (-6) = 8$
$a = 16$
$a + b - c = 16 + 2 - (-6) = 24$
$a - c = 16 - (-6) = 22$
$a + b + c = 16 + 2 + (-6) = 12$
$a - b = 16 - 2 = 14$
The magic square is then as follows.

18	20	10
8	16	24
22	12	14

35.

39	48	57	10	19	28	37
47	56	16	18	27	36	38
55	15	17	26	35	44	46
14	23	25	34	43	45	54
22	24	33	42	51	53	13
30	32	41	50	52	12	21
31	40	49	58	11	20	29

$$MS = \frac{7(2\cdot 10+7^2-1)}{2} = \frac{7(20+49-1)}{2} = \frac{7(68)}{2} = 238$$

37. There are many ways to find the magic sum. One way is by adding the top row:
$52 + 61 + 4 + 13 + 20 + 29 + 36 + 45 = 260$

39. $52 + 45 + 16 + 17 + 54 + 43 + 10 + 23$
$= 260$

41. Start by placing 1 in the fourth row, second column. Move up two, right one and place 2 in the second row, third column. If we now move up two, right one again, we will go outside the square. Drop down 5 cells (one complete column) to the bottom of the fourth column to place 3. Move up two, right one, to place 4 in the third row, fifth column. Moving up two, right one, we again go outside the square; move 5 cells to the left to place 5 in the first row, first column. Moving up two, right one, takes us two rows outside the square. Counting downward 5 cells, find that the fourth row, second column is blocked with a 1 already there. The number 6 is then placed just below the entry 5. Continue in this manner until all 24 numbers have been placed. Notice that in trying to enter the number 21, it is blocked by 16 which is already in the cell. Because 20 is already in the bottom cell of the last row, dropping a cell just "below" this one moves it to the top row, third column. The completed magic square is shown here.

		14	22	10	18
		20	3	16	24
5	13	21	9	17	5
6	19	2	15	23	11
12	25	8	16	4	12
18	1	14	22	10	
24	7	20	3	11	

43. First find the magic sum. Consider the known entries on the front of the cube. Let x = the unknown number in the column between the entries 4 and 27. The sum of this column is $x + 4 + 27 = x + 31$. The sum of the entries in the top row must be the same, but the known entries have a sum of 30. So the unknown entry in that row must have the value $x + 1$. Similarly, if y is the unknown entry in the bottom row, then $27 + y + 10 = 37 + y$. Also the sum of the known entries in the far right column is 36, so the unknown entry in that column must be $y + 1$. Then we know the following:
$4 + x + 27 = 27 + y + 10$ (1)
and the sum in the middle row is
$x + 25 + y + 1$, and
$x + 25 + y + 1 = 27 + y + 10$ (2)
Solve the first equation for x.
$x = y + 6$
Substitute the value into the second equation.

$$\begin{aligned} y+6+25+y+1 &= 27+y+10 \\ 2y+32 &= y+37 \\ y &= 5 \end{aligned}$$

Thus, the magic sum is
$27 + y + 10 = 27 + 5 + 10 = 42$. Because every other number in the "magic cube" is given, now that the magic sum is known the unknown entries are easy to find. The completed cube is shown.

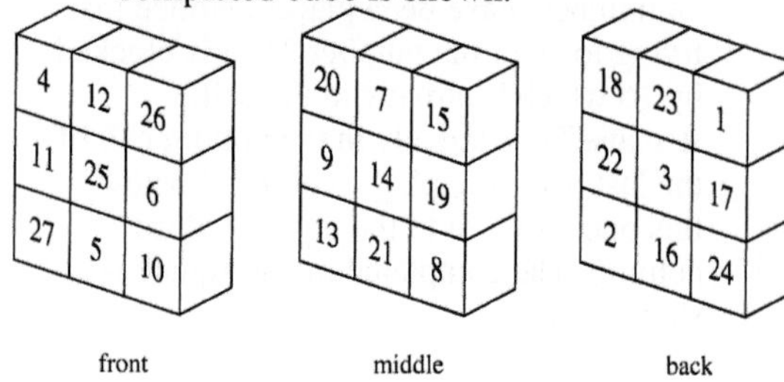

5 Exercises

1. The total number of subsets is 2^4 for a set with 4 elements. The only subset which is not a proper subset is the given set itself. Thus, by the complements principle, the number of proper subsets is
$2^4 - 1 = 16 - 1 = 15.$

3. By the fundamental counting principle, there are 2^7 different outcomes if seven coins are tossed. There is only one way to get no heads (all tails); thus, by the complements principle, there are
$2^7 - 1 = 128 - 1 = 127$ outcomes with at least one head.

5. By the fundamental counting principle, there are 2^7 different outcomes if seven coins are tossed. Of these, there is 1 way to get zero tails, and there are 7 ways to get one tail. Since "at least two" is the complement of "zero or one," the number of ways to get at least two tails is
$2^7 - (1 + 7) = 128 - 8 = 120.$

Refer to Table 2 in the first section of the textbook chapter.

7. In Table 2 all columns except the first represent "at least 2 on all the green die." Thus, there are $36 - 6 = 30$ ways to achieve this outcome.

9. Counting the number of outcomes in row 4 (4 on red die) + those in column 4 (4 on green die) and subtracting the outcome counted twice, the number of outcomes with "a 4 on at least one of the dice" is
$6 + 6 - 1 = 11.$

11. Since there is only one "ace of spades" in the deck, there must be 51 other cards. Thus, there are 51 ways to draw "a card other than the ace of spades."

13. There are nine two-digit multiples of 10 (10, 20, 30, ..., 90). Altogether there are $9 \cdot 10 = 90$ two-digit numbers by the fundamental counting principle. Thus, by the complements principle, the number of "two-digit numbers which are not multiples of ten" is $90 - 9 = 81$.

15. **(a)** The number of different sets of three albums she could choose is ${}_{10}C_3 = 120$.

(b) The number which would not include *Southern Voice* is ${}_9C_3 = 84$.

(c) The number that would contain *Southern Voice* is 120 – 84 = 36.

17. The total number of ways of choosing any three days of the week is ${}_7C_3$. The number of ways of choosing three days of the week that do not begin with S is ${}_5C_3$. Thus, the number of ways of choosing any three days of the week such that "at least one of them begin with S" is ${}_7C_3 - {}_5C_3 = 25$.

19. If the order of selection is important, the number of choices of restaurants is ${}_8P_4$. The number of choices of restaurants that would not include seafood is ${}_5P_4$. Thus, the number of choices such that at least one of the four will serve seafood is
${}_8P_4 - {}_5P_4 = 1560$.

21. The total number of ways to arrange 3 people among ten seats is ${}_{10}P_3$. The number of ways to arrange three people among the seven (non-aisle) seats is ${}_7P_3$. Therefore, by the complements principle, the number of arrangements with at least one aisle seat is ${}_{10}P_3 - {}_7P_3 = 510$.

23. For the stations with 3 call letters, there are 2 choices for the first letter, 26 choices for the second letter, and 26 choices for the third letter, or $2 \cdot 26^2$ possibilities. Similarly, for stations with 4 call letters, there are $2 \cdot 26^3$ possibilities. So the total number of different call letter combinations is $2 \cdot 26^2 + 2 \cdot 26^3 = 36{,}504$.

25. "At least one officer" is the complement of "no officers." The number of ways of choosing 4-member search teams is ${}_{12}C_4$. The number of ways to choose 4-member search teams with no officers included is ${}_8C_4$. The total number of ways to choose the search team with at least one officer included is ${}_{12}C_4 - {}_8C_4 = 425$.

27. Let C = the set of clubs and J = the set of jacks. Then, $C \cup J$ is the set of cards which are face cards or jacks, and $C \cap J$ is the set of cards which are both clubs and jacks, that is, the jack of clubs. Using the general additive counting principle, we obtain

$$\begin{aligned} n(C \cup J) &= n(C) + n(J) - n(C \cap J) \\ &= 13 + 4 - 1 \\ &= 16. \end{aligned}$$

29. Let M = the set of students who enjoy music and C = the set of students who enjoy cinema. Then $M \cup C$ is the set of students who enjoy music or cinema, and $M \cap C$ is the set of students who enjoy both music and cinema. Using the additive principle, we obtain

$$\begin{aligned} n(M \cup C) &= n(M) + n(C) - n(M \cap C) \\ &= 25 + 22 - 18 \\ &= 29. \end{aligned}$$

31. There are ${}_{13}C_5$ 5-card hands of hearts. Thus, by the complements principle, the number of hands containing "at least one card that is not a heart" is
$2{,}598{,}960 - {}_{13}C_5 = 2{,}597{,}673$.

33. The number of 5-card hands drawn from the 40 non-face cards in the deck is given by ${}_{40}C_5$. Thus, by the complements principle the number of 5-card hands with "at least one face card" is
$2{,}598{,}960 - {}_{40}C_5 = 1{,}940{,}952$.

35. If there are no duplicate flavors chosen, then the number of possible selections is ${}_6C_3 = 20$. But if we allow duplicate flavors, then after the first flavor is selected there are 6 choices for the second flavor and 6 choices for the third flavor, or 36 possible selections. So the total number of possible selections is 20 + 36 = 56.

37. "At most two elements" is the same as 0, 1, or 2 elements. Thus, the number of subsets is ${}_{10}C_0 + {}_{10}C_1 + {}_{10}C_2 = 56$.

39. "More than two elements" is the complement of "at most two elements." Find the number of subsets with "at most two elements" by adding the number of 0-element subsets, 1-element subsets, and 2-element subsets.
${}_{10}C_0 + {}_{10}C_1 + {}_{10}C_2 = 1 + 10 + 45 = 56$

There are 2^{10} subsets altogether. Thus, by the complements principle, the number of subsets of more than two elements is

$2^{10} - 56 = 968.$

41. The complement of "at least one letter or digit repeated" is "no letters or digits repeated." There are ${}_{26}P_2 \cdot {}_{10}P_3$ license plates with no digits repeated, and using the fundamental counting principle we have $26 \cdot 26 \cdot 10 \cdot 10 \cdot 10 = 26^2 \cdot 10^3$ license plates where any letter of digit can be repeated. By the complements principle, the number of different license plates with at least one letter or digit repeated is

$26^2 \cdot 10^3 - {}_{26}P_2 \cdot {}_{10}P_3 = 208{,}000.$

43. Writing exercise; answers will vary.

45. To choose sites in only one state works as follows: The number of ways to choose three monuments in New Mexico is ${}_4C_3$, The number of ways to choose three monuments in Arizona is ${}_3C_3$, and the number of ways to pick three monuments in California is ${}_5C_3$. Since these components are disjoint, we may use the special additive principle. The number of ways to choose the monuments is

${}_4C_3 + {}_3C_3 + {}_5C_3 = 4 + 1 + 10 = 15.$

47. "Sites in fewer than all three states" is the complement of choosing "sites in all three states." Since there are 12 monuments altogether, the total number of ways to select three monuments (with no restrictions) is ${}_{12}C_3$. Choosing sites in all three states requires choosing one site in each state, which can be done in $4 \cdot 3 \cdot 5$ ways. Using the complements principles, the number of ways to choose sites in fewer than all three states is

${}_{12}C_3 - 4 \cdot 3 \cdot 5 = 220 - 60 = 160.$

49. Writing exercise; answers will vary.

51. Writing exercise; answers will vary.

53. Writing exercise; answers will vary.

Chapter Test

1. To find three-digit numbers from the set $\{0, 1, 2, 3, 4, 5, 6\}$, use the fundamental counting principle: $\underline{6} \cdot \underline{7} \cdot \underline{7} = 294$.

2. To find odd three-digit numbers from the set $\{0, 1, 2, 3, 4, 5, 6\}$, use the fundamental counting principle: $\underline{6} \cdot \underline{7} \cdot \underline{3} = 126$.

3. To find three-digit numbers without repeated digits from the set $\{0, 1, 2, 3, 4, 5, 6\}$, use the fundamental counting principle: $\underline{6} \cdot \underline{6} \cdot \underline{5} = 180$.

4. To find three-digit multiples of five without repeated digits from the set $\{0, 1, 2, 3, 4, 5, 6\}$, use the fundamental counting principle and the special additive principle: Multiples of 5 end in "0" or "5." There are $\underline{6} \cdot \underline{5} \cdot \underline{1} = 30$ multiples that end in 0 and $\underline{5} \cdot \underline{5} \cdot \underline{1} = 25$ that end in 5. Thus, the number of three-digit multiples of five without repeated digits is $30 + 25 = 55$.

5. Make a systematic listing of triangles. Beginning with the smaller inside triangle, there are 4 right triangles off the horizontal bisector of the larger triangle. These triangles may be combined to create 4 larger isosceles triangles. There are 2 isosceles triangles—inside the upper left and lower left corners of the largest triangle and 1 larger right triangle above and 1 below the horizontal bisector of the larger triangle. Of course, count the largest isosceles triangle itself. The total number of triangles is $4 + 4 + 2 + 1 + 1 + 1 = 13$.

6.

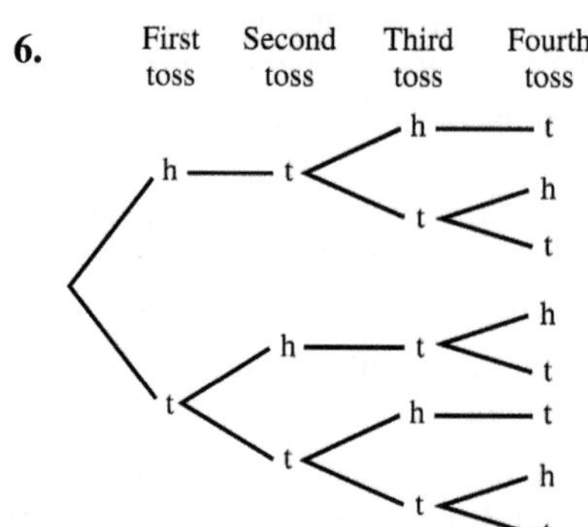

7. There is only one set of 4 digits that add to 30 ($9 + 8 + 7 + 6 = 30$). The number of arrangements of the digits 9876 is given by ${}_4P_4 = 4! = 24$.

8. Counting clockwise, Tia and Jo can sit either 1 seat, 2 seats, or 3 seats apart, leaving 4 empty seats for their four friends. There are 3 arrangements for Tia and Jo and 4! arrangements for their four friends, so the total number of ways they can be arranged is $3 \cdot 4! = 72$.

9. $6! = 6 \cdot 5 \cdot 4 \cdot 3 \cdot 2 \cdot 1 = 720$

10. $\dfrac{8!}{6!} = \dfrac{8 \cdot 7 \cdot 6!}{6!} = 8 \cdot 7 = 56$

11.
$$\begin{aligned} {}_{12}P_3 &= \frac{12!}{(12-3)!} \\ &= \frac{12!}{9!} \\ &= \frac{12 \cdot 11 \cdot 10 \cdot 9!}{9!} \\ &= 12 \cdot 11 \cdot 10 \\ &= 1320 \end{aligned}$$

12.
$$\begin{aligned} {}_8C_5 &= \frac{8!}{5!(8-5)!} \\ &= \frac{8!}{5! \cdot 3!} \\ &= \frac{8 \cdot 7 \cdot 6 \cdot 5!}{5! \cdot 3 \cdot 2 \cdot 1} \\ &= \frac{8 \cdot 7 \cdot 6}{3 \cdot 2 \cdot 1} \\ &= 56 \end{aligned}$$

13. Since the arrangement of the letters is important and no repetitions are allowed, use ${}_{26}P_5$.

$${}_{26}P_5 = 26 \cdot 25 \cdot 24 \cdot 23 \cdot 22 = 7{,}893{,}600$$

14. Since repetitions are allowed, sue the fundamental counting principle.

$$32^5 = 33{,}554{,}432$$

15. Since the order of the assignments is important, use ${}_7P_2$.

$${}_7P_2 = \frac{7!}{(7-2)!} = \frac{7!}{5!} = \frac{7 \cdot 6 \cdot 5!}{5!} = 7 \cdot 6 = 42$$

16. Since the order of the remaining five assignments is important, use ${}_5P_5$ or 5!.

$${}_5P_5 = 5! = 5 \cdot 4 \cdot 3 \cdot 2 \cdot 1 = 120$$

17. There are 6 letters to be arranged, but two letters are repeated: G appears 2 times and O appears 3 times. To account for this, we must divide out combinations that would imply order mattered. Thus, the number of arrangements is

$$\frac{6!}{2! \cdot 3!} = \frac{6 \cdot 5 \cdot 4 \cdot 3!}{2 \cdot 1 \cdot 3!} = \frac{6 \cdot 5 \cdot 4}{2} = 60.$$

18. Since order is not important, use ${}_{10}C_4$.

$$\begin{aligned} {}_{10}C_4 &= \frac{10!}{4!(10-4)!} \\ &= \frac{10!}{4!6!} \\ &= \frac{10 \cdot 9 \cdot 8 \cdot 7 \cdot 6!}{4 \cdot 3 \cdot 2 \cdot 1 \cdot 6!} \\ &= 210 \end{aligned}$$

19. Use the fundamental counting principle and account for any unwanted ordering.

$$\frac{{}_{10}C_2 \cdot {}_8C_2}{2!} = 630$$

20. Use the fundamental counting principle and account for any unwanted ordering.

$$\frac{{}_{10}C_5 \cdot {}_5C_5}{2!} = 126$$

21. Use the fundamental counting principle and account for any unwanted ordering.

$$\frac{{}_{10}C_4 \cdot {}_6C_4}{2!} = 1575$$

22. The complement of "a group of three or more of the players" is "zero, one, or two of the players." The total number of subsets of the 10 players is $2^{10} = 1024$.
The total number of 0-member subsets, 1-member subsets, and 2-member subsets is ${}_{10}C_0 + {}_{10}C_1 + {}_{10}C_2 = 1 + 10 + 45 = 56$.
By the complements principle, the number of ways to select a group of three or more of the players is

$$\begin{aligned} 2^{10} - ({}_{10}C_0 + {}_{10}C_1 + {}_{10}C_2) &= 1024 - 56 \\ &= 968. \end{aligned}$$

23. With no restrictions, use the fundamental counting principle to determine the number of positions that a row of five switches may be set.

$$2 \cdot 2 \cdot 2 \cdot 2 \cdot 2 = 2^5 = 32$$

24. Use the fundamental counting principle to determine the number of positions that a row of five switches may be set if the first and fifth switches must be on.

$$1 \cdot 2 \cdot 2 \cdot 2 \cdot 1 = 2^3 = 8$$

25. Use the fundamental counting principle to determine the number of positions that a row of five switches may be set if the first and fifth switches must be set the same.

$$2 \cdot 2 \cdot 2 \cdot 2 \cdot 1 = 2^4 = 16$$

26. The following represent switch settings where "no two adjacent switches can both be off." Remember that "0" represents an "off" switch.

01010	10101	10111
01011	10110	11101
01101	11010	11110
01110	11011	
01111	11111	

There are 13 switch settings that satisfy the restriction.

27. There are only 2 switch settings in which no two adjacent switches can be set the same:
01010 10101

28. The complement of "at least two switches must be on" is "zero or one switch is on." Without restrictions there are $2^5 = 32$ different switch settings. There is only 1 way for zero switches to be on and 5 ways for only 1 switch to be on. Thus, by the complements principle, the number of ways for at least two switches to be on is $32 - (1 + 5) = 26$.

29. Since the letter B must be a member, all that is necessary is to choose two members from the remaining six members. The number of three-element subsets is ${}_6C_2 = 15$.

30. Since the letters A and E must be members, all that is necessary is to choose one member from the five remaining members. The number of three-element subsets is ${}_5C_1 = 5$.

31. ${}_5C_2$ represents the number of three-element subsets that contain exactly one of the letters but not the other. There will be twice this number if we do the same for the 2nd letter. Thus, the number of three-element subsets with either A or E but not both is $2 \cdot {}_5C_2 = 20$.

32. Since the letters A and D must be members, all that is necessary is to choose one member from the remaining five members. The number of three-element subsets is then ${}_5C_1 = 5$.

33. "More consonants than vowels" can happen two ways. One, with 3 consonants and no vowels, can be found by ${}_5C_3$. The second, with 2 consonants and 1 vowel, can be found by choosing the 1 vowel ${}_2C_1$ ways. Since one or the other will satisfy the restrictions (and they cannot both happen at the same time) apply the special addition principle to find the total number of subset choices for "more consonants than vowels."
${}_5C_3 + {}_5C_2 \cdot {}_2C_1 = 30$

34. All possible paths are 9 blocks long, and 4 of those must be in an eastward direction. Thus, there are ${}_9C_4 = 126$ different paths to the garage.

35. Writing exercise; answers will vary.

36. Because ${}_nC_r$ and ${}_nC_{r+1}$ are the two entries just above ${}_{n+1}C_{r+1}$, evaluate ${}_{n+1}C_{r+1}$ by adding their values.
${}_{n+1}C_{r+1} = {}_nC_r + {}_nC_{r+1} = 495 + 220 = 715$

37. The sequence of numbers obtained is 1, 2, 3, 4, 5, ...

38. Writing exercise; answers will vary.

PROBABILITY

Everett Collection

Suppose you're on a game show, and you're given the choice of three doors: Behind one of the doors is a car, and behind the other doors, goats. Of course, you want to win the car. You pick one of the doors, say Door 1, and the host, who knows what's behind the other doors, opens another door, say Door 3, to reveal a goat. He then says to you, "Do you want to change your choice?" Is it to your advantage to switch to Door 2?

This question appeared in *Parade* magazine in a column written by Marilyn vos Savant in the early 1990s. This probability problem, known as the Monty Hall Problem, was named after the host of the popular game show *Let's Make a Deal.* Marilyn's answer caused an incredible amount of discussion and argument among the general public at that time.

The answer and its justification can also be found at the interactive Web site www.math.ucsd.edu/~crypto/Monty/monty .html. *Would YOU switch doors?*

1 BASIC CONCEPTS

Historical Background • Probability • The Law of Large Numbers • Probability in Genetics • Odds

If the **Pascal–Fermat correspondence** of 1654 marks the birth of probability theory, it wasn't an easy birth. In his 2010 book, *The Unfinished Game: Pascal, Fermat, and the Seventeenth-Century Letter that Made the World Modern* (see the photo above), Keith Devlin describes how the two "struggled for several weeks" to solve the unfinished game problem. In fact, this is no exception, but rather the rule, even for the greatest mathematicians. The reams of scratch work behind the elegant results are seldom seen and rarely published.

Historical Background

The modern mathematical theory of probability came mainly from the Russian scholars P. L. Chebyshev (1821–1922), A. A. Markov (1856–1922), and Andrei Nikolaevich Kolmogorov (1903–1987). But the basic ideas arose much earlier, mostly in questions of games and gambling. In 1654, two French mathematicians, Pierre de Fermat (about 1601–1665) and Blaise Pascal (1623–1662), corresponded with each other regarding a problem posed by the Chevalier de Méré, a gambler and member of the aristocracy.

> *If the two players of a game are forced to quit before the game is finished, how should the pot be divided?*

Pascal and Fermat solved the problem by developing basic methods of determining each player's chance, or probability, of winning.

The Dutch mathematician and scientist Christiaan Huygens (1629–1695) wrote a formal treatise on probability. It appeared in 1657 and was based on the Pascal–Fermat correspondence.

One of the first to apply probability to matters other than gambling was the French mathematician Pierre Simon de Laplace (1749–1827), who is usually credited with being the "father" of probability theory.

Probability

If you go to a supermarket and select five pounds of peaches at 89¢ per pound, you can easily predict the amount you will be charged at the checkout counter.

$$5 \cdot \$0.89 = \$4.45.$$

This is an example of a **deterministic phenomenon.** It can be predicted exactly on the basis of obtainable information, namely, in this case, number of pounds and cost per pound.

On the other hand, consider the problem faced by the produce manager of the market, who must order peaches to have on hand each day without knowing exactly how many pounds customers will buy during the day. Customer demand is an example of a **random phenomenon.** It fluctuates in such a way that its value (on a given day) cannot be predicted exactly with obtainable information.

The study of probability is concerned with such random phenomena. Even though we cannot be certain whether a given result will occur, we often can obtain a good measure of its *likelihood,* or **probability.** This chapter discusses various ways of finding and using probabilities.

Any observation, or measurement, of a random phenomenon is an **experiment.** The possible results of the experiment are **outcomes,** and the set of all possible outcomes is the **sample space.**

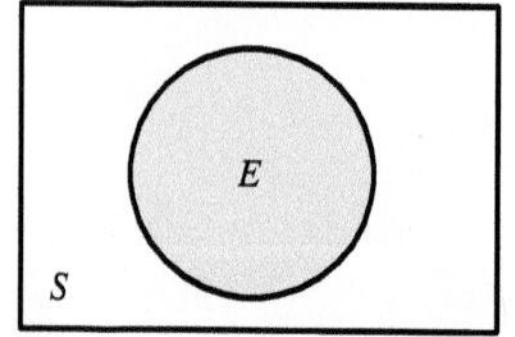

Every event is a subset of the sample space.

Usually we are interested in some particular collection of the possible outcomes. Any such subset of the sample space is an **event.** Outcomes that belong to the event are "favorable outcomes," or "successes." Any time a success is observed, we say that the event has "occurred." The probability of an event, being a numerical measure of the event's likelihood, is determined in one of two ways, either *theoretically* (mathematically) or *empirically* (experimentally).

Mary Evans Picture Library/Alamy Images

"But is it probable," asked Pascal, "that probability gives assurance? Nothing gives certainty but truth; nothing gives rest but the sincere search for truth." When Pascal wrote that, he had gone to live at the Jansenist convent of Port-Royal after a carriage accident in 1654.

Pascal's notes on Christianity were collected after his death in the *Pensées* (thoughts). The above quotation is included. Another develops Pascal's "rule of the wager": If you bet God exists and live accordingly, you will have gained much even if God does not exist; if you bet the opposite and God does exist, you will have lost the reason for living right—hence everything.

EXAMPLE 1 Finding Probability When Tossing a Coin

If a single coin is tossed, find the probability that it will land heads up.

SOLUTION

There is no apparent reason for one side of a coin to land up any more often than the other (in the long run), so we assume that heads and tails are equally likely.

The experiment here is the tossing of a single fair coin, the sample space is $S = \{h, t\}$, and the event whose probability we seek is $E = \{h\}$. Since one of the two equally likely outcomes is a head, the probability of heads is the quotient of 1 and 2.

$$\text{Probability (heads)} = \frac{1}{2}, \quad \text{written} \quad P(\text{h}) = \frac{1}{2} \quad \text{or} \quad P(E) = \frac{1}{2}.$$

EXAMPLE 2 Finding Probability When Tossing a Cup

If a Styrofoam cup is tossed, find the probability that it will land on its top.

SOLUTION

Intuitively, it seems that such a cup will land on its side much more often than on its top or its bottom. But just how much more often is not clear. To get an idea, we performed the experiment of tossing such a cup 50 times. It landed on its side 44 times, on its top 5 times, and on its bottom just 1 time. By the frequency of "success" in this experiment, we concluded for the cup we used that

$$P(\text{top}) \approx \frac{5}{50} = \frac{1}{10}.$$

Write in lowest terms.

In **Example 1** involving the tossing of a fair coin, the number of possible outcomes was obviously two, both were equally likely, and one of the outcomes was a head. No actual experiment was required. The desired probability was obtained *theoretically.* Theoretical probabilities apply to dice rolling, card games, roulette, lotteries, and so on, and apparently to many phenomena in nature.

Laplace, in his famous *Analytic Theory of Probability,* published in 1812, gave a formula that applies to any such theoretical probability, as long as the sample space S is finite and all outcomes are equally likely. (It is sometimes referred to as the *classical definition of probability.*)

Theoretical Probability Formula

If all outcomes in a sample space S are equally likely, and E is an event within that sample space, then the **theoretical probability** of event E is given by the following formula.

$$P(E) = \frac{\textbf{number of favorable outcomes}}{\textbf{total number of outcomes}} = \frac{n(E)}{n(S)}$$

On the other hand, **Example 2** involved the tossing of a cup, where the likelihoods of the various outcomes were not intuitively clear. It took an actual experiment to arrive at a probability value of $\frac{1}{10}$, and that value, based on a portion of all possible tosses of the cup, should be regarded as an approximation of the true theoretical probability. The value was found according to the *experimental,* or *empirical,* probability formula.

In 1827, **Robert Brown** (1773–1858), a Scottish physician and botanist, described the irregular motion of microscopic pollen grains suspended in water. Such "Brownian motion," as it came to be called, was not understood until 1905 when Albert Einstein explained it by treating molecular motion as a random phenomenon.

Library of Congress Prints and Photographs Division [LC-USZ62-75479]

Empirical Probability Formula

If E is an event that may happen when an experiment is performed, then an **empirical probability** of event E is given by the following formula.

$$P(E) = \frac{\textbf{number of times event } E \textbf{ occurred}}{\textbf{number of times the experiment was performed}}$$

Usually it is clear in applications which probability formula should be used.

EXAMPLE 3 Finding the Probability of Having Daughters

Kathy Campbell wants to have exactly two daughters. Assuming that boy and girl babies are equally likely, find her probability of success if

(a) she has a total of two children. **(b)** she has a total of three children.

SOLUTION

(a) The equal likelihood assumption allows the use of theoretical probability. But how can we determine the number of favorable outcomes and the total number of possible outcomes?

One way is to use a tree diagram to enumerate the possibilities, as shown in **Figure 1**. From the outcome column we obtain the sample space $S = \{gg, gb, bg, bb\}$. Only one outcome, marked with an arrow, is favorable to the event of exactly two daughters: $E = \{gg\}$.

$$P(E) = \frac{n(E)}{n(S)} = \frac{1}{4} \quad \text{Theoretical probability formula}$$

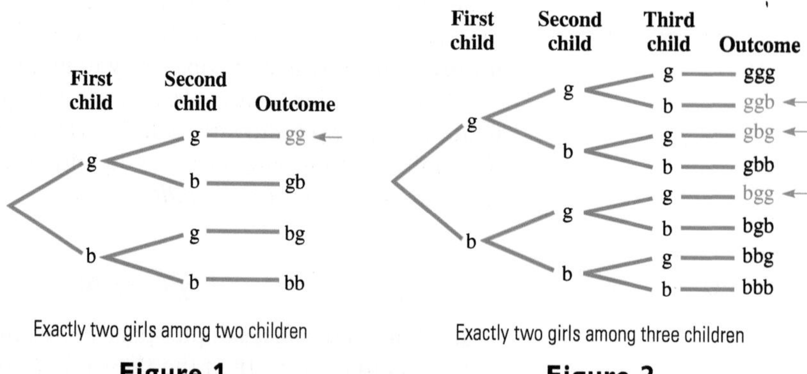

Exactly two girls among two children

Figure 1

Exactly two girls among three children

Figure 2

(b) For three children altogether, we construct another tree diagram, as shown in **Figure 2**. In this case, we see that

$$S = \{ggg, ggb, gbg, gbb, bgg, bgb, bbg, bbb\} \quad \text{and} \quad E = \{ggb, gbg, bgg\},$$

so $P(E) = \frac{3}{8}$.

When dealing (or drawing) cards, as in the next example, the dealing is generally done "without replacement." Once dealt, a card is *not* replaced in the deck. So all cards in a hand are distinct. (Repetitions are *not* allowed.) In many cases, such as building three-digit numbers, repetition of digits *is* allowed. For example, 255 is a legitimate three-digit number. So digit selection is done "with replacement."

EXAMPLE 4 Finding Probability When Dealing Cards

Table 1 Number of Poker Hands in 5-Card Poker; Nothing Wild

Event E	Number of Outcomes Favorable to E
Royal flush	4
Straight flush	36
Four of a kind	624
Full house	3744
Flush	5108
Straight	10,200
Three of a kind	54,912
Two pairs	123,552
One pair	1,098,240
No pair	1,302,540
Total	2,598,960

Find the probability of being dealt each of the following hands in five-card poker. Use a calculator to obtain answers to eight decimal places.

(a) a full house (three of one denomination and two of another)

(b) a royal flush (the five highest cards—ace, king, queen, jack, ten—of a single suit)

SOLUTION

(a) **Table 1** summarizes the various possible kinds of five-card hands. Since the 2,598,960 possible individual hands all are equally likely, we can enter the appropriate numbers from the table into the theoretical probability formula.

$$P(\text{full house}) = \frac{3744}{2{,}598{,}960} = \frac{6}{4165} \approx 0.00144058$$

(b) The table shows that there are four royal flushes, one for each suit.

$$P(\text{royal flush}) = \frac{4}{2{,}598{,}960} = \frac{1}{649{,}740} \approx 0.00000154$$

Examples 3 and 4 both utilized the theoretical probability formula because we were able to enumerate all possible outcomes and all were equally likely. In **Example 3,** however, the equal likelihood of girl and boy babies was *assumed.* In fact, male births typically occur a little more frequently. (At the same time, there usually are more females living at any given time, due to higher infant mortality rates among males and longer female life expectancy in general.) **Example 5** shows a way of incorporating such empirical information.

EXAMPLE 5 Finding the Probability of the Gender of a Resident

According to *Pocket World in Figures,* 2009 edition, published by *The Economist,* the U.S. population at the end of 2006 included 148.2 million males and 152.8 million females. If a person were selected randomly from the population in that year, what is the probability that the person would be a male?

SOLUTION

In this case, we calculate the empirical probability from the given experimental data.

$$\begin{aligned} P(\text{male}) &= \frac{\text{number of males}}{\text{total number of persons}} \\ &= \frac{148.2 \text{ million}}{148.2 \text{ million} + 152.8 \text{ million}} \\ &\approx 0.492 \end{aligned}$$

The Law of Large Numbers

Recall the cup of **Example 2.** If we tossed it 50 more times, we would have 100 total tosses upon which to base an empirical probability of the cup landing on its top. The new value would likely be (at least slightly) different from what we obtained before. It would still be an empirical probability, but it would be "better" in the sense that it is based upon a larger set of outcomes.

The **law of large numbers** also can be stated as follows.

A theoretical probability really says nothing about one, or even a few, repetitions of an experiment, but only about the proportion of successes we would expect over the long run.

If, as we increase the number of tosses, the resulting empirical probability values approach some particular number, that number can be defined as the theoretical probability of that particular cup landing on its top. We could determine this "limiting" value only as the actual number of observed tosses approaches the total number of possible tosses of the cup. Since there are potentially an infinite number of possible tosses, we could never actually find the theoretical probability. But we can still assume such a number exists. And as the number of actual observed tosses increases, the resulting empirical probabilities should tend ever closer to the theoretical value.

This very important principle is known as the **law of large numbers** (or sometimes as the "law of averages").

Law of Large Numbers

As an experiment is repeated more and more times, the proportion of outcomes favorable to any particular event will tend to come closer and closer to the theoretical probability of that event.

EXAMPLE 6 Graphing a Sequence of Proportions

A fair coin was tossed 35 times, producing the following sequence of outcomes.

tthhh, ttthh, hthtt, hhthh, ttthh, thttt, hhthh

Calculate the ratio of heads to total tosses after the first toss, the second toss, and so on through all 35 tosses, and plot these ratios on a graph.

SOLUTION

After the first toss, we have 0 heads out of 1 toss, for a ratio of $\frac{0}{1} = 0.00$. After two tosses, we have $\frac{0}{2} = 0.00$. After three tosses, we have $\frac{1}{3} \approx 0.33$. Verify that the first six ratios are

$$0.00, \quad 0.00, \quad 0.33, \quad 0.50, \quad 0.60, \quad 0.50.$$

The thirty-five ratios are plotted as points in **Figure 3**. The fluctuations away from 0.50 become smaller as the number of tosses increases, and the ratios appear to approach 0.50 toward the right side of the graph, in keeping with the law of large numbers.

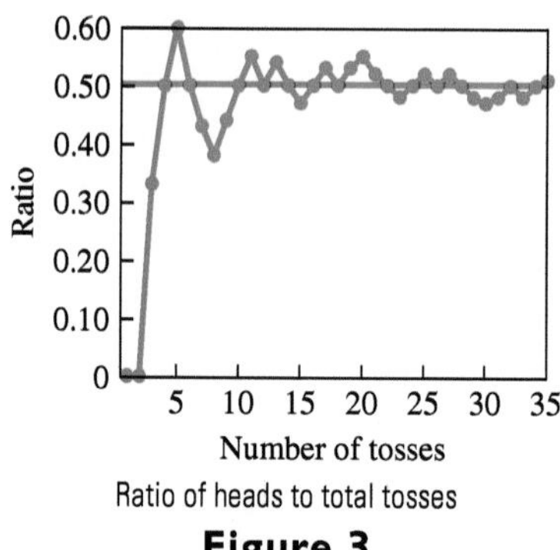

Ratio of heads to total tosses

Figure 3

Comparing Empirical and Theoretical Probabilities

A series of repeated experiments provides an *empirical probability* for an event, which, by *inductive reasoning,* is an *estimate* of the event's *theoretical probability*. (Increasing the number of repetitions increases the reliability of the estimate.)

Likewise, an established *theoretical probability* for an event enables us, by *deductive reasoning,* to *predict* the proportion of times the event will occur in a series of repeated experiments. (The prediction should be more accurate for larger numbers of repetitions.)

Gregor Johann Mendel (1822–1884) came from a peasant family who managed to send him to school. By 1847 he had been ordained and was teaching at the Abbey of St. Thomas. He finished his education at the University of Vienna and returned to the abbey to teach mathematics and natural science.

Mendel began to carry out experiments on plants in the abbey garden, notably pea plants, whose distinct traits (unit characters) he had puzzled over. In 1865 he published his results. His work was not appreciated at the time even though he had laid the foundation of **classical genetics.**

Probability in Genetics

Probabilities, both empirical and theoretical, have been valuable tools in many areas of science. An important early example was the work of the Austrian monk Gregor Mendel, who used the idea of randomness to help establish the study of genetics.

In an effort to understand the mechanism of character transmittal from one generation to the next in plants, Mendel counted the number of occurrences of various characteristics. He found that the flower color in certain pea plants obeyed this scheme:

Pure red crossed with pure white produces red.

Mendel theorized that red is "dominant" (symbolized with the capital letter R), while white is "recessive" (symbolized with the lowercase letter r). The pure red parent carried only genes for red (R), and the pure white parent carried only genes for white (r). The offspring would receive one gene from each parent, hence one of the four combinations shown in the body of **Table 2.** Because every offspring receives one gene for red, that characteristic dominates and the offspring exhibits the color red.

Table 2 First to Second Generation

		Second Parent	
		r	**r**
First Parent	**R**	Rr	Rr
	R	Rr	Rr

Table 3 Second to Third Generation

		Second Parent	
		R	**r**
First Parent	**R**	RR	Rr
	r	rR	rr

Now each of these second-generation offspring, though exhibiting the color red, still carries one of each gene. So when two of them are crossed, each third-generation offspring will receive one of the gene combinations shown in **Table 3**. Mendel theorized that each of these four possibilities would be equally likely and produced experimental counts that were close enough to support this hypothesis.

EXAMPLE 7 Finding Probabilities of Flower Colors

Referring to **Table 3**, determine the probability that a third-generation offspring will exhibit each flower color. Base the probabilities on the sample space of equally likely outcomes: $S = \{\text{RR}, \text{Rr}, \text{rR}, \text{rr}\}$.

(a) red **(b)** white

SOLUTION

(a) Since red dominates white, any combination with at least one gene for red (R) will result in red flowers. Since three of the four possibilities meet this criterion, $P(\text{red}) = \frac{3}{4}$.

(b) Only the combination rr has no gene for red, so $P(\text{white}) = \frac{1}{4}$.

Odds

Whereas probability compares the number of favorable outcomes to the total number of outcomes, **odds** compare the number of favorable outcomes to the number of unfavorable outcomes. Odds are commonly quoted, rather than probabilities, in horse racing, lotteries, and most other gambling situations. And the odds quoted normally are odds "against" rather than odds "in favor."

Smoking 1.4 cigarettes
Spending 1 hour in a coal mine
Living 2 days in New York or Boston
Eating 40 teaspoons of peanut butter
Living 2 months with a cigarette smoker
Flying 1000 miles in a jet
Traveling 300 miles in a car
Riding 10 miles on a bicycle

Risk is the probability that a harmful event will occur. Almost every action or substance exposes a person to some risk, and the assessment and reduction of risk accounts for a great deal of study and effort in our world. The list above, from *Calculated Risk*, by J. Rodricks, contains activities that carry an annual increased risk of death by one chance in a million.

Odds

If all outcomes in a sample space are equally likely, a of them are favorable to the event E, and the remaining b outcomes are unfavorable to E, then the **odds in favor** of E are a to b, and the **odds against** E are b to a.

EXAMPLE 8 Finding the Odds of Getting an Intern Position

Theresa Cortesini has been promised one of six jobs, three of which would be intern positions at the state capitol. If she has equal chances for all six jobs, find the odds that she will get one of the intern positions.

SOLUTION

Since three possibilities are favorable and three are not, the odds of becoming an intern at the capitol are 3 to 3 (or 1 to 1 in reduced terms). Odds of 1 to 1 are often termed "even odds," or a "50–50 chance."

EXAMPLE 9 Finding the Odds of Winning a Raffle

Bob Barickman has purchased 12 tickets for an office raffle in which the winner will receive an iPad. If 104 tickets were sold altogether and each has an equal chance of winning, what are the odds against Bob's winning the iPad?

SOLUTION

Bob has 12 chances to win and $104 - 12 = 92$ chances to lose, so the odds against winning are 92 to 12, or 23 to 3. (Divide both 92 and 12 by 4.)

Converting between Probability and Odds

Let E be an event.

1. If $P(E) = \frac{a}{b}$, then the odds in favor of E are a to $(b - a)$.
2. If the odds in favor of E are a to b, then $P(E) = \frac{a}{a + b}$.

EXAMPLE 10 Converting from Probability to Odds

There is a 30% chance of rain tomorrow. Give this information in terms of odds.

SOLUTION

$$P(\text{rain}) = 0.30 = \frac{30}{100} = \frac{3}{10}$$

Convert the decimal fraction to a quotient of integers and reduce.

By conversion formula 1 above, the odds in favor of rain are 3 to 10 – 3, or 3 to 7. Or, we can say the odds are 7 to 3 against rain tomorrow.

EXAMPLE 11 Converting from Odds to Probability

In a certain sweepstakes, your odds of winning are 1 to 99,999. What is the probability that you will win?

SOLUTION

$$P(\text{win}) = \frac{1}{1 + 99{,}999} = \frac{1}{100{,}000} = 0.00001 \quad \text{Conversion formula 2}$$

1 EXERCISES

In Exercises 1–4, give the probability that the spinner shown would land on **(a)** *red,* **(b)** *yellow,* **(c)** *blue.*

1. 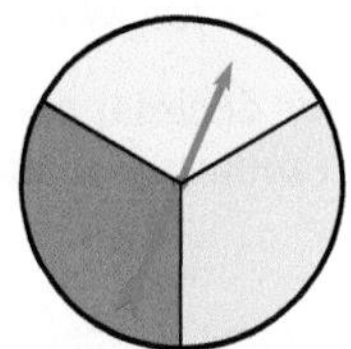

2. 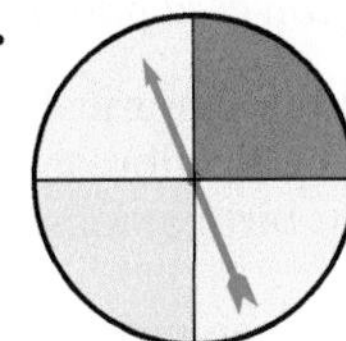

3. 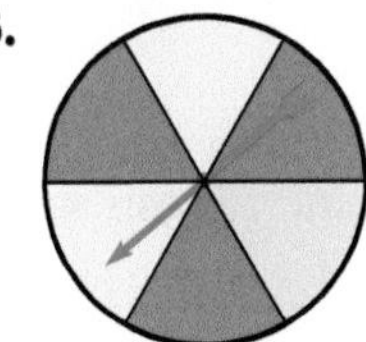

4. 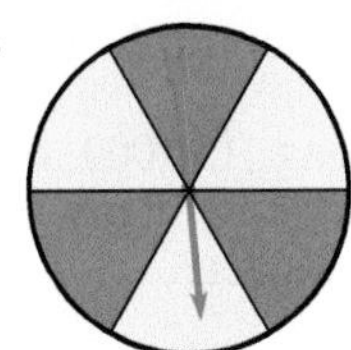

Solve each probability problem.

5. *Using Spinners to Generate Numbers* Suppose the spinner shown here is spun once, to determine a single-digit number, and we are interested in the event E that the resulting number is odd. Give each of the following.

(a) the sample space

(b) the number of favorable outcomes

(c) the number of unfavorable outcomes

(d) the total number of possible outcomes

(e) the probability of an odd number

(f) the odds in favor of an odd number

6. *Lining Up Preschool Children* Kim Lenaghan's group of preschool children includes nine girls and seven boys. If Kim randomly selects one child to be first in line, with E being the event that the one selected is a girl, give each of the following.

(a) the total number of possible outcomes

(b) the number of favorable outcomes

(c) the number of unfavorable outcomes

(d) the probability of event E

(e) the odds in favor of event E

7. *Using Spinners to Generate Numbers* The spinner of **Exercise 5** is spun twice in succession to determine a two-digit number. Give each of the following.

(a) the sample space

(b) the probability of an odd number

(c) the probability of a number with repeated digits

(d) the probability of a number greater than 30

(e) the probability of a prime number

8. *Probabilities in Coin Tossing* Two fair coins are tossed (say a dime and a quarter). Give each of the following.

(a) the sample space

(b) the probability of heads on the dime

(c) the probability of heads on the quarter

(d) the probability of getting both heads

(e) the probability of getting the same outcome on both coins

9. *Drawing Balls from an Urn* Anne Kelly randomly chooses a single ball from the urn shown here. Find the odds against each event.

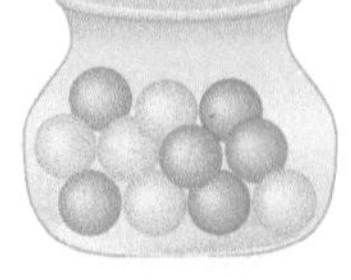

(a) red **(b)** yellow **(c)** blue

10. *Random Selection of Club Officers* Five people (Alan, Bill, Cathy, David, and Evelyn) form a club $N = \{A, B, C, D, E\}$. If they choose a president randomly, find the odds against each result.

(a) Cathy **(b)** a woman

(c) a person whose name begins with a consonant

11. *Random Selection of Fifties Music* Butch LeBeau has fifty hit singles from the fifties, including exactly one by Smiley Lewis, two by The Drifters, three by Bobby Darin, four by The Coasters, and five by Fats Domino. If Butch randomly selects one hit from his collection of fifty, find the probability it will be by each of the following.

(a) Smiley Lewis **(b)** The Drifters

(c) Bobby Darin **(d)** The Coasters

(e) Fats Domino

12. *Probabilities in Coin Tossing* Three fair coins are tossed.

(a) Write out the sample space.

Determine the probability of each event.

(b) no heads **(c)** exactly one head

(d) exactly two heads **(e)** three heads

13. *Number Sums for Rolling Two Dice* The sample space for the rolling of two fair dice appears as **Table 21** at end of this chapter. Reproduce that table, but replace each of the 36 equally likely ordered pairs with its corresponding sum (for the two dice). Then find the probability of rolling each sum.

(a) 2 **(b)** 3 **(c)** 4

(d) 5 **(e)** 6 **(f)** 7

(g) 8 **(h)** 9 **(i)** 10

(j) 11 **(k)** 12

In Exercises 14 and 15, give answers to three decimal places.

14. *Probability of Seed Germination* In a hybrid corn research project, 200 seeds were planted, and 175 of them germinated. Find the empirical probability that any particular seed of this type will germinate.

15. ***Probability of Forest Land in California*** According to *The World Almanac and Book of Facts 2010,* California has 155,959 square miles of land area, 51,250 square miles of which are forested. Find the probability that a randomly selected location in California will be forested.

16. ***Probabilities of Two Daughters Among Four Children*** In **Example 3,** what would be Kathy's probability of having exactly two daughters if she were to have four children altogether? (You may want to use a tree diagram to construct the sample space.)

17. ***Rolling Altered Dice*** A six-sided die has been altered so that the side that had been a single dot is now a blank face. Another die has a blank face instead of the face with four dots. What is the probability that a sum of 7 is rolled when the two dice are thrown? (*Mathematics Teacher* calendar problem)

18. ***Probability of Location in a Tunnel*** Mr. Davis is driving through a tunnel that is eight miles long. At this instant, what is the probability that he is at least six miles from one end of the tunnel? (*Mathematics Teacher* calendar problem)

Genetics in Snapdragons *Mendel found no dominance in snapdragons (in contrast to peas) with respect to red and white flower color. When pure red and pure white parents are crossed (see* **Table 2***), the resulting* Rr *combination (one of each gene) produces second-generation offspring with* pink *flowers. These second-generation pinks, however, still carry one red and one white gene, so when they are crossed the third generation is still governed by* **Table 3**.

Find each probability for third-generation snapdragons.

19. P(red) 20. P(pink) 21. P(white)

Genetics in Pea Plants *Mendel also investigated various characteristics besides flower color. For example, round peas are dominant over recessive wrinkled peas. First, second, and third generations can again be analyzed using* **Tables 2 and 3**, *where* R *represents round and* r *represents wrinkled.*

22. Explain why crossing pure round and pure wrinkled first-generation parents will always produce round peas in the second-generation offspring.

23. When second-generation round pea plants (each of which carries both R and r genes) are crossed, find the probability that a third-generation offspring will have
(a) round peas, **(b)** wrinkled peas.

Genetics of Cystic Fibrosis Cystic fibrosis *is one of the most common inherited diseases in North America (including the United States), occurring in about* 1 *of every* 2000 *Caucasian births and about* 1 *of every* 250,000 *non-Caucasian births. Even with modern treatment, victims usually die from lung damage by their early twenties.*

If we denote a cystic fibrosis gene with a c *and a disease-free gene with a* C *(since the disease is recessive), then only a* cc *person will actually have the disease. Such persons would ordinarily die before parenting children, but a child can also inherit the disease from two* Cc *parents (who themselves are healthy, that is, have no symptoms but are "carriers" of the disease). This is like a pea plant inheriting white flowers from two red-flowered parents that both carry genes for white.*

24. Find the empirical probability (to four decimal places) that cystic fibrosis will occur in a randomly selected infant birth among U.S. Caucasians.

25. Find the empirical probability (to six decimal places) that cystic fibrosis will occur in a randomly selected infant birth among U.S. non-Caucasians.

26. Among 150,000 North American Caucasian births, about how many occurrences of cystic fibrosis would you expect?

Suppose that both partners in a marriage are cystic fibrosis carriers (a rare occurrence). Construct a chart similar to **Table 3** *and determine the probability of each of the following events.*

27. Their first child will have the disease.

28. Their first child will be a carrier.

29. Their first child will neither have nor carry the disease.

Suppose a child is born to one cystic fibrosis carrier parent and one non-carrier parent. Find the probability of each of the following events.

30. The child will have cystic fibrosis.

31. The child will be a healthy cystic fibrosis carrier.

32. The child will neither have nor carry the disease.

Genetics of Sickle-Cell Anemia Sickle-cell anemia *occurs in about* 1 *of every* 500 *black baby births and about* 1 *of every* 160,000 *non-black baby births. It is ordinarily fatal in early childhood. There is a test to identify carriers. Unlike cystic fibrosis, which is recessive, sickle-cell anemia is* **codominant.** *This means that inheriting two sickle-cell genes causes the disease, while inheriting just one sickle-cell gene causes a mild (non-fatal) version (which is called* **sickle-cell trait***). This is similar to a snapdragon plant manifesting pink flowers by inheriting one red gene and one white gene.*

In Exercises 33 and 34, find the empirical probabilities of the given events.

33. A randomly selected black baby will have sickle-cell anemia. (Give your answer to three decimal places.)

34. A randomly selected non-black baby will have sickle-cell anemia. (Give your answer to six decimal places.)

35. Among 80,000 births of black babies, about how many occurrences of sickle-cell anemia would you expect?

Find the theoretical probability of each condition in a child both of whose parents have sickle-cell trait.

36. The child will have sickle-cell anemia.

37. The child will have sickle-cell trait.

38. The child will be healthy.

39. ***Women's 100-Meter Run*** In the history of track and field, no woman has broken the 10-second barrier in the 100-meter run.

(a) From the statement above, find the empirical probability that a woman runner will break the 10-second barrier next year.

(b) Can you find the theoretical probability for the event of part (a)?

(c) Is it possible that the event of part (a) will occur?

40. Is there any way a coin could fail to be "fair"? Explain.

41. On page 27 of their book *Descartes' Dream,* Philip Davis and Reuben Hersh ask the question, "Is probability real or is it just a cover-up for ignorance?" What do you think? Are some things truly random, or is everything potentially deterministic?

42. If $P(E) = 0.37$, find

(a) the odds in favor of E, **(b)** the odds against E.

43. If the odds in favor of event E are 12 to 19, find $P(E)$.

44. If the odds against event E are 10 to 3, find $P(E)$.

Probabilities of Poker Hands *In 5-card poker, find the probability of being dealt each of the following. Give each answer to eight decimal places. (Refer to* **Table 1***.)*

45. a straight flush

46. two pairs

47. four of a kind

48. four queens

49. a hearts flush (*not* a royal flush or a straight flush)

50. ***Probabilities in Dart Throwing*** If a dart hits the square target shown here at random, what is the probability that it will hit in a colored region? (*Hint:* Compare the area of the colored regions to the total area of the target.)

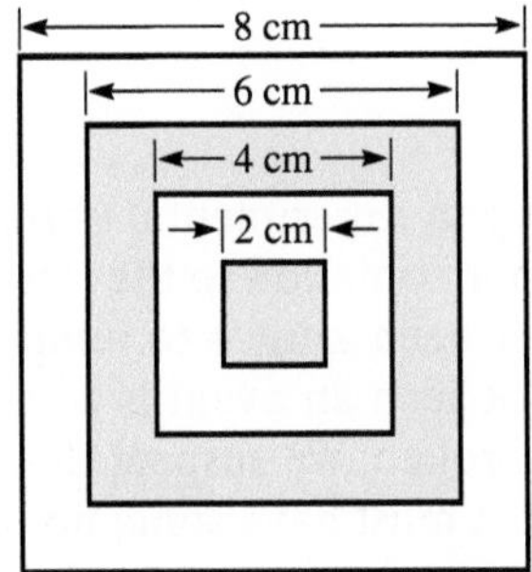

51. ***Probabilities in Olympic Curling*** In the Olympic event of curling, the scoring area (shown here) consists of four concentric circles on the ice with radii of 6 inches, 2 feet, 4 feet, and 6 feet.

If a team member lands a (43-pound) stone *randomly* within the scoring area, find the probability that it ends up centered on

(a) red, **(b)** white, **(c)** blue.

52. ***Drawing Cards*** When drawing cards without replacement from a standard 52-card deck, find the maximum number of cards you could possibly draw and still get

(a) fewer than three black cards,

(b) fewer than six spades,

(c) fewer than four face cards,

(d) fewer than two kings.

The remaining exercises require careful thought to determine n(E) and n(S). (In some cases, you may want to employ counting methods, such as the fundamental counting principle, permutations, or combinations.)

Probabilities of Seating Arrangements *Six people (three married couples) arrange themselves randomly in six consecutive seats in a row. Find the probability of each event in Exercises 53–56. (Hint: In each case the denominator of the probability fraction will be* $6! = 720$*, the total number of ways to arrange six items.)*

53. Each man will sit immediately to the left of his wife.

54. Each man will sit immediately to the left of a woman.

55. The women will be in three adjacent seats.

56. The women will be in three adjacent seats, as will the men.

57. ***Selecting Slopes*** If two distinct numbers are chosen randomly from the set $\{-2, -\frac{4}{3}, -\frac{1}{2}, 0, \frac{1}{2}, \frac{3}{4}, 3\}$, find the probability that they will be the slopes of two perpendicular lines.

58. ***Racing Bets*** At most horse-racing tracks, the "trifecta" is a particular race in which you win if you correctly pick the "win," "place," and "show" horses (the first-, second-, and third-place winners), in their proper order. If five horses of equal ability are entered in today's trifecta race, and Tracy Light selects an entry, what is the probability that she will be a winner?

59. ***Probabilities of Student Course Schedules*** Suppose you plan to take three courses next term. If you select them randomly from a listing of twelve courses, five of which are science courses, what is the probability that all three courses you select will be science courses?

60. ***Selecting Symphony Performances*** Rhonda Goedeker randomly selects three symphony performances to attend this season, choosing from a schedule of ten performances, three of which will feature works by Beethoven. Find the probability that Rhonda will select all of the Beethoven programs.

AbleStock/Thinkstock

Selecting Class Reports *Assuming that Ben, Jill, and Pam are three of the 26 members of the class, and that three of the class members will be chosen randomly to deliver their reports during the next class meeting, find the probability (to six decimal places) of each event.*

61. Ben, Jill, and Pam are selected, in that order.

62. Ben, Jill, and Pam are selected, in any order.

63. ***Random Selection of Prime Numbers*** If two distinct prime numbers are randomly selected from among the first eight prime numbers, what is the probability that their sum will be 24?

64. ***Building Numbers from Sets of Digits*** The digits 1, 2, 3, 4, and 5 are randomly arranged to form a five-digit number. Find the probability of each event.
    (a) The number is even.
    (b) The first and last digits of the number both are even.

65. ***Random Sums*** Two integers are randomly selected from the set $\{1, 2, 3, 4, 5, 6, 7, 8, 9\}$ and are added together. Find the probability that their sum is 11 if they are selected
    (a) with replacement, **(b)** without replacement.

66. ***Random Sums and Products*** Tamika selects two different numbers at random from the set $\{8, 9, 10\}$ and adds them. Carlos takes two different numbers at random from the set $\{3, 5, 6\}$ and multiplies them. What is the probability that Tamika's result is greater than Carlos's result? (*Mathematics Teacher* calendar problem)

67. ***Divisibility of Random Products*** When a fair six-sided die is tossed on a tabletop, the bottom face cannot be seen. What is the probability that the product of the numbers on the five faces that can be seen is divisible by 6? (*Mathematics Teacher* calendar problem)

68. ***Building Fractions with Dice*** Lisa has one red die and one green die, which she rolls to make up fractions. The green die is the numerator, and the red die is the denominator. Some of the fractions have terminating decimal representations. How many different terminating decimal results can these two dice represent? What is the probability of rolling a fraction with a terminating decimal representation? (*Mathematics Teacher* calendar problem)

Finding Palindromic Numbers *Numbers that are* **palindromes** *read the same forward and backward. For example,* 30203 *is a five-digit palindrome. If a single number is chosen randomly from each of the following sets, find the probability that it will be palindromic.*

69. the set of all two-digit numbers

70. the set of all three-digit numbers

Six people, call them A, B, C, D, E, and F, are randomly divided into three groups of two. Find the probability of each event. (Do not impose unwanted ordering among groups.)

71. A and B are in the same group, as are C and D.

72. E and F are in the same group.

2 EVENTS INVOLVING "NOT" AND "OR"

Properties of Probability • Events Involving "Not" • Events Involving "Or"

Properties of Probability

Recall that an empirical probability, based upon experimental observation, may be the best value available but still is only an approximation to the ("true") theoretical probability. For example, no human has ever been known to jump higher than 8.5 feet vertically, so the empirical probability of such an event is zero. Observing the rate at which high jump records have been broken, we suspect that the event is, in fact, possible and may one day occur. Hence it must have some nonzero theoretical probability, even though we have no way of assessing its exact value.

Newscom

Pierre Simon de Laplace (1749–1827) began in 1773 to solve the problem of why Jupiter's orbit seems to shrink and Saturn's orbit seems to expand. Eventually Laplace worked out a complete theory of the solar system. *Celestial Mechanics* resulted from almost a lifetime of work. In five volumes, it was published between 1799 and 1825 and gained for Laplace the reputation "Newton of France."

Laplace's work on probability was actually an adjunct to his celestial mechanics. He needed to demonstrate that probability is useful in interpreting scientific data.

Recall also that the theoretical probability formula,

$$P(E) = \frac{n(E)}{n(S)},$$

is valid only when all outcomes in the sample space S are equally likely. For the experiment of tossing two fair coins, we can write $S = \{\text{hh, ht, th, tt}\}$ and compute

$$P(\text{both heads}) = \frac{1}{4}, \qquad \text{which is } \textit{correct},$$

whereas if we define the sample space with non-equally likely outcomes as $S = \{\text{both heads, both tails, one of each}\}$, we are led to

$$P(\text{both heads}) = \frac{1}{3}, \qquad \text{which is } \textit{incorrect}.$$

(To convince yourself that $\frac{1}{4}$ is a better value than $\frac{1}{3}$, toss two fair coins 100 times or so to see what the empirical fraction seems to approach.)

For any event E within a sample space S, we know that $0 \le n(E) \le n(S)$. Dividing all members of this inequality by $n(S)$ gives

$$\frac{0}{n(S)} \le \frac{n(E)}{n(S)} \le \frac{n(S)}{n(S)}, \quad \text{or} \quad \mathbf{0 \le P(E) \le 1.}$$

In words, the probability of any event is a number from 0 through 1, inclusive.

If event E is *impossible* (cannot happen), then $n(E)$ must be 0 (E is the empty set), so $P(E) = 0$. If event E is *certain* (cannot help but happen), then $n(E) = n(S)$, so

$$P(E) = \frac{n(E)}{n(S)} = \frac{n(S)}{n(S)} = 1.$$

Properties of Probability

Let E be an event within the sample space S. That is, E is a subset of S. Then the following properties hold.

1. $\mathbf{0 \le P(E) \le 1}$ (The probability of an event is a number from 0 through 1, inclusive.)
2. $\mathbf{P(\emptyset) = 0}$ (The probability of an impossible event is 0.)
3. $\mathbf{P(S) = 1}$ (The probability of a certain event is 1.)

EXAMPLE 1 Finding Probability When Rolling a Die

When a single fair die is rolled, find the probability of each event.

(a) the number 2 is rolled **(b)** a number other than 2 is rolled

(c) the number 7 is rolled **(d)** a number less than 7 is rolled

SOLUTION

(a) Since one of the six possibilities is a 2, $P(2) = \frac{1}{6}$.

(b) There are five such numbers, 1, 3, 4, 5, and 6, so $P(\text{a number other than 2}) = \frac{5}{6}$.

(c) None of the possible outcomes is 7. Thus, $P(7) = \frac{0}{6} = 0$.

(d) Since all six of the possible outcomes are less than 7,

$$P(\text{a number less than 7}) = \frac{6}{6} = 1.$$

No probability in **Example 1** was less than 0 or greater than 1, which illustrates probability property 1. The "impossible" event of part (c) had probability 0, illustrating property 2. The "certain" event of part (d) had probability 1, illustrating property 3.

Events Involving "Not"

Table 4 look at these correspondences are the basis for the probability rules. For example, the probability of an event *not* happening involves the *complement* and *subtraction,* according to row 1 of the table.

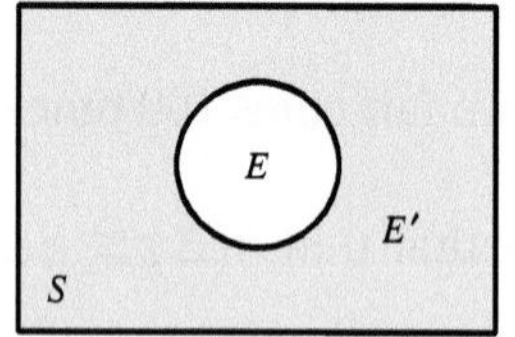

The logical connective "not" corresponds to "complement" in set theory.

$P(\text{not } E) = P(S) - P(E)$
$= 1 - P(E)$

Figure 4

Table 4 Set Theory/Logic/Arithmetic Correspondences

	Set Theory	Logic	Arithmetic
1. Operation or Connective (Symbol)	Complement (′)	Not (~)	Subtraction (−)
2. Operation or Connective (Symbol)	Union (∪)	Or (∨)	Addition (+)
3. Operation or Connective (Symbol)	Intersection (∩)	And (∧)	Multiplication (·)

The rule for the probability of a complement follows and is illustrated in **Figure 4.**

Probability of a Complement (for Not *E*)

The probability that an event *E* will *not* occur is equal to one minus the probability that it *will* occur.

$$P(\textbf{not } E) = 1 - P(E)$$

Notice that the events of **Examples 1(a) and (b),** namely "2" and "not 2," are complements of one another, and that their probabilities add up to 1. This illustrates the above probability rule. The equation

$$P(E) + P(E') = 1$$

is a rearrangement of the formula for the probability of a complement. Another form of the equation that is also useful at times follows.

$$P(E) = 1 - P(E')$$

EXAMPLE 2 Finding the Probability of a Complement

When a single card is drawn from a standard 52-card deck, what is the probability that it will not be a king?

SOLUTION

$$P(\text{not a king}) = 1 - P(\text{king}) = 1 - \frac{4}{52} = \frac{48}{52} = \frac{12}{13}$$

Remember to write in lowest terms.

EXAMPLE 3 Finding the Probability of a Complement

If five fair coins are tossed, find the probability of obtaining at least two heads.

SOLUTION

There are $2^5 = 32$ possible outcomes for the experiment of tossing five fair coins. Most include at least two heads. In fact, only the outcomes

tttt, htttt, thttt, tthtt, tttht, and tttth

do *not* include at least two heads. If E denotes the event "at least two heads," then E' is the event "not at least two heads,"

$$P(E) = 1 - P(E') = 1 - \frac{6}{32} = \frac{26}{32} = \frac{13}{16}$$

Photos/Thinkstock

Mary Somerville (1780–1872) is associated with Laplace because of her brilliant exposition of his *Celestial Mechanics.*

Somerville studied Euclid thoroughly and perfected her Latin so she could read Newton's *Principia.* In about 1816 she went to London and soon became part of its literary and scientific circles.

Somerville's book on Laplace's theories came out in 1831 with great acclaim. Then followed a panoramic book, *Connection of the Physical Sciences* (1834). A statement in one of its editions suggested that irregularities in the orbit of Uranus might indicate that a more remote planet, not yet seen, existed. This caught the eye of the scientists who worked out the calculations for Neptune's orbit.

Events Involving "Or"

Examples 2 and 3 showed how the probability of an event can be approached *indirectly,* by first considering the complement of the event. Another indirect approach is to break the event into simpler component events. Row 2 of **Table 4** indicates that the probability of one event *or* another should involve the *union* and *addition.*

EXAMPLE 4 Selecting From a Set of Numbers

If one number is selected randomly from the set $\{1, 2, 3, 4, 5, 6, 7, 8, 9, 10\}$, find the probability that it will be

(a) odd or a multiple of 4 **(b)** odd or a multiple of 3.

SOLUTION

Define the following events:

$S = \{1, 2, 3, 4, 5, 6, 7, 8, 9, 10\}$ Sample space

$A = \{1, 3, 5, 7, 9\}$ Odd outcomes

$B = \{4, 8\}$ Multiples of 4

$C = \{3, 6, 9\}$ Multiples of 3

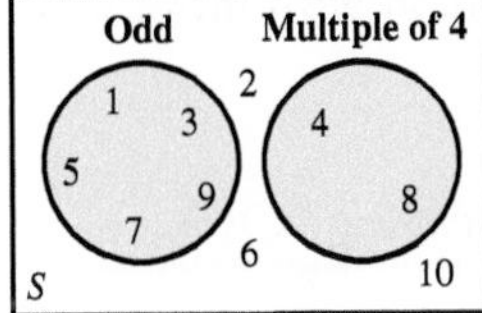

Figure 5

(a) Figure 5 shows the positioning of the 10 integers within the sample space and within the pertinent sets A and B. The composite event "A or B" corresponds to the set $A \cup B = \{1, 3, 4, 5, 7, 8, 9\}$. By the theoretical probability formula,

$$P(A \text{ or } B) = \frac{7}{10}.$$ Of 10 total outcomes, 7 are favorable.

(b) Figure 6 shows the situation.

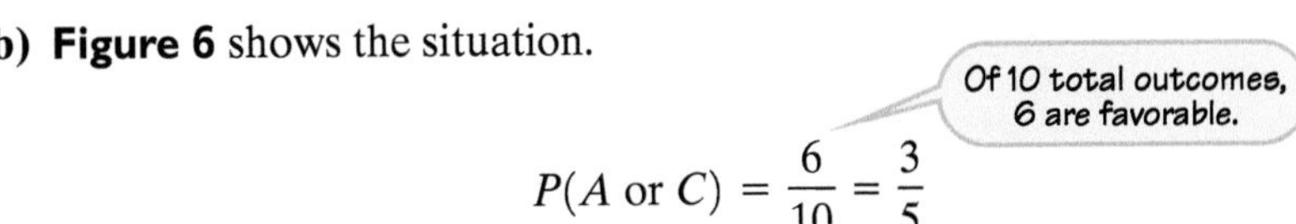

$$P(A \text{ or } C) = \frac{6}{10} = \frac{3}{5}$$

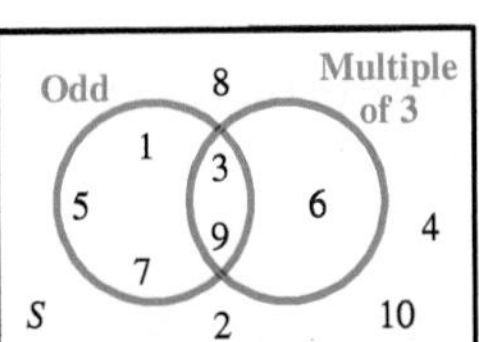

Figure 6

Would an addition formula have worked in **Example 4**? Let's check.

Part (a): $P(A \text{ or } B) = P(A) + P(B) = \frac{5}{10} + \frac{2}{10} = \frac{7}{10}$ Correct

Part (b): $P(A \text{ or } C) = P(A) + P(C) = \frac{5}{10} + \frac{3}{10} = \frac{8}{10} = \frac{4}{5}$ Incorrect

The trouble in part (b) is that A and C are not disjoint sets. They have outcomes in common. Just as with the additive counting principle, an adjustment must be made here to compensate for counting the common outcomes twice.

$$P(A \text{ or } C) = P(A) + P(C) - P(A \text{ and } C)$$
$$= \frac{5}{10} + \frac{3}{10} - \frac{2}{10} = \frac{6}{10} = \frac{3}{5} \quad \text{Correct}$$

In probability theory, events that are disjoint sets are called *mutually exclusive events.*

Mutually Exclusive Events

Two events A and B are **mutually exclusive events** if they have no outcomes in common. (Mutually exclusive events cannot occur simultaneously.)

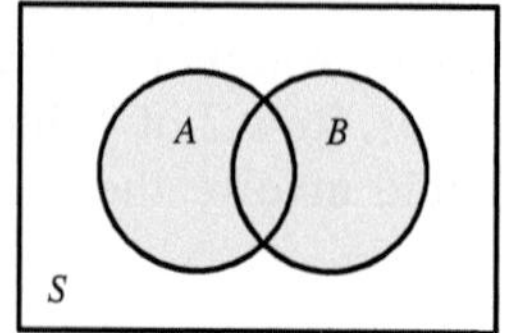

The logical connective "or" corresponds to "union" in set theory.

$P(A \text{ or } B)$
$= P(A) + P(B) - P(A \text{ and } B)$

Figure 7

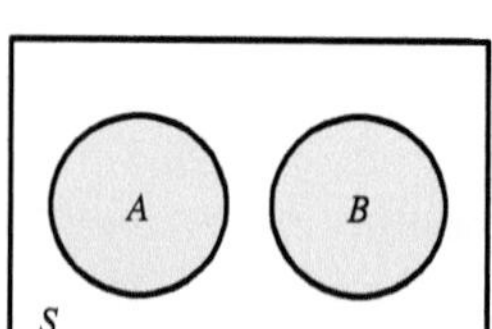

When A and B are mutually exclusive, $P(A \text{ or } B) = P(A) + P(B)$.

Figure 8

The results observed in **Example 4** are generalized as follows. The two possibilities are illustrated in **Figures 7 and 8**.

Addition Rule of Probability (for A or B)

If A and B are any two events, then

$$P(A \text{ or } B) = P(A) + P(B) - P(A \text{ and } B).$$

If A and B are mutually exclusive, then

$$P(A \text{ or } B) = P(A) + P(B).$$

Actually, the first formula in the addition rule applies in all cases. (The third term on the right drops out when A and B are mutually exclusive, because $P(A \text{ and } B) = 0$.) Still it is good to remember the second formula in the preceding box for the many cases where the component events are mutually exclusive. In this section, we consider only cases where the event "A and B" is simple. We deal with more involved composites involving "and" in the next section.

EXAMPLE 5 Finding the Probability of an Event Involving "Or"

If a single card is drawn from a standard 52-card deck, what is the probability that it will be a spade or a red card?

SOLUTION

First note that "spade" and "red" cannot both occur, because there are no red spades. (All spades are black.) Therefore, we can use the formula for mutually exclusive events. There are 13 spades and 26 red cards in the deck.

$$P(\text{spade or red}) = P(\text{spade}) + P(\text{red}) = \frac{13}{52} + \frac{26}{52} = \frac{39}{52} = \frac{3}{4}$$

We often need to consider composites of more than two events. When each event involved is mutually exclusive of all the others, we extend the addition rule to the appropriate number of components.

EXAMPLE 6 Treating Unions of Several Components

Amy Hogan plans to spend from 1 to 6 hours on her homework. If x represents the number of hours to be spent, then the probabilities of the various values of x, rounded to the nearest hour, are shown in **Table 5**. Find the probabilities that Amy will spend

Table 5

x	$P(x)$
1	0.05
2	0.10
3	0.20
4	0.40
5	0.10
6	0.15

(a) fewer than 3 hours

(b) more than 2 hours

(c) more than 1 but no more than 5 hours

(d) fewer than 5 hours.

SOLUTION

Because the time periods in **Table 5** are mutually exclusive of one another, we can simply add the appropriate component probabilities.

(a)
$$\begin{aligned} P(\text{fewer than } 3) &= P(1 \text{ or } 2) && \text{Fewer than 3 means 1 or 2.} \\ &= P(1) + P(2) && \text{Addition rule} \\ &= 0.05 + 0.10 && \text{Substitute values from Table 5.} \\ &= 0.15 \end{aligned}$$

(b)
$$\begin{aligned} P(\text{more than } 2) &= P(3 \text{ or } 4 \text{ or } 5 \text{ or } 6) && \text{More than 2 means 3, 4, 5, or 6.} \\ &= P(3) + P(4) + P(5) + P(6) && \text{Addition rule} \\ &= 0.20 + 0.40 + 0.10 + 0.15 && \text{Substitute values from Table 5.} \\ &= 0.85 \end{aligned}$$

(c) $P(\text{more than 1 but no more than 5})$
$$\begin{aligned} &= P(2 \text{ or } 3 \text{ or } 4 \text{ or } 5) && \text{2, 3, 4, and 5 are more than 1 and no more than 5.} \\ &= P(2) + P(3) + P(4) + P(5) && \text{Addition rule} \\ &= 0.10 + 0.20 + 0.40 + 0.10 && \text{Substitute values from Table 5.} \\ &= 0.80 \end{aligned}$$

(d) Although we could take a direct approach here, as in parts (a), (b), and (c), we will combine the complement rule with the addition rule.

$$\begin{aligned} P(\text{fewer than } 5) &= 1 - P(\text{not fewer than } 5) && \text{Complement rule} \\ &= 1 - P(5 \text{ or more}) && \text{5 or more is equivalent to not fewer than 5.} \\ &= 1 - P(5 \text{ or } 6) && \text{5 or more means 5 or 6.} \\ &= 1 - [P(5) + P(6)] && \text{Addition rule} \\ &= 1 - (0.10 + 0.15) && \text{Substitute values from Table 5.} \\ &= 1 - 0.25 && \text{Add inside the parentheses first.} \\ &= 0.75 \end{aligned}$$

Table 5 in **Example 6** lists all possible time intervals so the corresponding probabilities add up to 1, a necessary condition for the way part (d) was done. The time spent on homework here is an example of a **random variable.** (It is "random" since we cannot predict which of its possible values will occur.)

A listing like **Table 5**, which shows all possible values of a random variable, along with the probabilities that those values will occur, is called a **probability distribution** for that random variable. Since *all* possible values are listed, they make up the entire sample space, and so the listed probabilities must add up to 1 (by probability property 3). Probability distributions will occur in **Exercises 32 and 33** of this section and will be discussed further in later sections.

EXAMPLE 7 Finding the Probability of an Event Involving "Or"

Find the probability that a single card drawn from a standard 52-card deck will be a diamond or a face card.

SOLUTION

The component events "diamond" and "face card" can occur simultaneously. (The jack, queen, and king of diamonds belong to both events.) So, we must use the first formula of the addition rule. We let D denote "diamond" and F denote "face card."

$$P(D \text{ or } F) = P(D) + P(F) - P(D \text{ and } F) \quad \text{Addition rule}$$

$$= \frac{13}{52} + \frac{12}{52} - \frac{3}{52} \quad \text{There are 13 diamonds, 12 face cards, and 3 that are both.}$$

$$= \frac{22}{52} \quad \text{Add and subtract.}$$

$$= \frac{11}{26} \quad \text{Write in lowest terms.}$$

EXAMPLE 8 Finding the Probability of an Event Involving "Or"

Of 20 elective courses, Emily Horowitz plans to enroll in one, which she will choose by throwing a dart at the schedule of courses. If 8 of the courses are recreational, 9 are interesting, and 3 are both recreational and interesting, find the probability that the course Emily chooses will have at least one of these two attributes.

SOLUTION

If R denotes "recreational" and I denotes "interesting," then $P(R) = \frac{8}{20}$, $P(I) = \frac{9}{20}$, and $P(R \text{ and } I) = \frac{3}{20}$. R and I are not mutually exclusive.

$$P(R \text{ or } I) = \frac{8}{20} + \frac{9}{20} - \frac{3}{20} = \frac{14}{20} = \frac{7}{10} \quad \text{Addition rule; lowest terms}$$

2 EXERCISES

1. ***Determining Whether Events Are Mutually Exclusive*** Amanda Crotts has three office assistants. If A is the event that at least two of them are men and B is the event that at least two of them are women, are A and B mutually exclusive?

2. ***Determining Whether Events Are Mutually Exclusive*** Jeanne Jalufka earned her college degree several years ago. Consider the following four events.

   Her alma mater is in the East.
   Her alma mater is a private college.
   Her alma mater is in the Northwest.
   Her alma mater is in the South.

   Are these events all mutually exclusive of one another?

3. Explain the difference between the two formulas in the addition rule of probability on **page 592,** illustrating each one with an appropriate example.

Probabilities for Rolling a Die *For the experiment of rolling a single fair die, find the probability of each event.*

4. not less than 2
5. not prime
6. odd or less than 5
7. even or prime
8. odd or even
9. less than 3 or greater than 4

Probability and Odds for Drawing a Card *For the experiment of drawing a single card from a standard 52-card deck, find* **(a)** *the probability, and* **(b)** *the odds in favor, of each event.*

10. not an ace
11. king or queen
12. club or heart
13. spade or face card

14. not a heart, or a 7

15. neither a heart nor a 7

Number Sums for Rolling a Pair of Dice *For the experiment of rolling an ordinary pair of dice, find the probability that the sum will be each of the following. (You may want to use a table showing the sum for each of the 36 equally likely outcomes.)*

16. 11 or 12

17. even or a multiple of 3

18. odd or greater than 9

19. less than 3 or greater than 9

20. Find the probability of getting a prime number in each case.

(a) A number is chosen randomly from the set $\{1, 2, 3, 4, \ldots, 12\}$.

(b) Two dice are rolled and the sum is observed.

21. Suppose, for a given experiment, A, B, C, and D are events, all mutually exclusive of one another, such that $A \cup B \cup C \cup D = S$ (the sample space). By extending the addition rule of probability to this case, and utilizing probability property 3, what statement can you make?

Probabilities of Poker Hands *If you are dealt a 5-card hand (this implies without replacement) from a standard 52-card deck, find the probability of getting each of the following. Refer to* **Table 1** *of* ***Section 1,*** *and give answers to six decimal places.*

22. a flush or three of a kind

23. a full house or a straight

24. a black flush or two pairs

25. nothing any better than two pairs

Probabilities in Golf Scoring *The table gives golfer Brian Donahue's probabilities of scoring in various ranges on a par-70 course. In a given round, find the probability of each event in Exercises 26–30.*

26. 95 or higher

27. par or above

28. in the 80s

29. less than 90

30. not in the 70s, 80s, or 90s

31. What are the odds of Brian's scoring below par?

x	$P(x)$
Below 60	0.04
60–64	0.06
65–69	0.14
70–74	0.30
75–79	0.23
80–84	0.09
85–89	0.06
90–94	0.04
95–99	0.03
100 or above	0.01

32. ***Drawing Balls from an Urn*** Anne Kelly randomly chooses a single ball from the urn shown here, and x represents the color of the ball chosen. Construct a complete probability distribution for the random variable x.

33. Let x denote the sum of two distinct numbers selected randomly from the set $\{1, 2, 3, 4, 5\}$. Construct the probability distribution for the random variable x.

34. ***Comparing Empirical and Theoretical Probabilities for Rolling Dice*** Roll a pair of dice 50 times, keeping track of the number of times the sum is "less than 3 or greater than 9" (that is 2, 10, 11, or 12).

(a) From your results, calculate an empirical probability for the event "less than 3 or greater than 9."

(b) By how much does your answer differ from the *theoretical* probability of **Exercise 19?**

For Exercises 35–38, let A be an event within the sample space S, and let $n(A) = a$ and $n(S) = s$.

35. Use the complements principle of counting to find an expression for $n(A')$.

36. Use the theoretical probability formula to express $P(A)$ and $P(A')$.

37. Evaluate, and simplify, $P(A) + P(A')$.

38. What rule have you proved?

The remaining exercises require careful thought for the determination of $n(E)$ and $n(S)$. (In some cases, you may want to employ counting methods, such as the fundamental counting principle, permutations, or combinations.)

Building Numbers from Sets of Digits *Suppose we want to form three-digit numbers using the set of digits*

$$\{0, 1, 2, 3, 4, 5\}.$$

For example, 501 and 224 are such numbers but 035 is not.

39. How many such numbers are possible?

40. How many of these numbers are multiples of 5?

41. If one three-digit number is chosen at random from all those that can be made from the above set of digits, find the probability that the one chosen is not a multiple of 5.

42. ***Multiplying Numbers Generated by Spinners*** An experiment consists of spinning both spinners shown here and multiplying the resulting numbers together. Find the probability that the resulting product will be even.

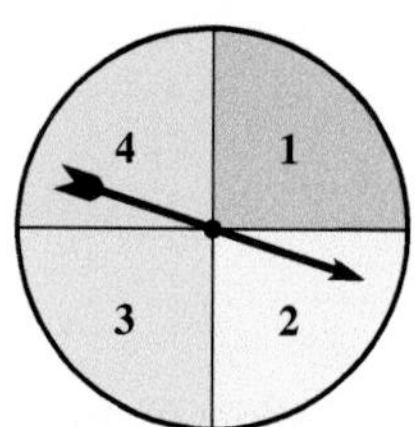

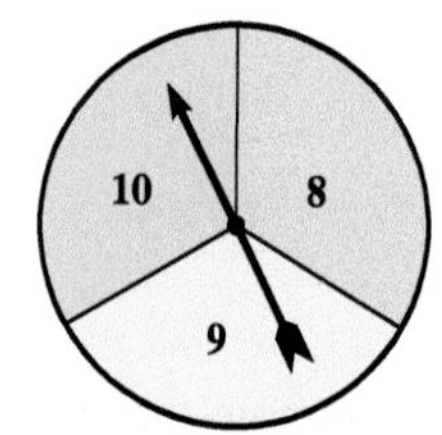

43. ***Drawing Colored Marbles from Boxes*** A bag contains fifty blue and fifty green marbles. Two marbles at a time are randomly selected. If both are green, they are placed in box A; if both are blue, in box B; if one is green and the other is blue, in box C. After all marbles are drawn, what is the probability that the numbers of marbles in box A and box B are the same? (*Mathematics Teacher* calendar problem)

44. ***Random Births on the Same Day of the Week*** What is the probability that, of three people selected at random, at least two were born on the same day of the week? (*Mathematics Teacher* calendar problem)

3 CONDITIONAL PROBABILITY; EVENTS INVOLVING "AND"

Conditional Probability • Events Involving "And"

Beth Anderson

Even **a rare occurrence** can sometimes cause widespread controversy. When Mattel Toys marketed a new talking Barbie doll a few years ago, some of the Barbies were programmed to say "Math class is tough." The National Council of Teachers of Mathematics (NCTM), the American Association of University Women (AAUW), and numerous consumers voiced complaints about the damage such a message could do to the self-confidence of children and to their attitudes toward school and mathematics. Mattel subsequently agreed to erase the phrase from the microchip to be used in future doll production.

Each Barbie was programmed to say four different statements, randomly selected from a pool of 270 prerecorded statements. Therefore, the probability of getting one that said "Math class is tough" was only

$$\frac{1 \cdot {}_{269}C_3}{{}_{270}C_4} \approx 0.015.$$

Other messages included in the pool were "I love school, don't you?," "I'm studying to be a doctor," and "Let's study for the quiz."

Conditional Probability

Sometimes the probability of an event must be computed using the knowledge that some other event has happened (or is happening, or will happen—the timing is not important). This type of probability is called *conditional probability*.

Conditional Probability

The probability of event B, computed on the assumption that event A has happened, is called the **conditional probability of B given A**, and is denoted

$$P(B|A).$$

EXAMPLE 1 Selecting from a Set of Numbers

From the sample space $S = \{1, 2, 3, 4, 5, 6, 7, 8, 9, 10\}$, a single number is to be selected randomly. Find each probability given the events

A: The selected number is odd, and B: The selected number is a multiple of 3.

(a) $P(B)$ **(b)** $P(A \text{ and } B)$ **(c)** $P(B|A)$

SOLUTION

(a) $B = \{3, 6, 9\}$, so $P(B) = \frac{n(B)}{n(S)} = \frac{3}{10}$.

(b) A and B is the set $A \cap B = \{1, 3, 5, 7, 9\} \cap \{3, 6, 9\} = \{3, 9\}$.

$$P(A \text{ and } B) = \frac{n(A \cap B)}{n(S)} = \frac{2}{10} = \frac{1}{5}$$

(c) The given condition, that A occurs, effectively reduces the sample space from S to A, and the elements of the new sample space A that are also in B are the elements of $A \cap B$.

$$P(B|A) = \frac{n(A \cap B)}{n(A)} = \frac{2}{5}$$

Walter G. Arce/Shutterstock

A **cosmic impact,** the collision of a meteor, comet, or asteroid with Earth, could be as catastrophic as full-scale nuclear war, killing a billion or more people. The Web site www.impact.arc.nasa.gov reports that a large enough object (1 kilometer or more in diameter) could even put the human species at risk of annihilation by causing drastic climate changes and destroying food crops.

The Spaceguard Survey has discovered more than half of the estimated number of near-Earth asteroids (NEAs) in this size range and hopes to locate 90% of them in the next decade. Although the risk of finding one on a collision course with the Earth is slight, it is anticipated that, if we did, we would be able to deflect it before impact.

The photo above shows a crater in Arizona, 4000 feet in diameter and 570 feet deep, thought to have been formed 20,000 to 50,000 years ago by a meteorite about 50 meters across, hitting the ground at several kilometers per second. (See http://en.wikipedia.org/wiki/Meteor_Crater.)

Example 1 illustrates some important points. First, because

$$\frac{n(A \cap B)}{n(A)} = \frac{\frac{n(A \cap B)}{n(S)}}{\frac{n(A)}{n(S)}} \qquad \text{Multiply numerator and denominator by } \tfrac{1}{n(S)}.$$

$$= \frac{P(A \cap B)}{P(A)}, \qquad \text{Theoretical probability formula}$$

the final line of the example gives the following convenient formula.

Conditional Probability Formula

The **conditional probability of *B* given *A*** is calculated as follows.

$$P(B|A) = \frac{P(A \cap B)}{P(A)} = \frac{P(A \text{ and } B)}{P(A)}$$

A second observation from **Example 1** is that the conditional probability of B, given A, was $\frac{2}{5}$, whereas the "unconditional" probability of B (with no condition given) was $\frac{3}{10}$, so the condition did make a difference.

EXAMPLE 2 Finding Probabilities of Boys and Girls in a Family

Given a family with two children, find the probabilities that

(a) both are girls, given that at least one is a girl, and

(b) both are girls, given that the older child is a girl.

(Assume boys and girls are equally likely.)

SOLUTION

We define the following events.

$$S = \{\text{gg, gb, bg, bb}\} \qquad \text{Sample space}$$
$$A = \{\text{gg}\} \qquad \text{Both are girls.}$$
$$B = \{\text{gg, gb, bg}\} \qquad \text{At least one is a girl.}$$
$$C = \{\text{gg, gb}\} \qquad \text{The older one is a girl.}$$

Note that $A \cap B = \{\text{gg}\}$.

(a) $P(A|B) = \dfrac{P(A \text{ and } B)}{P(B)} = \dfrac{\frac{1}{4}}{\frac{3}{4}} = \dfrac{1}{4} \div \dfrac{3}{4} = \dfrac{1}{4} \cdot \dfrac{4}{3} = \dfrac{1}{3}$

(b) $P(A|C) = \dfrac{P(A \text{ and } C)}{P(C)} = \dfrac{\frac{1}{4}}{\frac{2}{4}} = \dfrac{1}{4} \div \dfrac{2}{4} = \dfrac{1}{4} \cdot \dfrac{4}{2} = \dfrac{1}{2}$ ∎

Sometimes a conditional probability is no different than the corresponding unconditional probability, in which case we call the two events *independent.*

Independent Events

Two events A and B are called **independent events** if knowledge about the occurrence of one of them has no effect on the probability of the other one, that is, if

$$P(B|A) = P(B), \quad \text{or, equivalently,} \quad P(A|B) = P(A).$$

EXAMPLE 3 Checking Events for Independence

A single card is to be drawn from a standard 52-card deck. (The sample space S has 52 elements.) Given the events

A: The selected card is a face card, and B: The selected card is black,

(a) Find $P(B)$.

(b) Find $P(B|A)$.

(c) Determine whether events A and B are independent.

SOLUTION

(a) There are 26 black cards in the 52-card deck.

$$P(B) = \frac{26}{52} = \frac{1}{2} \quad \text{Theoretical probability formula}$$

(b)
$$\begin{aligned} P(B|A) &= \frac{P(B \text{ and } A)}{P(A)} && \text{Conditional probability formula} \\ &= \frac{\frac{6}{52}}{\frac{12}{52}} && \text{Of 52 cards, 12 are face cards and 6 are black face cards.} \\ &= \frac{6}{52} \cdot \frac{52}{12} && \text{To divide, multiply by the reciprocal.} \\ &= \frac{1}{2} && \text{Calculate and write in lowest terms.} \end{aligned}$$

(c) Because $P(B|A) = P(B)$, events A and B are independent. ∎

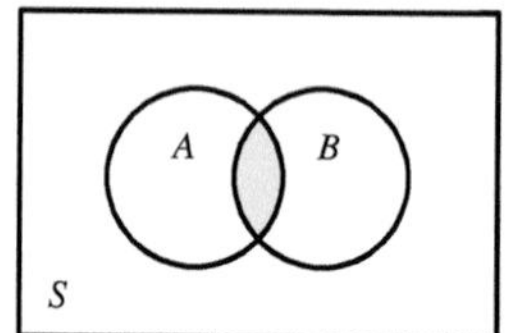

The logical connective "and" corresponds to "intersection" in set theory.

$P(A \text{ and } B) = P(A) \cdot P(B|A)$

Figure 9

Events Involving "And"

If we multiply both sides of the conditional probability formula by $P(A)$, we obtain an expression for $P(A \cap B)$, which applies to events of the form "A and B." The resulting formula is related to the fundamental counting principle. It is illustrated in **Figure 9.**

Just as the calculation of $P(A \text{ or } B)$ is simpler when A and B are mutually exclusive, the calculation of $P(A \text{ and } B)$ is simpler when A and B are independent.

Multiplication Rule of Probability (for A and B)

If A and B are any two events, then

$$P(A \text{ and } B) = P(A) \cdot P(B|A).$$

If A and B are independent, then

$$P(A \text{ and } B) = P(A) \cdot P(B).$$

The first formula in the multiplication rule actually applies in all cases. ($P(B|A) = P(B)$ when A and B are independent.) Still, the independence of the component events is clear in many cases, so it is good to remember the second formula as well.

EXAMPLE 4 Selecting from a Set of Books

Each year, Jacqui Carper adds to her book collection a number of new publications that she believes will be of lasting value and interest. She has categorized each of her twenty acquisitions for 2011 as hardcover or paperback and as fiction or nonfiction. The numbers of books in the various categories are shown in **Table 6.**

Table 6 Year 2011 Books

	Fiction (F)	Nonfiction (N)	Totals
Hardcover (H)	3	5	8
Paperback (P)	8	4	12
Totals	11	9	20

If Jacqui randomly chooses one of these 20 books, find the probability it will be

(a) hardcover, **(b)** fiction, given it is hardcover, **(c)** hardcover and fiction.

SOLUTION

(a) Eight of the 20 books are hardcover, so $P(H) = \frac{8}{20} = \frac{2}{5}$.

(b) The given condition that the book is hardcover reduces the sample space to eight books. Of those eight, just three are fiction, so $P(F|H) = \frac{3}{8}$.

(c) $P(H \text{ and } F) = P(H) \cdot P(F|H) = \frac{2}{5} \cdot \frac{3}{8} = \frac{3}{20}$ Multiplication rule

It is easier here if we simply notice, directly from **Table 6**, that 3 of the 20 books are "hardcover and fiction." This verifies that the general multiplication rule of probability did give us the correct answer.

EXAMPLE 5 Selecting from a Set of Planets

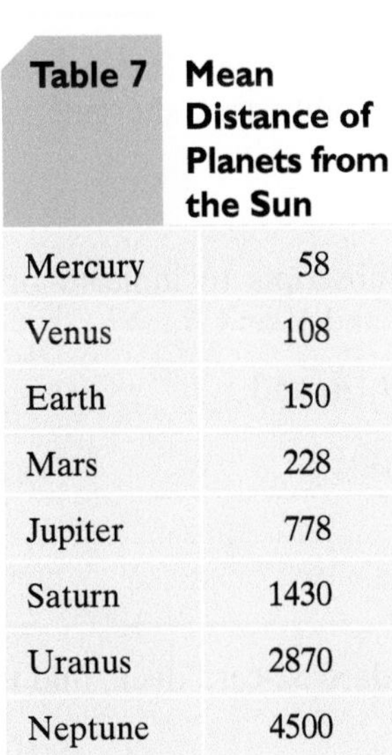

Table 7 Mean Distance of Planets from the Sun

Mercury	58
Venus	108
Earth	150
Mars	228
Jupiter	778
Saturn	1430
Uranus	2870
Neptune	4500

Table 7 lists the eight planets of our solar system together with their mean distances from the sun, in millions of kilometers. (Data is from *The World Almanac and Book of Facts 2010.*) Carrie Ayers must choose two distinct planets to cover in her astronomy report. If she selects randomly, find the probability that the first one selected is closer to the sun than Mars and the second is closer than Saturn.

SOLUTION

We define the events

A: The first is closer than Mars, and B: The second is closer than Saturn.

Then $P(A) = \frac{3}{8}$. (Three of the original eight choices are favorable.) If the planet selected first is closer than Mars, it is also closer than Saturn, and since that planet is no longer available, $P(B|A) = \frac{4}{7}$. (Four of the remaining seven are favorable.)

$$P(A \text{ and } B) = P(A) \cdot P(B|A) = \frac{3}{8} \cdot \frac{4}{7} = \frac{3}{14} \approx 0.214 \quad \text{Multiplication rule}$$

In **Example 5,** the condition that A had occurred changed the probability of B, since the selection was done, in effect, without replacement. (Repetitions were not allowed.) Events A and B were not independent. On the other hand, in the next example, the same events, A and B, will be independent.

EXAMPLE 6 Selecting from a Set of Planets

Carrie must again select two planets, but this time one is for an oral report, the other is for a written report, and they need not be distinct. (The same planet may be selected for both reports.) Again find the probability that, if she selects randomly, the first is closer than Mars and the second is closer than Saturn.

SOLUTION

Defining events A and B as in **Example 5,** we have $P(A) = \frac{3}{8}$, just as before. But the selection is now done *with* replacement. (Repetitions *are* allowed.) Event B is independent of event A, so we can use the second form of the multiplication rule.

$$P(A \text{ and } B) = P(A) \cdot P(B) = \frac{3}{8} \cdot \frac{5}{8} = \frac{15}{64} \approx 0.234$$

Answer is different than in **Example 5.**

EXAMPLE 7 Selecting from a Deck of Cards

A single card is drawn from a standard 52-card deck. Let B denote the event that the card is black, and let D denote the event that it is a diamond. Are events B and D

(a) independent? **(b)** mutually exclusive?

SOLUTION

(a) For the unconditional probability of D, we get $P(D) = \frac{13}{52} = \frac{1}{4}$. (Thirteen of the 52 cards are diamonds.) But for the conditional probability of D, given B, we have $P(D|B) = \frac{0}{26} = 0$. (None of the 26 black cards are diamonds.) Since the conditional probability $P(D|B)$ is different than the unconditional probability $P(D)$, B and D are not independent.

(b) Mutually exclusive events are events that cannot both occur for a given performance of an experiment. Since no card in the deck is both black and a diamond, B and D are mutually exclusive.

EXAMPLE 8 Selecting from an Urn of Balls

Anne is still drawing balls from the same urn (shown at the side). This time she draws three balls, without replacement. Find the probability that she gets red, yellow, and blue balls, in that order.

SOLUTION

Using appropriate letters to denote the colors, and subscripts to indicate first, second, and third draws, the event can be symbolized R_1 and Y_2 and B_3.

$$P(R_1 \text{ and } Y_2 \text{ and } B_3) = P(R_1) \cdot P(Y_2|R_1) \cdot P(B_3|R_1 \text{ and } Y_2)$$
$$= \frac{4}{11} \cdot \frac{5}{10} \cdot \frac{2}{9} = \frac{4}{99} \approx 0.0404$$

EXAMPLE 9 Selecting from a Deck of Cards

If five cards are drawn without replacement from a standard 52-card deck, find the probability that they all are hearts.

SOLUTION

Each time a heart is drawn, the number of available cards decreases by one and the number of hearts decreases by one.

$$P(\text{all hearts}) = \frac{13}{52} \cdot \frac{12}{51} \cdot \frac{11}{50} \cdot \frac{10}{49} \cdot \frac{9}{48} = \frac{33}{66{,}640} \approx 0.000495$$

The **search for extraterrestrial intelligence (SETI)** may have begun in earnest as early as 1961 when Dr. Frank Drake presented an equation for estimating the number of possible civilizations in the Milky Way galaxy whose communications we might detect. Over the years, the effort has been advanced by many scientists, including the late astronomer and exobiologist Carl Sagan, who popularized the issue in TV appearances and in his book *The Cosmic Connection: An Extraterrestrial Perspective* (Dell Paperback). "There must be other starfolk," said Sagan. In fact, some astronomers have estimated the odds against life on Earth being the only life in the universe at one hundred billion billion to one.

Other experts disagree. Freeman Dyson, a noted mathematical physicist and astronomer, says in his book *Disturbing the Universe* that after considering the same evidence and arguments, he believes it is just as likely as not (even odds) that there never was any other intelligent life out there.

Giovanni Benintende/ Shutterstock

If you studied counting methods, you may prefer to solve the problem of **Example 9** by using the theoretical probability formula and combinations. The total possible number of 5-card hands, drawn without replacement, is ${}_{52}C_5$, and the number of those containing only hearts is ${}_{13}C_5$.

$$P(\text{all hearts}) = \frac{{}_{13}C_5}{{}_{52}C_5} = \frac{\frac{13!}{5!8!}}{\frac{52!}{5!47!}} \approx 0.000495 \quad \text{Use a calculator.}$$

EXAMPLE 10 Using Both Addition and Multiplication Rules

The local garage employs two mechanics, Arnie and Burt. Your consumer club has found that Arnie does twice as many jobs as Burt, Arnie does a good job three out of four times, and Burt does a good job only two out of five times. If you plan to take your car in for repairs, find the probability that a good job will be done.

SOLUTION

We define the events

A: work done by Arnie; B: work done by Burt; G: good job done.

Since Arnie does twice as many jobs as Burt, the (unconditional) probabilities of events A and B are, respectively, $\frac{2}{3}$ and $\frac{1}{3}$. Since Arnie does a good job three out of four times, the probability of a good job, given that Arnie did the work, is $\frac{3}{4}$. And since Burt does well two out of five times, the probability of a good job, given that Burt did the work, is $\frac{2}{5}$. (These last two probabilities are conditional.) These four values can be summarized.

$$P(A) = \frac{2}{3}, \quad P(B) = \frac{1}{3}, \quad P(G|A) = \frac{3}{4}, \quad \text{and} \quad P(G|B) = \frac{2}{5}.$$

Event G can occur in two mutually exclusive ways: Arnie could do the work and do a good job $(A \cap G)$, or Burt could do the work and do a good job $(B \cap G)$.

$$\begin{aligned} P(G) &= P(A \cap G) + P(B \cap G) && \text{Addition rule} \\ &= P(A) \cdot P(G|A) + P(B) \cdot P(G|B) && \text{Multiplication rule} \\ &= \frac{2}{3} \cdot \frac{3}{4} + \frac{1}{3} \cdot \frac{2}{5} && \text{Substitute the values.} \\ &= \frac{1}{2} + \frac{2}{15} = \frac{19}{30} \approx 0.633 \end{aligned}$$

Multiply first, then add.

The tree diagram in **Figure 10** shows a graphical way to organize the work of **Example 10.** Use the given information to draw the tree diagram, then find the probability of a good job by adding the probabilities from the indicated branches of the tree.

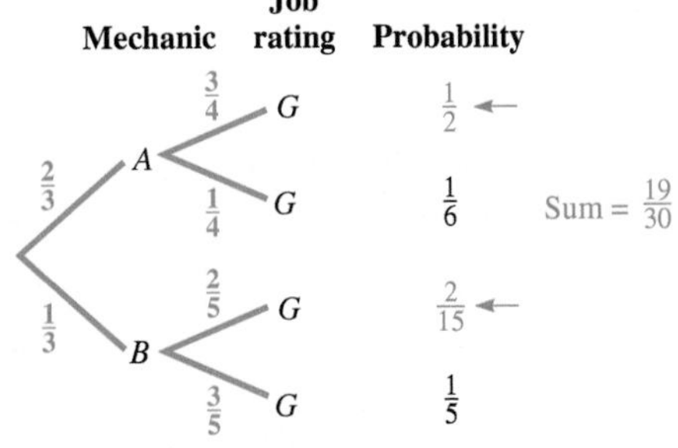

Garage mechanics experiment

Figure 10

EXAMPLE 11 Selecting Door Prizes

The **search for extraterrestrial intelligence (SETI)** has been mainly accomplished over the last decade through **SETI@HOME,** the largest distributed computing program on Earth. Most of the data are collected by the world's largest radio telescope, built into a 20-acre natural bowl in Aricebo, Puerto Rico (pictured above), and processed by millions of personal computers around the world.

To learn more, or for a chance to be the first to "contact" an extraterrestrial civilization, check out www.setiathome.ssl.berkeley.edu.

Courtesy of the National Astronomy and Ionosphere Center–Arecibo Observatory, a facility of the NSF

Rob Brown is among five door prize winners at a Christmas party. The five winners are asked to choose, without looking, from a bag which, they are told, contains five tokens, four of them redeemable for candy canes and one specific token redeemable for a \$100 gift certificate. Can Rob improve his chance of getting the gift certificate by drawing first among the five people?

SOLUTION

We denote candy cane by C, gift certificate by G, and first draw, second draw, and so on by subscripts 1, 2, ... Then if Rob draws first, his probability of getting the gift certificate is

$$P(G_1) = \frac{1}{5}.$$

If he draws second, his probability of getting the gift certificate is

$$\begin{aligned} P(G_2) &= P(C_1 \text{ and } G_2) \\ &= P(C_1) \cdot P(G_2 | C_1) \\ &= \frac{4}{5} \cdot \frac{1}{4} = \frac{1}{5}. \quad \text{Same result as above} \end{aligned}$$

For the third draw,

$$\begin{aligned} P(G_3) &= P(C_1 \text{ and } C_2 \text{ and } G_3) \\ &= P(C_1) \cdot P(C_2 | C_1) \cdot P(G_3 | C_1 \text{ and } C_2) \\ &= \frac{4}{5} \cdot \frac{3}{4} \cdot \frac{1}{3} = \frac{1}{5}. \quad \text{Same result as above} \end{aligned}$$

The probability of getting the gift certificate is $\frac{1}{5}$ when drawing fourth or fifth. The order in which the five winners draw does not affect Rob's chances.

For Further Thought

The Birthday Problem

A classic problem (with a surprising result) involves the probability that a given group of people will include at least one pair of people with the same birthday (the same day of the year, not necessarily the same year). This problem can be analyzed using the probability of a complement formula (**Section 2**) and the multiplication rule of probability from this section. Suppose there are three people in the group.

$$\begin{aligned} &P(\text{at least one duplication of birthdays}) \\ &= 1 - P(\text{no duplications}) \quad \text{Complement formula} \\ &= 1 - P(\text{2nd is different than 1st and 3rd is different than 1st and 2nd}) \\ &= 1 - \frac{364}{365} \cdot \frac{363}{365} \quad \text{Multiplication rule} \\ &\approx 1 - 0.992 \\ &= 0.008 \end{aligned}$$

(To simplify the calculations, we have assumed 365 possible birth dates, ignoring February 29.)

By doing more calculations like the one above, we find that the smaller the group, the smaller the probability of a duplication. The larger the group, the larger the probability of a duplication. The table on the next page shows the probability of at least one duplication for numbers of people from 2 through 52.

For Group or Individual Investigation

1. Based on the data shown in the table, what are the odds in favor of a duplication in a group of 30 people?
2. Estimate from the table the least number of people for which the probability of duplication is at least $\frac{1}{2}$.
3. How small a group is required for the probability of a duplication to be *exactly* 0?
4. How large a group is required for the probability of a duplication to be *exactly* 1?

Number of People	Probability of at Least One Duplication	Number of People	Probability of at Least One Duplication	Number of People	Probability of at Least One Duplication
2	0.003	19	0.379	36	0.832
3	0.008	20	0.411	37	0.849
4	0.016	21	0.444	38	0.864
5	0.027	22	0.476	39	0.878
6	0.040	23	0.507	40	0.891
7	0.056	24	0.538	41	0.903
8	0.074	25	0.569	42	0.914
9	0.095	26	0.598	43	0.924
10	0.117	27	0.627	44	0.933
11	0.141	28	0.654	45	0.941
12	0.167	29	0.681	46	0.948
13	0.194	30	0.706	47	0.955
14	0.223	31	0.730	48	0.961
15	0.253	32	0.753	49	0.966
16	0.284	33	0.775	50	0.970
17	0.315	34	0.795	51	0.974
18	0.347	35	0.814	52	0.978

3 EXERCISES

For each experiment, determine whether the two given events are independent.

1. ***Tossing Coins*** A fair coin is tossed twice. The events are "head on the first" and "head on the second."

2. ***Rolling Dice*** A pair of dice are rolled. The events are "even on the first" and "odd on the second."

3. ***Comparing Planets' Mean Distances from the Sun*** Two planets are selected, without replacement, from the list in **Table 7**. The events are "the first selected planet is closer than Jupiter" and "the second selected planet is farther than Mars."

4. ***Comparing Mean Distances from the Sun*** Two celestial bodies are selected, with replacement, from the list in **Table 7**. The events are "the first selected body is closer than Earth" and "the second selected body is farther than Uranus."

5. ***Guessing Answers on a Multiple-choice Test*** The answers are all guessed on a twenty-question multiple-choice test. The events are "the first answer is correct" and "the last answer is correct."

6. ***Selecting Committees of U.S. Senators*** A committee of five is randomly selected from the 100 U.S. Senators. The events are "the first member selected is a Republican" and "the second member selected is a Republican." (Assume that there are both Republicans and non-Republicans in the Senate.)

Comparing Gender and Career Motivation of College Students *One hundred college seniors attending a career fair at a university were categorized according to gender and according to primary career motivation, as summarized here.*

	Primary Career Motivation			
	Money	Allowed to be Creative	Sense of Giving to Society	Total
Male	19	15	14	48
Female	12	23	17	52
Total	31	38	31	100

If one of these students is to be selected at random, find the probability that the student selected will satisfy each condition in Exercises 7–12.

7. female

8. motivated primarily by creativity

9. not motivated primarily by money

10. male and motivated primarily by money

11. male, given that primary motivation is a sense of giving to society

12. motivated primarily by money or creativity, given that the student is female

Selecting Pets *A pet store has seven puppies, including four poodles, two terriers, and one retriever. If Rebecka and Aaron, in that order, each select one puppy at random,* with replacement *(they may both select the same one), find the probability of each event in Exercises 13–16.*

13. both select a poodle

14. Rebecka selects a retriever, Aaron selects a terrier

15. Rebecka selects a terrier, Aaron selects a retriever

16. both select a retriever

Selecting Pets *Suppose two puppies are selected as earlier, but this time* without replacement *(Rebecka and Aaron cannot both select the same puppy). Find the probability of each event in Exercises 17–22.*

17. both select a poodle

18. Aaron selects a terrier, given Rebecka selects a poodle

19. Aaron selects a retriever, given Rebecka selects a poodle

20. Rebecka selects a retriever

21. Aaron selects a retriever, given Rebecka selects a retriever

22. both select a retriever

Dealing Cards *Let two cards be dealt successively,* without replacement, *from a standard 52-card deck. Find the probability of each event in Exercises 23–27.*

23. spade second, given spade first

24. club second, given diamond first

25. two face cards

26. no face cards

27. The first card is a jack and the second is a face card.

28. Given events A and B within the sample space S, the following sequence of steps establishes formulas that can be used to compute conditional probabilities. Justify each statement.

(a) $P(A \text{ and } B) = P(A) \cdot P(B \mid A)$

(b) Therefore, $P(B \mid A) = \dfrac{P(A \text{ and } B)}{P(A)}$.

(c) Therefore, $P(B \mid A) = \dfrac{n(A \text{ and } B)/n(S)}{n(A)/n(S)}$.

(d) Therefore, $P(B \mid A) = \dfrac{n(A \text{ and } B)}{n(A)}$.

Considering Conditions in Card Drawing *Use the results of* ***Exercise 28*** *to find each probability when a single card is drawn from a standard 52-card deck.*

29. $P(\text{queen} \mid \text{face card})$

30. $P(\text{face card} \mid \text{queen})$

31. $P(\text{red} \mid \text{diamond})$

32. $P(\text{diamond} \mid \text{red})$

Investigating P(A and B) *Complete Exercises 33 and 34 to discover a general property of the probability of an event of the form A and B.*

33. If one number is chosen randomly from the integers 1 through 10, the probability of getting a number that is *odd and prime,* by the multiplication rule, is

$$P(\text{odd}) \cdot P(\text{prime} \mid \text{odd}) = \frac{5}{10} \cdot \frac{3}{5} = \frac{3}{10}.$$

Compute the product $P(\text{prime}) \cdot P(\text{odd} \mid \text{prime})$, and compare to the product above.

34. What does **Exercise 33** imply, in general, about the probability of an event of the form A and B?

35. ***Gender in Sequences of Babies*** Two authors of this book each have three sons and no daughters. Assuming boy and girl babies are equally likely, what is the probability of this event?

36. ***Rolling Dice*** Three dice are tossed. What is the probability that the numbers shown will all be different? (*Mathematics Teacher* calendar problem)

The remaining exercises, and groups of exercises, may require concepts from earlier sections, such as the complements principle of counting and addition rules, as well as the multiplication rule of this section.

Probabilities in Warehouse Grocery Shopping *Therese Felser manages a grocery warehouse which encourages volume shopping on the part of its customers. Therese has discovered that, on any given weekday, 70 percent of the customer sales amount to more than \$100. That is, any given sale on such a day has a probability of 0.70 of being for more than \$100. (Actually, the conditional probabilities throughout the day would change slightly, depending on earlier sales, but this effect would be negligible for the first several sales of the day, so we can treat them as independent.)*

Find the probability of each event in Exercises 37–40. (Give answers to three decimal places.)

37. The first two sales on Wednesday are both for more than \$100.

38. The first three sales on Wednesday are all for more than \$100.

39. None of the first three sales on Wednesday is for more than \$100.

40. Exactly one of the first three sales on Wednesday is for more than \$100.

Pollution from the Space Shuttle Launch Site *One problem encountered by developers of the space shuttle program is air pollution in the area surrounding the launch site. A certain direction from the launch site is considered critical in terms of hydrogen chloride pollution from the exhaust cloud. It has been determined that weather conditions would cause emission cloud movement in the critical direction only 5% of the time.*

NASA

In Exercises 41–44, find the probability for each event. Assume that probabilities for a particular launch in no way depend on the probabilities for other launches. (Give answers to two decimal places.)

41. A given launch will not result in cloud movement in the critical direction.

42. No cloud movement in the critical direction will occur during any of 5 launches.

43. Any 5 launches will result in at least one cloud movement in the critical direction.

44. Any 10 launches will result in at least one cloud movement in the critical direction.

Ordering Job Interviews *Three men and three women are waiting to be interviewed for jobs. If they are all selected in random order, find the probability of each event in Exercises 45–47.*

45. All the women will be interviewed first.

46. The first three interviewees will all be the same sex.

47. No man will be interviewed until at least two women have been interviewed.

48. ***Cutting Up a Cube*** A 4″ × 4″ × 4″ cube is painted and then cut into sixty-four 1″ × 1″ × 1″ cubes. A unit cube is then randomly selected and rolled. What is the probability that the top face of the rolled cube is painted? Express your answer as a common fraction. (*Mathematics Teacher* calendar problem)

49. ***Tossing a Two-Headed Coin?*** A gambler has two coins in his pocket—one fair coin and one two-headed coin. He selects a coin at random and flips it twice. If he gets two heads, what is the probability that he selected the fair coin? (*Mathematics Teacher* calendar problem)

50. In **Example 8,** where Anne draws three balls without replacement, what would be her probability of getting one of each color, where the order does not matter?

51. ***Gender in Sequences of Babies*** Assuming boy and girl babies are equally likely, find the probability that it would take

(a) at least three births to obtain two girls,

(b) at least four births to obtain two girls,

(c) at least five births to obtain two girls.

Comstock/ Thinkstock

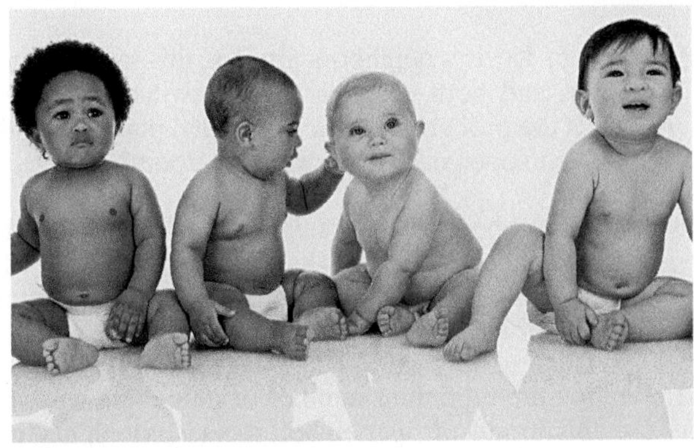

52. ***Drawing Cards*** Cards are drawn, without replacement, from an ordinary 52-card deck.

(a) How many must be drawn before the probability of obtaining at least one face card is greater than $\frac{1}{2}$?

(b) How many must be drawn before the probability of obtaining at least one king is greater than $\frac{1}{2}$?

Fair Decisions from Biased Coins *Many everyday decisions, like who will drive to lunch, or who will pay for the coffee, are made by the toss of a (presumably fair) coin and using the criterion "heads, you will; tails, I will." This criterion is not quite fair, however, if the coin is biased (perhaps due to slightly irregular construction or wear). John von Neumann suggested a way to make perfectly fair decisions even with a possibly biased coin. If a coin, biased so that*

$$P(\text{h}) = 0.5200 \quad \text{and} \quad P(\text{t}) = 0.4800,$$

is tossed twice, find each probability. (Give answers to four decimal places.)

53. $P(\text{hh})$

54. $P(\text{ht})$

55. $P(\text{th})$

56. $P(\text{tt})$

57. Having completed **Exercises 53–56,** can you suggest what von Neumann's scheme may have been?

Programming a Garage Door Opener *Kevin Frye installed a certain brand of automatic garage door opener that utilizes a transmitter control with six independent switches, each one set on or off. The receiver (wired to the door) must be set with the same pattern as the transmitter. (Exercises 58–61 are based on ideas similar to those of the "birthday problem" in the* ***For Further Thought*** *feature in this section.)*

P.J. Cross/Shutterstock

58. How many different ways can Kevin set the switches?

59. If one of Kevin's neighbors also has this same brand of opener, and both of them set the switches randomly, what is the probability, to four decimal places, that they are able to open each other's garage doors?

60. If five neighbors with the same type of opener set their switches independently, what is the probability of at least one pair of neighbors using the same settings? (Give your answer to four decimal places.)

61. What is the minimum number of neighbors who must use this brand of opener before the probability of at least one duplication of settings is greater than $\frac{1}{2}$?

62. ***Choosing Cards*** There are three cards, one that is green on both sides, one that is red on both sides, and one that is green on one side and red on the other. One of the three cards is selected randomly and laid on the table. If it happens that the card on the table has a red side up, what is the probability that it is also red on the other side?

Weather Conditions on Successive Days *In November, the rain in a certain valley tends to fall in storms of several days' duration. The unconditional probability of rain on any given day of the month is* 0.500. *But the probability of rain on a day that follows a rainy day is* 0.800, *and the probability of rain on a day following a nonrainy day is* 0.300. *Find the probability of each event in Exercises 63–66. Give answers to three decimal places.*

63. rain on two randomly selected consecutive days in November

64. rain on three randomly selected consecutive days in November

65. rain on November 1 and 2, but not on November 3

66. rain on the first four days of November, given that October 31 was clear all day

Engine Failures in a Vintage Aircraft *In a certain four-engine vintage aircraft, now quite unreliable, each engine has a* 10% *chance of failure on any flight, as long as it is carrying its one-fourth share of the load. But if one engine fails, then the chance of failure increases to* 20% *for each of the other three engines. And if a second engine fails, each of the remaining two has a* 30% *chance of failure.*

Assuming that no two engines ever fail simultaneously, and that the aircraft can continue flying with as few as two operating engines, find each probability for a given flight of this aircraft. (Give answers to four decimal places.)

67. no engine failures

68. exactly one engine failure (any one of four engines)

69. exactly two engine failures (any two of four engines)

70. a failed flight

One-and-one Free Throw Shooting in Basketball *In basketball, "one-and-one" free throw shooting (commonly called foul shooting) is done as follows: if the player makes the first shot (*1 *point), he is given a second shot. If he misses the first shot, he is not given a second shot (see the tree diagram).*

First shot	Second shot	Total points
Point	Point	2
	No point	1
No point		0

Christine Ellington, a basketball player, has a 70% *foul shot record. (She makes* 70% *of her foul shots.) Find the probability that, on a given one-and-one foul shooting opportunity, Christine will score each number of points.*

71. no points

72. one point

73. two points

74. ***Comparing Empirical and Theoretical Probabilities in Dice Rolling*** Roll a pair of dice until a sum of seven appears, keeping track of how many rolls it took. Repeat the process a total of 50 times, each time recording the number of rolls it took to get a sum of seven.

(a) Use your experimental data to compute an empirical probability (to two decimal places) that it would take at least three rolls to get a sum of seven.

(b) Find the theoretical probability (to two decimal places) that it would take at least three rolls to obtain a sum of seven.

75. Go to the Web site mentioned in the *cosmic impact* margin note in this section and write a report on the threat to humanity of cosmic impacts. Include an explanation of the abbreviation *NEO*.

4 BINOMIAL PROBABILITY

Binomial Probability Distribution • Binomial Probability Formula

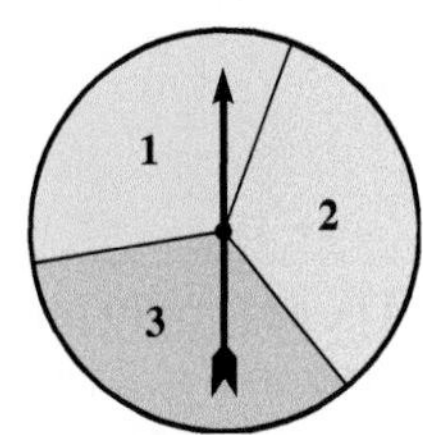

Binomial Probability Distribution

Suppose the spinner in the margin is spun twice. We are interested in the number of times a 2 is obtained. (Assume that 1, 2, and 3 all are equally likely on a given spin.) We can think of the outcome 2 as a "success," while a 1 or a 3 would be a "failure."

When the outcomes of an experiment are divided into just two categories, success and failure, the associated probabilities are called "binomial" (the prefix *bi* meaning *two*). Repeated performances of such an experiment, where the probability of success remains constant throughout all repetitions, are also known as repeated **Bernoulli trials** (after James Bernoulli). If we use an ordered pair to represent the result of each pair of spins, then the sample space for this experiment is

$$S = \{(1, 1), (1, 2), (1, 3), (2, 1), (2, 2), (2, 3), (3, 1), (3, 2), (3, 3)\}.$$

Table 8 Probability Distribution for the Number of 2s in Two Spins

x	$P(x)$
0	$\frac{4}{9}$
1	$\frac{4}{9}$
2	$\frac{1}{9}$
	Sum $= \frac{9}{9} = 1$

The nine outcomes in S are all equally likely. (This follows from the numbers 1, 2, and 3 being equally likely on a particular spin.)

If x denotes the number of 2s occurring on each pair of spins, then x is an example of a *random variable.* Although we cannot predict the result of any particular pair of spins, we can find the probabilities of various events from the sample space listing. In S, the number of 2s is 0 in four cases, 1 in four cases, and 2 in one case, as reflected in **Table 8**. Because the table includes all possible values of x, together with their probabilities, it is an example of a *probability distribution.* In this case, we have a **binomial probability distribution.** Notice that the probability column in **Table 8** has a sum of 1, in agreement with property 3 of probability (**Section 2**).

In order to develop a general formula for binomial probabilities, we can consider another way to obtain the probability values in **Table 8.** The various spins of the spinner are independent of one another, and on each spin the probability of success (S) is $\frac{1}{3}$ and the probability of failure (F) is $\frac{2}{3}$. We will denote success on the first spin by S_1, failure on the second by F_2, and so on.

$$\begin{aligned} P(x = 0) &= P(F_1 \text{ and } F_2) \\ &= P(F_1) \cdot P(F_2) && \text{Multiplication rule} \\ &= \frac{2}{3} \cdot \frac{2}{3} && \text{Substitute values.} \\ &= \frac{4}{9} && \text{Multiply.} \end{aligned}$$

$$\begin{aligned} P(x = 1) &= P[(S_1 \text{ and } F_2) \text{ or } (F_1 \text{ and } S_2)] && \text{2 ways to get } x = 1 \\ &= P(S_1 \text{ and } F_2) + P(F_1 \text{ and } S_2) && \text{Addition rule} \\ &= P(S_1) \cdot P(F_2) + P(F_1) \cdot P(S_2) && \text{Multiplication rule} \\ &= \frac{1}{3} \cdot \frac{2}{3} + \frac{2}{3} \cdot \frac{1}{3} && \text{Substitute values.} \\ &= \frac{2}{9} + \frac{2}{9} && \text{Multiply.} \\ &= \frac{4}{9} && \text{Add.} \end{aligned}$$

Interfoto/Alamy Images

James Bernoulli (1654–1705) is also known as Jacob or Jacques. He was charmed away from theology by the writings of Leibniz, became his pupil, and later headed the mathematics faculty at the University of Basel. His results in probability are contained in the *Art of Conjecture*, which was published in 1713, after his death, and which also included a reprint of the earlier Huygens paper. Bernoulli also made many contributions to calculus and analytic geometry.

$$\begin{aligned} P(x = 2) &= P(S_1 \text{ and } S_2) \\ &= P(S_1) \cdot P(S_2) && \text{Multiplication rule} \\ &= \frac{1}{3} \cdot \frac{1}{3} && \text{Substitute values.} \\ &= \frac{1}{9} && \text{Multiply.} \end{aligned}$$

Notice the following pattern in the above calculations. There is only one way to get $x = 0$ (namely, F_1 and F_2). And there is only one way to get $x = 2$ (namely, S_1 and S_2). But there are two ways to get $x = 1$. One way is S_1 and F_2; the other is F_1 and S_2. There are two ways because the one success required can occur on the first spin or on the second spin. How many ways can exactly one success occur in two repeated trials? This question is equivalent to:

How many size-one subsets are there of the set of two trials?

The answer is ${}_2C_1 = 2$. (The expression ${}_2C_1$ denotes "combinations of 2 things taken 1 at a time.") Each of the two ways to get exactly one success has a probability equal to $\frac{1}{3} \cdot \frac{2}{3}$, the probability of success times the probability of failure.

If the same spinner is spun three times rather than two, then x, the number of successes (2s) could have values of 0, 1, 2, or 3. Then the number of ways to get exactly 1 success is ${}_3C_1 = 3$. They are: S_1 and F_2 and F_3, F_1 and S_2 and F_3, F_1 and F_2 and S_3. The probability of each of these three ways is $\frac{1}{3} \cdot \frac{2}{3} \cdot \frac{2}{3} = \frac{4}{27}$.

$$P(x = 1) = 3 \cdot \frac{4}{27} = \frac{12}{27} = \frac{4}{9}$$

Figure 11 shows all possibilities for three spins, and **Table 9** gives the associated probability distribution. In the tree diagram, the number of ways of getting two successes in three trials is 3, in agreement with the fact that ${}_3C_2 = 3$. Also the sum of the $P(x)$ column in **Table 9** is again 1.

Table 9 Probability Distribution for the Number of 2s in Three Spins

x	$P(x)$
0	$\frac{8}{27}$
1	$\frac{12}{27}$
2	$\frac{6}{27}$
3	$\frac{1}{27}$
	Sum $= \frac{27}{27} = 1$

First spin	Second spin	Third spin	Number of successes	Probability
S ($\frac{1}{3}$)	S ($\frac{1}{3}$)	S ($\frac{1}{3}$)	3	$\frac{1}{3} \cdot \frac{1}{3} \cdot \frac{1}{3} = \frac{1}{27}$
		F ($\frac{2}{3}$)	2	$\frac{1}{3} \cdot \frac{1}{3} \cdot \frac{2}{3} = \frac{2}{27}$
	F ($\frac{2}{3}$)	S ($\frac{1}{3}$)	2	$\frac{1}{3} \cdot \frac{2}{3} \cdot \frac{1}{3} = \frac{2}{27}$
		F ($\frac{2}{3}$)	1	$\frac{1}{3} \cdot \frac{2}{3} \cdot \frac{2}{3} = \frac{4}{27}$
F ($\frac{2}{3}$)	S ($\frac{1}{3}$)	S ($\frac{1}{3}$)	2	$\frac{2}{3} \cdot \frac{1}{3} \cdot \frac{1}{3} = \frac{2}{27}$
		F ($\frac{2}{3}$)	1	$\frac{2}{3} \cdot \frac{1}{3} \cdot \frac{2}{3} = \frac{4}{27}$
	F ($\frac{2}{3}$)	S ($\frac{1}{3}$)	1	$\frac{2}{3} \cdot \frac{2}{3} \cdot \frac{1}{3} = \frac{4}{27}$
		F ($\frac{2}{3}$)	0	$\frac{2}{3} \cdot \frac{2}{3} \cdot \frac{2}{3} = \frac{8}{27}$

Tree diagram for three spins

Figure 11

PROBLEM-SOLVING HINT One problem-solving strategy is "Look for a pattern." Having constructed complete probability distributions for binomial experiments with 2 and 3 repeated trials (and probability of success $\frac{1}{3}$), we can now generalize the observed pattern to any binomial experiment, as shown next.

Binomial Probability Formula

Define the following quantities.

n = the number of repeated trials

p = the probability of success on any given trial

$q = 1 - p$ = the probability of failure on any given trial

x = the number of successes that occur

Note that p remains fixed throughout all n trials. This means that all trials are independent of one another. The random variable x (number of successes) can have any integer value from 0 through n. In general, x successes can be assigned among n repeated trials in ${}_nC_x$ different ways, since this is the number of different subsets of x positions among a set of n positions. Also, regardless of which x of the trials result in successes, there will always be x successes and $n - x$ failures, so we multiply x factors of p and $n - x$ factors of q together.

Binomial Probability Formula

When n independent repeated trials occur, where

p = probability of success and q = probability of failure

with p and q (where $q = 1 - p$) remaining constant throughout all n trials, the probability of exactly x successes is calculated as follows.

$$P(x) = {}_nC_x p^x q^{n-x} = \frac{n!}{x!(n-x)!}p^x q^{n-x}$$

Binomial probabilities for particular values of n, p, and x can be found directly using tables, statistical software, and some handheld calculators. In the following examples, we use the formula derived above.

From the DISTR menu

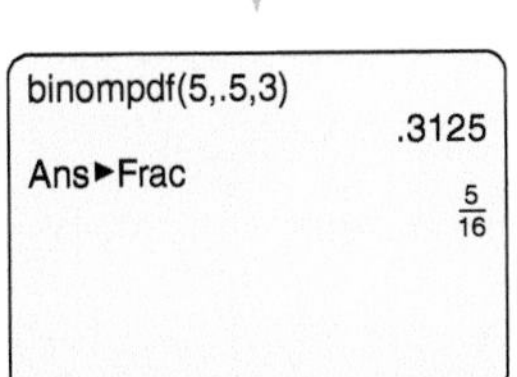

The TI-83/84 Plus calculator will find the probability discussed in **Example 1.**

EXAMPLE 1 Finding Probability in Coin Tossing

Find the probability of obtaining exactly three heads in five tosses of a fair coin.

SOLUTION

Let heads be "success." Then this is a binomial experiment with $n = 5$, $p = \frac{1}{2}$, $q = \frac{1}{2}$, and $x = 3$.

$$P(3) = {}_5C_3\left(\frac{1}{2}\right)^3\left(\frac{1}{2}\right)^2 = 10 \cdot \frac{1}{8} \cdot \frac{1}{4} = \frac{5}{16}$$ Binomial probability formula ■■■

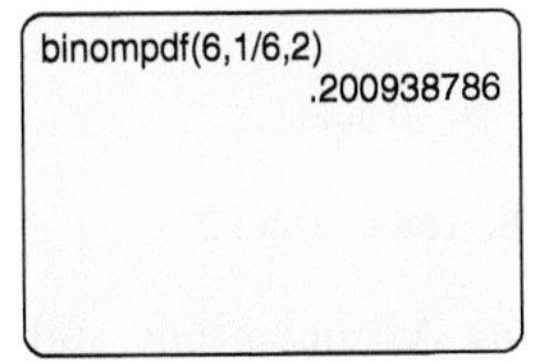

This screen supports the answer in **Example 2.**

EXAMPLE 2 Finding Probability in Dice Rolling

Find the probability of obtaining exactly two 5s in six rolls of a fair die.

SOLUTION

Let 5 be "success." Then $n = 6$, $p = \frac{1}{6}$, $q = \frac{5}{6}$, and $x = 2$.

$$P(2) = {}_6C_2\left(\frac{1}{6}\right)^2\left(\frac{5}{6}\right)^4 = 15 \cdot \frac{1}{36} \cdot \frac{625}{1296} = \frac{3125}{15{,}552} \approx 0.201$$ ■■■

In the case of repeated independent trials, when an event involves more than one specific number of successes, we can employ the binomial probability formula along with the complement or addition rules.

EXAMPLE 3 Finding Probability of Female Children

A couple plans to have 5 children. Find the probability they will have more than 3 girls. (Assume girl and boy babies are equally likely.)

SOLUTION

Let a girl be "success." Then $n = 5, p = q = \frac{1}{2}$, and $x > 3$.

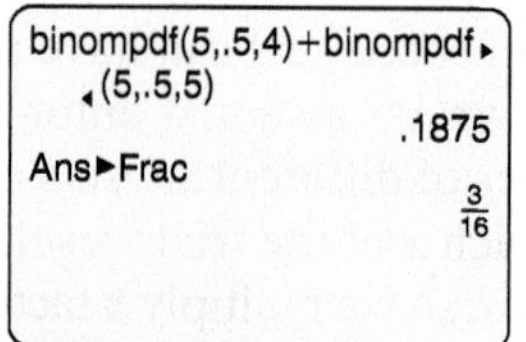

This screen supports the answer in **Example 3.**

$$\begin{aligned} P(x > 3) &= P(x = 4 \text{ or } 5) && \text{More than 3 means 4 or 5.} \\ &= P(4) + P(5) && \text{Addition rule} \\ &= {}_5C_4\left(\frac{1}{2}\right)^4\left(\frac{1}{2}\right)^1 + {}_5C_5\left(\frac{1}{2}\right)^5\left(\frac{1}{2}\right)^0 && \text{Binomial probability formula} \\ &= 5 \cdot \frac{1}{16} \cdot \frac{1}{2} + 1 \cdot \frac{1}{32} \cdot 1 && \text{Simplify.} \\ &= \frac{5}{32} + \frac{1}{32} = \frac{6}{32} = \frac{3}{16} = 0.1875 \end{aligned}$$

EXAMPLE 4 Finding Probability of Hits in Baseball

Andrew Crowley, a baseball player, has a well-established career batting average of .300. In a brief series with a rival team, Andrew will bat 10 times. Find the probability that he will get more than two hits in the series.

SOLUTION

This "experiment" involves $n = 10$ repeated Bernoulli trials, with probability of success (a hit) given by $p = 0.3$ (which implies $q = 1 - 0.3 = 0.7$). Since, in this case, "more than 2" means

"3 or 4 or 5 or 6 or 7 or 8 or 9 or 10" (eight different possibilities),

it will be less work to apply the complement rule.

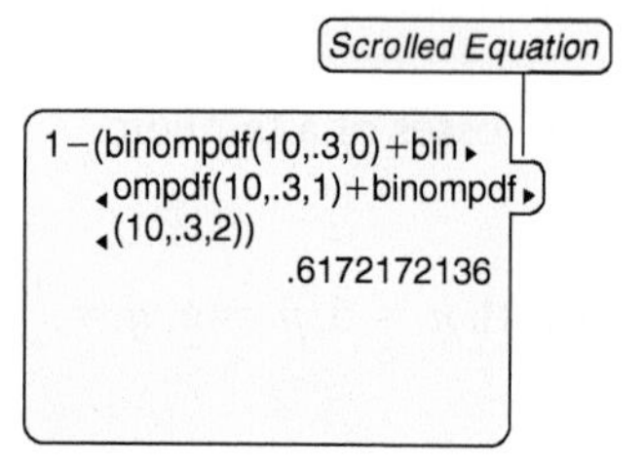

This screen supports the answer in **Example 4.**

$$\begin{aligned} P(x > 2) &= 1 - P(x \le 2) && \text{Complement rule} \\ &= 1 - P(x = 0 \text{ or } 1 \text{ or } 2) && \text{Only three different possibilities} \\ &= 1 - [P(0) + P(1) + P(2)] && \text{Addition rule} \\ &= 1 - [{}_{10}C_0(0.3)^0(0.7)^{10} && \text{Binomial probability formula} \\ &\quad + {}_{10}C_1(0.3)^1(0.7)^9 + {}_{10}C_2(0.3)^2(0.7)^8] \\ &\approx 1 - [0.0282 + 0.1211 + 0.2335] && \text{Simplify.} \\ &= 1 - 0.3828 \\ &= 0.6172 \end{aligned}$$

4 EXERCISES

For Exercises 1–24, give all numerical answers as common fractions reduced to lowest terms. For Exercises 25–54, give all numerical answers to three decimal places.

Coin Tossing *If three fair coins are tossed, find the probability of each number of heads.*

1. 0 **2.** 1 **3.** 2

4. 3 **5.** 1 or 2 **6.** at least 1

7. no more than 1 **8.** fewer than 3

9. *Gender in Sequences of Babies* Assuming boy and girl babies are equally likely, find the probability that a family with three children will have exactly two boys.

10. ***Relating Pascal's Triangle to Coin Tossing*** Pascal's triangle is shown in **Table 22** at the end of this chapter. Explain how the probabilities in **Exercises 1–4** here relate to row 3 of the "triangle." (Recall that we referred to the topmost row of the triangle as "row number 0" and to the leftmost entry of each row as "entry number 0.")

11. Generalize the pattern in **Exercise 10** to complete the following statement. If n fair coins are tossed, the probability of exactly x heads is the fraction whose numerator is entry number _____ of row number _____ in Pascal's triangle, and whose denominator is the sum of the entries in row number _____.

Binomial Probability Applied to Tossing Coins *Use the pattern noted in **Exercises 10 and 11** to find the probabilities of each number of heads when seven fair coins are tossed.*

12. 0 **13.** 1 **14.** 2 **15.** 3

16. 4 **17.** 5 **18.** 6 **19.** 7

Binomial Probability Applied to Rolling Dice *A fair die is rolled three times. A 4 is considered "success," while all other outcomes are "failures." Find the probability of each number of successes.*

20. 0 **21.** 1 **22.** 2 **23.** 3

24. **Exercises 10 and 11** established a way of using Pascal's triangle rather than the binomial probability formula to find probabilities of different numbers of successes in coin-tossing experiments. Explain why the same process would not work for **Exercises 20–23.**

For n repeated independent trials, with constant probability of success p for all trials, find the probability of exactly x successes in each of Exercises 25–28.

25. $n = 5,\ \ p = \frac{1}{3},\ \ x = 4$

26. $n = 10,\ \ p = 0.7,\ \ x = 5$

27. $n = 20,\ \ p = \frac{1}{8},\ \ x = 2$

28. $n = 30,\ \ p = 0.6,\ \ x = 22$

For Exercises 29–31, refer to ***Example 4.***

29. ***Batting Averages in Baseball*** Does Andrew's probability of a hit really remain constant at exactly 0.300 through all ten times at bat? Explain your reasoning.

30. ***Batting Averages in Baseball*** If Andrew's batting average is exactly .300 going into the series, and that value is based on exactly 1200 career hits out of 4000 previous times at bat, what is the greatest his average could possibly be (to three decimal places) when he goes up to bat the tenth time of the series? What is the least his average could possibly be when he goes up to bat the tenth time of the series?

31. Do you think the use of the binomial probability formula was justified in **Example 4,** even though p is not strictly constant? Explain your reasoning.

Random Selection of Answers on a Multiple-choice Test *Beth Dahlke is taking a ten-question multiple-choice test for which each question has three answer choices, only one of which is correct. Beth decides on answers by rolling a fair die and marking the first answer choice if the die shows* 1 *or* 2, *the second if it shows* 3 *or* 4, *and the third if it shows* 5 *or* 6. *Find the probability of each event in Exercises 32–35.*

32. exactly four correct answers

33. exactly seven correct answers

34. fewer than three correct answers

35. at least seven correct answers

Side Effects of Prescription Drugs *It is known that a certain prescription drug produces undesirable side effects in* 35% *of all patients who use it. Among a random sample of eight patients using the drug, find the probability of each event.*

36. None have undesirable side effects.

37. Exactly one has undesirable side effects.

38. Exactly two have undesirable side effects.

39. More than two have undesirable side effects.

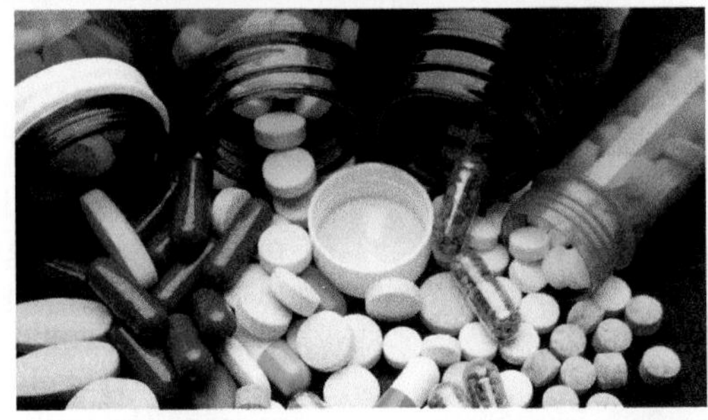

StillFX/Shutterstock

Likelihood of Capable Students Attending College *In a certain state, it has been shown that only* 60% *of the high school graduates who are capable of college work actually enroll in colleges. Find the probability that, among nine capable high school graduates in this state, each number will enroll in college.*

40. exactly 4 **41.** from 4 through 6

42. all 9 **43.** at least 3

44. ***Student Ownership of Personal Computers*** At a large midwestern university, 90% of all students have their own personal computers. If five students at that university are selected at random, find the probability that exactly three of them have their own computers.

45. ***Frost Survival Among Orange Trees*** If it is known that 65% of all orange trees will survive a hard frost, then what is the probability that at least half of a group of six trees will survive such a frost?

46. ***Rate of Favorable Media Coverage of an Incumbent President*** During a presidential campaign, 64% of the political columns in a certain group of major newspapers were favorable to the incumbent president. If a sample of fifteen of these columns is selected at random, what is the probability that exactly ten of them will be favorable?

Selecting Balls From a Bag *A bag contains only white balls and black balls. Let p be the probability that a ball selected at random is black. Each time a ball is selected, it is placed back in the bag before the next ball is selected. Four balls are selected at random.*

47. What is the probability that two of the four balls are black and two are white? (*Mathematics Teacher* calendar problem) (*Hint*: Use the binomial probability formula to express the probability in terms of p.)

48. Evaluate the probability of **Exercise 47** in case the bag actually contains 15 black balls and 25 white balls. Give your answer to four decimal places.

Taking a Random Walk *Abby Gartland is parked at a mile marker on an east-west country road. She decides to toss a fair coin 10 times, each time driving 1 mile east if it lands heads up and 1 mile west if it lands tails up. The term "random walk" applies to this process, even though Abby drives rather than walks. It is a simplified model of Brownian motion. (See also **Exercises 9–12** in the **Extension** at the end of this chapter.)*

In each of Exercises 49–56, find the probability that Abby's "walk" will end as described.

49. 10 miles east of the start

50. 6 miles east of the start

51. 6 miles west of the start

52. 5 miles west of the start

53. 2 miles east of the start

54. at least 2 miles east of the start

55. at least 2 miles from the start

56. exactly at the start

5 EXPECTED VALUE

Expected Value • Games and Gambling • Investments • Business and Insurance

Expected Value

Table 10

x	$P(x)$
1	0.05
2	0.10
3	0.20
4	0.40
5	0.10
6	0.15

The probability distribution in **Table 10**, from **Example 6** of **Section 2,** shows the probabilities assigned by Amy to the various lengths of time her homework may take on a given night. If Amy's friend Tara asks her how many hours her studies will take, what would be her best guess? Six different time values are possible, with some more likely than others. One thing Amy could do is calculate a "weighted average" by multiplying each possible time value by its probability and then adding the six products.

$$1(0.05) + 2(0.10) + 3(0.20) + 4(0.40) + 5(0.10) + 6(0.15)$$
$$= 0.05 + 0.20 + 0.60 + 1.60 + 0.50 + 0.90 = 3.85$$

Thus 3.85 hours is the **expected value** (or the **mathematical expectation**) of the quantity of time to be spent. Since the original time values in the table were rounded to the nearest hour, the expected value also should be rounded, to 4 hours.

Expected Value

If a random variable x can have any of the values $x_1, x_2, x_3, \ldots, x_n$, and the corresponding probabilities of these values occurring are $P(x_1), P(x_2), P(x_3), \ldots, P(x_n)$, then the **expected value of x** is calculated as follows.

$$E(x) = x_1 \cdot P(x_1) + x_2 \cdot P(x_2) + x_3 \cdot P(x_3) + \cdots + x_n \cdot P(x_n)$$

EXAMPLE 1 Finding the Expected Number of Boys

Find the expected number of boys for a three-child family (that is, the expected value of the number of boys). Assume girls and boys are equally likely.

SOLUTION

The sample space for this experiment is

$$S = \{\text{ggg, ggb, gbg, bgg, gbb, bgb, bbg, bbb}\}.$$

The probability distribution is shown in **Table 11**, along with the products and their sum, which gives the expected value.

Table 11

Number of Boys x	Probability $P(x)$	Product $x \cdot P(x)$
0	$\frac{1}{8}$	0
1	$\frac{3}{8}$	$\frac{3}{8}$
2	$\frac{3}{8}$	$\frac{6}{8}$
3	$\frac{1}{8}$	$\frac{3}{8}$
		Expected value: $E(x) = \frac{12}{8} = \frac{3}{2}$

The expected number of boys is $\frac{3}{2}$, or 1.5. This result seems reasonable. Since boys and girls are equally likely, "half" the children are expected to be boys. ∎∎∎

Everett Collection

Solution to the Chapter Opener Problem One way to look at the problem, given that the car is *not* behind Door 3, is that Doors 1 and 2 are now equally likely to contain the car. Thus, switching doors will neither help nor hurt your chances of winning the car.

However, there is another way to look at the problem. When you picked Door 1, the probability was $\frac{1}{3}$ that it contained the car. Being shown the goat behind Door 3 doesn't really give you any new information; after all, you knew that there was a goat behind at least one of the other doors. So seeing the goat behind Door 3 does nothing to change your assessment of the probability that Door 1 has the car. It remains $\frac{1}{3}$. But because Door 3 has been ruled out, the probability that Door 2 has the car is now $\frac{2}{3}$. Thus, you should switch.

Analysis of this problem depends on the psychology of the host. If we suppose that the host must *always* show you a losing door and then give you an option to switch, then you should switch. This was not specifically stated in the problem as posed above but was pointed out by many mathematicians who became involved in the discussion.

(The authors wish to thank David Berman of the University of New Orleans for his assistance with this explanation.)

For a convincing simulation of the Monty Hall problem, see http://www.grand-illusions.com/simulator/montysim.htm

The expected value for the number of boys in the family could never actually occur. It is only a kind of long run average of the various values that *could* occur. If we record the number of boys in many different three-child families, then by the law of large numbers, as the number of observed families increases, the observed average number of boys should approach the expected value.

Games and Gambling

EXAMPLE 2 Finding Expected Winnings

A player pays \$3 to play the following game: He tosses three fair coins and receives back "payoffs" of \$1 if he tosses no heads, \$2 for one head, \$3 for two heads, and \$4 for three heads. Find the player's expected net winnings for this game.

SOLUTION

Display the information as in **Table 12** on the next page. (Notice that, for each possible event, "net winnings" are "gross winnings" (payoff) minus cost to play.) Probabilities are derived from the sample space.

$$S = \{\text{ttt, htt, tht, tth, hht, hth, thh, hhh}\}$$

The expected net loss of 50 cents is a long-run average only. On any particular play of this game, the player would lose \$2 or lose \$1 or break even or win \$1. Over a long series of plays, say 100, there would be some wins and some losses, but the total net result would likely be around a $100 \cdot (\$0.50) = \$50$ *loss*.

Table 12

Number of Heads	Payoff	Net Winnings x	Probability $P(x)$	Product $x \cdot P(x)$
0	\$1	$-\$2$	$\frac{1}{8}$	$-\$\frac{2}{8}$
1	2	-1	$\frac{3}{8}$	$-\frac{3}{8}$
2	3	0	$\frac{3}{8}$	0
3	4	1	$\frac{1}{8}$	$\frac{1}{8}$
				Expected value: $E(x) = -\$\frac{1}{2} = -\$0.50$

A game in which the expected net winnings are zero is called a **fair game.** The game in **Example 2** has negative expected net winnings, so it is unfair against the player. A game with positive expected net winnings is unfair in favor of the player.

EXAMPLE 3 Finding the Fair Cost to Play a Game

The \$3 cost to play the game of **Example 2** makes the game unfair against the player (since the player's expected net winnings are negative). What cost would make this a fair game?

SOLUTION

We already computed, in **Example 2,** that the \$3 cost to play resulted in an expected net loss of \$0.50. Therefore we can conclude that the \$3 cost was 50 cents too high. A fair cost to play the game would then be $\$3 - \$0.50 = \$2.50$.

The result in **Example 3** can be verified. Disregard the cost to play and find the expected *gross* winnings (by summing the products of payoff times probability).

$$E(\text{gross winnings}) = \$1 \cdot \frac{1}{8} + \$2 \cdot \frac{3}{8} + \$3 \cdot \frac{3}{8} + \$4 \cdot \frac{1}{8} = \frac{\$20}{8} = \$2.50$$

Expected gross winnings (payoff) are \$2.50, so this amount is a fair cost to play.

EXAMPLE 4 Finding the Fair Cost to Play a Game

In a certain state lottery, a player chooses three digits, in a specific order. (Leading digits may be 0, so numbers such as 028 and 003 are legitimate entries.) The lottery operators randomly select a three-digit sequence, and any player matching their selection receives a payoff of \$600. What is a fair cost to play this game?

SOLUTION

In this case, no cost has been proposed, so we have no choice but to compute expected *gross* winnings. The probability of selecting all three digits correctly is $\frac{1}{10} \cdot \frac{1}{10} \cdot \frac{1}{10} = \frac{1}{1000}$, and the probability of not selecting all three correctly is $1 - \frac{1}{1000} = \frac{999}{1000}$. The expected gross winnings are

$$E(\text{gross winnings}) = \$600 \cdot \frac{1}{1000} + \$0 \cdot \frac{999}{1000} = \$0.60.$$

Thus the fair cost to play this game is 60 cents. (In fact, the lottery charges \$1 to play, so players should expect to lose 40 cents per play *on the average.*)

Photodisc

Roulette ("little wheel") was invented in France in the seventeenth or early eighteenth century. It has been a featured game of chance in the gambling casino of Monte Carlo.

The disk is divided into red and black alternating compartments, numbered 1 to 36 (but not in that order). There is a compartment also for 0 (and for 00 in the United States). In roulette, the wheel is set in motion, and an ivory ball is thrown into the bowl opposite to the direction of the wheel. When the wheel stops, the ball comes to rest in one of the compartments—the number and color determine who wins.

The players bet against the banker (person in charge of the pool of money) by placing money or equivalent chips in spaces on the roulette table corresponding to the wheel's colors or numbers. Bets can be made on one number or several, on odd or even, on red or black, or on combinations. The banker pays off according to the odds against the particular bet(s). For example, the classic payoff for a winning single number is $36 for each $1 bet.

State lotteries must be unfair against players because they are designed to help fund benefits (such as the state's school system) as well as to cover administrative costs and certain other expenses. Among people's reasons for playing may be a willingness to support such causes, but most people undoubtedly play for the chance to "beat the odds" and be one of the few net winners.

Gaming casinos are major business enterprises, by no means designed to break even; the games they offer are always unfair in favor of the house. The bias does not need to be great, however, since even relatively small average losses per player multiplied by large numbers of players can result in huge profits for the house.

EXAMPLE 5 Finding Expected Winnings in Roulette

One simple type of *roulette* is played with an ivory ball and a wheel set in motion. The wheel contains thirty-eight compartments. Eighteen of the compartments are black, eighteen are red, one is labeled "zero," and one is labeled "double zero." (These last two are neither black nor red.) In this case, assume the player places $1 on either red or black. If the player picks the correct color of the compartment in which the ball finally lands, the payoff is $2; otherwise the payoff is zero. Find the expected net winnings.

SOLUTION

By the expected value formula, expected net winnings are

$$E(\text{net winnings}) = (\$1)\frac{18}{38} + (-\$1)\frac{20}{38} = -\$\frac{1}{19}.$$

The expected net *loss* here is $\$\frac{1}{19}$, or about 5.3¢, per play. ■■■

Investments

EXAMPLE 6 Finding Expected Investment Profits

Nick Jovanovich has $5000 to invest and will commit the whole amount, for six months, to one of three technology stocks. A number of uncertainties could affect the prices of these stocks, but Nick is confident, based on his research, that one of only several possible profit scenarios will prove true of each one at the end of the six-month period. His complete analysis is shown in **Table 13**. (For example, stock *ABC* could lose $400, gain $800, or gain $1500.)

Table 13

Company *ABC*		Company *RST*		Company *XYZ*	
Profit or Loss x	Probability $P(x)$	Profit or Loss x	Probability $P(x)$	Profit or Loss x	Probability $P(x)$
−$400	0.2	$500	0.8	$0	0.4
800	0.5	1000	0.2	700	0.3
1500	0.3			1200	0.1
				2000	0.2

Find the expected profit (or loss) for each of the three stocks and select Nick's optimum choice based on these calculations. (The solution is on the next page.)

Matthew Heinrichs/Alamy

The first **Silver Dollar Slot Machine** was fashioned in 1929 by the Fey Manufacturing Company, San Francisco, inventors of the 3-reel, automatic payout machine (1895).

SOLUTION

Apply the expected value formula.

ABC: $-\$400 \cdot (0.2) + \$800 \cdot (0.5) + \$1500 \cdot (0.3) = \$770$

RST: $\$500 \cdot (0.8) + \$1000 \cdot (0.2) = \$600$

XYZ: $\$0 \cdot (0.4) + \$700 \cdot (0.3) + \$1200 \cdot (0.1) + \$2000 \cdot (0.2) = \$730$

The largest expected profit is \$770. By this analysis, Nick should invest the money in stock ABC.

Of course, by investing in stock ABC, Nick may in fact *lose* \$400 over the six months. The "expected" return of \$770 is only a long-run average over many identical situations. Since this particular investment situation may never occur again, you may argue that using expected values is not the best approach for Nick to use.

An optimist would ignore most possibilities and focus on the *best* that each investment could do, while a pessimist would focus on the *worst* possibility for each investment.

EXAMPLE 7 Choosing Stock Investments

Decide which stock of **Example 6** Nick would pick in each case.

(a) He is an optimist. **(b)** He is a pessimist.

SOLUTION

(a) Disregarding the probabilities, he would focus on the best case for each stock. Since ABC could return as much as \$1500, RST as much as \$1000, and XYZ as much as \$2000, the optimum is \$2000. He would buy stock XYZ (the best of the three *best* cases).

(b) In this situation, he would focus on the worst possible cases. Since ABC might return as little as $-\$400$ (a \$400 loss), RST as little as \$500, and XYZ as little as \$0, he would buy stock RST (the best of the three *worst* cases).

Business and Insurance

EXAMPLE 8 Finding Expected Lumber Revenue

Mike Crenshaw, a lumber wholesaler, is considering the purchase of a (railroad) carload of varied dimensional lumber. Mike calculates that the probabilities of reselling the load for \$10,000, \$9000, or \$8000 are 0.22, 0.33, and 0.45, respectively. In order to ensure an *expected* profit of at least \$3000, how much can Mike afford to pay for the load?

SOLUTION

The expected revenue (or income) from resales can be found in **Table 14.**

Table 14 Expected Lumber Revenue

Income x	Probability $P(x)$	Product $x \cdot P(x)$
\$10,000	0.22	\$2200
9000	0.33	2970
8000	0.45	3600
	Expected revenue:	\$8770

In general, we have the relationship

$$\text{profit} = \text{revenue} - \text{cost}.$$

Therefore, in terms of expectations,

$$\text{expected profit} = \text{expected revenue} - \text{cost}.$$

So \$3000 = \$8770 − cost, or equivalently, cost = \$8770 − \$3000 = \$5770. Mike can pay up to \$5770 and still maintain an expected profit of at least \$3000. ■■■

EXAMPLE 9 Analyzing an Insurance Decision

Jeff Marsalis, a farmer, will realize a profit of \$150,000 on his wheat crop, unless there is rain before harvest, in which case he will realize only \$40,000. The long-term weather forecast assigns rain a probability of 0.16. (The probability of no rain is 1 − 0.16 = 0.84.) An insurance company offers crop insurance of \$150,000 against rain for a premium of \$20,000. Should Jeff buy the insurance?

SOLUTION

In order to make a wise decision, Jeff computes his expected profit under both options: to insure and not to insure. The complete calculations are summarized in the two "expectation" **Tables 15 and 16.**

For example, if insurance is purchased and it rains, Jeff's net profit is

$$\begin{bmatrix}\text{Insurance}\\ \text{proceeds}\end{bmatrix} + \begin{bmatrix}\text{Reduced}\\ \text{crop profit}\end{bmatrix} - \begin{bmatrix}\text{Insurance}\\ \text{premium}\end{bmatrix} \quad \text{Net profit}$$

$$\downarrow \qquad\qquad \downarrow \qquad\qquad \downarrow \qquad\qquad \downarrow$$

$$\$150{,}000 + \$40{,}000 - \$20{,}000 = \$170{,}000.$$

Table 15 Expectation when Insuring

	Net Profit x	Probability $P(x)$	Product $x \cdot P(x)$
Rain	\$170,000	0.16	\$27,200
No rain	130,000	0.84	109,200
			Expected profit: \$136,400

Table 16 Expectation when Not Insuring

	Net Profit x	Probability $P(x)$	Product $x \cdot P(x)$
Rain	\$40,000	0.16	\$6400
No rain	150,000	0.84	126,000
			Expected profit: \$132,400

By comparing expected profits (136,400 > 132,400), we conclude that Jeff is better off buying the insurance. ■■■

For Further Thought

Expected Value of Games of Chance

Slot machines are a popular game for those who want to lose their money with very little mental effort. We cannot calculate an expected value applicable to all slot machines since payoffs vary from machine to machine. But we can calculate the "typical expected value."

A player operates a slot machine by pulling a handle after inserting a coin or coins. Reels inside the machine then rotate, and come to rest in some random order. Assume that three reels show the pictures listed in **Table 17.** For example, of the 20 pictures on the first reel, 2 are cherries, 5 are oranges, 5 are plums, 2 are bells, 2 are melons, 3 are bars, and 1 is the number 7.

A picture of cherries on the first reel, but not on the second, leads to a payoff of 3 coins (*net* winnings: 2 coins); a picture of cherries on the first two reels, but not the third, leads to a payoff of 5 coins (*net* winnings: 4 coins). These and all other winning combinations are listed in **Table 18.**

Since, according to **Table 17,** there are 2 ways of getting cherries on the first reel, 15 ways of *not* getting cherries on the second reel, and 20 ways of getting anything on the third reel, we have a total of $2 \cdot 15 \cdot 20 = 600$ ways of getting a net payoff of 2. Since there are 20 pictures per reel, there are a total of $20 \cdot 20 \cdot 20 = 8000$ possible outcomes. Hence, the probability of receiving a net payoff of 2 coins is 600/8000.

Courtesy of John Hornsby

This Cleveland Indians fan hit four 7s in a row on a progressive nickel slot machine at the Sands Casino in Las Vegas in 1988.

Table 17 Pictures on Reels

	Reels		
Pictures	**1**	**2**	**3**
Cherries	2	5	4
Oranges	5	4	5
Plums	5	3	3
Bells	2	4	4
Melons	2	1	2
Bars	3	2	1
7s	1	1	1
Totals	20	20	20

Table 18 Calculating Expected Loss on a Three-Reel Slot Machine

Winning Combinations	Number of Ways	Probability	Number of Coins Received	Net Winnings (in coins)	Probability Times Net Winnings
1 cherry (on first reel)	$2 \cdot 15 \cdot 20 = 600$	600/8000	3	2	1200/8000
2 cherries (on first two reels)	$2 \cdot 5 \cdot 16 = 160$	160/8000	5	4	640/8000
3 cherries	$2 \cdot 5 \cdot 4 = 40$	40/8000	10	9	360/8000
3 oranges	$5 \cdot 4 \cdot 5 = 100$	100/8000	10	9	900/8000
3 plums	$5 \cdot 3 \cdot 3 = 45$	45/8000	14	13	585/8000
3 bells	_ · _ · _ = __	__/8000	18	__	__/8000
3 melons (jackpot)	_ · _ · _ = __	__/8000	100	__	__/8000
3 bars (jackpot)	_ · _ · _ = __	__/8000	200	__	__/8000
3 7s (jackpot)	_ · _ · _ = __	__/8000	500	__	__/8000
Totals	__				6318/8000

Table 18 takes into account all *winning* outcomes, with the necessary products for finding expectation added in the last column. However, since a *nonwinning* outcome can occur in

$$8000 - 988 = 7012 \text{ ways (with winnings of } -1 \text{ coin)},$$

the product $(-1) \cdot 7012/8000$ must also be included. Hence, the expected value of this particular slot machine is

$$\frac{6318}{8000} + (-1) \cdot \frac{7012}{8000} \approx -0.087 \text{ coin}.$$

On a machine costing one dollar per play, the expected *loss* (per play) is about

$$(0.087)\,(1 \text{ dollar}) = 8.7 \textit{ cents}.$$

Actual slot machines vary in expected loss per dollar of play. But author Hornsby was able to beat a Las Vegas slot machine in 1988. (See the photo on **the previous page.**)

Table 19 comes from an article by Andrew Sterrett in *The Mathematics Teacher* (March 1967), in which he discusses rules for various games of chance and calculates their expected values. He uses expected values to find expected times it would take to lose $1000 if you played continually at the rate of $1 per play and one play per minute.

For Group or Individual Investigation

1. Explain why the entries of the "Net Winnings" column of **Table 18** are all one fewer than the corresponding entries of the "Number of Coins Received" column.
2. Find the 29 missing values in **Table 18.** (Refer to **Table 17** for the values in the "Number of Ways" column.)
3. In order to make your money last as long as possible in a casino, which game should you play?

Table 19 Expected Time to Lose $1000

Game	Expected Value	Days	Hours	Minutes
Roulette (with one 0)	−$0.027	25	16	40
Roulette (with 0 and 00)	−$0.053	13	4	40
Chuck-a-luck	−$0.079	8	19	46
Keno (one number)	−$0.200	3	11	20
Numbers	−$0.300	2	7	33
Football pool (4 winners)	−$0.375	1	20	27
Football pool (10 winners)	−$0.658	1	1	19

5 EXERCISES

1. Explain in words what is meant by "expected value of a random variable."

2. Explain what a couple means by the statement, "We expect to have 1.5 sons."

3. ***Tossing Coins*** Five fair coins are tossed. Find the expected number of heads.

4. ***Drawing Cards*** Two cards are drawn, with replacement, from a standard 52-card deck. Find the expected number of diamonds.

Expected Winnings in a Die-rolling Game *For Exercises 5 and 6, a game consists of rolling a single fair die and pays off as follows: $3 for a 6, $2 for a 5, $1 for a 4, and no payoff otherwise.*

5. Find the expected winnings for this game.

6. What is a fair price to pay to play this game?

Expected Winnings in a Die-rolling Game *For Exercises 7 and 8, consider a game consisting of rolling a single fair die, with payoffs as follows. If an even number of spots turns up, you receive as many dollars as there are spots up. But if an odd number of spots turns up, you must pay as many dollars as there are spots up.*

7. Find the expected net winnings of this game.

8. Is this game fair, or unfair against the player, or unfair in favor of the player?

9. ***Expected Winnings in a Coin-tossing Game*** A certain game involves tossing 3 fair coins, and it pays 10¢ for 3 heads, 5¢ for 2 heads, and 3¢ for 1 head. Is 5¢ a fair price to pay to play this game? (That is, does the 5¢ cost to play make the game fair?)

10. ***Expected Winnings in Roulette*** In a form of roulette slightly different from that in **Example 5,** a more generous management supplies a wheel having only thirty-seven compartments, with eighteen red, eighteen black, and one zero. Find the expected net winnings if you bet on red in this game.

11. ***Expected Number of Absences in a Math Class*** In a certain mathematics class, the probabilities have been empirically determined for various numbers of absentees on any given day. These values are shown in the table below. Find the expected number of absentees on a given day. (Give the answer to two decimal places.)

Number absent	0	1	2	3	4
Probability	0.18	0.26	0.29	0.23	0.04

12. ***Expected Profit of an Insurance Company*** An insurance company will insure a $200,000 home for its total value for an annual premium of $650. If the company spends $25 per year to service such a policy, the probability of total loss for such a home in a given year is 0.002, and you assume that either total loss or no loss will occur, what is the company's expected annual gain (or profit) on each such policy?

Profits from a College Foundation Raffle *A college foundation raises funds by selling raffle tickets for a new car worth* $36,000.

13. If 600 tickets are sold for $120 each, determine

(a) the expected *net* winnings of a person buying one of the tickets,

(b) the total profit for the foundation, assuming they had to purchase the car,

(c) the total profit for the foundation, assuming the car was donated.

14. For the raffle described in **Exercise 13,** if 720 tickets are sold for $120 each, determine

(a) the expected *net* winnings of a person buying one of the tickets,

(b) the total profit for the foundation, assuming they had to purchase the car,

(c) the total profit for the foundation, assuming the car was donated.

Winnings and Profits of a Raffle *Five thousand raffle tickets are sold. One first prize of* $1000, *two second prizes of* $500 *each, and three third prizes of* $100 *each will be awarded, with all winners selected randomly.*

15. If you purchased one ticket, what are your expected gross winnings?

16. If you purchased ten tickets, what are your expected gross winnings?

17. If the tickets were sold for $1 each, how much profit goes to the raffle sponsor?

18. ***Expected Sales at a Theater Snack Bar*** A children's theater found in a random survey that 58 customers bought one snack bar item, 49 bought two items, 31 bought three items, 4 bought four items, and 8 avoided the snack bar altogether. Use this information to find the expected number of snack bar items per customer. (Round your answer to the nearest tenth.)

Fuse/Getty Images

19. ***Expected Number of Children to Attend an Amusement Park*** An amusement park, considering adding some new attractions, conducted a study over several typical days and found that, of 10,000 families entering the park, 1020 brought just one child (defined as younger than age twelve), 3370 brought two children, 3510 brought three children, 1340 brought four children, 510 brought five children, 80 brought six children, and 170 brought no children at all. Find the expected number of children per family attending this park. (Round your answer to the nearest tenth.)

20. ***Expected Sums of Randomly Selected Numbers*** Four cards are numbered 1 through 4. Two of these cards are chosen randomly (without replacement), and the numbers on them are added. Find the expected value of this sum.

21. ***Prospects for Electronics Jobs in a City*** In a certain California city, projections for the next year are that there is a 20% chance that electronics jobs will increase by 200, a 50% chance that they will increase by 300, and a 30% chance that they will decrease by 800. What is the expected change in the number of electronics jobs in that city in the next year?

22. ***Expected Winnings in Keno*** In one version of the game *keno,* the house has a pot containing 80 balls, numbered 1 through 80. A player buys a ticket for $1 and marks one number on it (from 1 to 80). The house then selects 20 of the 80 numbers at random. If the number selected by the player is among the 20 selected by the management, the player is paid $3.20. Find the expected net winnings for this game.

23. Refer to **Examples 6 and 7.** Considering the three different approaches (expected values, optimist, and pessimist), which one seems most reasonable to you, and why?

Contractor Decisions Based on Expected Profits *Lori Hales, a commercial building contractor, will commit her company to one of three projects depending on her analysis of potential profits or losses as shown here.*

Project *A*		Project *B*		Project *C*	
Profit or Loss x	**Probability** $P(x)$	**Profit or Loss** x	**Probability** $P(x)$	**Profit or Loss** x	**Probability** $P(x)$
$60,000	0.10	$0	0.20	$40,000	0.65
180,000	0.60	210,000	0.35	340,000	0.35
250,000	0.30	290,000	0.45		

Determine which project Lori should choose according to each approach.

24. expected values

25. the optimist viewpoint

26. the pessimist viewpoint

Expected Winnings in a Game Show *A game show contestant is offered the option of receiving a computer system worth* $2300 *or accepting a chance to win either a luxury vacation worth* $5000 *or a boat worth* $8000. *If the second option is chosen the contestant's probabilities of winning the vacation or the boat are* 0.20 *and* 0.15, *respectively.*

27. If the contestant were to turn down the computer system and go for one of the other prizes, what would be the expected winnings?

28. Purely in terms of monetary value, what is the contestant's wiser choice?

Evaluating an Insurance Purchase *David Glenn, the promoter of an outdoor concert, expects a gate profit of* $100,000, *unless it rains, which would reduce the gate profit to* $30,000. *The probability of rain is* 0.20. *For a premium of* $25,000 *David can purchase insurance coverage that would pay him* $100,000 *in case of rain.*

Use this information for Exercises 29–32.

29. Find the expected net profit when the insurance is purchased.

30. Find the expected net profit when the insurance is not purchased.

31. Based on expected values, which is David's wiser choice in this situation?

32. If you were the promoter, would you base your decision on expected values? Explain your reasoning.

Expected Values in Book Sales *Jessica Lasda, an educational publisher representative, presently has five accounts, and her manager is considering assigning her three more accounts. The new accounts would bring potential volume to her business, and some of her present accounts have potential for growth as well. See the following table and continue on the next page.*

1	2	3	4	5	6
Account Number	**Existing Volume**	**Potential Additional Volume**	**Probability of Getting Additional Volume**	**Expected Value of Additional Volume**	**Existing Volume plus Expected Value of Additional Volume**
1	$10,000	$10,000	0.40	$4000	$14,000
2	30,000	0	—	—	30,000
3	25,000	15,000	0.20	3000	
4	35,000	0	—	—	
5	15,000	5,000	0.30		
6	0	30,000	0.10		
7	0	25,000	0.70		
8	0	45,000	0.60		

Use the previous table to work Exercises 33–37.

33. Compute the four missing expected values in column 5.

34. Compute the six missing amounts in column 6.

35. What is Jessica's total "expected" additional volume?

36. If Jessica achieved her expected additional volume in all accounts, what would be the total volume of all her accounts?

37. If Jessica achieved her expected additional volume in all accounts, by what percentage (to the nearest tenth of a percent) would she increase her total volume?

38. ***Expected Winnings in Keno*** Recall that in the game keno of **Exercise 22,** the house randomly selects 20 numbers from the counting numbers 1–80. In the variation called 6-spot keno, the player pays 60¢ for his ticket and marks 6 numbers of his choice. If the 20 numbers selected by the house contain at least 3 of those chosen by the player, he gets a payoff according to this scheme.

3 of the player's numbers among the 20	\$0.35
4 of the player's numbers among the 20	2.00
5 of the player's numbers among the 20	60.00
6 of the player's numbers among the 20	1250.00

Find the player's expected net winnings in this game. [*Hint:* The four probabilities required here can be found using combinations the fundamental counting principle, and the theoretical probability formula (**Section 1**).]

EXTENSION Estimating Probabilities by Simulation

Simulating Genetic Traits • Simulating Human Births

		Second Parent	
		R	r
First Parent	**R**	RR	Rr
	r	rR	rr

Simulation methods, also called **"Monte Carlo" methods,** require huge numbers of random digits, so computers are used to produce them. A computer, however, cannot toss coins. It must use an algorithmic process, programmed into the computer, which is called a **random number generator.** It is very difficult to avoid all nonrandom patterns in the results, so the digits produced are called "pseudorandom" numbers. They must pass a battery of tests of randomness before being "approved for use."

Computer scientists and physicists have been encountering unexpected difficulties with even the most sophisticated random number generators. Therefore, they must be carefully checked along with each new simulation application proposed.

Simulating Genetic Traits

An important area within probability theory is the process called **simulation.** It is possible to study a complicated, or unclear, phenomenon by *simulating,* or imitating, it with a simpler phenomenon involving the same basic probabilities.

For example, recall from **Section 1** Mendel's discovery that when two Rr pea plants (red-flowered but carrying both red and white genes) are crossed, the offspring will have red flowers if an R gene is received from either parent or from both. This is because red is dominant and white is recessive. **Table 3**, reproduced here in the margin, shows that three of the four equally likely possibilities result in red-flowered offspring.

Now suppose we want to estimate the probability that three offspring in a row will have red flowers. It is much easier (and quicker) to toss coins than to cross pea plants. And the equally likely outcomes, heads and tails, can be used to simulate the transfer of the equally likely genes, R and r. If we toss two coins, say a nickel and a penny, then we can interpret the results as follows.

hh ⇒ RR ⇒ red gene from first parent and red gene from second parent
⇒ red flowers

ht ⇒ Rr ⇒ red gene from first parent and white gene from second parent
⇒ red flowers

th ⇒ rR ⇒ white gene from first parent and red gene from second parent
⇒ red flowers

tt ⇒ rr ⇒ white gene from first parent and white gene from second parent
⇒ white flowers

Although nothing is certain for a few tosses, the law of large numbers indicates that larger and larger numbers of tosses should become better and better indicators of general trends in the genetic process.

EXAMPLE 1 Simulating Genetic Processes

Toss two coins 50 times and use the results to approximate the probability that the crossing of Rr pea plants will produce three successive red-flowered offspring.

SOLUTION

We actually tossed two coins 50 times and got the following sequence.

th, hh, th, tt, th, hh, ht, th, ht, th, hh, hh, tt, th, hh,
ht, ht, ht, ht, th, hh, hh, hh, tt, ht, tt, hh, ht, ht, hh, tt,
tt, tt, th, tt, tt, hh, ht, ht, ht, hh, tt, th, hh, tt, hh, ht,
tt, tt, tt

By the color interpretation described on the previous page, this gives the following sequence of flower colors in the offspring.

Only "both tails" gives white.

red–red–red–white–red–red–red–red–red–red–red–red–white–
red–red–red–red–red–red–red–red–red–red–white–red–white–
red–red–red–red–white–white–white–red–white–white–red–red–
red–red–red–white–red–red–white–red–red–white–white–white

We now have an experimental list of 48 sets of three successive plants, the 1st, 2nd, and 3rd entries, then the 2nd, 3rd, and 4th entries, and so on. Do you see why there are 48 in all?

Now we just count up the number of these sets of three that are "red-red-red." Since there are 20 of those, our empirical probability of three successive red offspring, obtained through simulation, is $\frac{20}{48} = \frac{5}{12}$, or about 0.417. By applying the multiplication rule of probability (with all outcomes independent of one another), we find that the theoretical value is $\left(\frac{3}{4}\right)^3 = \frac{27}{64}$, or about 0.422, so our approximation obtained by simulation is very close.

Simulating Human Births In human births boys and girls are (essentially) equally likely. Therefore, an individual birth can be simulated by tossing a fair coin, letting a head correspond to a girl and a tail to a boy.

EXAMPLE 2 Simulating Births with Coin Tossing

A sequence of 40 actual coin tosses produced the results below.

bbggb, gbbbg, gbgbb, bggbg, bbbbg, gbbgg, gbbgg, bgbbg

(For every head we have written g, for girl. For every tail, b, for boy.)

(a) How many pairs of two successive births are represented by the sequence?

(b) How many of those pairs consist of both boys?

(c) Find the empirical probability, based on this simulation, that two successive births both will be boys. Give your answer to three decimal places.

SOLUTION

(a) Beginning with the 1st–2nd pair and ending with the 39th–40th pair, there are 39 pairs.

(b) Observing the sequence of boys and girls, we count 11 pairs of two consecutive boys.

(c) Utilizing parts (a) and (b), we have $\frac{11}{39} \approx 0.282$.

David Loh/Reuters/Corbis

Pilots, astronauts, race car drivers, and others train in **simulators.** Some of these devices, which may be viewed as very technical, high-cost versions of video games, imitate conditions to be encountered later in the "real world." A simulator session allows estimation of the likelihood, or probability, of different responses that the learner would display under actual conditions. Repeated sessions help the learner to develop more successful responses before actual equipment and lives are put at risk.

Table 20

→51592
77876
36500
40571
04822
→53033
92080
01587
36006
63698
→17297
22841
→91979
96480
74949
76896
47588
45521
02472
55184
40177
84861
86937
20931
22454
→73219
→55707
48007
→65191
06772
94928
→15709
39922
96365
14655
65587
76905
12369
54219
89329
90060
06975
05050
69774
→78351
11464
84086
→51497
12307
68009

Another way to simulate births, and other phenomena, is with random numbers. The spinner in **Figure 12** can be used to obtain a table of random digits, like in **Table 20.** The 250 random digits generated have been grouped conveniently so that we can easily follow down a column or across a row to carry out a simulation.

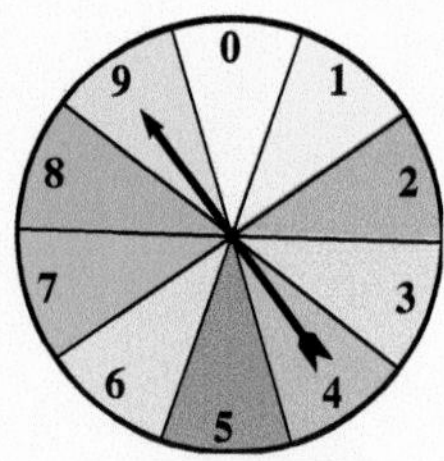

Figure 12

EXAMPLE 3 Simulating Births with Random Numbers

A couple plans to have five children. Use random number simulation to estimate the probability they will have more than three boys.

SOLUTION

Let each sequence of five digits, as they appear in **Table 20,** represent a family with five children, and (arbitrarily) associate odd digits with boys, even digits with girls. (Recall that 0 is even.) Verify that, of the fifty families simulated, only the ten marked with arrows have more than 3 boys (4 boys or 5 boys). Therefore, the estimated (empirical) probability is

$$P(\text{more than 3 boys}) = \frac{10}{50} = 0.20.$$

The theoretical value for the probability in **Example 3** above would be the same as that obtained in **Example 3** of **Section 4.** It was 0.1875. Our estimate above was fairly close. In light of the law of large numbers, a larger sampling of random digits (more than 50 simulated families) would likely yield a closer approximation.

EXAMPLE 4 Simulating Card Drawing with Random Numbers

Use random number simulation to estimate the probability that two cards drawn from a standard deck with replacement both will be of the same suit.

SOLUTION

Use this correspondence: 0 and 1 mean clubs, 2 and 3 mean diamonds, 4 and 5 mean hearts, 6 and 7 mean spades, 8 and 9 are disregarded. Now refer to **Table 20.** If we (arbitrarily) use the first digit of each five-digit group, omitting 8s and 9s, we obtain the sequence

5–7–3–4–0–5–0–3–6–1–2–7–7–4–4–0–5–4–2–2–
7–5–4–6–0–1–3–1–6–7–1–5–0–0–6–7–1–5–1–6.

First digits of all groups

This 40-digit sequence of digits yields the sequence of suits shown next.

5 gives hearts, 7 gives spades, 3 gives diamonds, and so on.

hearts–spades–diamonds–hearts–clubs–hearts–clubs–diamonds–spades–
clubs–diamonds–spades–spades–hearts–hearts–clubs–hearts–hearts–
diamonds–diamonds–spades–hearts–hearts–spades–clubs–clubs–
diamonds–clubs–spades–spades–clubs–hearts–clubs–clubs–spades–
spades–clubs–hearts–clubs–spades

Verify that, of the 39 successive pairs of suits (hearts–spades, spades–diamonds, diamonds–hearts, etc.), 9 of them are pairs of the same suit. This makes the estimated probability $\frac{9}{39} \approx 0.23$. (For comparison, the theoretical value is 0.25.)

EXTENSION EXERCISES

1. ***Simulating Pea Plant Reproduction with Coin Tossing*** Explain why, in **Example 1,** fifty tosses of the coins produced only 48 sets of three successive offspring.

2. ***Simulating Pea Plant Reproduction with Coin Tossing*** Use the sequence of flower colors of **Example 1** to approximate the probability that *four* successive offspring all will have red flowers.

3. ***Comparing the Likelihoods of Girl and Boy Births*** Should the probability of two successive girl births be any different from that of two successive boy births?

4. ***Finding Empirical Probability*** Simulate 40 births by tossing coins yourself, and obtain an empirical probability for two successive girls.

5. ***Simulating Boy and Girl Children with Random Numbers*** Use **Table 20** to simulate fifty families with three children. Let 0–4 correspond to boys and 5–9 to girls, and use the middle three digits of the 5-digit groupings (159, 787, 650, and so on). Estimate the probability of exactly two boys in a family of three children. Compare with the theoretical probability, which is $\frac{3}{8} = 0.375$.

Simulating One-and-One Foul Shooting with Random Numbers *In **Exercises 71–73** of **Section 3**, Christine, who had a 70% foul-shooting record, had probabilities of scoring* 0, 1, *or* 2 *points of* 0.30, 0.21, *and* 0.49, *respectively.*

Use **Table 20** *(with digits 0–6 representing hit and 7–9 representing miss) to simulate 50 one-and-one shooting opportunities for Christine. Begin at the top left (5, 7, 3, etc., to the bottom), then move to the second column (1, 7, 6, etc.), going until 50 one-and-one opportunities are obtained. (Some "opportunities" involve one shot and one random digit, while others involve two shots and two random digits.) Keep a tally of the numbers of times* 0, 1, *and* 2 *points are scored.*

Number of Points	Tally
0	
1	
2	

From the tally, find the empirical probability (to two decimal places) of each event.

6. no points 7. 1 point 8. 2 points

Determining the Path of a Random Walk Using a Die and a Coin ***Exercises 49–56** of **Section 4** illustrated a simple version of the idea of a "random walk." Atomic particles released in nuclear fission also move in a random fashion. During World War II, John von Neumann and Stanislaw Ulam used simulation with random numbers to study particle motion in nuclear reactions. Von Neumann coined the name "Monte Carlo" for the methods used.*

The figure suggests a model for random motion in two dimensions. Assume that a particle moves in a series of 1-unit "jumps," each one in a random direction, any one of 12 equally likely possibilities. One way to choose directions is to roll a fair die and toss a fair coin. The die determines one of the directions 1–6, coupled with heads on the coin. Tails on the coin reverses the direction of the die, so that the die coupled with tails gives directions 7–12. So 3h (meaning 3 with the die and heads with the coin) gives direction 3; 3t *gives direction* 9 *(opposite to 3); and so on.*

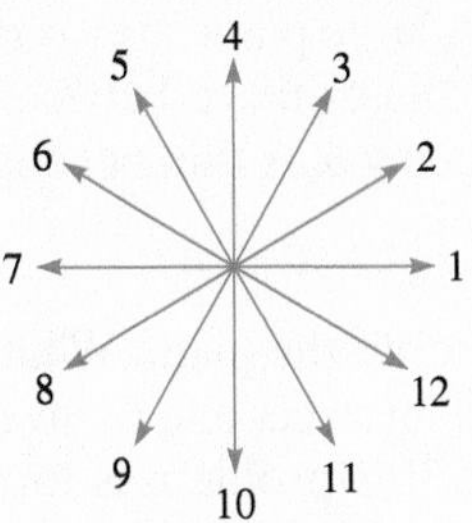

9. Simulate the motion described above with 10 rolls of a die (and tosses of a coin). Draw the 10-jump path you get. Make your drawing accurate enough so you can estimate (by measuring) how far from its starting point the particle ends up.

10. Repeat the experiment of **Exercise 9** four more times. Measure distance from start to finish for each of the 5 "random trips." Add these 5 distances and divide the sum by 5, to arrive at an "expected net distance" for such a trip.

For Exercises 11 and 12, consider another two-dimensional random walk governed by the following conditions.

- *Start out from a given street corner, and travel one block north. At each intersection:*
- *Turn left with probability* $\frac{1}{6}$.
- *Go straight with probability* $\frac{2}{6}\ (= \frac{1}{3})$.
- *Turn right with probability* $\frac{3}{6}\ (= \frac{1}{2})$.

(Never turn around.)

11. ***A Random Walk Using a Fair Die*** Explain how a fair die could be used to simulate this random walk.

12. ***A Random Walk Using a Random Number Table*** Use **Table 20** to simulate this random walk. For every 1 encountered in the table, turn left and proceed for another block. For every 2 or 3, go straight and proceed for another block. For every 4, 5, or 6, turn right and proceed for another block. Disregard all other digits, that is, 0s, 7s, 8s, and 9s. (Do you see how this scheme satisfies the probabilities given before **Exercise 11**?) This time begin at the upper right corner of the table, running down the column 2, 6, 0, and so on, to the bottom. When this column of digits is used up, stop the "walk." Describe, in terms of distance and direction, where you have ended up relative to your starting point.

COLLABORATIVE INVESTIGATION

Finding Empirical Values of π

The information in this investigation was obtained from Burton's History of Mathematics: An Introduction, *Third Edition, by David M. Burton, published by Wm. C. Brown, 1995, page 440.*

The following problem was posed by Georges Louis Leclerc, Comte de Buffon (1707–1788) in his *Histoire Naturelle* in 1777. A large plane area is ruled with equidistant parallel lines, the distance between two consecutive lines of the series being a. A thin needle of length

$$\ell < a$$

is tossed randomly onto the plane. What is the probability that the needle will intersect one of these lines?

The answer to this problem is found using integral calculus, and the probability p is shown to be $p = \frac{2\ell}{\pi a}$. Solving for π gives us the formula

$$\pi = \frac{2\ell}{pa}, \qquad \textbf{(1)}$$

which can be used to approximate the value of π experimentally. This was first observed by Pierre Simon de Laplace, and such an experiment was carried out by Johann Wolf, a professor of astronomy at Bern, in about 1850. In this investigation, we will perform a similar experiment.

See http://webspace.ship.edu/deensley/mathdl/stats/Buffon.html for a dynamic illustration of this Buffon Needle Problem.

Topics for Discussion

Divide the class into groups of 3 or 4 students each. Each group will need the materials listed in the next column.

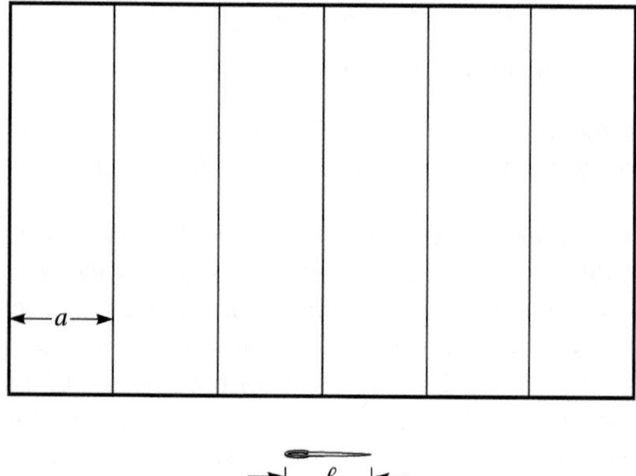

1. a sheet of paper with a series of parallel lines evenly spaced across it
2. a thin needle, or needlelike object, with a length less than the distance between adjacent parallel lines on the paper

Each group should carry out these steps:

1. Measure and record the distance between lines (a) and the length of the needle (ℓ), using the same units for both.
2. Assign one member to drop the needle onto the paper, another to determine whether the needle "hits" a line or not, and another to keep a tally of hits and misses.
3. Discuss ways to minimize bias so that the position and orientation of the dropped needle will be as random as possible.
4. Drop the needle 100 times, and record the number of hits.
5. Calculate the probability p = (number of hits)/100. Is this probability value theoretical or empirical?
6. Enter the calculated value of p and the measured values of a and ℓ into formula (1) to obtain a value of π. Round this value to four decimal places.

Now come back together as a class and record the various values obtained for π. Discuss the following questions.

1. The correct value of π, to four decimal places, is 3.1416. Which value of π, reported by the various groups, is most accurate? How far off is it?
2. Was it necessary to drop the needle 100 times, or could more or fewer tosses have been used?
3. Wolf tossed his needle 5000 times and it hit a line 2532 times, leading to an experimental value of π equal to 3.1596. How far off was Wolf's value?
4. How could the experiment be modified to produce "better" values for π?
5. Why could different groups use different ℓ to a ratios and still all obtain legitimate approximations for π?
6. Does the simulation method investigated here seem like a reasonable way to approximate π? Why, or why not?

CHAPTER TEST

1. Explain the difference between *empirical* and *theoretical* probabilities.

2. State the *law of large numbers,* and use coin tossing to illustrate it.

Drawing Cards *A single card is chosen at random from a standard 52-card deck. Find the odds against its being each of the following.*

3. a heart

4. a red queen

5. a king or a black face card

Genetics of Cystic Fibrosis *The chart represents genetic transmission of cystic fibrosis.* C *denotes a normal gene while* c *denotes a cystic fibrosis gene. (Normal is dominant.) Both parents in this case are* Cc, *which means that they inherited one of each gene, and are, therefore, carriers but do not have the disease.*

		Second Parent	
		C	c
First Parent	C		Cc
	c		

6. Complete the chart, showing all four equally likely gene arrangements.

7. Find the probability that a child of these parents will also be a carrier without the disease.

8. What are the odds that a child of these parents actually will have cystic fibrosis?

Days Off for Pizza Parlor Workers *The manager of a pizza parlor (which operates seven days a week) allows each of three employees to select one day off next week. Assuming the selection is done randomly and independently, find the probability of each event.*

9. All three select different days.

10. All three select the same day, given that all three select a day beginning with the same letter.

11. Exactly two of them select the same day.

Building Numbers from Sets of Digits *Two numbers are randomly selected without replacement from the set* $\{1, 2, 3, 4, 5\}$. *Find the probability of each event.*

12. Both numbers are even.

13. Both numbers are prime.

14. The sum of the two numbers is odd.

15. The product of the two numbers is odd.

Selecting Committees *A three-member committee is selected randomly from a group consisting of three men and two women.*

16. Let x denote the number of men on the committee, and complete the probability distribution table.

x	$P(x)$
0	0
1	
2	
3	

17. Find the probability that the committee members are not all men.

18. Find the expected number of men on the committee.

Rolling Dice *A pair of dice are rolled. Find the following.*

19. the probability of "doubles" (the same number on both dice)

20. the odds in favor of a sum greater than 2

21. the odds against a sum of "7 or 11"

22. the probability of a sum that is even and less than 5

Making Par in Golf *Ted Krischak has a* 0.78 *chance of making par on each hole of golf that he plays. Today he plans to play just three holes. Find the probability of each event. Round answers to three decimal places.*

23. He makes par on all three holes.

24. He makes par on exactly two of the three holes.

25. He makes par on at least one of the three holes.

26. He makes par on the first and third holes but not on the second.

Drawing Cards *Two cards are drawn, without replacement, from a standard 52-card deck. Find the probability of each event.*

27. Both cards are red.

28. Both cards are the same color.

29. The second card is a queen, given that the first card is an ace

30. The first card is a face card and the second is black.

Table 21 Rolling Two Fair Dice

		Green Die					
		1	**2**	**3**	**4**	**5**	**6**
Red Die	**1**	(1, 1)	(1, 2)	(1, 3)	(1, 4)	(1, 5)	(1, 6)
	2	(2, 1)	(2, 2)	(2, 3)	(2, 4)	(2, 5)	(2, 6)
	3	(3, 1)	(3, 2)	(3, 3)	(3, 4)	(3, 5)	(3, 6)
	4	(4, 1)	(4, 2)	(4, 3)	(4, 4)	(4, 5)	(4, 6)
	5	(5, 1)	(5, 2)	(5, 3)	(5, 4)	(5, 5)	(5, 6)
	6	(6, 1)	(6, 2)	(6, 3)	(6, 4)	(6, 5)	(6, 6)

Table 22 Pascal's Triangle

Row Number		Row Sum
0	1	1
1	1 1	2
2	1 2 1	4
3	1 3 3 1	8
4	1 4 6 4 1	16
5	1 5 10 10 5 1	32
6	1 6 15 20 15 6 1	64
7	1 7 21 35 35 21 7 1	128
8	1 8 28 56 70 56 28 8 1	256
9	1 9 36 84 126 126 84 36 9 1	512
10	1 10 45 120 210 252 210 120 45 10 1	1024

ANSWERS TO SELECTED EXERCISES

1 Exercises

1. (a) $\frac{1}{3}$ **(b)** $\frac{1}{3}$ **(c)** $\frac{1}{3}$ **3. (a)** $\frac{1}{2}$ **(b)** $\frac{1}{3}$ **(c)** $\frac{1}{6}$
5. (a) $\{1, 2, 3\}$ **(b)** 2 **(c)** 1 **(d)** 3 **(e)** $\frac{2}{3}$ **(f)** 2 to 1
7. (a) $\{11, 12, 13, 21, 22, 23, 31, 32, 33\}$ **(b)** $\frac{2}{3}$ **(c)** $\frac{1}{3}$
(d) $\frac{1}{3}$ **(e)** $\frac{4}{9}$ **9. (a)** 7 to 4 **(b)** 6 to 5 **(c)** 9 to 2
11. (a) $\frac{1}{50}$ **(b)** $\frac{2}{50} = \frac{1}{25}$ **(c)** $\frac{3}{50}$ **(d)** $\frac{4}{50} = \frac{2}{25}$
(e) $\frac{5}{50} = \frac{1}{10}$ **13. (a)** $\frac{1}{36}$ **(b)** $\frac{2}{36} = \frac{1}{18}$ **(c)** $\frac{3}{36} = \frac{1}{12}$
(d) $\frac{4}{36} = \frac{1}{9}$ **(e)** $\frac{5}{36}$ **(f)** $\frac{6}{36} = \frac{1}{6}$ **(g)** $\frac{5}{36}$ **(h)** $\frac{4}{36} = \frac{1}{9}$
(i) $\frac{3}{36} = \frac{1}{12}$ **(j)** $\frac{2}{36} = \frac{1}{18}$ **(k)** $\frac{1}{36}$ **15.** 0.329 **17.** $\frac{1}{9}$
19. $\frac{1}{4}$ **21.** $\frac{1}{4}$ **23. (a)** $\frac{3}{4}$ **(b)** $\frac{1}{4}$
25. $\frac{1}{250{,}000} = 0.000004$ **27.** $\frac{1}{4}$ **29.** $\frac{1}{4}$ **31.** $\frac{2}{4} = \frac{1}{2}$
33. $\frac{1}{500} = 0.002$ **35.** about 160 **37.** $\frac{2}{4} = \frac{1}{2}$ **39. (a)** 0
(b) no **(c)** yes **41.** Answers will vary. **43.** $\frac{12}{31}$
45. $\frac{36}{2{,}598{,}960} \approx 0.00001385$ **47.** $\frac{624}{2{,}598{,}960} \approx 0.00024010$
49. $\frac{1}{4} \cdot \frac{5108}{2{,}598{,}960} \approx 0.00049135$ **51. (a)** $\frac{5}{9}$ **(b)** $\frac{49}{144}$
(c) $\frac{5}{48}$ **53.** $3 \cdot 1 \cdot 2 \cdot 1 \cdot 1 \cdot 1 = 6$; $\frac{6}{720} = \frac{1}{120} \approx 0.0083$
55. $4 \cdot 3! \cdot 3! = 144$; $\frac{144}{720} = \frac{1}{5} = 0.2$
57. $\frac{2}{{}_7C_2} = \frac{2}{21} \approx 0.095$ **59.** $\frac{{}_5C_3}{{}_{12}C_3} = \frac{1}{22} \approx 0.045$
61. $\frac{1}{{}_{26}P_3} \approx 0.000064$ **63.** $\frac{3}{28} \approx 0.107$
65. (a) $\frac{8}{9^2} = \frac{8}{81} \approx 0.099$ **(b)** $\frac{4}{{}_9C_2} = \frac{1}{9} \approx 0.111$ **67.** 1
69. $\frac{9}{9 \cdot 10} = \frac{1}{10}$ **71.** $\frac{1}{15}$

2 Exercises

1. yes **3.** Answers will vary. **5.** $\frac{1}{2}$ **7.** $\frac{5}{6}$ **9.** $\frac{2}{3}$
11. (a) $\frac{2}{13}$ **(b)** 2 to 11 **13. (a)** $\frac{11}{26}$ **(b)** 11 to 15
15. (a) $\frac{9}{13}$ **(b)** 9 to 4 **17.** $\frac{2}{3}$ **19.** $\frac{7}{36}$

21. $P(A) + P(B) + P(C) + P(D) = 1$ **23.** 0.005365
25. 0.971285 **27.** 0.76 **29.** 0.92 **31.** 6 to 19

33.

x	$P(x)$
3	0.1
4	0.1
5	0.2
6	0.2
7	0.2
8	0.1
9	0.1

35. $n(A') = s - a$
37. $P(A) + P(A') = 1$
39. 180 **41.** $\frac{2}{3}$ **43.** 1

3 Exercises

1. independent **3.** not independent **5.** independent
7. $\frac{52}{100} = \frac{13}{25}$ **9.** $\frac{69}{100}$ **11.** $\frac{14}{31}$ **13.** $\frac{4}{7} \cdot \frac{4}{7} = \frac{16}{49}$
15. $\frac{2}{7} \cdot \frac{1}{7} = \frac{2}{49}$ **17.** $\frac{4}{7} \cdot \frac{3}{6} = \frac{2}{7}$ **19.** $\frac{1}{6}$ **21.** 0
23. $\frac{12}{51} = \frac{4}{17}$ **25.** $\frac{12}{52} \cdot \frac{11}{51} = \frac{11}{221}$ **27.** $\frac{4}{52} \cdot \frac{11}{51} = \frac{11}{663}$
29. $\frac{1}{3}$ **31.** 1 **33.** $\frac{3}{10}$ (the same)
35. $\frac{1}{2} \cdot \frac{1}{2} \cdot \frac{1}{2} \cdot \frac{1}{2} \cdot \frac{1}{2} \cdot \frac{1}{2} = \frac{1}{64}$ **37.** 0.490 **39.** 0.027
41. 0.95 **43.** 0.23 **45.** $\frac{1}{20}$ **47.** $\frac{1}{5}$ **49.** $\frac{1}{5}$ **51. (a)** $\frac{3}{4}$
(b) $\frac{1}{2}$ **(c)** $\frac{5}{16}$ **53.** 0.2704 **55.** 0.2496
57. Answers will vary. **59.** $\frac{1}{64} \approx 0.0156$ **61.** 10
63. 0.400 **65.** 0.080 **67.** $(0.90)^4 = 0.6561$
69. ${}_4C_2 \cdot (0.10) \cdot (0.20) \cdot (0.70)^2 = 0.0588$ **71.** 0.30
73. 0.49 **75.** Answers will vary.

4 Exercises

1. $\frac{1}{8}$ **3.** $\frac{3}{8}$ **5.** $\frac{3}{4}$ **7.** $\frac{1}{2}$ **9.** $\frac{3}{8}$ **11.** $x; n; n$ **13.** $\frac{7}{128}$
15. $\frac{35}{128}$ **17.** $\frac{21}{128}$ **19.** $\frac{1}{128}$ **21.** $\frac{25}{72}$ **23.** $\frac{1}{216}$ **25.** 0.041
27. 0.268 **29.** Answers will vary. **31.** Answers will vary.
33. 0.016 **35.** 0.020 **37.** 0.137 **39.** 0.572 **41.** 0.669
43. 0.975 **45.** 0.883 **47.** $6p^2(1 - p)^2$
49. $\frac{1}{1024} \approx 0.001$ **51.** $\frac{45}{1024} \approx 0.044$
53. $\frac{210}{1024} = \frac{105}{512} \approx 0.205$ **55.** $\frac{772}{1024} \approx 0.754$

5 Exercises

1. Answers will vary. **3.** $\frac{5}{2}$ **5.** \$1 **7.** \$0.50
9. no (expected net winnings: $-\frac{3}{4}$¢) **11.** 1.69
13. (a) −\$60 **(b)** \$36,000 **(c)** \$72,000 **15.** \$0.46
17. \$2700 **19.** 2.7 **21.** a decrease of 50 **23.** Answers will vary. **25.** Project C **27.** \$2200 **29.** \$81,000
31. Do not purchase the insurance (because \$86,000 > \$81,000). **33.** \$1500; \$3000; \$17,500; \$27,000
35. \$56,000 **37.** 48.7%

Extension Exercises

1. Answers will vary. **3.** no **5.** $\frac{18}{50} = 0.36$ (This is quite close to 0.375, the theoretical value.) **7.** $\frac{6}{50} = 0.12$
9. Answers will vary. **11.** Answers will vary.

Chapter Test

1. Answers will vary. **2.** Answers will vary. **3.** 3 to 1
4. 25 to 1 **5.** 11 to 2 **6.** row 1: CC; row 2: cC, cc
7. $\frac{1}{2}$ **8.** 1 to 3 **9.** $\frac{7}{7} \cdot \frac{6}{7} \cdot \frac{5}{7} = \frac{30}{49}$ **10.** $\frac{7}{19}$
11. $1 - \left(\frac{30}{49} + \frac{1}{49}\right) = \frac{18}{49}$ **12.** $\frac{{}_2C_2}{{}_5C_2} = \frac{1}{10}$
13. $\frac{{}_3C_2}{{}_5C_2} = \frac{3}{10}$ **14.** $\frac{6}{10} = \frac{3}{5}$ **15.** $\frac{3}{10}$
16. $\frac{3}{10}; \frac{6}{10}; \frac{1}{10}$ **17.** $\frac{9}{10}$ **18.** $\frac{18}{10} = \frac{9}{5}$ **19.** $\frac{6}{36} = \frac{1}{6}$
20. 35 to 1 **21.** 7 to 2 **22.** $\frac{4}{36} = \frac{1}{9}$ **23.** $(0.78)^3 \approx 0.475$
24. ${}_3C_2 \cdot (0.78)^2 \cdot (0.22) \approx 0.402$
25. $1 - (0.22)^3 \approx 0.989$
26. $(0.78) \cdot (0.22) \cdot (0.78) \approx 0.134$ **27.** $\frac{25}{102}$ **28.** $\frac{25}{51}$
29. $\frac{4}{51}$ **30.** $\frac{3}{26}$

Probability

Exercise Set 1

The sample space is {red, yellow, blue}.

1. The number of regions in the sample space is $n(S) = 3$. Each region has the same area and thus, has the same likelihood of occurring. Therefore,

(a) $P(\text{red}) = \dfrac{n(\text{red regions})}{n(S)} = \dfrac{1}{3}.$

(b) $P(\text{yellow}) = \dfrac{n(\text{yellow regions})}{n(S)} = \dfrac{1}{3}.$

(c) $P(\text{blue}) = \dfrac{n(\text{blue regions})}{n(S)} = \dfrac{1}{3}.$

3. The number of regions in the sample space is $n(S) = 6$. Each region (piece of the pie) has the same area and thus, has the same likelihood of occurring. The probability of landing on any one of the six regions is $\dfrac{1}{6}$, but we must account for the fact that some colors shade more than one region. Therefore,

(a) $P(\text{red}) = \dfrac{n(\text{red regions})}{n(S)} = \dfrac{3}{6} = \dfrac{1}{2}.$

(b)
$$\begin{aligned} P(\text{yellow}) &= \frac{n(\text{yellow regions})}{n(S)} \\ &= \frac{2}{6} \\ &= \frac{1}{3}. \end{aligned}$$

(c) $P(\text{blue}) = \dfrac{n(\text{blue regions})}{n(S)} = \dfrac{1}{6}.$

5. **(a)** The sample space is $\{1, 2, 3\}$.

(b) The number of favorable outcomes is 2.

(c) The number of unfavorable outcomes is 1.

(d) The total number of possible outcomes is 3.

(e) The probability of an odd number is given by
$$\begin{aligned} &P(\text{odd number}) \\ &= P(E) \\ &= \frac{\text{number of favorable outcomes}}{\text{total number of outcomes}} \\ &= \frac{2}{3}. \end{aligned}$$

(f) The odds in favor of an odd number is given by
$$\begin{aligned} &\text{Odds in favor} \\ &= \frac{\text{number of favorable outcomes}}{\text{number of unfavorable outcomes}} \\ &= \frac{2}{1}, \text{ or 2 to 1} \end{aligned}$$

7. **(a)** The sample space is $\{11, 12, 13, 21, 22, 23, 31, 32, 33\}$.

(b) The probability of an odd number is given by
$$\begin{aligned} &P(\text{odd number}) \\ &= P(E) \\ &= \frac{\text{number of favorable outcomes}}{\text{total number of outcomes}} \\ &= \frac{6}{9} \\ &= \frac{2}{3}. \end{aligned}$$

(c) The probability of a number with repeated digit is given by
$$\begin{aligned} P(\text{number with repeated digits}) &= \frac{3}{9} \\ &= \frac{1}{3}. \end{aligned}$$

(d) The probability of a number greater than 30 is given by
$$P(\text{number greater than 30}) = \frac{3}{9} = \frac{1}{3}.$$

(e) The primes are $\{11, 13, 23, 31\}$. Thus, the probability for a prime number is given by $P(\text{prime number}) = \dfrac{4}{9}.$

9. **(a)** The odds against selecting a red ball is given by
Odds against
$= \dfrac{\text{number of unfavorable outcomes}}{\text{number of favorable outcomes}}$
$= \dfrac{7}{4}$ or 7 to 4.

(b) The odds against selecting a yellow ball is given by
Odds against
$= \dfrac{\text{number of unfavorable outcomes}}{\text{number of favorable outcomes}}$
$= \dfrac{6}{5}$ or 6 to 5.

(c) The odds against selecting a blue ball is given by
Odds against
$= \dfrac{\text{number of unfavorable outcomes}}{\text{number of favorable outcomes}}$
$= \dfrac{9}{2}$ or 9 to 2.

11. **(a)** $P(\text{Smiley Lewis}) = \dfrac{1}{50}$

(b) $P(\text{The Drifters}) = \dfrac{2}{50} = \dfrac{1}{25}$

(c) $P(\text{Bobby Darin}) = \dfrac{3}{50}$

(d) $P(\text{The Coasters}) = \dfrac{4}{50} = \dfrac{2}{25}$

(e) $P(\text{Fats Domino}) = \dfrac{5}{50} = \dfrac{1}{10}$

13. Product table for "sum"

2nd die

	+	1	2	3	4	5	6
	1	2	3	4	5	6	7
	2	3	4	5	6	7	8
1st die	3	4	5	6	7	8	9
	4	5	6	7	8	9	10
	5	6	7	8	9	10	11
	6	7	8	9	10	11	12

(a) Of the 36 possible outcomes, one gives a sum of 2, so $P(\text{sum is 2}) = \dfrac{1}{36}$.

(b) The sum of 3 appears 2 times in the body of the table. Thus,
$P(\text{sum of 3}) = \dfrac{2}{36} = \dfrac{1}{18}$.

(c) The sum of 4 appears 3 times in the body of the table. Thus,
$P(\text{sum of 4}) = \dfrac{3}{36} = \dfrac{1}{12}$.

(d) The sum of 5 appears 4 times in the table. Thus, $P(\text{sum of 5}) = \dfrac{4}{36} = \dfrac{1}{9}$.

(e) The sum of 6 appears 5 times in the table. Thus, $P(\text{sum of 6}) = \dfrac{5}{36}$.

(f) The sum of 7 appears 6 times in the table. Thus, $P(\text{sum of 7}) = \dfrac{6}{36} = \dfrac{1}{6}$.

(g) The sum of 8 appears 5 times in the table. Thus, $P(\text{sum of 8}) = \dfrac{5}{36}$.

(h) The sum of 9 appears 4 times in the table. Thus, $P(\text{sum of 9}) = \dfrac{4}{36} = \dfrac{1}{9}$.

(i) The sum of 10 appears 3 times in the table. Thus, $P(\text{sum of 10}) = \dfrac{3}{36} = \dfrac{1}{12}$.

(j) The sum of 11 appears 2 times in the table. Thus, $P(\text{sum of 11}) = \dfrac{2}{36} = \dfrac{1}{18}$.

(k) The sum of 12 appears 1 time in the table. Thus, $P(\text{sum of 12}) = \dfrac{1}{36}$.

In Exercise 15, answers are computed to three decimal places.

15. The probability that a randomly selected location in California will be forested is $\frac{51,250}{155,959} \approx 0.329$.

17. The possible ways to obtain a sum of 7 using regular 6-sided dice are 1 + 6, 2 + 5, 3 + 4, 4 + 3, 5 + 2, and 6 + 1, where the first number in each sum comes from the first die and the second number in each sum comes from the second die. Since these dice have been altered, the only possibilities for obtaining a sum of 7 are 2 + 5, 4 + 3, 5 + 2, and 6 + 1. So there are 4 possible ways out of a total of 36 possible sums, so the probability is $\frac{4}{36} = \frac{1}{9}$.

19. Since there is no dominance, only RR will result in red flowers. Thus, $P(\text{red}) = \frac{1}{4}$.

21. Since only rr will result in white flowers $P(\text{white}) = \frac{1}{4}$.

23. **(a)** Since round peas are dominant over wrinkled peas, the combinations RR, Rr, and rR will all result in round peas. Thus, $P(\text{round}) = \frac{3}{4}$.

(b) Since wrinkled peas are recessive, only rr will result in wrinkled peas. Thus, $P(\text{wrinkled}) = \frac{1}{4}$.

25. Cystic fibrosis occurs in 1 of every 250,000 non-Caucasian births, so the empirical probability that cystic fibrosis will occur in a randomly selected non-Caucasian birth is $P = \frac{1}{250,000} = 0.000004$.

Construct a chart similar to Table 2 in the textbook and determine the probability of each of the following events.

		Second Parent	
	+	*C*	*c*
First Parent	*C*	*CC*	*Cc*
	c	*cC*	*cc*

27. C represents the normal (disease-free gene) and c represents the cystic fibrosis gene. Since c is a recessive gene, only the combination cc results in a child with the disease. Thus, the probability that their first child will have the disease is given by $P = \frac{1}{4}$.

29. Only the combination CC results in a child who neither has nor carries the disease, so the required probability is given by $P = \frac{1}{4}$.

Create a table that gives the possibilities when one parent is a carrier and the other is a non-carrier to answer Exercises 30–32.

		Second Parent	
	+	*C*	*c*
First Parent	*C*	*CC*	*Cc*
	C	*CC*	*Cc*

31. The combination Cc results in a child who is a healthy cystic fibrosis carrier. This combination occurs twice in the table (while the other combination that gives a carrier, cC, does not occur). Thus, the required probability is given by $P = \frac{2}{4} = \frac{1}{2}$.

33. Sickle-cell anemia occurs in about 1 of every 500 black baby births, so the empirical probability that a randomly selected black baby will have sickle-cell anemia is $P = \frac{1}{500} = 0.002$.

35. From Exercise 33, the probability that a particular black baby will have sickle-cell anemia is 0.002. Therefore, among 80,000 black baby births, about 0.002(80,000) = 160 occurrences of sickle-cell anemia would be expected.

For Exercise 37 let S represent the normal gene and s represent the sickle-cell gene. The possibilities for a child with parents who both have sickle-cell trait are given in the following table that gives the possibilities when one parent is a carrier and the other is a non-carrier.

	+	Second Parent	
		S	*s*
First Parent	*S*	*SS*	*Ss*
	s	*sS*	*ss*

37. Since the combinations Ss and sS result in sickle-cell trait, the probability that the child will have sickle-cell trait is given by

$$P = \frac{1}{4} = \frac{1}{2}.$$

39. **(a)** The empirical probability formula is

$$P(E) = \frac{\text{number of times event occurred}}{\text{number of times experiment performed}}.$$

Since the number of times that the event described in the exercise has occurred is 0, the probability fraction has a numerator of 0. The denominator is some natural number n. Thus,

$$P(E) = \frac{0}{n} = 0.$$

(b) There is no basis for establishing a theoretical probability for this event.

(c) A woman may break the 10-second barrier at any time in the future, so it is possible that this event will occur.

41. Writing exercise; answers will vary.

One approach to Exercise 43 is to consider the following: Odds in favor $= \frac{a}{b}$*; Odds against* $= \frac{b}{a}$*;*

Probability of same event $= \frac{a}{a+b}$.

43. The odds in favor of event E are 12 to 19, where $a = 12$ and $b = 19$. Since

$P(E) = \frac{a}{a+b}$, we have

$$P(E) = \frac{12}{12+19} = \frac{12}{31}.$$

45. From Table 1 in the text, there are 2,598,960 5-card poker hands. Of these 36 are straight flushes. Thus,

$$P(\text{straight flush}) = \frac{36}{2{,}598{,}960} \approx 0.00001385.$$

Refer to Table 1 in the text. Answers are given to eight decimal places.

47. From Table 1 in the text, there are 2,598,960 5-card poker hands. Of these 624 are four of a kind. Thus,

$$P(\text{four of a kind}) = \frac{624}{2{,}598{,}960} \approx 0.00024010.$$

49. Since there are 4 different suits, a hearts flush is $\frac{1}{4}$ of all possible non-royal and non-straight flushes. Thus, the probability is

$$\left(\frac{1}{4}\right)\cdot\left(\frac{5108}{2{,}598{,}960}\right) \approx 0.00049135.$$

51. Compare the area of the colored regions to the total area of the target. Using $\frac{22}{7}$ to approximate π, the areas of the colored regions are given by

blue: $\frac{22}{7}(2\text{ ft})^2 - \frac{22}{7}\left(\frac{1}{2}\text{ ft}\right)^2 = \frac{165}{14}\text{ ft}^2$;

white: $\frac{22}{7}(4\text{ ft})^2 - \frac{165}{14}\text{ ft}^2 = \frac{77}{2}\text{ ft}^2$;

red: $\frac{22}{7}(6\text{ ft})^2 - \frac{22}{7}(4\text{ ft})^2 = \frac{440}{7}\text{ ft}^2$.

The total area is given by

$$\pi(6\text{ ft})^2 \approx \frac{22}{7}\cdot 36\text{ ft}^2 = \frac{792}{7}\text{ ft}^2.$$

Thus, the probability of hitting a colored region is given by

$$P(\text{red}) = \left(\frac{440}{7}\right) \div \left(\frac{792}{7}\right) = \left(\frac{440}{7}\right)\cdot\left(\frac{7}{792}\right) = \frac{5}{9};$$

$$P(\text{white}) = \left(\frac{77}{2}\right) \div \left(\frac{792}{7}\right) = \left(\frac{77}{2}\right) \cdot \left(\frac{7}{792}\right) = \frac{49}{144};$$

$$P(\text{blue}) = \left(\frac{165}{14}\right) \div \left(\frac{792}{7}\right) = \left(\frac{165}{14}\right) \cdot \left(\frac{7}{792}\right) = \frac{5}{48}.$$

53. Use the fundamental counting principle to determine the number of favorable seating arrangements where each man will sit immediately to the left of his wife.
The first seat can be occupied by one of the three men, the second by his wife, the third by one of the two remaining men, etc. or, $3 \cdot 1 \cdot 2 \cdot 1 \cdot 1 \cdot 1 = 6$; since there are $6! = 720$ possible arrangements of the six people in the six seats, we have

$$P = \frac{6}{720} = \frac{1}{120} \approx 0.0083.$$

55. Use the fundamental counting principle to determine the number of ways the women can sit in three adjacent seats.
The first task is to decide in which seat the first woman is to sit. There are 4 choices (seats 1, 2, 3 or 4). Once this is decided, a second task would be to decide how many arrangements the three women can make sitting together (3!). The last task is to decide how many arrangements the three men could make sitting in the remaining three seats (3!). Thus, there are $4 \cdot 3! \cdot 3! = 144$ ways to accommodate the three women sitting together.
The probability of this occurring is given by $P = \frac{144}{720} = \frac{1}{5} = 0.2,$ where $6! = 720$ is the total number of seating arrangements possible.

57. Two distinct numbers are chosen randomly from the set $\left\{-2, -\frac{4}{3}, -\frac{1}{2}, 0, \frac{1}{2}, \frac{3}{4}, 3\right\}.$
To evaluate the probability that they will be the slopes of two perpendicular lines, find the size of the sample space and the size of the event of interest. The size of the sample space, $n(S)$, is given by ${}_7C_2 = 21,$ since we are choosing 2 items from a set of 7. The size of the event of interest, $n(E)$, is 2 (remember that perpendicular lines must have slopes that are the negative reciprocals of each other). These are either -2 and $\frac{1}{2}$ (either order) or $-\frac{4}{3}$ and $\frac{3}{4}$. Thus,

$$P = \frac{n(E)}{n(S)} = \frac{2}{21} \approx 0.095.$$

59. Since repetitions are not allowed and order is not important in selecting courses, use combinations. The number of ways of choosing any three courses from the list of twelve is $C(12, 3)$. Let F be the event of interest "all three courses selected are science courses." Then,

$$P(F) = \frac{\text{number of favorable outcomes}}{\text{total number of outcomes}} = \frac{{}_5C_3}{{}_{12}C_3} = \frac{10}{220} = \frac{1}{22} \approx 0.045.$$

61. The total number of ways to make the three selections, in order, is given by ${}_{26}P_3 = 15,600.$
Only 1 of these ways represents a success.
Thus, $P = \frac{1}{15,600} \approx 0.000064.$

63. The first eight primes are 2, 3, 5, 7, 11, 13, 17, 19. The sample space consists of all combinations of the set of 8 elements taken 2 at a time, the size of which is given by ${}_8C_2 = 28.$ Thus,
$E = \{19 + 5, 17 + 7, 13 + 11\}$ and

$$P = \frac{n(E)}{n(S)} = \frac{3}{28} \approx 0.107.$$

65. Two integers are randomly selected from the set $\{1, 2, 3, 4, 5, 6, 7, 8, 9\}$ and are added together. Find the probability that their sum is 11 if they are selected as follows:

(a) With replacement, the event of interest is $E = \{2 + 9, 9 + 2, 3 + 8, 8 + 3, 4 + 7, 7 + 4, 5 + 6, 6 + 5\}$.
Thus, $n(E) = 8$. Since there are

$9 \cdot 9 = 9^2 = 81$ ways of selecting the two digits to add together, we have $n(S) = 81$ and

$$P(\text{sum is eleven}) = \frac{8}{81} \approx 0.099.$$

(b) Without replacement, the event of interest is $E = \{2+9, 3+8, 4+7, 5+6\}$ and $n(E) = 4$. However (without replacement), $n(S) = C(9, 2) = 36$. Thus,

$$P(\text{sum is eleven}) = \frac{4}{36} = \frac{1}{9} \approx 0.111.$$

67. Only one number cannot be seen. If that number is six, the product of the remaining five sides is divisible by 6 because the factors 2 and 3 are part of the product. If the number that cannot be seen is not 6, then the product has a factor of 6 and is divisible by 6.

69. Let S be the sample space, which is the set of all two-digit numbers. Since the tens digit can be any of the nine digits 1 through 9 and the units digit can be any of the ten digits 0 through 9, $n(S) = 9 \cdot 10 = 90$.
Let E be the event "a palindromic two-digit number is chosen." A two-digit number will be palindromic only if both digits are the same. This repeated digit can be any of the nine digits 1 through 9, that is, $E = \{11, 22, 33, \ldots, 99\}$.
Thus, $n(E) = 9$, and

$$P(E) = \frac{n(E)}{n(S)} = \frac{9}{90} = \frac{1}{10}.$$

71. The number of possible groupings is $5 \cdot 3 = 15$. If A and B are in the same group and C and D are in the same group, then E and F must be in the same group, and there is only one possible grouping. Thus the probability of this event is $\frac{1}{15}$.

2 Exercises

1. Yes, since event A and event B cannot happen at the same time.

3. Writing exercise; answers will vary.

Use the sample space $S = \{1, 2, 3, 4, 5, 6\}$ for Exercises 5–9.

5. Let E be the event "not prime." Then, $E = \{1, 4, 6\}$, the non-prime numbers in S.
Thus, $P(E) = \frac{3}{6} = \frac{1}{2}$.

7. Let $E = \{2, 4, 6\}$ and $F = \{2, 3, 5\}$.

$$\begin{aligned} P(E \text{ or } F) &= P(E) + P(F) - P(E \text{ and } F) \\ &= \frac{3}{6} + \frac{3}{6} - \frac{1}{6} \\ &= \frac{5}{6}, \end{aligned}$$

by the general addition rule of probability.

9. Let A be the event "less than 3" and B be the event "greater than 4." Thus, $A = \{1, 2\}$ and $B = \{5, 6\}$.
Since A and B are mutually exclusive events, use the special addition rule of probability:

$$P(A \text{ or } B) = P(A) + P(B) = \frac{2}{6} + \frac{2}{6} = \frac{4}{6} = \frac{2}{3}.$$

11. (a) Since the two events, drawing a king (K) and drawing a queen (Q) are mutually exclusive, use the special addition rule:

$$\begin{aligned} P(K \text{ or } Q) &= P(K) + P(Q) \\ &= \frac{4}{52} + \frac{4}{52} \\ &= \frac{8}{52} \\ &= \frac{2}{13}. \end{aligned}$$

(b) Use the formula for finding odds in favor of an event E:

Odds in favor of $E = \frac{P(E)}{P(E')}$. Thus,

$$\begin{aligned} \frac{P(E)}{P(E')} &= \frac{P(K \text{ or } Q)}{P(\text{not } (K \text{ or } Q))} \\ &= \frac{P(K \text{ or } Q)}{1 - P(K \text{ or } Q)} \\ &= \frac{\frac{2}{13}}{1 - \left(\frac{2}{13}\right)} \\ &= \frac{\frac{2}{13}}{\frac{11}{13}} \\ &= \frac{2}{13} \cdot \frac{13}{11} \\ &= \frac{2}{11}, \text{ or 2 to 11.} \end{aligned}$$

13. **(a)** Let S be the event of "drawing a spade" and F be the event of "drawing a face card." Then, $n(S) = 13$ and $n(F) = 12$. (There are 3 face cards in each of the 4 suits.) There are 3 face cards that are also spades so that $n(S \text{ and } F) = 3$. Thus, by the general additive rule for probability,

$$\begin{aligned} P(S \text{ or } F) &= P(S) + P(F) - P(S \text{ and } F) \\ &= \frac{13}{52} + \frac{12}{52} - \frac{3}{52} \\ &= \frac{11}{26}. \end{aligned}$$

(b) Use the formula for finding odds in favor of an event E:

Odds in favor of $E = \frac{P(E)}{P(E')}$. Thus,

$$\begin{aligned} \frac{P(E)}{P(E')} &= \frac{P(S \text{ or } F)}{P(\text{not } (S \text{ or } F))} \\ &= \frac{P(S \text{ or } F)}{1 - P(S \text{ or } F)} \\ &= \frac{\frac{11}{26}}{1 - \left(\frac{11}{26}\right)} \\ &= \frac{\frac{11}{26}}{\frac{15}{26}} \\ &= \frac{11}{26} \cdot \frac{26}{15} \\ &= \frac{11}{15}, \text{ or 11 to 15.} \end{aligned}$$

15. **(a)** Let H be the event "a heart is drawn" and S be the event "a seven is drawn." We want to find $P(H \text{ or } S)'$, or $P(H \cup S)'$. Since there are 13 hearts in the deck and 3 other sevens which are not hearts, $n(H \cup S) = 16$ and $P(H \cup S) = \frac{16}{52} = \frac{4}{13}$.

$$\begin{aligned} \text{Thus, } P(H \cup S)' &= 1 - P(H \cup S) \\ &= 1 - \frac{4}{13} \\ &= \frac{9}{13}. \end{aligned}$$

(b) The number of cards which are hearts or are sevens totals 16. Thus the number of cards which are not hearts nor sevens is 52 – 16 = 36. The odds in favor of not hearts nor sevens are 36 to 16, or 9 to 4.

Construct a table showing the sum for each of the 36 equally likely outcomes.

		2nd die					
	+	1	2	3	4	5	6
	1	2	3	4	5	6	7
	2	3	4	5	6	7	8
1st die	3	4	5	6	7	8	9
	4	5	6	7	8	9	10
	5	6	7	8	9	10	11
	6	7	8	9	10	11	12

17. Let E be the event of getting a sum which is an even number. Counting the number of occurrences in the sum table for these even outcomes represents the numerator of the probability fraction. Then, $P(E) = \frac{18}{36}$.

Let M be the event of getting sums which are multiples of three, $\{3, 6, 9, 12\}$. Counting the number of occurrences in the sum table for these outcomes represents the numerator of the probability fraction.

Then, $P(M) = \frac{12}{36}$ and $P(E \text{ and } M) = \frac{6}{36}$.

Thus, by the general addition rule,

$$\begin{aligned} P(E \cup M) &= P(E) + P(M) - P(E \text{ and } M) \\ &= \frac{18}{36} + \frac{12}{36} - \frac{6}{36} \\ &= \frac{24}{36} \\ &= \frac{2}{3}. \end{aligned}$$

19. Since these are mutually exclusive events, use the special additive rule. Since there is only one sum less than 3 (the sum of 2), $P(\text{sum less than } 3) = \frac{1}{36}$, and since there are six sums greater than 9, $P(\text{sum greater than } 9) = \frac{6}{36}$.

$$\begin{aligned} \text{Thus, } &P(\text{sum less than 3 or greater than 9}) \\ &= \frac{1}{36} + \frac{6}{36} \\ &= \frac{7}{36}. \end{aligned}$$

21.
$$\begin{aligned} P(S) &= P(A \cup B \cup C \cup D) \\ &= P(A) + P(B) + P(C) + P(D) \\ &= 1 \end{aligned}$$

Refer to Table 1 in the textbook and give answers to six decimal places.

23. Let F be the event of drawing a full house and S be the event of drawing a straight. Using Table 1 in the text to determine $n(F) = 3744$ and $n(S) = 10{,}200$, we have

$$P(F) = \frac{3744}{2{,}598{,}960} \text{ and } P(S) = \frac{10{,}200}{2{,}598{,}960}.$$

Since the events are mutually exclusive,

$$\begin{aligned} P(F \text{ or } S) &= P(F) + P(S) \\ &= \frac{3{,}744}{2{,}598{,}960} + \frac{10{,}200}{2{,}598{,}960} \\ &= \frac{13{,}944}{2{,}598{,}960} \approx 0.005365. \end{aligned}$$

25. The events are mutually exclusive, so use the special addition rule:

P(nothing any better than two pairs)

$= P(\text{no pair}) + P(\text{one pair}) + P(\text{two pairs})$

$= \dfrac{1{,}302{,}540}{2{,}598{,}960} + \dfrac{1{,}098{,}240}{2{,}598{,}960} + \dfrac{123{,}552}{2{,}598{,}960}$

$= \dfrac{2{,}524{,}332}{2{,}598{,}960} \approx 0.971285$

27. "Par or above" is represented by all categories from 70 up. Since these are mutually exclusive, use the special addition rule:

P(Par or above)

$= 0.30 + 0.23 + 0.09 + 0.06 + 0.04 + 0.03 + 0.01$

$= 0.76$

29. "Less than 90" is represented by all categories under the 90–94 category. Since these are mutually exclusive, use the special addition rule:

P(Less than 90)

$= 0.04 + 0.06 + 0.14 + 0.30 + 0.23 + 0.09 + 0.06$

$= 0.92$

31. Odds of Brian's shooting below par

$= \dfrac{P(\text{below par})}{P(\text{par or above})}$

$P(\text{par or above}) = 0.76$ (Exercise 27), and

$$\begin{aligned} P(\text{below par}) &= 1 - P(\text{par or above}) \\ &= 1 - 0.76 \\ &= 0.24, \end{aligned}$$

by the complements rule of probability.

Thus, odds in favor $= \dfrac{0.24}{0.76} = \dfrac{6}{19}$, or 6 to 19.

33. Let x denote the sum of two distinct numbers selected randomly from the set $\{1, 2, 3, 4, 5\}$. Construct the probability distribution for the random variable x. Create a "sum table" to list the elements in the sample space. Note: can't use 1 + 1 = 2, etc. Why?

+	1	2	3	4	5
1	–	3	4	5	6
2	3	–	5	6	7
3	4	5	–	7	8
4	5	6	7	–	9
5	6	7	8	9	–

Thus, the probability distribution is as follows.

x	$P(x)$
3	$\frac{2}{20} = 0.1$
4	$\frac{2}{20} = 0.1$
5	$\frac{4}{20} = 0.2$
6	$\frac{4}{20} = 0.2$
7	$\frac{4}{20} = 0.2$
8	$\frac{2}{20} = 0.1$
9	$\frac{2}{20} = 0.1$

For Exercises 35–37, let A be an event within the sample space S, and let n(A) = a and n(S) = s.

35. $n(A') + n(A) = n(S)$

$n(A') + a = s$

Thus, $n(A') = s - a$.

37. $P(A) + P(A') = \dfrac{a}{s} + \dfrac{s-a}{s} = \dfrac{a+s-a}{s} = \dfrac{s}{s} = 1$

We want to form three-digit numbers using the set of digits {0, 1, 2, 3, 4, 5}. For example, 501 and 224 are such numbers but 035 is not.

39. The number of three-digit numbers is, by the fundamental counting principle, $5 \cdot 6 \cdot 6 = 180$. Remember that we can't choose "0" for the first digit.

41. If one three-digit number is chosen at random from all those that can be made from the above set of digits, find the probability that the one chosen is not a multiple of 5.
The number of three-digit numbers is, by the fundamental counting principle, $5 \cdot 6 \cdot 6 = 180$ (Exercise 39).
There are $5 \cdot 6 \cdot 2 = 60$ three-digit numbers that are multiples of 5 (Exercise 40). Thus,
$P(\text{multiple of } 5) = \frac{60}{180} = \frac{1}{3}.$
By the complements rule,
$$\begin{aligned} P(\text{not a multiple of } 5) &= 1 - P(\text{multiple of } 5) \\ &= 1 - \frac{60}{180} \\ &= 1 - \frac{1}{3} \\ &= \frac{2}{3}. \end{aligned}$$

43. Since box C contains the same number of green marbles as blue and the number of green and blue marbles was the same to begin with, then box A and box B must contain exactly the same number of marbles after all the marbles are drawn. Because this is certain, the probability is 1.

3 Exercises

1. The events are independent since the outcome on the first toss has no effect on the outcome of the second toss.

3. The two planets are selected, without replacement, from the list in Table 7. The events "first is closer than Jupiter" and "second is farther than Neptune" are not independent. This is because the first selection was not replaced, which may affect the outcome of the second choice.

5. The answers are all guessed on a twenty-question multiple choice test. Let A be the event "first answer correct" and let B be the event "last answer correct." The events A and B are independent since the first answer choice does not affect the last answer choice.

7. The probability that the student selected is "female" is $\frac{52}{100} = \frac{13}{25}$.

9. Since a total of $100 - 31 = 69$ of the 100 students are "not motivated primarily by money," the probability is $\frac{69}{100}$.

11. Given that the student selected is motivated primarily by "sense of giving to society," the sample space is reduced to 31 students. Of these 14 are male, so the probability is $\frac{14}{31}$.

In Exercises 13–15 the first puppy chosen is replaced before the second is chosen. Note that "with replacement" means that the events may be considered independent and we can apply the special multiplication rule of probability.

13. The probability that "both select a poodle" is
$$\begin{aligned} P(P_1 \text{ and } P_2) &= P(P_1) \cdot P(P_2) \\ &= \left(\frac{4}{7}\right) \cdot \left(\frac{4}{7}\right) \\ &= \frac{16}{49}. \end{aligned}$$

15. The probability that "Rebecka selects a terrier and Aaron selects a retriever" is given by
$$\begin{aligned} P(T_1 \text{ and } R_2) &= P(T_1) \cdot P(R_2) \\ &= \left(\frac{2}{7}\right) \cdot \left(\frac{1}{7}\right) \\ &= \frac{2}{49}. \end{aligned}$$

In Exercises 17–21, the first puppy chosen is not replaced before the second is chosen. Thus, the events are not independent. Therefore, apply the general multiplication rule of probability.

17. The probability that "both select a poodle" is given by
$$\begin{aligned} P(P_1 \text{ and } P_2) &= P(P_1) \cdot P(P_2 | P_1) \\ &= \left(\frac{4}{7}\right) \cdot \left(\frac{3}{6}\right) \\ &= \frac{2}{7}. \end{aligned}$$
Remember that the second probability is conditional to the first event as having occurred and hence, the sample space is reduced.

19. The probability that "Aaron selects a retriever," given "Rebecka selects a poodle" is found by $P(R_2 | P_1) = \frac{1}{6}$.
Note that Rebecka's choice decreased the sample space by one dog.

21. The probability that "Aaron selects a retriever," given "Rebecka selects a retriever" is found by $P(R_2|R_1) = \frac{0}{6} = 0.$

Note that after Rebecka's selection, there are no remaining retrievers for Aaron to select.

23. Since the cards are dealt without replacement, when the second card is drawn, there will be 51 cards left, of which 12 are spades. Thus, $P(S_2|S_1) = \frac{12}{51} = \frac{4}{17}.$

Note that both the event of interest (numerator) and the sample space (denominator) were reduced by the selection of the first card, a spade.

25. Since the cards are dealt without replacement, the events "first is face card" and "second is face card" are not independent, so be sure to use the general multiplication rule of probability. Let F_1 be the event "first is a face card" and F_2 be the event "second is a face card." Then,

$$\begin{aligned} P(\text{two face cards}) &= P(F_1 \text{ and } F_2) \\ &= P(F_1)\cdot P(F_2|F_1) \\ &= \frac{12}{52}\cdot\frac{11}{51} \\ &= \frac{3}{13}\cdot\frac{11}{51} \\ &= \frac{11}{221}. \end{aligned}$$

27. The probability that the "first card dealt is a jack and the second is a face card" is found by

$$\begin{aligned} P(J_1 \text{ and } F_2) &= P(J_1)\cdot(F_2|J_1) \\ &= \frac{4}{52}\cdot\frac{11}{51} \\ &= \frac{11}{663}. \end{aligned}$$

Remember that there are only 11 face cards left once the jack is drawn.

Use the results of Exercise 28 to find each of the following probabilities when a single card is drawn from a standard 52-card deck.

29. $P(\text{queen}|\text{face card}) = \frac{n(F \text{ and } Q)}{n(F)} = \frac{4}{12} = \frac{1}{3}$

31. $P(\text{red}|\text{diamond}) = \frac{n(D \text{ and } R)}{n(D)} = \frac{13}{13} = 1$

33. From the integers 1 through 10, the set of primes are $\{2, 3, 5, 7\}$. The set of odds are $\{1, 3, 5, 7, 9\}$. Since there are only three odd numbers in the set of 4 primes, the second probability fraction becomes $\frac{3}{4}$ and

$$P(\text{prime})\cdot P(\text{odd}|\text{prime}) = \frac{4}{10}\cdot\frac{3}{4} = \frac{3}{10}.$$

This is the same value as computed in the text for $P(\text{odd}) \cdot P(\text{prime}|\text{odd})$, that is, the probability of selecting an integer from the set which is "odd and prime."

35. Since the birth of a boy (or girl) is independent of previous births, the probability of both authors having three boys successively is

$$\left(\frac{1}{2}\right)\cdot\left(\frac{1}{2}\right)\cdot\left(\frac{1}{2}\right)\cdot\left(\frac{1}{2}\right)\cdot\left(\frac{1}{2}\right)\cdot\left(\frac{1}{2}\right) = \frac{1}{64}.$$

37. Let S represent a sale purchase for more than \$100. Then,

$$\begin{aligned} &P(\text{both sales more than } \$100) \\ &= P(S_1 \text{ and } S_2) \\ &= P(S_1)\cdot P(S_2) \\ &= (0.70)\cdot(0.70) \\ &= 0.490 \end{aligned}$$

39. Let S represent a sale purchase for more than \$100. Then, S' represents a sale purchase that is not more than \$100. Since $P(S) = 0.70,\ P(S') = 1 - 0.70 = 0.30,$ by the complements principle.

$$\begin{aligned} &P(\text{none of the first 3 sales more than } \$100) \\ &= P(\text{not } S_1 \text{ and not } S_2 \text{ and not } S_3) \\ &= P(S_1')\cdot P(S_2')\cdot P(S_3') \\ &= (0.30)\cdot(0.30)\cdot(0.30) \\ &= 0.027 \end{aligned}$$

41. Since the probability the cloud will move in the critical direction is 0.05, the probability that it will not move in the critical direction is 1 0.05 = 0.95, by the complements formula.

43. The probability that the cloud would not move in the critical direction for each launch is 1 – 0.05 = 0.95. The probability that the cloud would not move in the critical direction for any 5 launches is $(0.95)^5$ by the special multiplication rule. The probability that any 5 launches will result in at least one cloud movement in the critical direction is the complement of the probability that a cloud would not move in the critical direction for any 5 launches, or $1-(0.95)^5 \approx 0.23$.

Three men and three women are waiting to be interviewed for jobs. If they are all selected in random order, find the probability of each of the following events.

45. $P(\text{all women first})$
$= P(W_1)\cdot P(W_2|W_1)\cdot P(W_3|W_1 \text{ and } W_2)$
$= \frac{3}{6}\cdot\frac{2}{5}\cdot\frac{1}{4}$
$= \frac{1}{20}$

47. The probability that no man will be interviewed until at least two women have been interviewed is the same as the probability that the first two people interviewed are women. That is,

$P(\text{two women first}) = P(W_1)\cdot P\left(W_2|W_1\right)$
$= \frac{3}{6}\cdot\frac{2}{5}$
$= \frac{1}{5}$

49. The probability of selecting the fair coin out of the two coins is $\frac{1}{2}$. The probability of getting two heads using either coin is $\frac{2}{5}$.

So, the probability that the gambler selected the fair coin knowing he got two heads is $\frac{1}{2}\cdot\frac{2}{5}=\frac{1}{5}$.

51. **(a)** "At least three" is the complement of "one or two" and we can't get two girls from one birth. Thus, find only the probability of having 2 girls with two births.

$P(\text{gg}) = P(\text{g})\cdot P(\text{g}) = \frac{1}{2}\cdot\frac{1}{2}=\frac{1}{4}$.

Therefore, by the complements principle.

$P(\text{at least three births}) = 1-\frac{1}{4}=\frac{3}{4}$.

(b) "At least four births" is the complement of "two or three births." From (a) above

$P(\text{two births to get gg}) = \frac{1}{4}$.

To calculate P(three births to get gg) examine Figure 2 in the text. The three successes are ggb, gbg, and bgg. Don't count, however, the outcome ggb as a success since this has already been counted when computing the probability associated with two births.

$P(\text{three births to get gg}) = \frac{2}{8}=\frac{1}{4}$.

$P(\text{two or three births to get gg})$
$= P(\text{two births to get gg})$
$+ P(\text{three births to get gg})$
$= \frac{1}{4}+\frac{1}{4}$
$= \frac{2}{4}$
$= \frac{1}{2}$

Finally, the probability of "at least four births" may be calculated by the complements rule:

$P(\text{at least four births to get gg}) = 1-\frac{1}{2}$
$= \frac{1}{2}$.

(c) "At least five births" is the complement of "two or three or four births."
P(two or three or four births to obtain gg)
$= P(\text{two or three births to get gg})$
$+ P(\text{four births to get gg})$

$P(\text{two or three births to get gg}) = \frac{1}{2}$

was calculated in (b) above. To calculate P(four births to get gg) extend the tree diagram (Figure 2 in the text). Count all of the outcomes with gg (two girls) as successes except bggb and ggbb since they have already been used in calculating the earlier probability. There are then 3 outcomes which may be considered as successes. Thus,

$P(\text{four births to get gg}) = \frac{3}{16}$.

P(two or three or four births to obtain gg)
$= P$(two or three births to get gg) $+ P$(four births to get gg)
$=\frac{1}{2}+\frac{3}{16}$
$=\frac{8}{16}+\frac{3}{16}$
$=\frac{11}{16}$

Finally, the probability of "at least five births to obtain gg" may be calculated by the complements rule:
P(at least five births to obtain gg)
$=1-\frac{11}{16}$
$=\frac{5}{16}.$

A coin, biased so that P(h) = 0.5200 and P(t) = 0.4800, it tossed twice. Give answers to four decimal places.

53. Since the two tosses are independent events, use the special multiplication rule:
$P(hh) = P(h)\cdot P(h)$
$= (0.5200)\cdot(0.5200)$
$= 0.2704.$

55. Since the two tosses are independent events, use the special multiplication rule:
$P(th) = P(t)\cdot P(h)$
$= (0.4800)\cdot(0.5200)$
$= 0.2496.$

57. Writing exercise; answers will vary.

59. Using the fundamental counting principle, there are $2\cdot2\cdot2\cdot2\cdot2\cdot2 = 2^6 = 64$ different switch settings. The probability of randomly getting 1 of the 64 possible settings is $\frac{1}{64}\approx 0.0156.$

61. P(at least one duplication of switch settings)
$= 1 - P$(no duplication)
$=1-\frac{63}{64}$
≈ 0.016 for two neighbors;
$1-\frac{63}{64}\cdot\frac{62}{64}=1-\frac{63\cdot62}{(64^2)}$
≈ 0.046 for three neighbors;

$1-\frac{63\cdot62\cdot61\cdot60\cdot59\cdot58\cdot57\cdot56}{(64)^8}$
≈ 0.445 for nine neighbors;
and
$1-\frac{63\cdot62\cdot61\cdot60\cdot59\cdot58\cdot57\cdot56\cdot55}{(64)^9}$
$\approx 0.523 > \frac{1}{2}$ for ten neighbors.

Thus, the minimum number of neighbors who must use this brand of opener before the probability of at least one duplication of settings is greater than $\frac{1}{2}$ is ten.

63. Since the events are not independent, use the general multiplication rule. Let R_1 represent rain on the first day, R_2 represent rain on the second day.
P(rain on two consecutive days in November)
$= P(R_1 \cap R_2)$
$= P(R_1)\cdot P(R_2|\mathrm{R}_1)$
$= (0.500)\cdot(0.800)$
$= 0.400$

65. Since the events are not independent, use the general multiplication rule. Let R_1 represent rain on November 1, R_2 represent rain on November 2, and R_3 represent rain on November 3.
P(rain on November 1st and 2nd, but not on the 3rd)
$= P(R_1 \cap R_2 \cap \text{not } R_3)$
$= P(R_1)\cdot P(R_2|R_1)\cdot P(\text{not } R_3|R_2)$
$= (0.500)\cdot(0.800)\cdot(1-0.800)$
$= 0.080$

Note that the probability of not raining after a rainy day is the complement of the probability that it does rain.

67. To find the probability of "no engine failures," begin by letting F represent a failed engine. The probability that a given engine will fail, $P(F)$, is 0.10. This means that, by the complements principle, the probability that an engine will not fail is given by $P(\text{not } F) = 1 - 0.10 = 0.90$. Since engines "not failing" are independent events, use the special product rule.

$P(\text{no engine failures})$
$= P(\text{not } F_1 \cap \text{not } F_2 \cap \text{not } F_3 \cap \text{not } F_4)$
$= P(\text{not } F_1) \cdot P(\text{not } F_2) \cdot P(\text{not } F_3) \cdot P(\text{not } F_4)$
$= (0.90)^4$
$= 0.6561$

69. The probability of "exactly two engine failures" can be found by applying the fundamental counting principle, where the first task is to decide which two engines fail ${}_4C_2$; the second task, find the probability that one of these engines fails (0.10); followed by the second engine failing (0.20); followed by finding the probability the third engine does not fail (1 – 0.30 = 0.70); followed by the probability that last engine does not fail (1 – 0.30 = 0.70). Thus,

$$P = {}_4C_2 \cdot (0.10) \cdot (0.20) \cdot (0.70)^2 = 0.0588.$$

Refer to text discussion of the rules for "one-and-one" basketball. Christine Ellington, a basketball player, has a 70% foul shot record. (She makes 70% of her foul shots.) Find the probability that, on a given one-and-one foul shooting opportunity, Christine will score the following number of points.

71. A one-and-one foul shooting opportunity means that Christine gets a second shot only if she makes her first shot. The probability of scoring "no points" means that she missed her first shot. Thus,

$P(\text{scoring no points})$
$= 1 - P(\text{scoring at least one point})$
$= 1 - 0.70$
$= 0.30.$

73. The probability of "scoring two points" is given by

$P(\text{scoring two points})$
$= P(\text{scoring the 1st shot and scoring the 2nd shot})$
$= P(\text{scoring on 1st shot}) \cdot P(\text{scoring on 2nd shot})$
$= (0.70) \cdot (0.70)$
$= 0.49.$

75. Writing exercise; answers will vary.

4 Exercises

1. Let heads be "success."

Then $n = 3,\ p = q = \frac{1}{2},$ and $x = 0.$

By the binomial probability formula,

$$P(0) = {}_3C_0 \cdot \left(\frac{1}{2}\right)^0 \left(\frac{1}{2}\right)^{3-0} = \frac{3!}{0!(3-0)!} \cdot 1 \cdot \left(\frac{1}{2}\right)^3 = \frac{3!}{1 \cdot 3!} \cdot \frac{1}{2^3} = 1 \cdot \frac{1}{8} = \frac{1}{8}.$$

Note ${}_3C_0 = 1,$ and we could easily reason this result without using the combination formula since there is only one way to choose 0 things from a set of 3 things—take none out.

3. Let heads be "success."

Then $n = 3,\ p = q = \frac{1}{2},$ and $x = 2.$

By the binomial probability formula,

$$P(2 \text{ heads}) = {}_3C_2 \cdot \left(\frac{1}{2}\right)^2 \cdot \left(\frac{1}{2}\right)^{3-2} = \frac{3!}{2!(3-2)!} \cdot \frac{1}{4} \cdot \frac{1}{2} = \frac{3 \cdot 2 \cdot 1}{2 \cdot 1 \cdot 4 \cdot 2} = \frac{3}{8}.$$

5. Use the special addition rule for calculating the probability of "1 or 2 heads."

$P(1 \text{ or } 2 \text{ heads})$
$= P(1) + P(2)$
$= {}_3C_1 \cdot \left(\frac{1}{2}\right)^1 \cdot \left(\frac{1}{2}\right)^{3-1} + {}_3C_2 + \left(\frac{1}{2}\right)^2 \cdot \left(\frac{1}{2}\right)^{3-2}$
$= 3 \cdot \frac{1}{2} \cdot \frac{1}{4} + 3 \cdot \frac{1}{4} \cdot \frac{1}{2}$
$= \frac{6}{8}$
$= \frac{3}{4}$

7. "No more than 1" is the same as "0 or 1."
$P(0 \text{ or } 1)$
$= P(0) + P(1)$
$= {}_3C_0 \cdot \left(\frac{1}{2}\right)^0 \left(\frac{1}{2}\right)^3 + {}_3C_1 \cdot \left(\frac{1}{2}\right)^1 \left(\frac{1}{2}\right)^2$
$= 1 \cdot 1 \cdot \frac{1}{8} + 3 \cdot \frac{1}{2} \cdot \frac{1}{4}$
$= \frac{1}{8} + \frac{3}{8}$
$= \frac{1}{2}$

9. Assuming boy and girl babies are equally likely, find the probability that a family with three children will have exactly two boys.

$$P(2 \text{ boys}) = {}_3C_2 \cdot \left(\frac{1}{2}\right)^2 \left(\frac{1}{2}\right)^1 = 3 \cdot \frac{1}{4} \cdot \frac{1}{2} = \frac{3}{8}$$

11. If n fair coins are tossed, the probability of exactly x heads is the fraction whose numerator is entry number $\underline{x}$ of row number $\underline{n}$ in Pascal's triangle, and whose denominator is the sum of the entries in row number $\underline{n}$. That is x; n; n.

For Exercises 13–19, refer to Pascal's triangle. Since seven coins are tossed, we will use row number 7 of the triangle. (Recall that the first row is row number 0 and that the first entry in each row is entry number 0.) The sum of the numbers in row 7 is $2^7 = 128$, *which will be the denominator in each of the probability fractions.*

```
            1
          1   1
        1   2   1
      1   3   3   1
    1   4   6   4   1
  1   5  10  10   5   1
 1  6  15  20  15   6  1
1  7  21  35  35  21  7  1
```

13. For the probability "1 head," the numerator of the probability fraction is entry 1 of row 7 of Pascal's triangle, or 7, and the denominator is the sum of the elements in row 7, or
1 + 7 + 21 + 35 + 35 + 21 + 7 + 1 = 128.
Thus, $P(1 \text{ head}) = \frac{7}{128}$.

15. For the probability "3 heads," the numerator of the probability fraction is entry number 3 of row 7 of Pascal's triangle, or 35, and the denominator is the sum of the elements in row 7, or 128. Thus, $P(3 \text{ heads}) = \frac{35}{128}$.

17. For the probability "5 heads," the numerator of the probability fraction is entry number 5 of row 7 of Pascal's triangle, or 21, and the denominator is the sum of the elements in row 7, or 128. Thus, $P(5 \text{ heads}) = \frac{21}{128}$.

19. For the probability "7 heads," the numerator of the probability fraction is entry 7 of row 7 of Pascal's triangle, or 1, and the denominator is the sum of the elements in row 7, or 128. Thus, $P(7 \text{ heads}) = \frac{1}{128}$.

For Exercises 21–23, a fair die is rolled three times and a 4 is considered "success," while all other outcomes are "failures."

21. Here $n = 3$, $p = \frac{1}{6}$, $q = \frac{5}{6}$, and $x = 1$.

$$P(1) = {}_3C_1 \cdot \left(\frac{1}{6}\right)^1 \left(\frac{5}{6}\right)^2 = 3 \cdot \frac{1}{6} \cdot \frac{25}{36} = \frac{25}{72}$$

23. Here $n = 3$, $p = \frac{1}{6}$, $q = \frac{5}{6}$, and $x = 3$.

$$P(3) = {}_3C_3 \cdot \left(\frac{1}{6}\right)^3 \left(\frac{5}{6}\right)^0 = 1 \cdot \frac{1}{216} \cdot 1 = \frac{1}{216}$$

Answers are rounded to three decimal places.

25. Here $n = 5$, $p = \frac{1}{3}$, and $x = 4$. Since $p = \frac{1}{3}$,
$q = 1 - p = 1 - \frac{1}{3} = \frac{2}{3}$.
Substitute these values into the binomial probability formula:

$$P(4) = {}_5C_4 \cdot \left(\frac{1}{3}\right)^4 \left(\frac{2}{3}\right)^1 = 5 \cdot \frac{2}{3^5} \approx 0.041$$

27. Here $n = 20$, $p = \frac{1}{8}$, and $x = 2$. Since
$p = \frac{1}{8}$, $q = 1 - p = 1 - \frac{1}{8} = \frac{7}{8}$.
Substitute these values into the binomial

probability formula:

$$P(2) = {}_{20}C_2 \cdot \left(\frac{1}{8}\right)^2 \left(\frac{7}{8}\right)^{18}$$
$$= \frac{20!}{2!18!} \cdot \frac{7^{18}}{8^2 8^{18}}$$
$$= 190 \cdot \frac{7^{18}}{8^{20}}$$
$$\approx 0.268$$

29. Writing exercise; answers will vary.

31. Writing exercise; answers will vary.

For Exercises 33–35, let a correct answer be a "success." Then $n = 10$, $p = \frac{2}{6} = \frac{1}{3}$, *and* $q = 1 - p = \frac{2}{3}$.

33. The probability of getting "exactly 7 correct answers" is given by

$$P(7 \text{ correct answers }) = {}_{10}C_7 \cdot \left(\frac{1}{3}\right)^7 \left(\frac{2}{3}\right)^3$$
$$= 120 \cdot \frac{2^3}{3^{10}}$$
$$\approx 0.016.$$

35. "At least seven" means seven, eight, nine, or ten correct answers.

$P(7 \text{ or } 8 \text{ or } 9 \text{ or } 10)$
$$= P(7) + P(8) + P(9) + P(10)$$
$$= {}_{10}C_7 \cdot \left(\frac{1}{3}\right)^7 \left(\frac{2}{3}\right)^3 + {}_{10}C_8 \cdot \left(\frac{1}{3}\right)^8 \left(\frac{2}{3}\right)^2$$
$$+ {}_{10}C_9 \cdot \left(\frac{1}{3}\right)^9 \left(\frac{2}{3}\right)^1 + {}_{10}C_{10} \cdot \left(\frac{1}{3}\right)^{10} \left(\frac{2}{3}\right)^0$$
$$\approx 0.01626 + 0.00305 + 0.00034 + 0.00002$$
$$\approx 0.01967$$
$$\approx 0.020$$

37. For "exactly 1 to have undesirable side effects," $x = 1$ and $n = 8$, $p = 0.35$, $q = 1 - p = 0.65$. Thus,

$$P(1) = {}_8C_1 \cdot (0.35)^1 (1 - 0.35)^{8-1}$$
$$= 8(0.35)(0.65)^7$$
$$\approx 0.137$$

39. "More than two" is the complement of 0, 1, or 2. Thus,

$P(\text{more than two})$
$$= 1 - P(0,1, \text{ or } 2)$$
$$= 1 - [P(0) + P(1) + P(2)]$$
$$= 1 - [{}_8C_0 \cdot (0.35)^0 (0.65)^8$$
$$+ {}_8C_1 \cdot (0.35)^1 (0.65)^7$$
$$+ {}_8C_2 \cdot (0.35)^2 (0.65)^6]$$
$$\approx 1 - [1 \cdot 1 \cdot (0.03186448)$$
$$+ 8(0.35)(0.04902228)$$
$$+ (28)(0.1225)(0.07541889)]$$
$$\approx 0.572$$

41. For the probability that "from 4 through 6" will attend college, $n = 9$, $p = 0.60$, and $q = 1 - p = 0.40$. Thus,

$$P(4 \text{ or } 5 \text{ or } 6) = P(4) + P(5) + P(6)$$
$$= {}_9C_4 \cdot (0.60)^4 (0.40)^5$$
$$+ {}_9C_5 \cdot (0.60)^5 (0.40)^4$$
$$+ {}_9C_6 \cdot (0.60)^6 (0.40)^3$$
$$\approx 0.167 + 0.251 + 0.251$$
$$\approx 0.669$$

43. "At least 3" means three, four, five, six, seven, eight or nine enroll in college.

$P(3 \text{ or } 4 \text{ or } 5 \text{ or } 6 \text{ or } 7 \text{ or } 8 \text{ or } 9)$
$$= P(3) + P(4) + P(5) + P(6) + P(7)$$
$$+ P(8) + P(9)$$
$$= {}_9C_3 \cdot (0.60)^3 (0.40)^6$$
$$+ {}_9C_4 \cdot (0.60)^4 (0.40)^5$$
$$+ {}_9C_5 \cdot (0.60)^5 (0.40)^4$$
$$+ {}_9C_6 \cdot (0.60)^6 (0.40)^3$$
$$+ {}_9C_7 \cdot (0.60)^7 (0.40)^2$$
$$+ {}_9C_8 \cdot (0.60)^8 (0.40)^1$$
$$+ {}_9C_9 \cdot (0.60)^9 (0.40)^0$$
$$\approx 0.074 + 0.167 + 0.251 + 0.251 + 0.161$$
$$+ 0.060 + 0.010$$
$$\approx 0.974$$

45. "At least half of the 6 trees" is the complement of "0, 1, or 2 trees." Here $p = 0.65$, $q = 1 - 0.65 + 0.35$ and $n = 6$. Using the complements rule, the probability is found by

$P(\text{at least half})$
$= 1 - P(0 \text{ or } 1 \text{ or } 2)$
$= 1 - [P(0) + P(1) + P(2)]$
$= 1 - [{}_6C_0 \cdot (0.65)^0 (0.35)^6 + {}_6C_1 \cdot (0.65)^1 (0.35)^5 + {}_6C_2 \cdot (0.65)^2 (0.35)^4]$
$\approx 1 - [0.0018 + 0.0205 + 0.0951]$
$\approx 1 - 0.1174$
$\approx 0.883.$

47. If p is the probability that a ball selected at random is black, $x = 2$, and $n = 4$, then
$P(\text{two of four balls are black})$
$= {}_4C_2 \cdot p^2 (1-p)^2$
$= 6p^2 (1-p)^2$

49. To end up 10 miles east of the starting point, Abby must go 10 miles east and 0 miles west, so she must toss 10 heads and no tails. Use the binomial probability formula with
$n = 10,\ p = \frac{1}{2},\ q = \frac{1}{2},$ and $x = 10.$
Then
$P(10 \text{ heads, } 0 \text{ tails}) = P(10)$
$$= {}_{10}C_{10} \cdot \left(\frac{1}{2}\right)^{10} \left(\frac{1}{2}\right)^0 = 1 \cdot \frac{1}{1024} \cdot 1 = \frac{1}{1024} \approx 0.001.$$

51. To end up 6 miles west of the starting point, Abby must go 8 miles west and 2 miles east, so she must toss 8 tails and 2 heads. Use the binomial probability formula with $n = 10$,
$p = \frac{1}{2},\ q = \frac{1}{2},$ and $x = 8$. Then,
$P(8 \text{ tails, } 2 \text{ heads}) = P(8)$
$$= {}_{10}C_8 \cdot \left(\frac{1}{2}\right)^8 \left(\frac{1}{2}\right)^2 = 45 \cdot \left(\frac{1}{2}\right)^{10} = \frac{45}{1024} \approx 0.044.$$

53. To end up 2 miles east of the starting point, Abby must go 6 blocks east and 4 blocks west (since 6 + 4 = 10 and 6 − 4 = 2), so she must toss 6 heads and 4 tails. Use the binomial probability formula with $n = 10$,
$p = \frac{1}{2},\ q = \frac{1}{2},$ and $x = 6$. Then,
$P(6 \text{ heads, } 4 \text{ tails}) = P(6)$
$$= {}_{10}C_6 \cdot \left(\frac{1}{2}\right)^6 \left(\frac{1}{2}\right)^4 = 210\left(\frac{1}{1024}\right) = \frac{210}{1024} = \frac{105}{512} \approx 0.205.$$

55. To find the probability that Abby will end up at least 2 miles from the starting point, use the complements rule. The complement of "at least 2 miles from the start" is "less than 2 miles from the start" or "1 mile from the start" or "exactly at the start." However, it is impossible for Abby to end up 1 mile from the starting point (either east or west). In order for two integers to have a sum of 10, they must be both even or both odd. In either case, their difference will be even. Thus, Abby can never end up an odd number of miles from the starting point.
In order to end up at the starting point, Abby must go 5 miles east and 5 miles west. Let
$p = \frac{1}{2},\ q = \frac{1}{2},$ and $x = 5$:
$P(5 \text{ heads, } 5 \text{ tails}) = P(5)$
$$= {}_{10}C_5 \cdot \left(\frac{1}{2}\right)^5 \left(\frac{1}{2}\right)^5 = 252\left(\frac{1}{2}\right)^{10} = 252\left(\frac{1}{1024}\right) = \frac{252}{1024} = \frac{63}{256}$$
Then, the probability that Abby ends up at least 2 miles from the starting point is
$1 - P(5) = 1 - \frac{63}{256} = \frac{193}{256} \approx 0.754.$

5 Exercises

1. Writing exercise; answers will vary.

3. Five fair coins are tossed. A tree diagram may be helpful to create the following sample space.

Use the following sample space to create the individual probabilities.

hhhhh	hhhht	hhhth	hhhtt
hhthh	hhtht	hhtth	hhttt
hthhh	hthht	hthth	hthtt
htthh	httht	httth	htttt
thhhh	thhht	thhth	thhtt
ththh	ththt	thtth	thttt
tthhh	tthht	tthth	tthtt
ttthh	tttht	tttth	ttttt

Number of heads, x	Probability $P(x)$	Product $x \cdot P(x)$
0	$\frac{1}{32}$	0
1	$\frac{5}{32}$	$\frac{5}{32}$
2	$\frac{10}{32}$	$\frac{20}{32}$
3	$\frac{10}{32}$	$\frac{30}{32}$
4	$\frac{5}{32}$	$\frac{20}{32}$
5	$\frac{1}{32}$	$\frac{5}{32}$

Thus, the expected value is given by:
Expected number of heads

$$= 0 + \frac{5}{32} + \frac{20}{32} + \frac{30}{32} + \frac{20}{32} + \frac{5}{32}$$

$$= \frac{80}{32}$$

$$= \frac{5}{2}.$$

5. List the given information in a table. Then calculate $P(x)$, the product $x \cdot P(x)$, and their total.

Number Rolled	Payoff	Probability	Product
6	\$3	$\frac{1}{6}$	$\$\left(\frac{3}{6}\right)$
5	\$2	$\frac{1}{6}$	$\$\left(\frac{2}{6}\right)$
4	\$1	$\frac{1}{6}$	$\$\left(\frac{1}{6}\right)$
1–3	\$0	$\frac{3}{6}$	\$0

Expected value: $\$\left(\frac{6}{6}\right) = \$1$

7. List the given information in a table. Then complete the table as follows.

Number Rolled	Payoff	Probability	Product
1	–\$1	$\frac{1}{6}$	$-\$\left(\frac{1}{6}\right)$
2	\$2	$\frac{1}{6}$	$\$\left(\frac{2}{6}\right)$
3	–\$3	$\frac{1}{6}$	$-\$\left(\frac{3}{6}\right)$
4	\$4	$\frac{1}{6}$	$\$\left(\frac{4}{6}\right)$
5	–\$5	$\frac{1}{6}$	$-\$\left(\frac{5}{6}\right)$
6	\$6	$\frac{1}{6}$	$\$\left(\frac{6}{6}\right)$

Expected value: $\$\left(\frac{3}{6}\right) = 50¢$

The expected net winnings for this game are 50¢.

9. List the given information in a table, and complete the probability and product columns. Remember that the expected value is the sum of the product column.

Number of heads	Payoff	Probability $P(x)$	Product $x \cdot P(x)$
3	10¢	$\frac{1}{8}$	$\left(\frac{10}{8}\right)¢$
2	5¢	$\frac{3}{8}$	$\left(\frac{15}{8}\right)¢$
1	3¢	$\frac{3}{8}$	$\left(\frac{9}{8}\right)¢$
0	0¢	$\frac{1}{8}$	0¢

Expected value: $\left(\frac{34}{8}\right)¢ = \left(\frac{17}{4}\right)¢$

Since it costs 5¢ to play, the expected net winnings are $\frac{17}{4}¢ - 5¢ = \frac{17}{4}¢ - \frac{20}{4}¢ = -\frac{3}{4}¢.$
Because the expected net winnings are not zero, 5¢ is not a fair price to pay to play this game.

11. The expected number of absences on a given day is

$$x_1 \cdot P(x_1) + x_2 \cdot P(x_2) + x_3 \cdot P(x_3) + x_4 \cdot P(x_4) + x_5 \cdot P(x_5)$$
$$= 0(0.18) + 1(0.26) + 2(0.29) + 3(0.23) + 4(0.04)$$
$$= 1.69$$

A college foundation raises funds by selling raffle tickets for a new car worth $36,000.

13. **(a)** Since 600 tickets are sold, a person who buys one ticket will have a probability of $\frac{1}{600} \approx 0.00167$ of winning the car and a 1 – 0.0017 = 0.9983 probability of not winning anything. For this person, the expected value is $36,000(0.00167) + $0(0.9983) ≈ $60, and the expected *net* winnings (since the ticket costs $120) are $60 – $120 = –$60.

(b) By selling 600 tickets at $120 each, the foundation takes in 600($120) = $72,000. Since they had to spend $36,000 for the car, the total profit for the foundation is

revenue – cost = profit
$72,000 – $36,000 = $36,000.

(c) Without having to pay for the car, the foundation's total profit will be all of the revenue from the ticket sales, which is $72,000.

Five thousand raffle tickets are sold. One first prize of $1000, two second prizes of $500 each, and three third prizes of $100 each will be awarded, with all winners selected randomly.

15. The associated probabilities are

$$P(\text{1st prize}) = \frac{1}{5000}, \quad P(\text{2nd prize}) = \frac{2}{5000},$$

and $P(\text{3rd prize}) = \frac{3}{5000}$.

The expected winnings, ignoring the cost of the raffle ticket, are given by

$$\$1000\left(\frac{1}{5000}\right) + \$500\left(\frac{2}{5000}\right) + \$100\left(\frac{3}{5000}\right)$$
$$= \$.20 + \$.20 + \$.06$$
$$= \$.46, \text{ or } 46¢.$$

17. Since 5000 tickets were sold for $1 each, the sponsor's revenue was 5000($1) = $5000. The sponsor's cost was the sum of all the prizes:
1($1000) + 2($500) + 3($100) = $2300.
Therefore, the sponsor's profit is
revenue – cost = profit
$5000 – $2300 = $2700.

19. List the given information in a table, and complete the probability and product columns. Remember that the expected value is the sum of the product column.

Number of families	Probability $P(x)$	Product $x \cdot P(x)$
1020	$\frac{1020}{10000}$	$1 \cdot \left(\frac{1020}{10000}\right) = \frac{1020}{10000}$
3370	$\frac{3370}{10000}$	$2 \cdot \left(\frac{3370}{10000}\right) = \frac{6740}{10000}$
3510	$\frac{3510}{10000}$	$3 \cdot \left(\frac{3510}{10000}\right) = \frac{10530}{10000}$
1340	$\frac{1340}{10000}$	$4 \cdot \left(\frac{1340}{10000}\right) = \frac{5360}{10000}$
510	$\frac{510}{10000}$	$5 \cdot \left(\frac{510}{10000}\right) = \frac{2550}{10000}$
80	$\frac{80}{10000}$	$6 \cdot \left(\frac{80}{10000}\right) = \frac{480}{10000}$
170	$\frac{170}{10000}$	$0 \cdot \left(\frac{170}{10000}\right) = 0$

Expected value: $\frac{26680}{10000} \approx 2.7$

21. The expected value is
200(0.2) + 300(0.5) + (–800)(0.3)
= 40 + 150 – 240
= –50
Since this expected value is negative, the expected change in the number of electronics jobs is a decrease of 50.

23. Writing exercise; answers will vary.

25. The optimist viewpoint would ignore the probabilities and hope for the best possible outcome, which is Project *C* since it may return up to $340,000.

27. If the contestant takes a chance on the other two prizes, the expected winnings will be

$$\$5000(0.20) + \$8000(0.15) = \$1000 + \$1200 = \$2200.$$

29. Expectation for Insuring

	Net Profit x	Probability $P(x)$	Product $x \cdot P(x)$
Rain	\$100,000 + \$30,000 − \$25,000 = \$105,000	0.20	\$21,000
No rain	\$100,000 − \$25,000 = \$75,000	0.80	\$60,000
		Expected Profit:	\$81,000

31. Do not purchase the insurance because \$86,000 > \$81,000.

33. Compute the remaining values in Column 5 (Expected Value).
Row 5: 5000(0.30) = 1500
Row 6: 30,000(0.10) = 3000
Row 7: 25,000(0.70) = 17,500
Row 8: 45,000(0.60) = 27,000

35. Jessica's total "expected" additional volume is
\$4000 + \$3000 + \$1500 + \$3000 + \$17,500 + \$27,000
= \$56,000.

37. Her total existing volume is
\$10,000 + \$30,000 + \$25,000 + \$35,000 + \$15,000
= \$115,000.
The increase in volume would be
\$171,000 − \$115,000 = \$56,000.
That would be an increase of

$$\frac{56,000}{115,000} \approx 0.487, \text{ or } 48.7\%.$$

EXTENSION: ESTIMATING PROBABILITIES BY SIMULATION

1. Writing exercise; answers will vary.

3. No, since the probability of an individual girl's birth is (nearly) the same as that for a boy.

5. Let each of the 50 numbers correspond to one family. For example, the first number, 51592, with middle digits—1(boy), 5(girl), 9(girl)—represents a family with 2 girls and 1 boy. The last number whose middle digits are 800 represents the 50th family which has 1 girl and 2 boys—a success, and so on.

Examining each number, we count (tally) 18 successes. Therefore,

$$P(\text{2 boys and 1 girl}) = \frac{18}{50} = 0.36.$$

Observe that this is quite close to the 0.375 predicted by the theoretical value.

Refer to discussion in text regarding foul shooting in basketball. After completing the indicated tally, find the empirical probability that, on a given opportunity, Christine will score as follows.

To construct the tally for Exercise 7, begin as follows: Since the first number in the table of random digits is 5, which represents a hit, Christine will get a second shot. The second digit is 7, representing a miss on the second shot. Record the results of the first two shots (the first one-and-one opportunity) as "one point." The second and third opportunities correspond to the pair 3, 4 and 0, 5. Record each of these results as "two points." For the fourth opportunity, the digit 9 indicates that the first shot was missed, so Christine does not get a second shot. In this case only one digit is used. Record this result as "zero points." Continue in this manner until 50 one-and-one opportunities are obtained. The results of the tally are as follows. Note that this, in effect, is a frequency distribution.

Number of Points	Tally frequency
0	15
1	6
2	29
Total	50

7. From the tally, we see that 1 point shots occur 6 times. Thus,

$$P(\text{1 point}) = \frac{6}{50} = 0.12.$$

9. Answers will vary.

11. Writing exercise; answers will vary.

Chapter Test

1. Writing exercise; answers will vary.

2. Writing exercise; answers will vary.

3. There are 39 non-hearts and 13 hearts, so the odds against getting a heart are 39 to 13, or 3 to 1 (when reduced).

4. There are 2 red queens and 50 other cards, so the odds against getting a red queen are 50 to 2, or 25 to 1.

5. There are 12 face cards altogether. Of these, there are 6 black face cards and 2 more non-black kings for a total of 8 cards. There are 52 – 8 = 44 other cards in the deck. Thus, the odds against getting a black face card or king are 44 to 8, or 11 to 2.

6.

		Second Parent	
		C	c
First Parent	C	CC	Cc
	c	cC	cc

7. There are two outcomes (cC or Cc) indicating that the next child will be a carrier. Thus, $P(\text{carrier}) = \frac{2}{4} = \frac{1}{2}$.

8. There is one 'favorable' outcome (cc) and three 'unfavorable' outcomes (CC, Cc, and cC). Thus, the odds that a child will have the disease (cc) are 1 to 3.

9. Use the fundamental counting principle where the first task is to calculate the probability of the initial employee choosing any day of the week $\left(\frac{7}{7}\right)$, the second task is the probability for the second employee to choose any other day of the seek $\left(\frac{6}{7}\right)$. In a similar manner, the third employee's probability must involve a choice from one of the five remaining days with a resulting probability of $\left(\frac{5}{7}\right)$. Thus,

$$P = \frac{7}{7}\cdot\frac{6}{7}\cdot\frac{5}{7} = \frac{30}{49}.$$

10. Let E_1, E_2, and E_3 represent the 3 employees. The following seven outcomes would be considered a success, or favorable outcome, for our probability:
{(M: E_1, E_2, E_3), (Tue: E_1, E_2, E_3), (W: E_1, E_2, E_3), ..., (Sun: E_1, E_2, E_3)}.
The remainder of the sample space outcomes include those where employees are split between Tuesday and Thursday or Saturday and Sunday. Listing the Tuesday, Thursday possibilities we have:
{(Tue: E_1; Th: E_2, E_3),
(Tue: E_2; Th: E_1, E_3),
(Tue: E_3; Th: E_1, E_2),
(Tue: E_1, E_2; Th: E_3),
(Tue: E_1, E_3; Th: E_2),
(Tue: E_2, E_3; Th: E_1)} for a total of six more outcomes. Similarly, if all employees choose a day beginning with "S" i.e. Saturday or Sunday there would be an additional six outcomes for a total of nineteen outcomes in our sample space, i.e. $n(S) = 19$. Thus the probability that all employees choose the same day to work given that all three select a day beginning with the same letter is:

$$P = \frac{\text{number of favorable outcomes}}{\text{total number of outcomes, } n(S)} = \frac{7}{19}.$$

11. The complement of "exactly two choose the same day" is "all three choose different days (Exercise 9) or all three choose the same day." The probability that all three choose the same day is $\frac{7}{7}\cdot\frac{1}{7}\cdot\frac{1}{7} = \frac{1}{49}$. Thus, the probability of "exactly two choosing the same day" is given by

$$P = 1 - \left(\frac{30}{49} + \frac{1}{49}\right) = \frac{18}{49}.$$

Observe that the calculation involves both the complements rule and the special addition rule.

Two numbers are randomly selected without replacement from the set {1, 2, 3, 4, 5}.

12. To find the probability that "both numbers are even," use combinations to select the number of successes—ways of selecting the two even numbers, ${}_2C_2$, and to calculate the total number of ways of selecting two of the numbers from the 5, ${}_5C_2$. Thus,

$$P(\text{selecting two even numbers}) = \frac{{}_2C_2}{{}_5C_2} = \frac{1}{10}.$$

As in many of the exercises an alternate solution may be considered here: Let E_1 represent the event of selecting an even number as the first selection and E_2, selecting an even number as the second selection. Using the general multiplication rule the probability is given by

$$P(E_1 \text{ and } E_2) = P(E_1) \cdot P(E_2|E_1) = \frac{2}{5} \cdot \frac{1}{4} = \frac{1}{10}.$$

13. To find the probability that "both numbers are prime" use combinations. Since there are three prime numbers {2, 3, 5}, use ${}_3C_2$ to calculate the number of successes. To calculate the total number of ways of selecting two of the numbers from the 5, use ${}_5C_2$. Thus,

$$P(\text{selecting two prime numbers}) = \frac{{}_3C_2}{{}_5C_2} = \frac{3}{10}.$$

14. Create a "product (sum) table" to list the elements in the sample space and the successes (event of interest). Note that "without replacement," one can only use a selected number once. Hence, there are no diagonal values in the table.

		2nd number				
	+	1	2	3	4	5
	1	–	3	4	5	6
	2	3	–	5	6	7
2nd number	3	4	5	–	7	8
	4	5	6	7	–	9
	5	6	7	8	9	–

There are 12 odd sums in the table and a total of 20 sums in the sample space. Thus,

$$P(\text{sum is odd}) = \frac{12}{20} = \frac{3}{5}.$$

15. Similar to Exercise 14, create a "product table" to list the elements in the sample space and the successes (event of interest). Note that "without replacement," one can only use a selected number once. Hence, there are no diagonal values in the table.

		2nd number				
	×	1	2	3	4	5
	1	–	2	3	4	5
	2	2	–	6	8	10
2nd number	3	3	6	–	12	15
	4	4	8	12	–	20
	5	5	10	15	20	–

There are 6 odd products in the table and a total of 20 products in the sample space.

Thus, $P(\text{product is odd}) = \frac{6}{20} = \frac{3}{10}.$

A three-member committee is selected randomly from a group consisting of three men and two women.

16. Let x represent the number of men on the committee. Then,

x	$P(x)$
0	0
1	$\frac{3}{10}$
2	$\frac{6}{10}$
3	$\frac{1}{10}$

Where,

$$P(1) = \frac{C(3, 1) \cdot C(2, 2)}{C(5, 3)}$$

$$P(2) = \frac{C(3, 2) \cdot C(2, 1)}{C(5, 3)}$$

$$P(3) = \frac{C(3, 3) \cdot C(2, 0)}{C(5, 3)}$$

Why is $P(0) = 0$?

17. The probability that the "committee members are not all men" is the complement of the "committee are all men," $P(3)$. Hence, use the complements rule,

$$P(\text{committee members are not all men}) = 1 - P(3) = 1 - \frac{1}{10} = \frac{9}{10}.$$

18. Complete the table begun in Exercise 16 as an aid to calculating the expected number of men (sum of product column).

x	$P(x)$	$x \cdot P(x)$
0	0	0
1	$\frac{3}{10}$	$\frac{3}{10}$
2	$\frac{6}{10}$	$\frac{12}{10}$
3	$\frac{1}{10}$	$\frac{3}{10}$

Expected number: $\frac{18}{10} = \frac{9}{5}$

Create a "product (sum) table" such as below for the "sum" of rolling two dice.

2nd die

	+	1	2	3	4	5	6
	1	2	3	4	5	6	7
	2	3	4	5	6	7	8
1st die	3	4	5	6	7	8	9
	4	5	6	7	8	9	10
	5	6	7	8	9	10	11
	6	7	8	9	10	11	12

Use for Exercises 19–22.

19. There are 6 doubles values and 36 possible values. The probability of doubles is therefore, $\frac{6}{36} = \frac{1}{6}$.

20. There are 35 outcomes with a "sum greater than 2" and 36 possible outcomes. Thus the odds in favor of a "sum greater than 2" are 35 to 1.

21. To find the odds against a "sum of 7 or 11" count the sums that satisfy the condition "sum of 7 or 11." There are 8 such sums. It follows that there are 36 – 8 = 28 sums that are not 7 or 11. Thus, the odds against a "sum of 7 or 11" are 28 to 8, or 7 to 2.

22. Since there are 4 sums that are even and less than 5,

$$P(\text{sum that is even and less than 5}) = \frac{4}{36} = \frac{1}{9}.$$

For Exercises 23–26, the chance of making par on any one hole is 0.78.

23. By the special multiplication rule,

$$P(\text{making par on all three holes}) = 0.78^3 \approx 0.475$$

24. Use the fundamental counting principle, where the first task is to find the number of ways to choose the two holes he scores par on followed by the tasks of assigning a probability for each hole. Note that since 0.78 is the probability of scoring par, 1 – 0.78 = 0.22 is the probability of not scoring par on a hole.

$$\begin{aligned} &P(\text{makes par on exactly 2 holes}) \\ &= {}_3C_2 \cdot (0.78)^2 \cdot (0.22) \\ &= (3)(0.6084)(0.22) \\ &\approx 0.402 \end{aligned}$$

25. "At least one of the three holes" is the complement of "none of the three holes." Since the probability of not making par on any of the three holes is 0.22^3,

$$\begin{aligned} &P(\text{at least one of the three holes}) \\ &= 1 - (0.22)^3 \\ &= 1 - 0.010648 \\ &\approx 0.989. \end{aligned}$$

26. Use the special multiplication rule since these probabilities are independent. The probability that he makes par on the first and third holes but not on the second is found by

$P = (0.78)(0.22)(0.78) \approx 0.134.$

Two cards are drawn, without replacement, from a standard 52-card deck for Exercises 27–30.

27. Let R_1 and R_2 represent the two red cards. Since the cards are not replaced, the events are not independent. Use the general multiplication rule:

$$\begin{aligned} P(R_1 \text{ and } R_2) &= P(R_1) \cdot P(R_2 | R_1) \\ &= \frac{26}{52} \cdot \frac{25}{51} \\ &= \frac{1}{2} \cdot \frac{25}{51} \\ &= \frac{25}{102} \end{aligned}$$

28. Let C_1 and C_2 represent two cards of the same color. Since the cards are not replaced, the events are not independent. Use the general multiplication rule. Note that since it

doesn't matter what color the first card is, its probability is 1.
Thus, $P(C_1 \text{ and } C_2) = P(C_1)\cdot P(C_2|C_1)$

$$= \frac{52}{52}\cdot\frac{25}{51}$$
$$= \frac{25}{51}.$$

29. The first card drawn limits the sample space to 51 cards where all 4 queens are still in the deck. The probability then is given by
P(queen given the first card is an ace)
$= P(Q_2|A_1)$
$$= \frac{4}{51}.$$

30. In the event "the first card is a face card and the second is black," the first (face) card may be red or black. Since this affects the probability associated with the second card, look at both cases and use the special addition rule to add (since we are "or-ing") the results.
Case 1 (first card is a red face card):
$P(F_1 \text{ and } B_2) = P(F_1)\cdot P(B_2|F_1)$
$$= \frac{6}{52}\cdot\frac{26}{51}$$
$$= \frac{3}{51}$$
$$= \frac{1}{17}.$$
Case 2 (first card is a black face card):
$P(F_1 \text{ and } B_2) = P(F_1)\cdot P(B_2|F_1)$
$$= \frac{6}{52}\cdot\frac{25}{51}$$
$$= \frac{3}{26}\cdot\frac{25}{51}$$
$$= \frac{1}{26}\cdot\frac{25}{17}$$
$$= \frac{25}{26\cdot 17}.$$

The probability is $P(\text{Case 1 or Case 2})$
$$= P(\text{Case 1}) + P(\text{Case 2})$$
$$= \frac{1}{17} + \frac{25}{26\cdot 17}$$
$$= \frac{26\cdot 1}{26\cdot 17} + \frac{25}{26\cdot 17}$$
$$= \frac{26+25}{26\cdot 17}$$
$$= \frac{51}{26\cdot 17}$$
$$= \frac{3\cdot 17}{26\cdot 17}$$
$$= \frac{3}{26}.$$

STATISTICS

Mark Lennihan/AP Photo

The CBS television series, NUMB3RS, focused on how mathematics is used in solving crimes. In the December 5, 2008 episode Conspiracy Theory, agent Charlie Eppes wants to prove a point to one of his colleagues: "Go with what you know, not what you don't." He cites a case of Simpson's paradox, a puzzling statistical oddity.

> *In both these years, David Justice had a higher batting average than Derek Jeter. But if you factor in their uneven number of at-bats, Jeter beats him.*

What we know is that for the two-year period, Jeter is the better hitter, despite the fact that for both individual years, Justice had higher averages. To verify the paradox for yourself, see Further Thought later in this chapter.

1 VISUAL DISPLAYS OF DATA

Basic Concepts • Frequency Distributions • Grouped Frequency Distributions • Stem-and-Leaf Displays • Bar Graphs, Circle Graphs, and Line Graphs

Basic Concepts

Governments collect and analyze an amazing quantity of "statistics". The word itself comes from the Latin *statisticus,* meaning "of the state."

Population

Sample

Courtesy of Vern Heeren

In statistical work, a **population** includes *all* items of interest, and a **sample** includes *some* (but ordinarily not all) of the items in the population. See the Venn diagram in the margin.

To predict the outcome of an approaching presidential election, we may be interested in a population of many millions of voter preferences (those of all potential voters in the country). As a practical matter, however, even national polling organizations with considerable resources will obtain only a relatively small sample, say 2000, of those preferences.

The study of statistics is divided into two main areas. **Descriptive statistics** has to do with collecting, organizing, summarizing, and presenting data (information). **Inferential statistics,** has to do with drawing inferences or conclusions (making conjectures) about populations based on information from samples.

The photos below show two random samples drawn from a large bowl of 10,000 colored beads. The 25-bead sample contains 9 green beads, from which we infer, by inductive reasoning, that the bowl (the population) must contain about $\frac{9}{25}$, or 36%, that is, about 3600 green beads.

A population of 10,000

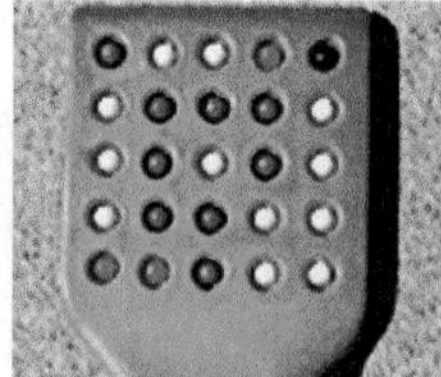

A random sample of 25

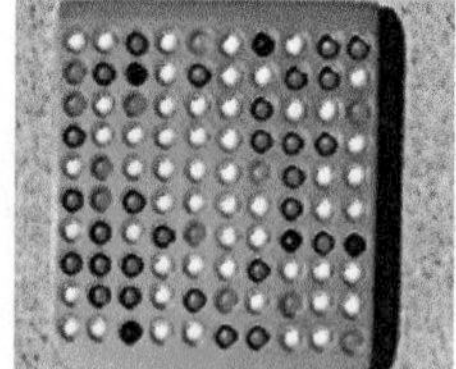

A random sample of 100

The 100-bead sample contains 28 green beads, leading to the inference that the population must contain about $\frac{28}{100}$, or 28%, that is, about 2800 green beads. This estimate, based on a larger sample, should be more accurate. In fact it is, since the bowl actually contains 30%, or 3000 green beads, and 2800 is closer to 3000 than 3600 is. (The "error" is one-third as much.)

Summarizing, if we know what a population is like, then probability theory enables us to predict what is likely to happen in a sample (deductive reasoning). If we know what a sample is like, then inferential statistics enables us to infer estimates about the population (inductive reasoning).

Information that has been collected but not yet organized or processed is called **raw data.** It is often **quantitative** (or **numerical**) but can also be **qualitative** (or **nonnumerical**), as illustrated in **Table 1**.

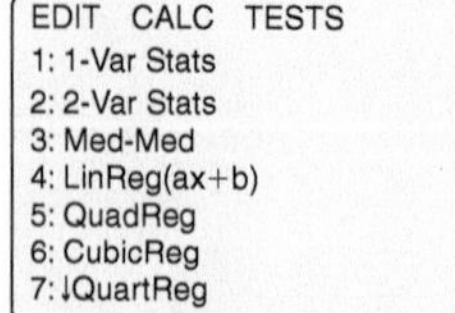

EDIT CALC TESTS
7: ↑QuartReg
8: LinReg(a+bx)
9: LnReg
0: ExpReg
A: PwrReg
B: Logistic
C: SinReg

Various statistical options on the TI-83/84 Plus.

Table 1 Examples of Raw Data

Quantitative data: The number of siblings in ten different families: 3, 1, 2, 1, 5, 4, 3, 3, 8, 2
Qualitative data: The makes of six different automobiles: Toyota, Ford, Nissan, Toyota, Chevrolet, Honda

Most scientific and graphing calculators will perform all computations we describe in this chapter, including sorting of data (once they are entered). So your purpose in studying this material should be to understand the meanings of the various computed quantities. It is recommended that the actual computations, especially for sizable collections of data, be done on a calculator (or a computer with suitable statistical software).

Quantitative data are generally more useful when they are **sorted,** or arranged in numerical order. In sorted form, the first list in **Table 1** appears as follows.

$$1, 1, 2, 2, 3, 3, 3, 4, 5, 8$$

Frequency Distributions

When a data set includes many repeated items, it can be organized into a **frequency distribution,** which lists the distinct data values (x) along with their frequencies (f). The frequency designates the number of times the corresponding item occurred in the data set.

It is also helpful to show the **relative frequency** of each distinct item. This is the fraction, or percentage, of the data set represented by the item. If n denotes the total number of items, and a given item, x, occurred f times, then the relative frequency of x is $\frac{f}{n}$. **Example 1** illustrates these ideas.

EXAMPLE 1 Constructing Frequency and Relative Frequency Distributions

The 25 members of a psychology class were polled as to the number of siblings in their individual families. Construct a frequency distribution and a relative frequency distribution for their responses, which are shown here.

$$2, 3, 1, 3, 3, 5, 2, 3, 3, 1, 1, 4, 2, 4, 2, 5, 4, 3, 6, 5, 1, 6, 2, 2, 2$$

SOLUTION

The data range from a low of 1 to a high of 6. The frequencies (obtained by inspection) and relative frequencies are shown in **Table 2**.

Table 2 Frequency and Relative Frequency Distributions for Numbers of Siblings

Number x	Frequency f	Relative Frequency $\frac{f}{n}$
1	4	$\frac{4}{25} = 16\%$
2	7	$\frac{7}{25} = 28\%$
3	6	$\frac{6}{25} = 24\%$
4	3	$\frac{3}{25} = 12\%$
5	3	$\frac{3}{25} = 12\%$
6	2	$\frac{2}{25} = 8\%$

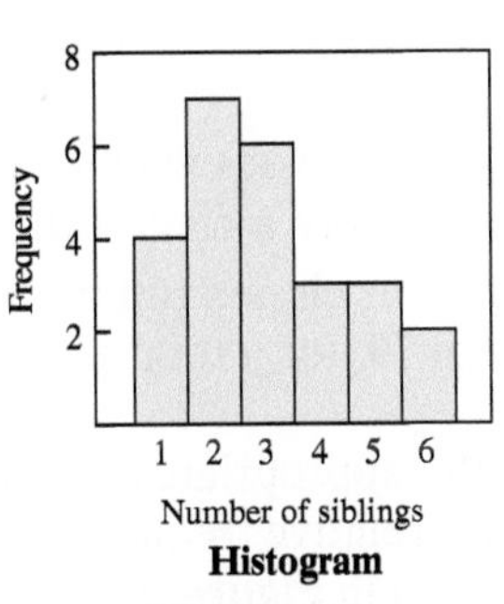

Histogram

Figure 1

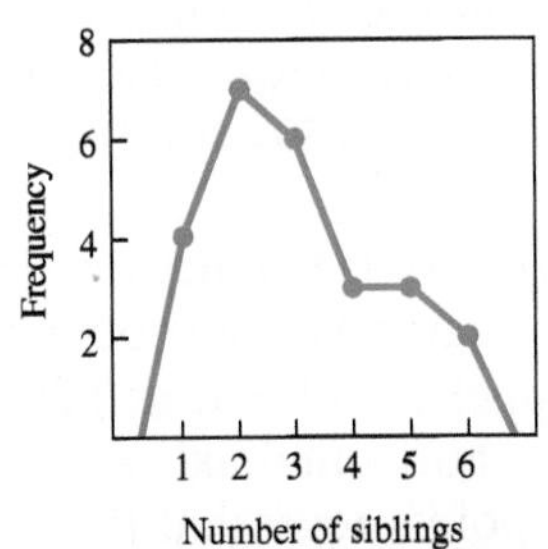

Frequency polygon

Figure 2

The numerical data of **Table 2** can more easily be interpreted with the aid of a **histogram.** A series of rectangles, whose lengths represent the frequencies, are placed next to one another as shown in **Figure 1**. On each axis, horizontal and vertical, a label and the numerical scale should be shown.

The information shown in the histogram in **Figure 1** can also be conveyed by a **frequency polygon,** as in **Figure 2**. Simply plot a single point at the appropriate height for each frequency, connect the points with a series of connected line segments, and complete the polygon with segments that trail down to the axis beyond 1 and 6.

The frequency polygon is an instance of the more general *line graph,* used for many kinds of data, not just frequencies.

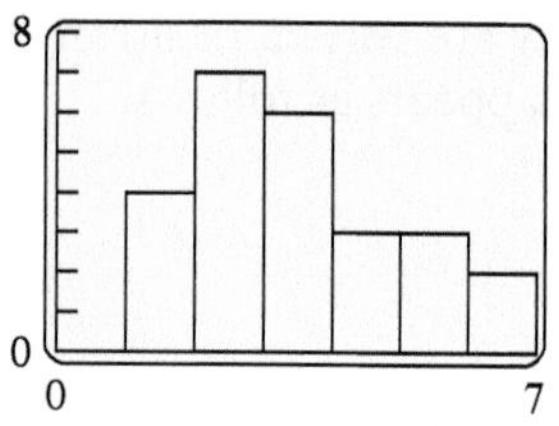

This histogram was generated with a graphing calculator using the data in **Table 2**. Compare with **Figure 1** on **the previous page**.

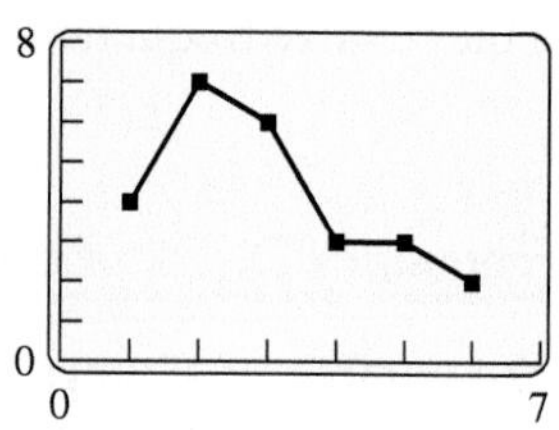

This line graph resembles the frequency polygon in **Figure 2** on **the previous page**. It was generated with a graphing calculator using the data in **Table 2**.

Grouped Frequency Distributions

Data sets containing large numbers of items are often arranged into groups, or *classes*. All data items are assigned to their appropriate classes, and then a **grouped frequency distribution** can be set up and a graph displayed. Although there are no fixed rules for establishing the classes, most statisticians agree on a few general guidelines.

Guidelines for the Classes of a Grouped Frequency Distribution

1. Make sure each data item will fit into one, and only one, class.
2. Try to make all classes the same width.
3. Make sure the classes do not overlap.
4. Use from 5 to 12 classes. (Too few or too many classes can obscure the tendencies in the data.)

EXAMPLE 2 Constructing a Histogram and a Frequency Polygon

Forty students, selected randomly in the school cafeteria one morning, were asked to estimate the number of hours they had spent studying in the past week (including both in-class and out-of-class time). Their responses are recorded here.

18 60 72 58 20 15 12 26 16 29
26 41 45 25 32 24 22 55 30 31
55 39 29 44 29 14 40 31 45 62
36 52 47 38 36 23 33 44 17 24

Tabulate a grouped frequency distribution and a grouped relative frequency distribution and construct a histogram and a frequency polygon for the given data.

SOLUTION

The data range from a low of 12 to a high of 72 (that is, over a range of $72 - 12 = 60$ units.). The widths of the classes should be uniform (by Guideline 2), and there should be from 5 to 12 classes (by Guideline 4). Five classes would imply a class width of about $\frac{60}{5} = 12$, while twelve classes would imply a class width of about $\frac{60}{12} = 5$. A class width of 10 will be convenient. We let our classes run from 10 through 19, from 20 through 29, and so on up to 70 through 79, for a total of seven classes. All four guidelines are met.

Next go through the data set, tallying each item into the appropriate class. The tally totals produce class frequencies, which in turn produce relative frequencies, as shown in **Table 3** on the next page. The histogram is displayed in **Figure 3**.

In **Table 3** (and **Figure 3**) the numbers 10, 20, 30, and so on are called the **lower class limits.** They are the smallest possible data values within the respective classes. The numbers 19, 29, 39, and so on are called the **upper class limits.** The common **class width** for the distribution is the difference of any two successive lower class limits (such as 30–20), or of any two successive upper class limits (such as 59–49). The class width for this distribution is 10, as noted earlier.

To construct a frequency polygon, notice that, in a *grouped* frequency distribution, the data items in a given class are generally not all the same. We can obtain the "middle" value, or **class mark,** by adding the lower and upper class limits and dividing this sum by 2. We locate all the class marks along the horizontal axis and plot points above the class marks. The heights of the plotted points represent the class frequencies. The resulting points are connected just as for an ordinary (nongrouped) frequency distribution. The result is shown in **Figure 4**.

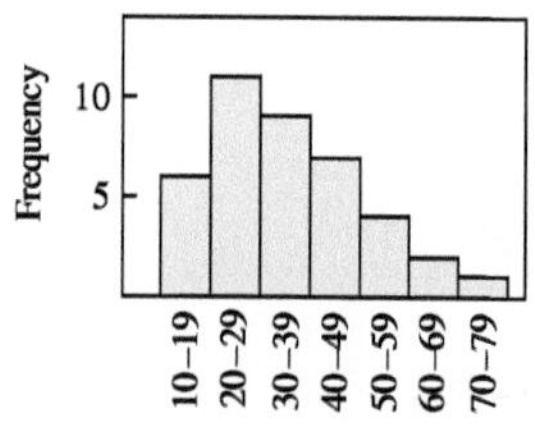

Grouped frequency histogram

Figure 3

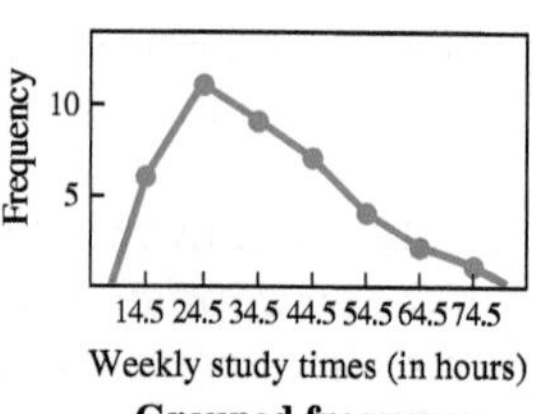

Grouped frequency polygon

Figure 4

Table 3 Grouped Frequency and Relative Frequency Distributions for Weekly Study Times

Class Limits	Tally	Frequency f	Relative Frequency $\frac{f}{n}$
10–19	𝍸 I	6	$\frac{6}{40} = 15.0\%$
20–29	𝍸 𝍸 I	11	$\frac{11}{40} = 27.5\%$
30–39	𝍸 IIII	9	$\frac{9}{40} = 22.5\%$
40–49	𝍸 II	7	$\frac{7}{40} = 17.5\%$
50–59	IIII	4	$\frac{4}{40} = 10.0\%$
60–69	II	2	$\frac{2}{40} = 5.0\%$
70–79	I	1	$\frac{1}{40} = 2.5\%$
		Total: $n = 40$	

Stem-and-Leaf Displays

In **Table 3**, the tally marks give a good visual impression of how the data are distributed. In fact, the tally marks are almost like a histogram turned on its side. Nevertheless, once the tallying is done, the tally marks are usually dropped, and the grouped frequency distribution is presented as in **Table 4**.

Table 4 Grouped Frequency Distribution for Weekly Study Times

Class Limits	Frequency
10–19	6
20–29	11
30–39	9
40–49	7
50–59	4
60–69	2
70–79	1

The pictorial advantage of the tally marks is now lost. Furthermore, we cannot tell, from the grouped frequency distribution itself (or from the tally marks either, for that matter), what any of the original items were. We only know, for example, that there were seven items in the class 40–49. We do not know specifically what any of them were.

One way to avoid these shortcoming is to employ a tool of exploratory data analysis, the **stem-and-leaf display,** as shown in **Example 3**.

EXAMPLE 3 Constructing a Stem-and-Leaf Display

Present the study times data of **Example 2** in a stem-and-leaf display.

SOLUTION

See **Example 2** for the original raw data. We arrange the numbers in **Table 5**. The tens digits, to the left of the vertical line, are the "stems," while the corresponding ones digits are the "leaves." We have entered all items from the first row of the original data, from left to right, then the items from the second row through the fourth row.

Table 5 Stem-and-Leaf Display for Weekly Study Times

1	8	5	2	6	4	7					
2	0	6	9	6	5	4	2	9	9	3	4
3	2	0	1	9	1	6	8	6	3		
4	1	5	4	0	5	7	4				
5	8	5	5	2							
6	0	2									
7	2										

Notice that the stem-and-leaf display of **Example 3** conveys at a glance the same pictorial impressions that a histogram would convey without the need for constructing the drawing. It also preserves the exact data values.

Bar Graphs, Circle Graphs, and Line Graphs

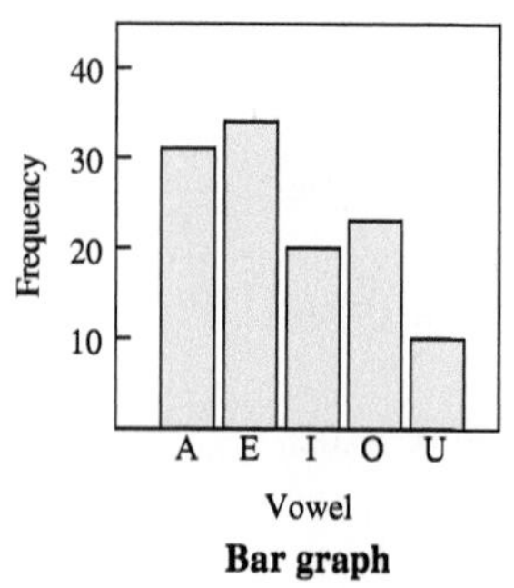

Figure 5

A frequency distribution of nonnumerical observations can be presented in the form of a **bar graph,** which is similar to a histogram except that the rectangles (bars) usually are not touching one another and sometimes are arranged horizontally rather than vertically. The bar graph of **Figure 5** shows the frequencies of occurrence of the vowels A, E, I, O, and U in this paragraph.

A graphical alternative to the bar graph is the **circle graph,** or **pie chart,** which uses a circle to represent the total of all the categories and divides the circle into sectors, or wedges (like pieces of pie), whose sizes show the relative magnitudes of the categories. The angle around the entire circle measures 360°. For example, a category representing 20% of the whole should correspond to a sector whose central angle is 20% of 360°, that is,

$$0.20(360°) = 72°.$$

A circle graph shows, at a glance, the relative magnitudes of various categories.

EXAMPLE 4 Constructing a Circle Graph

Cheri Goldberg found that, during her first semester of college, her expenses fell into categories as shown in **Table 6** below. Present this information in a circle graph.

SOLUTION

The central angle of the food sector is $0.30(360°) = 108°$. Rent is $0.25(360°) = 90°$. Calculate the other four angles similarly. Then draw a circle and mark off the angles with a protractor. The completed circle graph appears in **Figure 6**.

Table 6 Student Expenses

Expense	Percent of Total
Food	30%
Rent	25%
Entertainment	15%
Clothing	10%
Books	10%
Other	10%

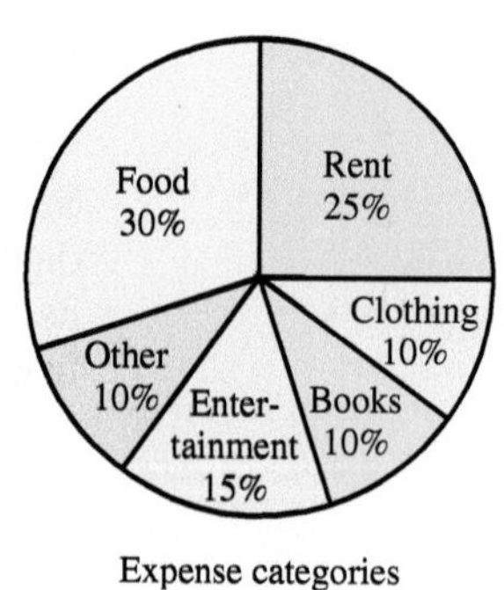

Figure 6

To demonstrate how a quantity *changes,* say with respect to time, use a **line graph.** Connect a series of line segments that rise and fall with time, according to the magnitude of the quantity being illustrated. To compare the patterns of change for two or more quantities, we can even plot multiple line graphs together in a "comparison line graph." (A line graph looks somewhat like a frequency polygon, but the quantities graphed are not necessarily frequencies.)

EXAMPLE 5 Constructing and Interpreting a Line Graph

Suppose Cheri, from **Example 4,** wanted to keep track of her major expenses, food and rent, over the course of four years of college (eight semesters), in order to see how each one's budget percentage changed with time and how the two compared. Use the data she collected (**Table 7**) to show this information in a line graph, and state any significant conclusions that are apparent from the graph.

Table 7 Food and Rent Expense Percentages

Semester	Food	Rent
First	30%	25%
Second	31	26
Third	30	28
Fourth	29	29
Fifth	28	34
Sixth	31	34
Seventh	30	37
Eighth	29	38

Francesco Ridolfi/Shutterstock

SOLUTION

A comparison line graph for the given data (**Figure 7**) shows that the food percentage stayed fairly constant over the four years (at close to 30%), while the rent percentage, starting several points below food, rose steadily, surpassing food after the fourth semester and finishing significantly higher than food.

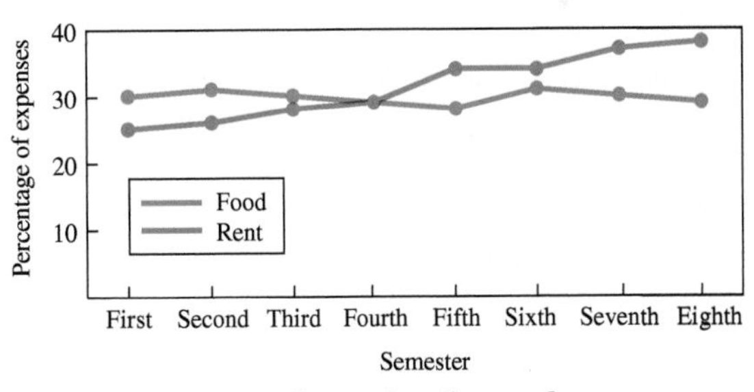

Comparison line graph

Figure 7

For Further Thought

Expected and Observed Frequencies

When fair coins are tossed, the results on particular tosses cannot be reliably predicted. As more and more coins are tossed, however, the proportions of heads and tails become more predictable. This is a consequence of the "law of large numbers."

For example, if five coins are tossed, then the resulting number of heads, denoted x, is a "random variable," whose possible values are

$$0, 1, 2, 3, 4, \text{and } 5.$$

If the five coins are tossed repeatedly, say 64 separate times, then the binomial probability formula can be used to get **expected frequencies** (or **theoretical frequencies**), as shown in the table on the next page. The first two columns of the table comprise the **expected frequency distribution** for 64 tosses of five fair coins.

(continued)

For Further Thought (cont.)

In an actual experiment, we could obtain **observed frequencies** (or **empirical frequencies**), which would most likely differ somewhat from the expected frequencies. But 64 repetitions of the experiment should be enough to provide fair consistency between expected and observed values.

For Group or Individual Investigation

Toss five coins a total of 64 times, keeping a record of the results.

1. Enter your experimental results in the third column of the table at the right, producing an **observed frequency distribution.**
2. Compare the second and third column entries.
3. Construct two histograms, one from the expected frequency distribution and one from your observed frequency distribution.
4. Compare the two histograms.

Number of Heads x	Expected Frequency e	Observed Frequency o
0	2	
1	10	
2	20	
3	20	
4	10	
5	2	

1 EXERCISES

In Exercises 1 and 2, use the given data to do the following:

(a) *Construct frequency and relative frequency distributions, in a table similar to* **Table 2.**

(b) *Construct a histogram.*

(c) *Construct a frequency polygon.*

1. ***Preparation for Summer*** According to *Newsmax* (May, 2010), the following are five popular "maintenance" activities performed as summer approaches.

1. Prep the car for road trips.
2. Clean up the house or apartment.
3. Groom the garden.
4. Exercise the body.
5. Organize the wardrobe.

The following data are the responses of 30 people who were asked, on June 1st, how many of the five they had accomplished.

1	1	3	1	0	3	0	0	2	1
2	2	0	0	5	3	4	0	1	0
4	2	0	2	0	1	0	1	2	3

2. ***Responses to "Pick a Number"*** The following data are the responses of 28 people asked to "pick a number from 1 to 10."

4	7	2	7	6	3	1
7	4	9	8	5	6	10
4	10	8	9	5	4	5
9	2	6	6	6	8	7

In Exercises 3–6, use the given data to do the following:

(a) *Construct grouped frequency and relative frequency distributions, in a table similar to* **Table 3.** *(Follow the suggested guidelines for class limits and class width.)*

(b) *Construct a histogram.*

(c) *Construct a frequency polygon.*

3. ***Exam Scores*** The scores of the 54 members of a sociology lecture class on a 70-point exam were as follows.

60	63	64	52	60	58	63	53	56
64	48	54	64	57	51	67	60	49
59	54	49	52	53	60	58	60	64
52	56	56	58	66	59	62	50	58
53	51	65	62	61	55	59	52	62
58	61	65	56	55	50	61	55	54

Use five classes with a uniform class width of 5 points, and use a lower limit of 45 points for the first class.

4. ***Charge Card Account Balances*** The following raw data represent the monthly account balances (to the nearest dollar) for a sample of 50 brand-new charge card users.

78	175	46	138	79	118	90	163	88	107
126	154	85	60	42	54	62	128	114	73
67	119	116	145	129	130	81	105	96	71
100	145	117	60	125	130	94	88	136	112
85	165	118	84	74	62	81	110	108	71

Use seven classes with a uniform width of 20 dollars, where the lower limit of the first class is 40 dollars.

5. ***Daily High Temperatures*** The following data represent the daily high temperatures (in degrees Fahrenheit) for the month of June in a southwestern U.S. city.

79	84	88	96	102	104	99	97	92	94
85	92	100	99	101	104	110	108	106	106
90	82	74	72	83	107	111	102	97	94

Use nine classes with a uniform width of 5 degrees, where the lower limit of the first class is 70 degrees.

6. ***IQ Scores of College Freshmen*** The following data represent IQ scores of a group of 50 college freshmen.

113	109	118	92	130	112	114	117	122	115
127	107	108	113	124	112	111	106	116	118
121	107	118	118	110	124	115	103	100	114
104	124	116	123	104	135	121	126	116	111
96	134	98	129	102	103	107	113	117	112

Use nine classes with a uniform width of 5, where the lower limit of the first class is 91.

In each of Exercises 7–10, construct a stem-and-leaf display for the given data. In each case, treat the ones digits as the leaves. For any single-digit data, use a stem of 0.

7. ***Games Won in the National Basketball Association*** Approaching midseason, the teams in the National Basketball Association had won the following numbers of games.

27	20	29	11	26	11	12	7	26	18
22	19	14	13	22	9	25	11	10	15
38	10	22	23	31	8	24	15	24	15

Paul J. Richards/AFP/Getty Images

8. ***Accumulated College Units*** The students in a biology class were asked how many college units they had accumulated to date. Their responses are shown below.

12	4	13	12	21	22	15	17	33	24
32	42	26	11	53	62	42	25	13	8
54	18	21	14	19	17	38	17	20	10

9. ***Distances to School*** The following data are the daily round-trip distances to school (in miles) for 30 randomly chosen students attending a community college in California.

16	30	10	11	18	26	34	18	8	12
21	14	5	22	4	25	9	10	6	21
12	18	9	16	44	23	4	13	36	8

10. ***Yards Gained in the National Football League*** The following data represent net yards gained per game by National Football League running backs who played during a given week of the season.

25	19	36	73	37	88	67	33	54	123	79
19	39	45	22	58	7	73	30	43	24	36
65	43	33	55	40	29	112	60	94	86	62
52	29	18	25	41	3	49	102	16	32	46

Federal Government Receipts *The graph shows U.S. government receipts and outlays (both on-budget and off-budget) for 2001–2011. Refer to the graph for Exercises 11–15.*

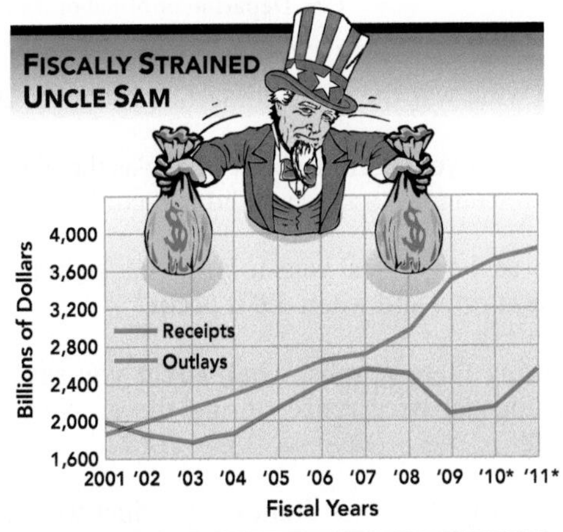

Source: Department of the Treasury, Office of Management and Budget.
*Data are estimates.

11. Of the period 2001–2011, list all years when receipts exceeded outlays.

12. Identify each of the following amounts and when it occurred.
    (a) the greatest one-year drop in receipts
    (b) the greatest one-year rise in outlays

13. In what years did receipts appear to climb faster than outlays?

14. About what was the greatest federal deficit, and in what year did it occur?

15. Plot a point for each year and draw a line graph showing the federal surplus (+) or deficit (−) over the years 2001–2011.

Reading Bar Graphs of Economic Indicators *The bar graphs here show trends in several economic indicators over the period 2004–2009. Refer to these graphs for Exercises 16–20.*

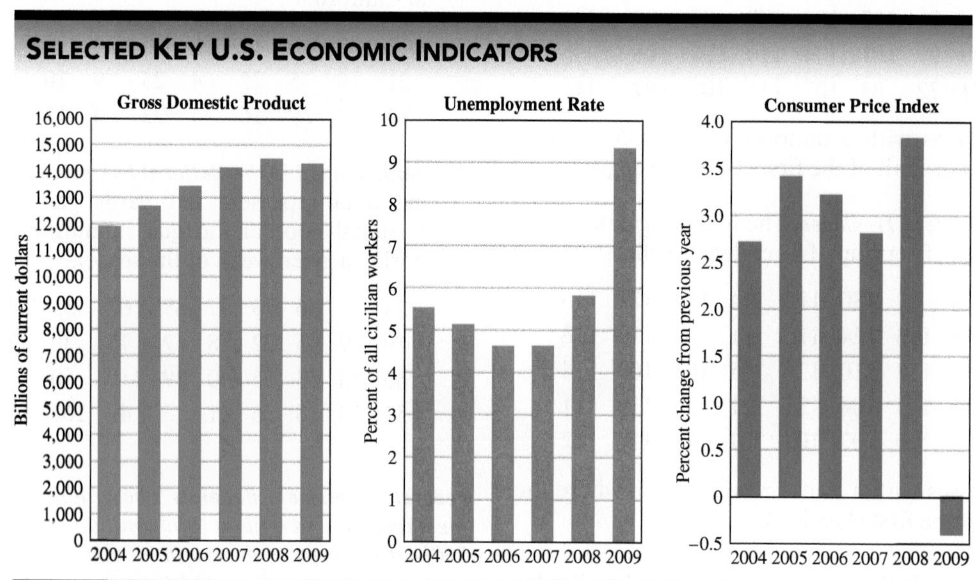

Sources: U.S. Department of Commerce, Bureau of Economic Analysis. U.S. Department of Labor, Bureau of Labor Statistics.

16. About what was the gross domestic product in 2008?

17. Over the six-year period, about what was the highest consumer price index, and when did it occur?

18. What was the greatest year-to-year change in the unemployment rate, and when did it occur?

19. Observing these graphs, what would you say was the most unusual occurrence during the six years represented?

20. Explain why the gross domestic product would generally increase when the unemployment rate decreases.

Reading a Circle Graph of Government Spending *The circle graph below shows categories of planned federal spending from 2011 to 2020. Use the graph for Exercises 21 and 22.*

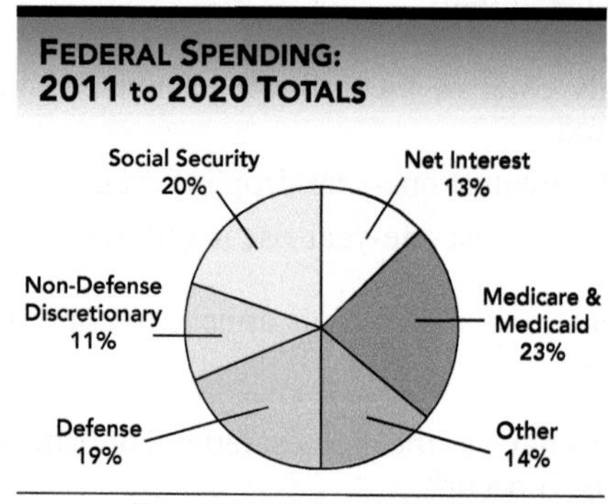

Source: Office of Management and Budget, January 2010.

21. What is the greatest single expense category? To the nearest degree, what is the central angle of that category's sector?

22. If federal spending over the decade leading up to 2020 increased by about 7.5% per year (as it did over the preceding decade), total spending for the decade would be about $54,200 billion. Of that total, what amount would go to Social Security, Medicare, and Medicaid benefits (combined)?

23. ***Sources of Job Training*** A survey asked American workers how they were trained for their jobs. The percentages who responded in various categories are shown in the table below. Use the information in the table to draw a circle graph.

Principal Source of Training	Approximate Percentage of Workers
Trained in school	33%
Informal on-the-job training	25
Formal training from employers	12
Trained in military, or correspondence or other courses	10
No particular training, or could not identify any	20

Source: Bureau of Labor Statistics.

24. ***Correspondence Between Education and Earnings*** Data for 2008 showed that the average annual earnings of American workers corresponded to educational level as shown in the table below. Draw a bar graph that shows this information.

Educational Level	Median Weekly Earnings
Less than a high school diploma	$453
High school graduate	618
Some college, no degree	699
Associate degree	757
Bachelor's degree	1012
Master's degree	1233
Professional degree	1531
Doctoral degree	1561

Source: Bureau of Labor Statistics.

Net Worth of Retirement Savings *Claire Kozar, wishing to retire at age 60, is studying the comparison line graph here, which shows (under certain assumptions) how the net worth of her retirement savings (initially* $400,000 *at age 60) will change as she gets older and as she withdraws living expenses from savings. Refer to the graph for Exercises 25–28.*

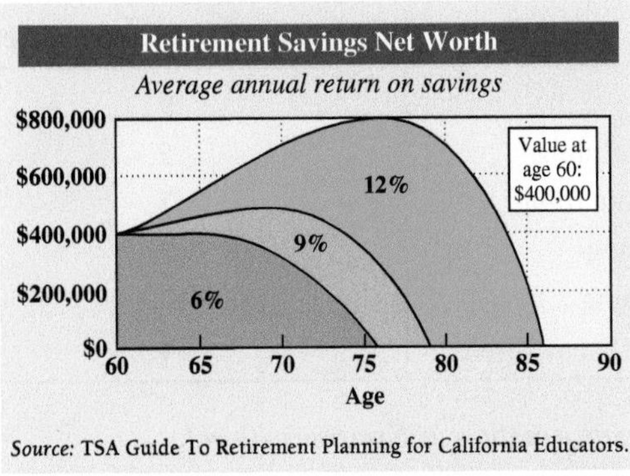

Source: TSA Guide To Retirement Planning for California Educators.

25. Assuming Claire can maintain an average annual return of 9%, how old will she be when her money runs out?

26. If she could earn an average of 12% annually, what maximum net worth would Claire achieve? At about what age would the maximum occur?

27. Suppose Claire reaches age 70, in good health, and the average annual return has proved to be 6%.

(a) About how much longer can she expect her money to last?

(b) What options might she consider in order to extend that time?

28. At age 77, about how many times more will Claire's net worth be if she averages a 12% return than if she averages a 9% return?

Sample Masses in a Geology Laboratory *Stem-and-leaf displays can be modified in various ways in order to obtain a reasonable number of stems. The following data, representing the measured masses (in grams) of thirty mineral samples in a geology lab, are shown in a* **double-stem** *display in* **Table 8**.

60.7	41.4	50.6	39.5	46.4
58.1	49.7	38.8	61.6	55.2
47.3	52.7	62.4	59.0	44.9
35.6	36.2	40.6	56.9	42.6
34.7	48.3	55.8	54.2	33.8
51.3	50.1	57.0	42.8	43.7

Table 8 Stem-and-Leaf Display for Mineral Sample Masses

(30–34)	3	4.7	3.8					
(35–39)	3	9.5	8.8	5.6	6.2			
(40–44)	4	1.4	4.9	0.6	2.6	2.8	3.7
(45–49)	4	6.4	9.7	7.3	8.3		
(50–54)	5	0.6	2.7	4.2	1.3	0.1	
(55–59)	5	8.1	5.2	9.0	6.9	5.8	7.0
(60–64)	6	0.7	1.6	2.4			

29. Describe how the stem-and-leaf display of **Table 8** was constructed.

30. Explain why **Table 8** is called a "double-stem" display.

31. In general, how many stems (total) are appropriate for a stem-and-leaf display? Explain your reasoning.

32. ***Record Temperatures*** According to the National Climatic Data Center, the highest temperatures (in degrees Fahrenheit) ever recorded in the 50 states (as of August, 2006) were as follows.

112	100	128	120	134	118	106	110	109	112
100	118	117	116	118	121	114	114	105	109
107	112	114	115	118	117	118	125	106	110
122	108	110	121	113	120	119	111	104	111
120	113	120	117	105	110	118	112	114	115

Present these data in a double-stem display.

"Retirement Savings Net Worth" graph. From *TSA Guide to Retirement Planning for California Educators.*

33. ***Letter Occurrence Frequencies in the English Language*** The table below shows commonly accepted percentages of occurrence for the various letters in English language usage. (Code breakers have carefully analyzed these percentages as an aid in deciphering secret codes.)

For example, notice that E is the most commonly occurring letter, followed by T, A, O, N, and so on. The letters Q and Z occur least often. Referring to **Figure 5** in the text, would you say that the relative frequencies of occurrence of the vowels in the associated paragraph were typical or unusual? Explain your reasoning.

Letter	Percent
E	13
T	9
A, O	8
N	7
I, R	$6\frac{1}{2}$
S, H	6
D	4

Letter	Percent
L	$3\frac{1}{2}$
C, M, U	3
F, P, Y	2
W, G, B	$1\frac{1}{2}$
V	1
K, X, J	$\frac{1}{2}$
Q, Z	$\frac{1}{5}$

Frequencies and Probabilities of Letter Occurrence *The percentages shown in* **Exercise 33** *are based on a very large sampling of English language text. Since they are based upon experiment, they are "empirical" rather than "theoretical." By converting each percent in that table to a decimal fraction, you can produce an* ***empirical probability distribution.***

For example, if a single letter is randomly selected from a randomly selected passage of text, the probability that it will be an E *is* 0.13. *The probability that a randomly selected letter would be a vowel* (A, E, I, O, *or* U) *is*

$$(0.08 + 0.13 + 0.065 + 0.08 + 0.03) = 0.385.$$

34. Rewrite the distribution shown in **Exercise 33** as an empirical probability distribution. Give values to three decimal places. Note that the 26 probabilities in this distribution—one for each letter of the alphabet—should add up to 1 (except for, perhaps, a slight round-off error).

35. **(a)** From your distribution of **Exercise 34,** construct an empirical probability distribution just for the vowels A, E, I, O, and U. (*Hint:* Divide each vowel's probability, from **Exercise 34,** by 0.385 to obtain a distribution whose five values add up to 1.) Give values to three decimal places.

(b) Construct an appropriately labeled bar chart from your distribution of part (a).

36. Based on the occurrences of vowels in the paragraph represented by **Figure 5**, construct a probability distribution for the vowels. Give probabilities to three decimal places. The frequencies are:

A–31, E–34, I–20, O–23, U–10.

37. Is the probability distribution of **Exercise 36** theoretical or empirical? Is it different from the distribution of **Exercise 35**? Which one is more accurate? Explain your reasoning.

38. ***Frequencies and Probabilities of Study Times*** Convert the grouped frequency distribution of **Table 3** to an empirical probability distribution, using the same classes and giving probability values to three decimal places.

39. ***Probabilities of Study Times*** Recall that the distribution of **Exercise 38** was based on weekly study times for a sample of 40 students. Suppose one of those students was chosen randomly. Using your distribution, find the probability that the study time in the past week for the student selected would have been in each of the following ranges.

(a) 30–39 hours **(b)** 40–59 hours

(c) fewer than 30 hours **(d)** at least 50 hours

Favorite Sports Among Recreation Students *The* 40 *members of a recreation class were asked to name their favorite sports. The table shows the numbers who responded in various ways.*

Sport	Number of Class Members
Sailing	9
Hang gliding	5
Snowboarding	7
Bicycling	3
Canoeing	12
Rafting	4

Use this information in Exercises 40–42.

40. If a member of this class is selected at random, what is the probability that the favorite sport of the person selected is snowboarding?

41. **(a)** Based on the data in the table, construct a probability distribution, giving probabilities to three decimal places.

(b) Is the distribution of part (a) theoretical or is it empirical?

(c) Explain your answer to part (b).

42. Explain why a frequency polygon trails down to the axis at both ends while a line graph ordinarily does not.

2 MEASURES OF CENTRAL TENDENCY

Mean • Median • Mode • Central Tendency from Stem-and-Leaf Displays • Symmetry in Data Sets • Summary

A small video recycling business had the following daily sales over a six-day period.

$305, $285, $240, $376, $198, $264

A single number that is, in some sense representative of this whole set of numbers, a kind of "middle" value, would be a **measure of central tendency.**

Mean

Many calculators find the **mean** (as well as other statistical measures) automatically when a set of data items are entered. To recognize these calculators, look for a key marked $\boxed{\bar{x}}$, or perhaps $\boxed{\mu}$, or look in a menu such as "LIST" for a listing of mathematical measures.

The most common measure of central tendency is the **mean** (or **arithmetic mean**). The mean of a sample is denoted $\bar{x}$ (read "*x* bar"), while the mean of a complete population is denoted μ (the lower case Greek letter *mu*). For our purposes here, data sets are considered to be samples, so we use $\bar{x}$.

The mean of a set of data items is found by adding up all the items and then dividing the sum by the number of items. (The mean is what most people associate with the word "average.") Since adding up, or summing, a list of items is a common procedure in statistics, we use the symbol for "summation," Σ (the capital Greek letter *sigma*). Therefore, the sum of n items, say $x_1, x_2, \ldots, x_n$, can be denoted

$$\Sigma x = x_1 + x_2 + \cdots + x_n.$$

Mean

The **mean** of n data items $x_1, x_2, \ldots, x_n$, is calculated as follows.

$$\bar{x} = \frac{\Sigma x}{n}$$

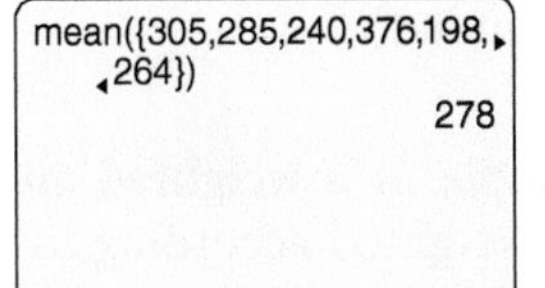

A calculator can find the mean of items in a list. This screen supports the text discussion of daily sales figures.

We use this formula to find the central tendency of the daily sales figures above.

$$\text{Mean} = \bar{x} = \frac{\Sigma x}{n}$$

$$= \frac{305 + 285 + 240 + 376 + 198 + 264}{6} \qquad \text{Add the daily sales. Divide by the number of days.}$$

$$= \frac{1668}{6}, \quad \text{or} \quad 278$$

The mean value (the "average daily sales") for the week is $278.

EXAMPLE 1 Finding the Mean of a List of Sales Figures

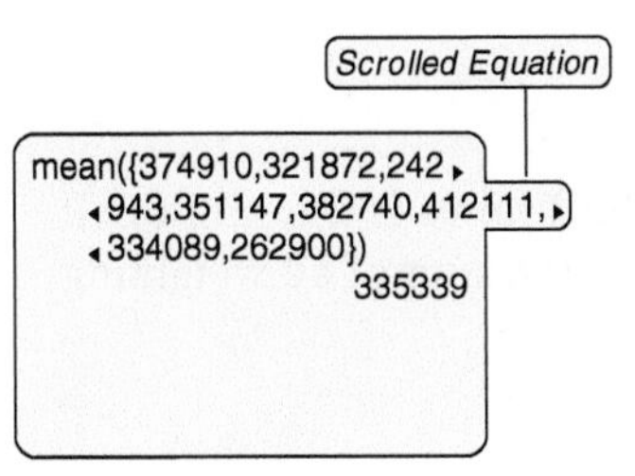

This screen supports the result in **Example 1.**

Last year's annual sales for eight different flower shops were as follows.

$374,910 $321,872 $242,943 $351,147
$382,740 $412,111 $334,089 $262,900

Find the mean annual sales for the eight shops.

SOLUTION

$$\bar{x} = \frac{\Sigma x}{n} = \frac{2{,}682{,}712}{8} = 335{,}339 \qquad \text{Add the sales. Divide by the number of shops.}$$

The mean annual sales amount is $335,339.

The following table shows the units and grades earned by one student last term.

Course	Grade	Units
Mathematics	A	3
History	C	3
Chemistry	B	5
Art	B	2
PE	A	1

In one common method of defining **grade-point average,** an A grade is assigned 4 points, with 3 points for B, 2 for C, and 1 for D. Compute grade-point average as follows.

Step 1 Multiply the number of units for a course and the number assigned to each grade.

Step 2 Add these products.

Step 3 Divide by the total number of units.

Course	Grade	Grade Points	Units	(Grade Points) · (Units)
Mathematics	A	4	3	12
History	C	2	3	6
Chemistry	B	3	5	15
Art	B	3	2	6
PE	A	4	1	4
		Totals:	14	43

$$\text{Grade-point average} = \frac{43}{14} = 3.07 \text{ (rounded)}$$

The calculation of a grade-point average is an example of a **weighted mean,** because the grade points for each course grade must be weighted according to the number of units of the course. (For example, five units of A is better than two units of A.) The number of units is called the **weighting factor.**

Weighted Mean

The **weighted mean** of n numbers, $x_1, x_2, \ldots, x_n$, that are weighted by the respective factors $f_1, f_2, \ldots, f_n$ is calculated as follows.

$$\overline{w} = \frac{\Sigma(x \cdot f)}{\Sigma f}$$

In words, the weighted mean of a group of (weighted) items is the sum of all products of items times weighting factors, divided by the sum of all weighting factors.

The weighted mean formula is commonly used to find the mean for a frequency distribution. In this case, the weighting factors are the frequencies.

Salary x	Number of Employees f
$12,000	8
$16,000	11
$18,500	14
$21,000	9
$34,000	2
$50,000	1

Scrolled Equation

```
mean({12000,16000,18500,▸
◂21000,34000,50000},{8,11,▸
◂14,9,2,1})
                18622.22222
```

In this screen supporting **Example 2,** the first list contains the salaries and the second list contains their frequencies.

EXAMPLE 2 Finding the Mean of a Frequency Distribution of Salaries

Find the mean salary for a small company that pays annual salaries to its employees as shown in the frequency distribution in the margin.

SOLUTION

According to the weighted mean formula, we can set up the work as follows.

Salary x	Number of Employees f	Salary · Number $x \cdot f$
$12,000	8	$ 96,000
$16,000	11	$176,000
$18,500	14	$259,000
$21,000	9	$189,000
$34,000	2	$ 68,000
$50,000	1	$ 50,000
Totals:	45	$838,000

$$\text{Mean salary} = \frac{\$838{,}000}{45} = \$18{,}622 \quad \text{(rounded)}$$

For some data sets the mean can be a misleading indicator of average. Consider Barry Matlock who runs a small business that employs five workers at the following annual salaries.

$16,500, $16,950, $17,800, $19,750, $20,000

The employees, knowing that Barry accrues vast profits to himself, decide to go on strike and demand a raise. To get public support, they go on television and tell about their miserable salaries, pointing out the mean salary in the company.

$$\bar{x} = \frac{\$16{,}500 + \$16{,}950 + \$17{,}800 + \$19{,}750 + \$20{,}000}{5}$$

$$= \frac{\$91{,}000}{5}, \quad \text{or} \quad \$18{,}200 \quad \text{Mean salary (employees)}$$

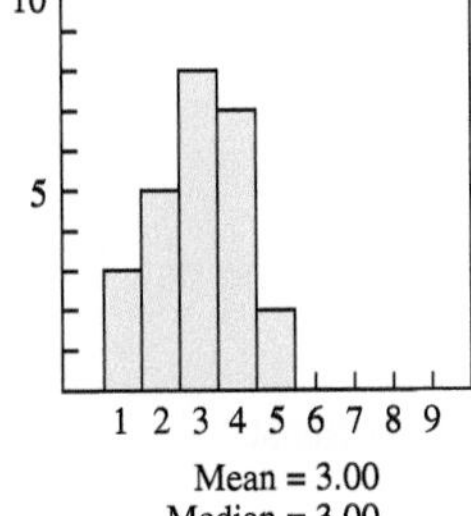

The local television station schedules an interview with Barry to investigate. In preparation, Barry calculates the mean salary of *all* workers (including his own salary of $188,000).

$$\bar{x} = \frac{\$16{,}500 + \$16{,}950 + \$17{,}800 + \$19{,}750 + \$20{,}000 + \$188{,}000}{6}$$

$$= \frac{\$279{,}000}{6}, \quad \text{or} \quad \$46{,}500 \quad \text{Mean salary (including Barry's)}$$

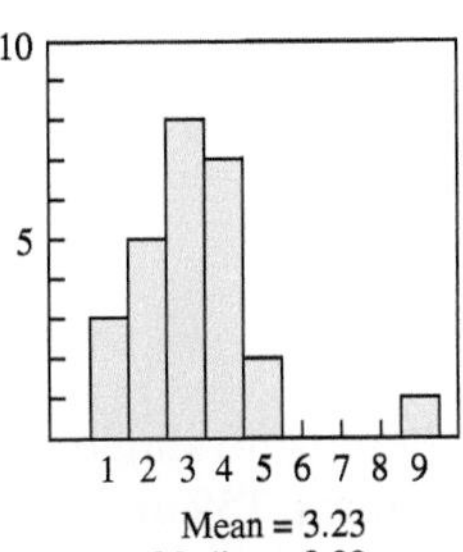

The introduction of a single "outlier" above increased the mean by 8 percent but left the median unaffected.

Outliers should usually be considered as *possible* errors in the data.

When the TV crew arrives, Barry calmly assures them that there is no reason for his employees to complain since the company pays a generous mean salary of $46,500.

The employees, of course, would argue that when Barry included his own salary in the calculation, it caused the mean to be a misleading indicator of average. This was so because Barry's salary is not typical. It lies a good distance away from the general grouping of the items (salaries). An extreme value like this is referred to as an **outlier.** Since a single outlier can have a significant effect on the value of the mean, we say that the mean is "highly sensitive to extreme values."

Median

Another measure of central tendency, which is not so sensitive to extreme values, is the **median.** This measure divides a group of numbers into two parts, with half the numbers below the median and half above it.

Median

Find the **median** of a group of items as follows.

Step 1 Rank the items (that is, arrange them in numerical order from least to greatest).

Step 2 If the number of items is *odd,* the median is the middle item in the list.

Step 3 If the number of items is *even,* the median is the mean of the two middle items.

For Barry Matlock's business, all salaries (including Barry's), arranged in numerical order, are shown here.

$16,500, $16,950, $17,800, $19,750, $20,000, $188,000

Thus,
$$\text{median} = \frac{\$17{,}800 + \$19{,}750}{2} = \frac{\$37{,}550}{2} = \$18{,}775.$$

This figure is a representative average, based on all six salaries, that the employees would probably agree is reasonable.

EXAMPLE 3 Finding Medians of Lists of Numbers

Find the median of each list of numbers.

(a) 6, 7, 12, 13, 18, 23, 24

(b) 17, 15, 9, 13, 21, 32, 41, 7, 12

(c) 147, 159, 132, 181, 174, 253

SOLUTION

(a) This list is already in numerical order. The number of values in the list, 7, is odd, so the median is the middle value, or 13.

(b) First, place the numbers in numerical order from least to greatest.

7, 9, 12, 13, 15, 17, 21, 32, 41
↑
Median

The middle number can now be picked out. The median is 15.

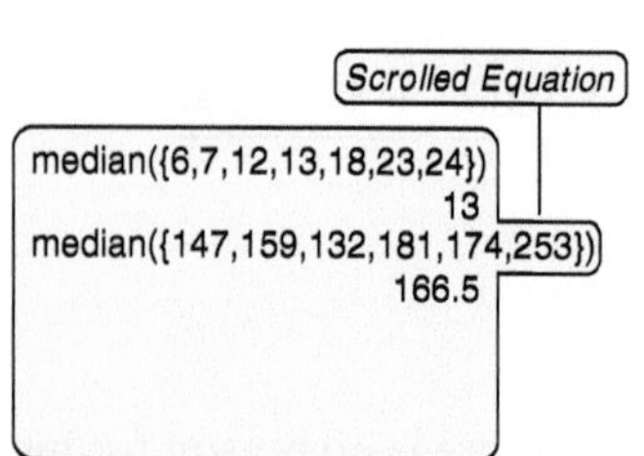

The calculator can find the median of the entries in a list. This screen supports the results in **Examples 3(a) and (c).**

(c) First write the numbers in numerical order.

132, 147, 159, 174, 181, 253

Since the list contains an even number of items, namely 6, there is no single middle item. Find the median by taking the mean of the two middle items, 159 and 174.

$$\frac{159 + 174}{2} = \frac{333}{2} = 166.5 \leftarrow \text{Median}$$

Locating the middle item (the median) of a frequency distribution, is a bit different. First find the total number of items in the set by adding the frequencies ($n = \Sigma f$). Then the median is the item whose *position* is given by the following formula.

Position of the Median in a Frequency Distribution

$$\textbf{Position of median} = \frac{n+1}{2} = \frac{\Sigma f + 1}{2}$$

This formula gives only the position, and not the actual value, of the median.

EXAMPLE 4 Finding Medians for Frequency Distributions

Find the medians for the following distributions.

(a)

Value	1	2	3	4	5	6
Frequency	1	3	2	4	8	2

(b)

Value	2	4	6	8	10
Frequency	5	8	10	6	6

SOLUTION

(a) Arrange the work as follows. Tabulate the values and frequencies, and the **cumulative frequencies,** which tell, for each different value, how many items have that value or a lesser value.

Value	Frequency	Cumulative Frequency	
1	1	1	1 item 1 or less
2	3	4	1 + 3 = 4 items 2 or less
3	2	6	4 + 2 = 6 items 3 or less
4	4	10	6 + 4 = 10 items 4 or less
5	8	18	10 + 8 = 18 items 5 or less
6	2	20	18 + 2 = 20 items 6 or less

Total: 20

Adding the frequencies shows that there are 20 items total.

$$\text{position of median} = \frac{20+1}{2} = \frac{21}{2} = 10.5$$

The median, then, is the average of the tenth and eleventh items. To find these items, make use of the cumulative frequencies. Since the value 4 has a cumulative frequency of 10, the tenth item is 4 and the eleventh item is 5, making the median

$$\frac{4+5}{2} = \frac{9}{2} = 4.5.$$

median({1,2,3,4,5,6},{1,3,2,4,8,2})
4.5

(b)

Value	Frequency	Cumulative Frequency
2	5	5
4	8	13
6	10	23
8	6	29
10	6	35

Total: 35

There are 35 items total.

$$\text{position of median} = \frac{35+1}{2} = \frac{36}{2} = 18$$

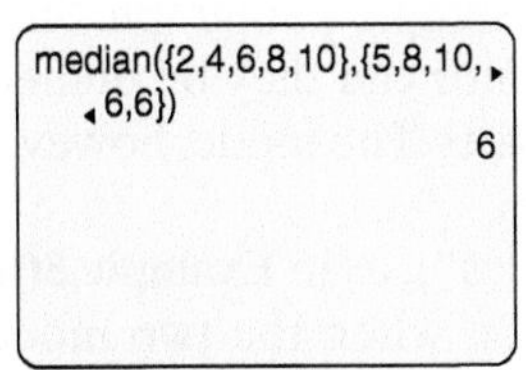

These two screens support the results in **Example 4.**

From the cumulative frequency column, the fourteenth through the twenty-third items are all 6s. This means the eighteenth item is a 6, so the median is 6.

Mode

The third important measure of central tendency is the **mode.** Suppose ten students earned the following scores on a business law examination.

74, 81, 39, 74, 82, 80, 100, 92, 74, 85

Notice that more students earned the score 74 than any other score.

Mode

The **mode** of a data set is the value that occurs most often.

EXAMPLE 5 Finding Modes for Sets of Data

Find the mode for each set of data.

(a) 51, 32, 49, 49, 74, 81, 92 **(b)** 482, 485, 483, 485, 487, 487, 489

(c) 10,708, 11,519, 10,972, 17,546, 13,905, 12,182

(d)

Value	19	20	22	25	26	28
Frequency	1	3	8	7	4	2

SOLUTION

(a) 51, 32, 49, 49, 74, 81, 92
The number 49 occurs more often than any other. Therefore, 49 is the mode. ***The numbers do not need to be in numerical order when looking for the mode.***

(b) 482, 485, 483, 485, 487, 487, 489
Both 485 and 487 occur twice. This list is said to have *two* modes, or to be **bimodal.**

(c) No number here occurs more than once. This list has no mode.

(d)

Value	**Frequency**	
19	1	
20	3	
22	8	← Greatest frequency
25	7	
26	4	
28	2	

The frequency distribution shows that the most frequently occurring value (and, thus, the mode) is 22.

It is traditional to include the mode as a measure of *central tendency*, because many important kinds of data sets do have their most frequently occurring values "centrally" located. However, there is no reason the mode cannot be one of the least values in the set or one of the greatest. In such a case, the mode really is not a good measure of "central tendency."

When the data items being studied are nonnumeric, the mode may be the only usable measure of central tendency. For example, the bar graph of **Figure 5** in **Section 1** showed frequencies of occurrence of vowels in a sample paragraph. Since A, E, I, O, and U are not numbers, they cannot be added, nor can they be numerically ordered. Thus, neither their mean nor their median exists. The mode, however, does exist. As the bar graph shows, the mode is the letter E.

Sometimes, a distribution is **bimodal** (literally, "two modes"), as in **Example 5(b).** In a large distribution, this term is commonly applied even when the two modes do not have exactly the same frequency. Three or more different items sharing the highest frequency of occurrence is not often useful information. We say that such a distribution has *no* mode.

Central Tendency from Stem-and-Leaf Displays

As shown in **Section 1,** data are sometimes presented in a stem-and-leaf display in order to give a graphical impression of their distribution. We can also calculate measures of central tendency from a stem-and-leaf display. The median and mode are more easily identified when the "leaves" are **ranked** (arranged in numerical order) on their "stems."

In **Table 9**, we have rearranged the leaves of **Table 5** in **Section 1** (which showed the weekly study times from **Example 2** of that section).

Table 9 Stem-and-Leaf Display for Weekly Study Times, with Leaves Ranked

1	2	4	5	6	7	8					
2	0	2	3	4	4	5	6	6	9	9	9
3	0	1	1	2	3	6	6	8	9		
4	0	1	4	4	5	5	7				
5	2	5	5	8							
6	0	2									
7	2										

EXAMPLE 6 Finding the Mean, Median, and Mode from a Stem-and-Leaf Display

For the data in **Table 9**, find the following.

(a) the mean

(b) the median

(c) the mode

SOLUTION

(a) A calculator with statistical capabilities will automatically compute the mean. Otherwise, add all items (reading from the stem-and-leaf display) and divide by $n = 40$.

$$\text{mean} = \frac{12 + 14 + 15 + \cdots + 60 + 62 + 72}{40} = \frac{1395}{40} = 34.875$$

(b) In this case, $n = 40$ (an even number), so the median is the average of the twentieth and twenty-first items, in order. Counting leaves, we see that these will be the third and fourth items on the stem 3.

$$\text{median} = \frac{31 + 32}{2} = 31.5$$

(c) By inspection, we see that 29 occurred three times and no other value occurred that often.

$$\text{mode} = 29$$

Symmetry in Data Sets

The most useful way to analyze a data set often depends on whether the distribution is **symmetric** or **nonsymmetric.** In a "symmetric" distribution, as we move out from the central point, the pattern of frequencies is the same (or nearly so) to the left and to the right. In a "nonsymmetric" distribution, the patterns to the left and right are different.

Figure 8 shows several types of symmetric distributions, while **Figure 9** shows some nonsymmetric distributions. A nonsymmetric distribution with a tail extending out to the left, shaped like a J, is called **skewed to the left.** If the tail extends out to the right, the distribution is **skewed to the right.** Notice that a bimodal distribution may be either symmetric or nonsymmetric.

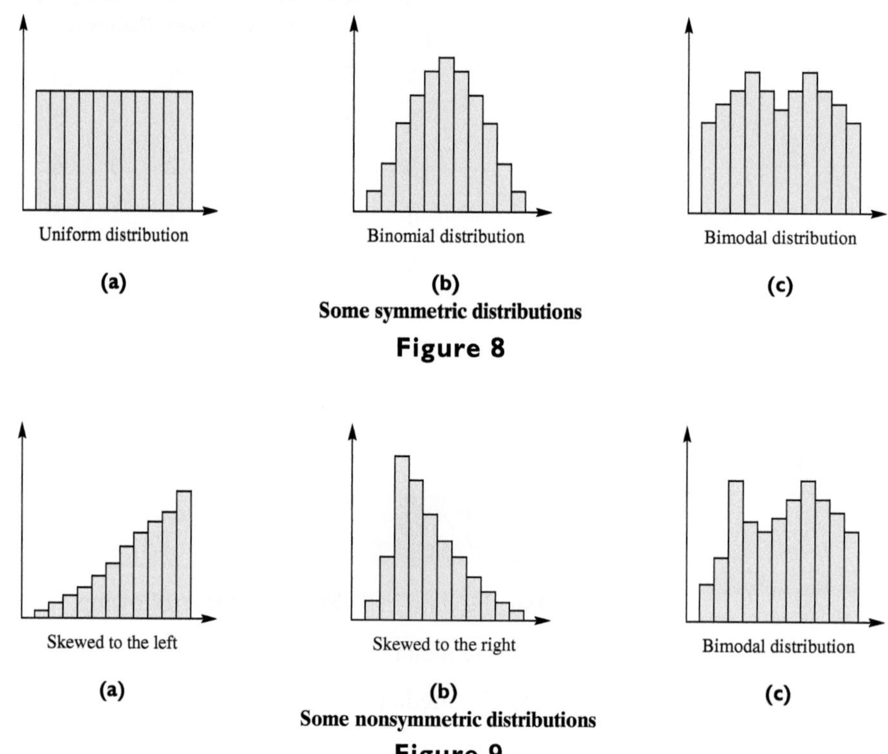

Some symmetric distributions

Figure 8

Some nonsymmetric distributions

Figure 9

Summary

We conclude this section with a summary of the measures presented and a brief discussion of their relative advantages and disadvantages.

Summary of the Common Measures of Central Tendency

The **mean** of a set of numbers is found by adding all the values in the set and dividing by the number of values.

The **median** is a kind of "middle" number. To find the median, first arrange the values in numerical order. For an *odd* number of values, the median is the middle value in the list. For an *even* number of values, the median is the mean of the two middle values.

The **mode** is the value that occurs most often. Some sets of numbers have two most frequently occurring values and are **bimodal**. Other sets have no mode at all (if no value occurs more often than the others or if more than two values occur most often).

Some helpful points of comparison follow.

1. For distributions of numeric data, the mean and median will always exist, while the mode may not exist. On the other hand, for nonnumeric data, it may be that none of the three measures exists, or that only the mode exists.
2. Because even a single change in the data may cause the mean to change, while the median and mode may not be affected at all, ***the mean is the most "sensitive" measure.***
3. In a symmetric distribution, the mean, median, and mode (if a single mode exists) will all be equal. In a nonsymmetric distribution, the mean is often unduly affected by relatively few extreme values and, therefore, may not be a good representative measure of central tendency. For example, distributions of salaries, family incomes, or home prices often include a few values that are much higher than the bulk of the items. In such cases, the median is a more useful measure.
4. ***The mode is the only measure covered here that must always be equal to one of the data items of the distribution.*** In fact, more of the data items are equal to the mode than to any other number. A fashion shop planning to stock only one hat size for next season would want to know the mode (the most common) of all hat sizes among their potential customers. Likewise, a designer of family automobiles would be interested in the most common family size. In examples like these, designing for the mean or the median might not be right for anyone.

Goodshoot/Thinkstock

For Further Thought

Simpson's Paradox

In baseball statistics, a player's "batting average" gives the average number of hits per time at bat. For example, a player who has gotten 84 hits in 250 times at bat has a batting average of $\frac{84}{250} = .336$. This "average" can be interpreted as the empirical probability of that player's getting a hit the next time at bat.

The following are actual comparisons of hits and at-bats for two major league players in the 1995, 1996, and 1997 seasons. The numbers illustrate a puzzling statistical occurrence known as **Simpson's paradox.** The example below, involving Dave Justice and Derek Jeter, was referred to in the "Conspiracy Theory" episode of the television series NUMB3RS. (*Source:* www.wikipedia.org)

For Group or Individual Investigation

1. Fill in the twelve blanks in the table, giving batting averages to three decimal places.
2. Which player had a better average in 1995?
3. Which player had a better average in 1996?
4. Which player had a better average in 1997?
5. Which player had a better average in 1995, 1996, and 1997 combined?
6. Did the results above surprise you? How can it be that one player's batting average leads another's for each of three years, and yet trails the other's for the combined years?

	Dave Justice			Derek Jeter		
	Hits	**At-bats**	**Batting Average**	**Hits**	**At-bats**	**Batting Average**
1995	104	411	______	12	48	______
1996	45	140	______	183	582	______
1997	163	495	______	190	654	______
Combined (1995–1997)	______	______	______	______	______	______

2 EXERCISES

For each list of data, calculate **(a)** *the mean,* **(b)** *the median, and* **(c)** *the mode or modes (if any). Round mean values to the nearest tenth.*

1. 7, 9, 12, 14, 34

2. 20, 27, 42, 45, 53, 62, 62, 64

3. 218, 230, 196, 224, 196, 233

4. 26, 31, 46, 31, 26, 29, 31

5. 3.1, 4.5, 6.2, 7.1, 4.5, 3.8, 6.2, 6.3

6. 14,320, 16,950, 17,330, 15,470

7. 0.78, 0.93, 0.66, 0.94, 0.87, 0.62, 0.74, 0.81

8. 0.53, 0.03, 0.28, 0.18, 0.39, 0.28, 0.14, 0.22, 0.04

9. 128, 131, 136, 125, 132, 128, 125, 127

10. 8.97, 5.64, 2.31, 1.02, 4.35, 7.68

Airline Fatalities in the United States *The table pertains to scheduled commercial carriers. Fatalities data include those on the ground except for the September 11, 2001, terrorist attacks. Use this information for Exercises 11–16.*

U.S. Airline Safety, 1999–2008

Year	Departures (millions)	Fatal Accidents	Fatalities
1999	10.9	2	12
2000	11.1	2	89
2001	10.6	6	531
2002	10.3	0	0
2003	10.2	2	22
2004	10.8	1	13
2005	10.9	3	22
2006	10.6	2	50
2007	10.7	0	0
2008	10.6	0	0

Source: The World Almanac and Book of Facts 2010.

For each category in Exercises 11–16, find **(a)** *the mean,* **(b)** *the median, and* **(c)** *the mode (if any).*

11. departures

12. fatal accidents

13. fatalities

The year 2001 was clearly an anomaly. If the data for that year are reduced by 4 fatal accidents and 265 fatalities, which of the three measures change and what are their new values for each of the following?

14. Exercise 12

15. Exercise 13

16. Following 2001, in what year did airline departures start to increase again?

Spending by U.S. Travelers *The table shows the top five U.S. states for domestic traveler spending in 2007.*

State	Spending (billions of dollars)
California	$96.2
Florida	68.9
New York	51.3
Texas	47.4
Nevada	34.5

Source: The World Almanac and Book of Facts 2010.

Find each of the following quantities for these five states.

17. the mean spending

18. the median spending

Measuring Elapsed Times *While doing an experiment, a physics student recorded the following sequence of elapsed times (in seconds) in a lab notebook.*

2.16, 22.2, 2.96, 2.20, 2.73, 2.28, 2.39

19. Find the mean.

20. Find the median.

The student from ***Exercises 19 and 20,*** *when reviewing the calculations later, decided that the entry 22.2 should have been recorded as 2.22, and made that change in the listing.*

21. Find the mean for the new list.

22. Find the median for the new list.

23. Which measure, the mean or the median, was affected more by correcting the error?

24. In general, which measure, mean or median, is affected less by the presence of an extreme value in the data?

Scores on Management Examinations *Rob Bates earned the following scores on his six management exams last semester.*

79, 81, 44, 89, 79, 90

25. Find the mean, the median, and the mode for Rob's scores.

26. Which of the three averages probably is the best indicator of Rob's ability?

27. If Rob's instructor gives him a chance to replace his score of 44 by taking a "make-up" exam, what must he score on the make-up to get an overall average (mean) of 85?

Exercises 28 and 29 give frequency distributions for sets of data values. For each set find the **(a)** *mean (to the nearest tenth),* **(b)** *median, and* **(c)** *mode or modes (if any).*

28.

Value	Frequency
12	3
14	1
16	8
18	4

29.

Value	Frequency
615	17
590	7
605	9
579	14
586	6
600	5

30. ***Average Employee Salaries*** A company has

5 employees with a salary of $19,500,
11 employees with a salary of $23,000,
7 employees with a salary of $28,300,
2 employees with a salary of $31,500,
4 employees with a salary of $38,900,
1 employee with a salary of $147,500.

Find the mean salary for the employees (to the nearest hundred dollars).

Grade-point Averages *Find the grade-point average for each of the following students. Assume* A = 4, B = 3, C = 2, D = 1, *and* F = 0. *Round to the nearest hundredth.*

31.

Units	Grade
4	C
7	B
3	A
3	F

32.

Units	Grade
2	A
6	B
5	C

Most Populous Countries *The table gives population (2009) and land area for the world's five most populous countries.*

Country	Population (millions)	Area (Thousands of square miles)
China	1339	3601
India	1157	1148
United States	307	3537
Indonesia	240	741
Brazil	199	3265

Source: World Almanac and Book of Facts 2010.

Use this information for Exercises 33–36.

33. Find the mean population (to the nearest million) for these 5 countries.

34. Find the mean area (to the nearest thousand square miles) for these 5 countries.

35. For each country, find the population density (to the nearest whole number of persons per square mile).

36. For the 5 countries combined, find the mean population density.

Personal Computer Use *Just six countries account for over half of all personal computers in use worldwide. The table shows figures for 2008. Use this information for Exercises 37 and 38.*

Country	PCs in use (millions)	Population (millions)
U.S.	303.8	264.10
China	1330.0	98.67
Japan	127.3	86.22
Germany	82.4	61.96
UK	60.9	47.04
France	64.7	43.11

Source: The World Almanac and Book of Facts 2010.

37. Estimate the mean number of PCs in use in 2008 for these six countries.

38. U.S. use was 22.19% of the worldwide total. How many PCs were in use in the world in 2008?

Crew, Passengers, and Hijackers on 9/11 Airliners *The table shows, for each hijacked flight on September 11, 2001, the numbers of crew members, passengers, and hijackers (not included as passengers). For each quantity in Exercises 39–41, find*

(a) *the mean, and* **(b)** *the median.*

Flight	Crew	Passengers	Hijackers
American #11	11	76	5
United #175	9	51	5
American #77	6	53	5
United #93	7	33	4

Source: www.911research.wtc7.net

39. number of crew members per plane

40. number of passengers per plane

41. total number of persons per plane

Olympic Medal Standings *The top ten medal-winning nations in the 2010 Winter Olympics at Vancouver, Canada, are shown in the table. Use the given information for Exercises 42–45.*

Medal Standings for the 2010 Winter Olympics

Nation	Gold	Silver	Bronze	Total
United States	9	15	13	37
Germany	10	13	7	30
Canada	14	7	5	26
Norway	9	8	6	23
Austria	4	6	6	16
Russia	3	5	7	15
South Korea	6	6	2	14
Sweden	5	2	4	11
China	5	2	4	11
France	2	3	6	11

Source: www.nbcolympics.com

Calculate the following for all nations shown.

42. the mean number of gold medals

43. the median number of silver medals

44. the mode, or modes, for the number of bronze medals

45. each of the following for the total number of medals

(a) mean

(b) median

(c) mode or modes

In Exercises 46 and 47, use the given stem-and-leaf display to identify

(a) *the mean,* **(b)** *the median, and* **(c)** *the mode (if any)*

for the data represented.

46. *Auto Repair Charges* The display here represents prices (to the nearest dollar) charged by 23 different auto repair shops for a new alternator (installed). Give answers to the nearest cent.

Stem	Leaves
9	7
10	2 4
10	5 7 9
11	1 3 4 4
11	5 5 8 8 9
12	0 4 4
12	5 7 7 9
13	8

47. *Scores on a Biology Exam* The display here represents scores achieved on a 100-point biology exam by the 34 members of the class.

Stem	Leaves
4	7
5	1 3 6
6	2 5 5 6 7 8 8
7	0 4 5 6 7 7 8 8 8 8 9
8	0 1 1 3 4 5 5
9	0 0 0 1 6

48. *Calculating a Missing Test Score* Katie Campbell's Business professor lost his grade book, which contained Katie's five test scores for the course. A summary of the scores (each of which was an integer from 0 to 100) indicates the following:

The mean was 88.

The median was 87.

The mode was 92.

(The data set was not bimodal.) What is the least possible number among the missing scores?

49. Explain what an "outlier" is and how it affects measures of central tendency.

50. *Consumer Preferences in Food Packaging* A food processing company that packages individual cups of instant soup wishes to find out the best number of cups to include in a package. In a survey of 22 consumers, they found that five prefer a package of 1, five prefer a package of 2, three prefer a package of 3, six prefer a package of 4, and three prefer a package of 6.

(a) Calculate the mean, median, and mode values for preferred package size.

(b) Which measure in part (a) should the food processing company use?

(c) Explain your answer to part (b).

51. ***Scores on a Math Quiz*** The following are scores earned by 15 college students on a 20-point math quiz.

0, 1, 3, 14, 14, 15, 16, 16, 17, 17, 18, 18, 18, 19, 20

(a) Calculate the mean, median, and mode values.

(b) Which measure in part (a) is most representative of the data?

In Exercises 52–55, begin a list of the given numbers, in order, starting with the least one. Continue the list only until the median of the listed numbers is a multiple of 4. Stop at that point and find **(a)** *the number of numbers listed, and* **(b)** *the mean of the listed numbers (to two decimal places).*

52. counting numbers

53. prime numbers

54. Fibonacci numbers

55. triangular numbers

56. Seven consecutive whole numbers add up to 147. What is the result when their mean is subtracted from their median?

57. If the mean, median, and mode are all equal for the set $\{70, 110, 80, 60, x\}$, find the value of x.

58. Mike Coons wants to include a fifth counting number, n, along with the numbers 2, 5, 8, and 9 so that the mean and median of the five numbers will be equal. How many choices does Mike have for the number n, and what are those choices?

For Exercises 59–61, refer to the grouped frequency distribution shown here.

Class Limits	Frequency f
21–25	5
26–30	3
31–35	8
36–40	12
41–45	21
46–50	38
51–55	35
56–60	20

59. Is it possible to identify, based on the data shown in the table, any specific data items that occurred in this sample?

60. Is it possible to compute the actual mean for this sample?

61. Describe how you might approximate the mean for this sample. Justify your procedure.

62. ***Average Employee Salaries*** Refer to the salary data of **Example 2,** specifically the dollar amounts given in the salary column of the table. Explain what is wrong with simply calculating the mean salary by adding those six numbers and dividing the result by 6.

3 MEASURES OF DISPERSION

Range • Standard Deviation • Interpreting Measures of Dispersion • Coefficient of Variation

Table 10

	A	B
	5	1
	6	2
	7	7
	8	12
	9	13
Mean	7	7
Median	7	7

The mean is a good indicator of the central tendency of a set of data values, but it does not completely describe the data. Compare distribution A with distribution B in **Table 10.**

Both distributions have the same mean and the same median, but they are quite different. In the first, 7 is a fairly typical value, but in the second, most of the values differ considerably from 7. What is needed here is some measure of the **dispersion,** or *spread,* of the data. Two of the most common measures of dispersion, the *range* and the *standard deviation,* are discussed in this section.

Range

The **range** of a data set is a straightforward measure of dispersion.

Range

For any set of data, the **range** of the set is defined as follows.

Range = (greatest value in the set) − (least value in the set)

For a short list of data, calculation of the range is simple. For a more extensive list, it is more difficult to be sure you have accurately identified the greatest and least values.

Once the data are entered, a calculator with statistical functions may actually show the range (among other things), or at least sort the data and identify the minimum and maximum items. (The associated symbols may be something like MIN Σ and MAX Σ, or min*X* and max*X*.) Given these two values, a simple subtraction produces the range.

EXAMPLE 1 Finding and Comparing Range Values

Find the ranges for distributions A and B in **Table 10**, and describe what they imply.

SOLUTION

In distribution A, the greatest value is 9 and the least is 5.

$$\text{Range} = \text{greatest} - \text{least} = 9 - 5 = 4$$

Distribution B is handled similarly.

$$\text{Range} = 13 - 1 = 12$$

We can say that even though the two distributions have identical averages, distribution B exhibits three times more dispersion, or *spread,* than distribution A. ∎

Table 11

Quiz	Max	Molly
1	28	27
2	22	27
3	21	28
4	26	6
5	18	27
Mean	23	23
Median	22	27
Range	10	22

The range can be misleading if it is interpreted unwisely. For example, look at the points scored by Max and Molly on five different quizzes, as shown in **Table 11.** The ranges for the two students make it tempting to conclude that Max is more consistent than Molly. However, Molly is actually more consistent, with the exception of one very poor score. That score, 6, is an outlier which, if not actually recorded in error, must surely be due to some special circumstance. (Notice that the outlier does not seriously affect Molly's median score, which is more typical of her overall performance than is her mean score.)

Standard Deviation

One of the most useful measures of dispersion, the *standard deviation,* is based on *deviations from the mean* of the data values.

EXAMPLE 2 Finding Deviations from the Mean

Find the deviations from the mean for all data values in the following sample.

32, 41, 47, 53, 57

SOLUTION

Add these values and divide by the total number of values, 5. The mean is 46. To find the deviations from the mean, subtract 46 from each data value.

Data value	32	41	47	53	57
Deviation	**−14**	**−5**	**1**	**7**	**11**

↑ $32 - 46 = -14$ ↑ $57 - 46 = 11$

To check your work, add the deviations. ***The sum of the deviations for a set of data is always 0.*** ∎

We cannot obtain a measure of dispersion by finding the mean of the deviations, because this number is always 0, since the positive deviations just cancel out the negative ones. To avoid this problem of positive and negative numbers canceling each other, we *square* each deviation.

The following chart shows the squares of the deviations for the data in **Example 2.**

Data value	32	41	47	53	57
Deviation	−14	−5	1	7	11
Square of deviation	**196**	**25**	**1**	**49**	**121**

$(-14) \cdot (-14) = 196$ $\quad$ $11 \cdot 11 = 121$

An average of the squared deviations could now be found by dividing their sum by the number of data values n (5 in this case), which we would do if our data values composed a population. However, since we are considering the data to be a sample, we divide by $n - 1$ instead.*

The average that results is itself a measure of dispersion, called the **variance,** but a more common measure is obtained by taking the square root of the variance. This makes up, in a way, for squaring the deviations earlier, and gives a kind of average of the deviations from the mean, which is called the sample **standard deviation.** It is denoted by the letter s. (The standard deviation of a population is denoted σ, the lowercase Greek letter *sigma.*)

Continuing our calculations from the chart above, we obtain

$$s = \sqrt{\frac{196 + 25 + 1 + 49 + 121}{4}} = \sqrt{\frac{392}{4}} = \sqrt{98} \approx 9.90.$$

Most calculators find square roots, such as $\sqrt{98}$, to as many digits as you need using a key like $\boxed{\sqrt{x}}$. In this book, we normally give from two to four significant figures for such calculations.

The algorithm (process) described above for finding the sample standard deviation can be summarized as follows.

```
stdDev({32,41,47,53,57})
                    9.899494937
√98
                    9.899494937
```

This screen supports the text discussion. Note that the standard deviation reported agrees with the approximation for $\sqrt{98}$.

Calculation of Standard Deviation

Let a sample of n numbers $x_1, x_2, \ldots, x_n$ have mean $\bar{x}$. Then the **sample standard deviation, s,** of the numbers is calculated as follows.

$$s = \sqrt{\frac{\Sigma(x - \bar{x})^2}{n - 1}}$$

The individual steps involved in this calculation are as follows.

Step 1 Calculate $\bar{x}$, the mean of the numbers.

Step 2 Find the deviations from the mean.

Step 3 Square each deviation.

Step 4 Sum the squared deviations.

Step 5 Divide the sum in Step 4 by $n - 1$.

Step 6 Take the square root of the quotient in Step 5.

The preceding description helps show why standard deviation measures the amount of spread in a data set. For actual calculation purposes, we recommend the use of a scientific calculator, or a statistical calculator, that does all the detailed steps automatically. We illustrate both methods in **Example 3** on the next page.

*Although the reasons cannot be explained at this level, dividing by $n - 1$ rather than n produces a sample measure that is more accurate for purposes of inference. In most cases, the results using the two divisors are only slightly different.

L1	L2	L3 1
7	------	------
9		
18		
22		
27		
29		
32		

L1(1)=7

The sample in **Example 3** is stored in a list. (The last entry, 40, is not shown here.)

EXAMPLE 3 Finding a Sample Standard Deviation

Find the standard deviation of the following sample by using **(a)** the step-by-step process, and **(b)** the statistical functions of a calculator.

$$7, 9, 18, 22, 27, 29, 32, 40$$

SOLUTION

(a) Carry out the six steps summarized above.

Step 1 Find the mean of the values.

$$\frac{7 + 9 + 18 + 22 + 27 + 29 + 32 + 40}{8} = 23$$

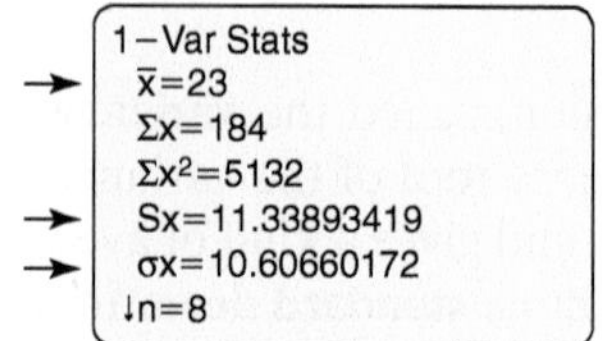

The arrows point to the mean and the sample and population standard deviations. See **Example 3.**

Step 2 Find the deviations from the mean.

Data value	7	9	18	22	27	29	32	40
Deviation	−16	−14	−5	−1	4	6	9	17

Step 3 Square each deviation.

Squares of deviations: 256 196 25 1 16 36 81 289

Step 4 Sum the squared deviations.

$$256 + 196 + 25 + 1 + 16 + 36 + 81 + 289 = 900$$

Step 5 Divide by $n - 1 = 8 - 1 = 7$: $\frac{900}{7} \approx 128.57$.

Step 6 Take the square root: $\sqrt{128.57} \approx 11.3$.

(b) Enter the eight data values. (The key for entering data may look something like [Σ+]. Find out which key it is on your calculator.) Then press the key for standard deviation. It may look like one of these.

[STDEV] or [SD] or [S_{n-1}] or [σ_{n-1}]

If your calculator also has a key that looks like σ_n, it is probably for *population* standard deviation, which involves dividing by n rather than by $n - 1$, as mentioned earlier.

The result should again be 11.3.

If you mistakenly used the population standard deviation key, the result would be 10.6.

For data given in the form of a frequency distribution, some calculators allow entry of both values and frequencies, or each value can be entered separately the number of times indicated by its frequency. Then press the standard deviation key.

The following example is included only to strengthen your understanding of frequency distributions and standard deviation, not as a practical algorithm for calculating.

Table 12

Value	Frequency
2	5
3	8
4	10
5	2

EXAMPLE 4 Finding the Standard Deviation of a Frequency Distribution

Find the sample standard deviation for the frequency distribution shown in **Table 12.**

SOLUTION

Complete the calculations as shown in **Table 13** on next page. To find the numbers in the "Deviation" column, first find the mean, and then subtract the mean from the numbers in the "Value" column.

```
stdDev({2,3,4,5},{5,8,10,2})
                  .9073771726
√19.76/24
                  .9073771726
```

The screen supports the result in **Example 4.**

Table 13

Value	Frequency	Value Times Frequency	Deviation	Squared Deviation	Squared Deviation Times Frequency
2	5	10	−1.36	1.8496	9.2480
3	8	24	−0.36	0.1296	1.0368
4	10	40	0.64	0.4096	4.0960
5	2	10	1.64	2.6896	5.3792
Sums	25	84			19.76

$$\overline{x} = \frac{84}{25} = 3.36 \qquad s = \sqrt{\frac{19.76}{24}} \approx \sqrt{0.8233} \approx 0.91$$

Central tendency and dispersion (or "spread tendency") are different and independent aspects of a set of data. Which one is more critical can depend on the specific situation.

For example, suppose tomatoes sell by the basket. Each basket costs the same, and each contains one dozen tomatoes. If you want the most fruit possible per dollar spent, you would look for the basket with the highest average weight per tomato (regardless of the dispersion of the weights). On the other hand, if the tomatoes are to be served on an hors d' oeuvre tray where "presentation" is important, you would look for a basket with uniform-sized tomatoes, that is a basket with the lowest weight dispersion (regardless of the average of the weights). See the illustration at the side.

The more desirable basket depends on your objective.

Another situation involves target shooting (also illustrated at the side). The five hits on the top target are, *on average,* very close to the bulls eye, but the large dispersion (spread) implies that improvement will require much effort. On the other hand, the bottom target exhibits a poorer average, but the smaller dispersion means that improvement will require only a minor adjustment of the gun sights. (In general, consistent errors can be corrected more easily than more dispersed errors.)

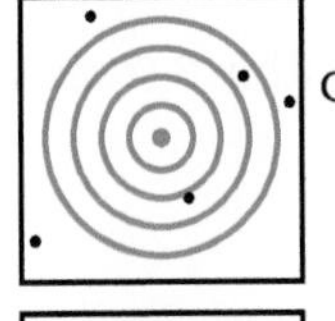

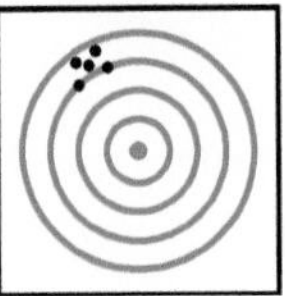

In this case, good consistency (lesser dispersion) is more desirable than a good average (central tendency).

Interpreting Measures of Dispersion

A main use of dispersion measures is to compare the amounts of spread in two (or more) data sets as we did with distributions A and B at the beginning of this section. A common technique in inferential statistics is to draw comparisons between populations by analyzing samples that come from those populations.

EXAMPLE 5 Comparing Populations Based on Samples

Two companies, A and B, sell 12-ounce jars of instant coffee. Five jars of each were randomly selected from markets, and the contents were carefully weighed, with the following results.

A: 12.02, 12.08, 11.99, 11.96, 11.99

B: 12.40, 12.21, 12.36, 12.22, 12.27

Find **(a)** which company provides more coffee in their jars, and **(b)** which company fills its jars more consistently.

SOLUTION

The mean and standard deviation values for both samples are shown in **Table 14.**

Table 14

Sample *A*	Sample *B*
$\overline{x}_A = 12.008$	$\overline{x}_B = 12.292$
$s_A = 0.0455$	$s_B = 0.0847$

(a) Since $\overline{x}_B$ is greater than $\overline{x}_A$, we *infer* that Company B most likely provides more coffee (greater mean) per jar.

(b) Since s_A is less than s_B, we *infer* that Company A seems more consistent (smaller standard deviation).

RIA Novosti/Alamy

Pafnuty Lvovich Chebyshev (1821–1894) was a Russian mathematician known mainly for his work on the theory of prime numbers. Chebyshev and French mathematician and statistician **Jules Bienaymé** (1796–1878) independently developed an important inequality of probability now known as the Bienaymé–Chebyshev inequality.

The conclusions drawn in **Example 5** are tentative, because the samples were small. We could place more confidence in our inferences if we used larger samples, for then it would be more likely that the samples were accurate representations of their respective populations.

It is clear that a larger dispersion value means more "spread" than a smaller one. But it is difficult to say exactly what a single dispersion value says about a data set. *It is impossible* (though it would be nice) to make a general statement like: "Exactly half of the items of any distribution lie within one standard deviation of the mean of the distribution." Such a statement can be made only of specialized kinds of distributions. (See, for example, **Section 5** on the normal distribution.) There is, however, one useful result that does apply to all data sets, no matter what their distributions are like. This result is named for the Russian mathematician Pafnuty Lvovich Chebyshev.

Chebyshev's Theorem

For any set of numbers, regardless of how they are distributed, the fraction of them that lie within k standard deviations of their mean (where $k > 1$) is *at least*

$$1 - \frac{1}{k^2}.$$

Be sure to notice the words *at least* in the theorem. In certain distributions the fraction of items within k standard deviations of the mean may be more than $1 - \frac{1}{k^2}$, but in no case will it ever be less. The theorem is meaningful for any value of k greater than 1 (integer or noninteger).

EXAMPLE 6 Applying Chebyshev's Theorem

What is the minimum percentage of the items in a data set that lie within 3 standard deviations of the mean?

SOLUTION

With $k = 3$, we calculate as follows.

$3^2 = 3 \cdot 3$, not $3 \cdot 2$

$$1 - \frac{1}{3^2} = 1 - \frac{1}{9} = \frac{8}{9} \approx 0.889 = 88.9\%$$ ← Minimum percentage

Coefficient of Variation

Look again at the top target pictured on **the previous page**. The dispersion, or spread, among the five bullet holes may not be especially impressive if the shots were fired from 100 yards, but would be much more so at, say, 300 yards. There is another measure, the *coefficient of variation*, which takes this distinction into account. It is not strictly a measure of dispersion, as it combines central tendency and dispersion. It expresses the standard deviation as a percentage of the mean. ***Often this is a more meaningful measure than a straight measure of dispersion, especially when comparing distributions whose means are appreciably different.***

Coefficient of Variation

For any set of data, the **coefficient of variation** is calculated as follows.

$$V = \frac{s}{\bar{x}} \cdot 100 \text{ for a sample} \quad \text{or} \quad V = \frac{\sigma}{\mu} \cdot 100 \text{ for a population}$$

EXAMPLE 7 Comparing Samples

Compare the dispersions in the two samples A and B.

A: 12, 13, 16, 18, 18, 20 B: 125, 131, 144, 158, 168, 193

Table 15

Sample A	Sample B
$\bar{x}_A = 16.167$	$\bar{x}_B = 153.167$
$s_A = 3.125$	$s_B = 25.294$
$V_A = 19.3$	$V_B = 16.5$

SOLUTION

Using a calculator, we obtain the values shown in **Table 15**. The values of V_A and V_B were found using the formula on the previous page. From the calculated values, we see that sample B has a much larger dispersion (standard deviation) than sample A. But sample A actually has the larger *relative* dispersion (coefficient of variation). The dispersion within sample A is larger as a percentage of the sample mean. ■■■

For Further Thought

Measuring Skewness in a Distribution

Section 2 included a discussion of "symmetry in data sets." Here we present a common method of measuring the amount of "skewness," or nonsymmetry, inherent in a distribution.

In a skewed distribution, the mean will be farther out toward the tail than the median, as shown in the sketch.

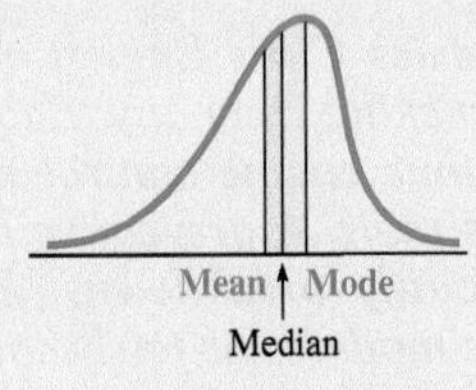

Skewed to the left

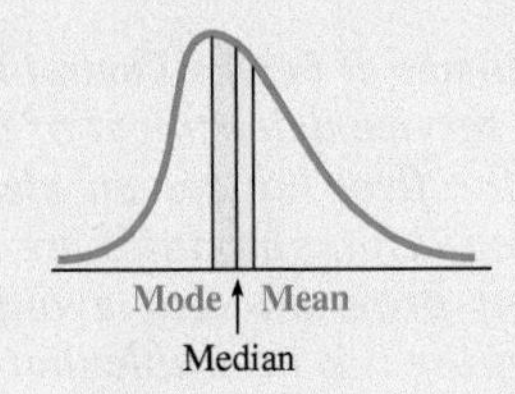

Skewed to the right

The degree of skewness can be measured by the **skewness coefficient**, which involves both central tendency and dispersion, and is calculated as follows.

$$\text{SK} = \frac{3 \cdot (\text{mean} - \text{median})}{\text{standard deviation}}$$

For Group or Individual Investigation

1. Under what conditions would the skewness coefficient be each of the following?
   (a) positive **(b)** negative
2. Explain why the mean of a skewed distribution is always farther out toward the tail than the median.
3. In a skewed distribution, how many standard deviations apart are the mean and median in each case?
   (a) $\text{SK} = \frac{1}{2}$ **(b)** $\text{SK} = 1$ **(c)** $\text{SK} = 3$

3 EXERCISES

1. If your calculator finds both kinds of standard deviation, the sample standard deviation and the population standard deviation, which of the two will be a larger number for a given set of data? (*Hint:* Recall the difference between how the two standard deviations are calculated.)

2. If your calculator finds only one kind of standard deviation, explain how you would determine whether it is sample or population standard deviation (assuming your calculator manual is not available).

Find **(a)** *the range, and* **(b)** *the standard deviation for each sample in Exercises 3–12. Round answers to the nearest hundredth.*

3. 2, 5, 6, 8, 9, 11, 15

4. 6, 5, 10, 8, 9, 15, 22, 16, 5

5. 27, 34, 22, 41, 30, 25, 31

6. 57, 81, 55, 63, 77, 61, 84, 72, 65

7. 348, 326, 330, 308, 316, 322, 310, 319, 324, 330

8. 4.7, 5.3, 9.4, 6.6, 7.4, 6.2, 7.1, 8.0, 8.8, 7.9, 7.1, 7.4, 7.9, 8.1

9. 84.96, 84.60, 84.58, 84.48, 84.72, 85.62, 85.03, 85.10, 84.53

10. 312.3, 310.4, 309.3, 311.1, 310.8, 313.5, 312.6, 310.5, 311.0, 314.2

11.

Value	Frequency
13	3
10	4
7	7
4	5
1	2

12.

Value	Frequency
14	6
16	12
18	14
20	15
22	10
24	4
26	3

Use Chebyshev's theorem for Exercises 13–28.

Find the least possible fraction of the numbers in a data set lying within the given number of standard deviations of the mean. Give answers as standard fractions reduced to lowest terms.

13. 2 **14.** 4 **15.** $\frac{5}{2}$ **16.** $\frac{7}{4}$

Find the least possible percentage (to the nearest tenth of a percent) of the items in a distribution lying within the given number of standard deviations of the mean.

17. 3 **18.** 6 **19.** $\frac{5}{3}$ **20.** $\frac{9}{2}$

In a certain distribution of numbers, the mean is 80 and the standard deviation is 8. At least what fraction of the numbers are between the following pairs of numbers? Give answers as common fractions reduced to lowest terms.

21. 64 and 96 **22.** 56 and 104

23. 48 and 112 **24.** 40 and 120

In the same distribution (mean 80 and standard deviation 8), find the largest fraction of the numbers that could meet the following requirements. Give answers as common fractions reduced to lowest terms.

25. less than 64 or more than 96

26. less than 60 or more than 100

27. less than 52 or more than 108

28. less than 62 or more than 98

Bonus Pay for a Baseball Team *Mairead Jacoby owns a minor league baseball team. Each time the team wins a game, Mairead pays the nine starting players, the manager, and two coaches bonuses, which are certain percentages of their regular salaries. The amounts paid are listed here.*

\$80,	\$105,	\$120,	\$175,	\$185,	\$190,
\$205,	\$210,	\$215,	\$300,	\$320,	\$325

Use this distribution of bonuses for Exercises 29–34.

29. Find the mean of the distribution.

30. Find the standard deviation of the distribution.

31. How many of the bonus amounts are within one standard deviation of the mean?

32. How many of the bonus amounts are within two standard deviations of the mean?

33. What does Chebyshev's theorem say about the number of the amounts that are within two standard deviations of the mean?

34. Explain any discrepancy between your answers for **Exercises 32 and 33.**

In Exercises 35 and 36, two samples are given. In each case, **(a)** *find both sample standard deviations,* **(b)** *find both sample coefficients of variation,* **(c)** *decide which sample has the higher dispersion, and* **(d)** *decide which sample has the higher relative dispersion.*

35. *A:* 3, 7, 4, 3, 8 *B:* 10, 8, 10, 6, 7, 3, 5

36. *A:* 68, 72, 69, 65, 71, 72, 68, 71, 67, 67
B: 26, 35, 30, 28, 31, 36, 38, 29, 34, 33

37. ***Comparing Battery Lifetimes*** Two brands of car batteries, both carrying 6-year warranties, were sampled and tested under controlled conditions. Five of each brand failed after the numbers of months shown here.

Brand A: 74, 65, 70, 64, 71

Brand B: 69, 70, 62, 72, 60

(a) Calculate both sample means.

(b) Calculate both sample standard deviations.

(c) Which brand apparently lasts longer?

(d) Which brand has the more consistent lifetime?

Lifetimes of Engine Control Modules *Chris Englert manages the service department of a trucking company. Each truck in the fleet utilizes an electronic engine control module. Long-lasting modules are desirable. A preventive replacement program also avoids costly breakdowns. For this purpose it is desirable that the modules be fairly consistent in their lifetimes, so that preventive replacements can be timed efficiently.*

Chris tested a sample of 20 Brand A modules, and they lasted 48,560 highway miles on the average (mean), with a standard deviation of 2116 miles. The listing below shows how long each of another sample of 20 Brand B modules lasted. Use these data for Exercises 38–40.

44,660,	51,300,	45,680,	48,840,	47,510,
61,220,	49,100,	48,660,	47,790,	47,210,
48,050,	49,920,	47,420,	45,880,	50,110,
52,910,	47,930,	45,800,	46,690,	49,240

38. According to the sampling, which brand of module has the longer average life (in highway miles)?

39. Which brand of module apparently has a more consistent (or uniform) length of life (in highway miles)?

40. If Brands A and B are the only modules available, which one should Chris purchase for the maintenance program? Explain your reasoning.

Utilize the following sample for Exercises 41–46.

13, 14, 17, 19, 21, 22, 25

41. Compute the mean and standard deviation for the sample (each to the nearest hundredth).

42. Now add 5 to each item of the given sample and compute the mean and standard deviation for the new sample.

43. Go back to the original sample. This time subtract 10 from each item, and compute the mean and standard deviation of the new sample.

44. Based on your answers for **Exercises 41–43,** make conjectures about what happens to the mean and standard deviation when all items of the sample have the same constant k added or subtracted.

45. Go back to the original sample again. This time multiply each item by 3, and compute the mean and standard deviation of the new sample.

46. Based on your answers for **Exercises 41 and 45,** make conjectures about what happens to the mean and standard deviation when all items of the sample are multiplied by the same constant k.

47. In **Section 2** we showed that the mean, as a measure of central tendency, is highly sensitive to extreme values. Which measure of dispersion, covered in this section, would be more sensitive to extreme values? Illustrate your answer with one or more examples.

A Cereal Marketing Survey *A food distribution company conducted a survey to determine whether a proposed premium to be included in boxes of their cereal was appealing enough to generate new sales. Four cities were used as test markets, where the cereal was distributed with the premium, and four cities as control markets, where the cereal was distributed without the premium. The eight cities were chosen on the basis of their similarity in terms of population, per capita income, and total cereal purchase volume. The results follow.*

		Percent Change in Average Market Share per Month
Test cities	1	+18
	2	+15
	3	+7
	4	+10
Control cities	1	+1
	2	−8
	3	−5
	4	0

48. Find the mean of the percent change in market share for the four test cities.

49. Find the mean of the percent change in market share for the four control cities.

50. Find the standard deviation of the percent change in market share for the test cities.

51. Find the standard deviation of the percent change in market share for the control cities.

52. Find the difference between the means of the test cities and the control cities. This difference represents the estimate of the percent change in sales due to the premium.

53. The two standard deviations from the test cities and the control cities were used to calculate an "error" of ± 7.95 for the estimate in **Exercise 52.** With this amount of error, what are the least and greatest estimates of the increase in sales?

(On the basis of the interval estimate of **Exercise 53** the company decided to mass produce the premium and distribute it nationally.)

For Exercises 54–56, refer to the grouped frequency distribution shown below. (Also refer to ***Exercises 59–61*** *in* ***Section 2.****)*

Class Limits	Frequency f
21–25	5
26–30	3
31–35	8
36–40	12
41–45	21
46–50	38
51–55	35
56–60	20

54. Is it possible to identify any specific data items that occurred in this sample?

55. Is it possible to compute the actual standard deviation for this sample?

56. Describe how you might approximate the standard deviation for this sample. Justify your procedure.

57. Suppose the frequency distribution of **Example 4** involved 50 or 100 (or even more) distinct data values, rather than just four. Explain why the procedure of that example would then be very inefficient.

58. A "J-shaped" distribution can be skewed either to the right or to the left. (When skewed right, it is sometimes called a "reverse J" distribution.)

   (a) In a J-shaped distribution skewed to the right, which data item would be the mode, the greatest or the least item?

   (b) In a J-shaped distribution skewed to the left, which data item would be the mode, the greatest or the least item?

   (c) Explain why the mode is a weak measure of central tendency for a J-shaped distribution.

4 MEASURES OF POSITION

The z-Score • Percentiles • Deciles and Quartiles • The Box Plot

The **top ten jobs of 2010** did not vary much from recent earlier rankings despite the treacherous economy of 2008–2010. All ten require considerable education and/or training, and most require a good deal of mathematical ability. The rankings are based on the following five criteria.

(a) stress level
(b) working environment
(c) physical demands
(d) income
(e) hiring outlook

The rankings:

1. Actuary
2. Software Engineer
3. Computer Systems Analyst
4. Biologist
5. Historian
6. Mathematician
7. Paralegal Assistant
8. Statistician
9. Accountant
10. Dental Hygienist

To learn more, go to www.careercast.com

Measures of central tendency and measures of dispersion give us an effective way of characterizing an overall set of data. Central tendency indicates where, along a number scale, the overall data set is centered. Dispersion indicates how much the data set is spread out from the center point. And Chebyshev's theorem, stated in the previous section, tells us in a general sense what portions of the data set may be dispersed different amounts from the center point.

In some cases, we are interested in certain individual items within a data set, rather than in that set as a whole. So we would like to measure how an item fits into the collection, how it compares to other items in the collection, or even how it compares to another item in another collection. There are several common ways of creating such measures. Since they measure an item's position within the data set, they usually are called **measures of position.**

The z-Score

Each individual item in a sample can be assigned a ***z*-score,** which is defined as follows.

The z-score

If x is a data item in a sample with mean $\bar{x}$ and standard deviation s, then the ***z*-score** of x is calculated as follows.

$$z = \frac{x - \bar{x}}{s}$$

Because $x - \bar{x}$ gives the amount by which x differs (or deviates) from the mean $\bar{x}$, $\frac{x - \bar{x}}{s}$ gives the number of standard deviations by which x differs from $\bar{x}$. Notice that z will be positive if x is greater than $\bar{x}$ but negative if x is less than $\bar{x}$. Chebyshev's theorem assures us that, in any distribution whatsoever, at least 89% (roughly) of the items will lie within three standard deviations of the mean. That is, at least 89% of the items will have z-scores between -3 and 3. In fact, many common distributions, especially symmetric ones, have considerably more than 89% of their items within three standard deviations of the mean (as we will see in the next section). Hence, a z-score greater than 3 or less than -3 is a rare occurrence.

EXAMPLE 1 Comparing Positions Using z-Scores

Two friends, Ann Kuick and Kay Allen, who take different history classes, had midterm exams on the same day. Ann's score was 86 while Kay's was only 78. Which student did relatively better, given the class data shown here?

	Ann	Kay
Class mean	73	69
Class standard deviation	8	5

SOLUTION

Calculate as follows.

$$\text{Ann: } z = \frac{86 - 73}{8} = 1.625 \qquad \text{Kay: } z = \frac{78 - 69}{5} = 1.8$$

Since Kay's z-score is higher, she was positioned relatively higher within her class than Ann was within her class.

Percentiles

When you take the Scholastic Aptitude Test (SAT), or any other standardized test taken by large numbers of students, your raw score usually is converted to a **percentile** score, which is defined as follows.

Percentile

If approximately n percent of the items in a distribution are less than the number x, then x is the ***n*th percentile** of the distribution, denoted P_n.

For example, if you scored at the eighty-third percentile on the SAT, it means that you outscored approximately 83% of all those who took the test. (It does *not* mean that you got 83% of the answers correct.) Since the percentile score gives the position of an item within the data set, it is another "measure of position." The following example approximates percentiles for a fairly small collection of data.

EXAMPLE 2 Finding Percentiles

The following are the numbers of dinner customers served by a restaurant on 40 consecutive days. (The numbers have been ranked least to greatest.)

46	51	52	55	56	56	58	59	59	59
61	61	62	62	63	63	64	64	64	65
66	66	66	67	67	67	68	68	69	69
70	70	71	71	72	75	79	79	83	88

For this data set, find **(a)** the thirty-fifth percentile, and **(b)** the eighty-sixth percentile.

SOLUTION

(a) The thirty-fifth percentile can be taken as the item below which 35 percent of the items are ranked. Since 35 percent of 40 is $0.35(40) = 14$, we take the fifteenth item, or 63, as the thirty-fifth percentile.

(b) Since 86 percent of 40 is $0.86(40) = 34.4$, we round *up* and take the eighty-sixth percentile to be the thirty-fifth item, or 72.

Technically, percentiles originally were conceived as a set of 99 values $P_1, P_2, P_3, \ldots, P_{99}$ (not necessarily data items) along the scale that would divide the data set into 100 equal-sized parts. They were computed only for very large data sets. With smaller data sets, as in **Example 2,** dividing the data into 100 parts would necessarily leave many of those parts empty. However, the modern techniques of exploratory data analysis seek to apply the percentile concept to even small data sets. Thus, we use approximation techniques as in **Example 2.** Another option is to divide the data into a lesser number of equal-sized (or nearly equal-sized) parts.

Deciles and Quartiles

Deciles are the nine values (denoted $D_1, D_2, \ldots, D_9$) along the scale that divide a data set into ten (approximately) equal-sized parts, and **quartiles** are the three values (Q_1, Q_2, and Q_3) that divide a data set into four (approximately) equal-sized parts. Since deciles and quartiles serve to position particular items within portions of a distribution, they also are "measures of position." We can evaluate deciles by finding their equivalent percentiles.

$$D_1 = P_{10}, \quad D_2 = P_{20}, \quad D_3 = P_{30}, \quad \ldots, \quad D_9 = P_{90}$$

EXAMPLE 3 Finding Deciles

Find the fourth decile for the dinner customer data of **Example 2.**

SOLUTION

Refer to the ranked data table. The fourth decile is the fortieth percentile, and 40% of 40 is $0.40(40) = 16$. We take the fourth decile to be the seventeenth item, or 64. ■■■

Although the three quartiles also can be related to corresponding percentiles, notice that the second quartile, Q_2, also is equivalent to the median, a measure of central tendency introduced in **Section 2.** A common convention for computing quartiles goes back to the way we computed the median.

Finding Quartiles

For any set of data (ranked in order from least to greatest):

The **second quartile, Q_2,** is just the median, the middle item when the number of items is odd, or the mean of the two middle items when the number of items is even.

The **first quartile, Q_1,** is the median of all items below Q_2.

The **third quartile, Q_3,** is the median of all items above Q_2.

EXAMPLE 4 Finding Quartiles

Find the three quartiles for the data of **Example 2.**

SOLUTION

Refer to the ranked data. The two middle data items are 65 and 66.

$$Q_2 = \frac{65 + 66}{2} = 65.5$$

The least 20 items (an even number) are all below Q_2, and the two middle items in that set are 59 and 61.

$$Q_1 = \frac{59 + 61}{2} = 60$$

The greatest 20 items are above Q_2.

$$Q_3 = \frac{69 + 70}{2} = 69.5$$

■■■

The Box Plot

A **box plot,** or **box-and-whisker plot,** involves the median (a measure of central tendency), the range (a measure of dispersion), and the first and third quartiles (measures of position), all incorporated into a simple visual display.

Box Plot

For a given set of data, a **box plot** (or **box-and-whisker plot**) consists of a rectangular box positioned above a numerical scale, extending from Q_1 to Q_3, with the value of Q_2 (the median) indicated within the box, and with "whiskers" (line segments) extending to the left and right from the box out to the minimum and maximum data items.

EXAMPLE 5 Constructing a Box Plot

Construct a box plot for the weekly study times data of **Example 2** in **Section 1.**

SOLUTION

1−Var Stats
↑n=40
minX=12
Q_1=24
Med=31.5
Q_3=44.5
maxX=72

This screen supports the results of **Example 5.**

To determine the quartiles and the minimum and maximum values more easily, we use the stem-and-leaf display (with leaves ranked), given in **Table 9** of **Section 2.**

1	2 4 5 6 7 8
2	0 2 3 4 4 5 6 6 9 9 9
3	0 1 1 2 3 6 6 8 9
4	0 1 4 4 5 5 7
5	2 5 5 8
6	0 2
7	2

The median (determined earlier in **Example 6** of **Section 2**) is

$$\frac{31 + 32}{2} = 31.5.$$

From the stem-and-leaf display,

$$Q_1 = \frac{24 + 24}{2} = 24 \quad \text{and} \quad Q_3 = \frac{44 + 45}{2} = 44.5.$$

The minimum and maximum items are evident from the stem-and-leaf display. They are 12 and 72. The box plot is shown in **Figure 10**.

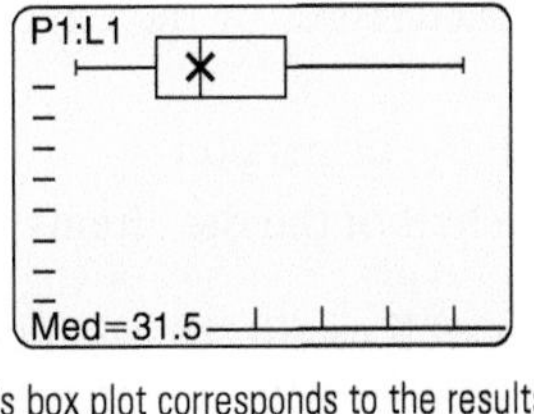

This box plot corresponds to the results of **Example 5.** It indicates the median in the display at the bottom. The TRACE function of the TI-83/84 Plus will locate the minimum, maximum, and quartile values as well.

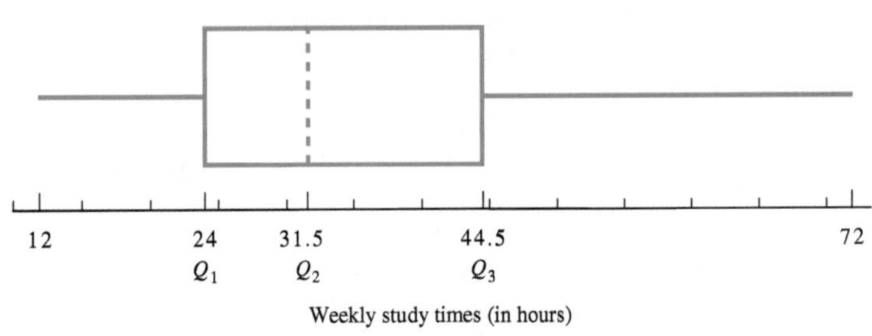

Box plot

Figure 10

The box plot in **Figure 10** conveys the following important information:

1. central tendency (the location of the median);
2. the location of the middle half of the data (the extent of the box);
3. dispersion (the range is the extent of the whiskers); and
4. skewness (the nonsymmetry of both the box and the whiskers).

4 EXERCISES

Numbers of Restaurant Customers *Refer to the dinner customers data of* **Example 2.** *Approximate each of the following. (Use the methods illustrated in this section.)*

1. the fifteenth percentile
2. the seventy-fifth percentile
3. the third decile
4. the eighth decile

In Exercises 5–8, make use of z-scores.

5. ***Relative Positions on Geometry Quizzes*** In a geometry class, Neil Hunnewell scored 5 on a quiz for which the class mean and standard deviation were 4.6 and 2.1, respectively. Janet Hunnius scored 6 on another quiz for which the class mean and standard deviation were 4.9 and 2.3, respectively. Relatively speaking, which student did better?

6. ***Relative Performances in Track Events*** In Saturday's track meet, Edgar Espina, a high jumper, jumped 6 feet 3 inches. Conference high jump marks for the past season had a mean of 6 feet even and a standard deviation of 3.5 inches. Kurt Massey, Edgar's teammate, achieved 18 feet 4 inches in the long jump. In that event the conference season average (mean) and standard deviation were 16 feet 6 inches and 1 foot 10 inches, respectively. Relative to this past season in this conference, which athlete had a better performance on Saturday?

Digital Vision/Thinkstock

7. ***Relative Lifetimes of Tires*** The lifetimes of Brand A tires are distributed with mean 45,000 miles and standard deviation 4500 miles, while Brand B tires last for only 38,000 miles on the average (mean) with standard deviation 2080 miles. Nicole Britt's Brand A tires lasted 37,000 miles and Yvette Angel's Brand B tires lasted 35,000 miles. Relatively speaking, within their own brands, which driver got the better wear?

8. ***Relative Ratings of Fish Caught*** In a certain lake, the trout average 12 inches in length with a standard deviation of 2.75 inches. The bass average 4 pounds in weight with a standard deviation of 0.8 pound. If Tobi Casper caught an 18-inch trout and Katrina Bass caught a 6-pound bass, then relatively speaking, which catch was the better trophy?

Leading U.S. Trade Partners *Countries in the table are ranked by value of 2008 imports to the United States from the countries. Exports are from the United States to the countries. Use this information for Exercises 9–20.*

Country	Population (millions)	Trade Volume (billion U.S. $) Imports	Exports
Canada	33	339	261
China	1339	338	70
Mexico	110	216	151
Japan	127	139	65
Germany	82	97	55
United Kingdom	61	59	54
Saudi Arabia	28	55	12
Venezuela	26	51	13
South Korea	48	48	35
France	64	44	29

Sources: The World Almanac and Book of Facts 2010, www.google.com

Compute z-scores (accurate to one decimal place) for Exercises 9–12.

9. Japan's population

10. imports from China

11. exports to Mexico

12. imports from Venezuela

In each of Exercises 13–16, determine which country occupied the given position.

13. the fifteenth percentile in population

14. the third quartile in exports

15. the fourth decile in imports

16. the first quartile in exports

17. Determine who was relatively higher: China in imports or Canada in exports.

18. Construct box plots for both exports and imports, one above the other in the same drawing.

19. What does your box plot of **Exercise 18** *for exports* indicate about the following characteristics of the exports data?

(a) the central tendency **(b)** the dispersion

(c) the location of the middle half of the data items

20. Comparing your two box plots of **Exercise 18,** what can you say about the 2008 trade balance with this group of countries?

21. The text stated that, for *any* distribution of data, at least 89% of the items will be within three standard deviations of the mean. Why couldn't we just move some items farther out from the mean to obtain a new distribution that would violate this condition?

22. Describe the basic difference between a measure of central tendency and a measure of position.

This chapter has introduced three major characteristics, central tendency, dispersion, and position, and has developed various ways of measuring them in numerical data. In each of Exercises 23–26, a new measure is described. Explain in each case which of the three characteristics you think it would measure and why.

23. Midrange $= \dfrac{\text{minimum item} + \text{maximum item}}{2}$

24. Midquartile $= \dfrac{Q_1 + Q_3}{2}$

25. Interquartile range $= Q_3 - Q_1$

26. Semi-interquartile range $= \dfrac{Q_3 - Q_1}{2}$

27. The "skewness coefficient" was defined in **For Further Thought** in the previous section, and it is calculated as follows.

$$SK = \frac{3 \cdot (\bar{x} - Q_2)}{s}$$

Is this a measure of individual data items or of the overall distribution?

28. For the U.S. trade partners data preceding **Exercise 9,** calculate the skewness coefficient for **(a)** exports, and **(b)** imports.

29. From **Exercise 28,** how would you compare the skewness of exports versus imports?

30. In a national standardized test, Kimberly Austin scored at the ninety-second percentile. If 67,500 individuals took the test, about how many scored higher than Kimberly did?

31. Let the three quartiles (from least to greatest) for a large population of scores be denoted Q_1, Q_2, and Q_3.

(a) Is it necessarily true that

$$Q_2 - Q_1 = Q_3 - Q_2?$$

(b) Explain your answer to part (a).

In Exercises 32–35, answer yes *or* no *and explain your answer. (Consult* ***Exercises 23–26*** *for definitions.)*

32. Is the midquartile necessarily the same as the median?

33. Is the midquartile necessarily the same as the midrange?

34. Is the interquartile range necessarily half the range?

35. Is the semi-interquartile range necessarily half the interquartile range?

	Raw Score	z-score
Omer	60	0.69
Alessandro	72	1.67

36. ***Relative Positions on a Standardized Chemistry Test*** Omer and Alessandro participated in the standardization process for a new statewide chemistry test. Within the large group participating, their raw scores and corresponding z-scores were as shown here.

Find the overall mean and standard deviation of the distribution of scores. (Give answers to two decimal places.)

Rating Passers in the National Football League *Since the National Football League began keeping official statistics in 1932, the passing effectiveness of quarterbacks has been rated by several different methods. The current system, adopted in 1973, is based on four performance components: completions, touchdowns, yards gained, and interceptions, as percentages of the number of passes attempted. The computation can be accomplished using the following formula.*

$$\text{Rating} = \frac{\left(250 \cdot \frac{C}{A}\right) + \left(1000 \cdot \frac{T}{A}\right) + \left(12.5 \cdot \frac{Y}{A}\right) + 6.25 - \left(1250 \cdot \frac{I}{A}\right)}{3},$$

where A = attempted passes,
C = completed passes,
T = touchdown passes,
Y = yards gained passing,
and I = interceptions.

In addition to the weighting factors (coefficients) appearing in the formula, the four category ratios are limited to nonnegative values with the following maximums.

$$0.775 \text{ for } \frac{C}{A}, \quad 0.11875 \text{ for } \frac{T}{A}, \quad 12.5 \text{ for } \frac{Y}{A}, \quad 0.095 \text{ for } \frac{I}{A}$$

These limitations are intended to prevent any one component of performance from having an undue effect on the overall rating. They are not often invoked but in special cases can have a significant effect.

The preceding formula rates all passers against the same performance standard and is applied, for example, after a single game, an entire season, or a career. The ratings for the ten leading passers in the league for 2009 regular season play are ranked in the following table.

Rank	NFL Passer	Rating Points
1	Drew Brees, New Orleans	109.6
2	Brett Favre, Minnesota	107.2
3	Philip Rivers, San Diego	104.4
4	Aaron Rodgers, Green Bay	103.2
5	Ben Roethlisberger, Pittsburgh	100.5
6	Peyton Manning, Indianapolis	99.9
7	Matt Schaub, Houston	98.6
8	Tony Romo, Dallas	97.6
9	Tom Brady, New England	96.2
10	Kurt Warner, Arizona	93.2

Source: www.espn.go.com

Find the measures (to one decimal place) in Exercises 37–42.

37. the three quartiles

38. the third decile

39. the sixty-fifth percentile

40. the midrange (See **Exercise 23.**)

41. the midquartile (see **Exercise 24.**)

42. the interquartile range (See **Exercise 25.**)

43. Construct a box plot for the rating points data.

44. The eleventh-ranked passer in the 2009 regular season was Eli Manning of the New York Giants. Eli attempted 509 passes, completed 317, passed for 27 touchdowns, gained 4021 yards passing, and was intercepted 14 times. Compute his rating.

45. If Eli Manning had completed one more pass in 2009, what would his rating have been?

Courtesy of John Hornsby

46. In the case of **Exercise 45,** how would Eli Manning have ranked for 2009?

47. Steve Young, of the San Francisco 49ers, set a full season rating record of 112.8 in 1994 and held that record until Peyton Manning achieved a rating of 121.1 in 2004. (As of 2010, Manning's all-time record holds.) If, in 2004, Manning had 336 completions, 49 touchdowns, and 4557 yards, for 497 attempts, how many times was he intercepted that year?

48. Refer to the passer rating formula and determine the highest rating possible (considered a "perfect" passer rating).

Archie Manning, father of NFL quarterbacks Peyton and Eli, signed this photo for author Hornsby's son, Jack.

5 THE NORMAL DISTRIBUTION

Discrete and Continuous Random Variables • Definition and Properties of a Normal Curve • A Table of Standard Normal Curve Areas • Interpreting Normal Curve Areas

Discrete and Continuous Random Variables

A random variable that can take on only certain fixed values is called a **discrete random variable.** For example, the number of heads in 5 tosses of a coin is discrete since its only possible values are 0, 1, 2, 3, 4, and 5. A variable whose values are not restricted in this way is a **continuous random variable.** For example, the diameter of camellia blossoms would be a continuous variable, spread over a scale perhaps from 5 to 25 centimeters. The values would not be restricted to whole numbers, or even to tenths, or hundredths, etc. A discrete random variable takes on only a countable number of values, whereas a continuous random variable takes on an uncountable number of values.

Most distributions discussed earlier in this chapter were *empirical* (based on observation). The distributions covered in this section are *theoretical* (based on theoretical probabilities). A knowledge of theoretical distributions enables us to identify when actual observations are inconsistent with stated assumptions, which is the key to inferential statistics.

The theoretical probability distribution for the discrete random variable "number of heads" when 5 fair coins are tossed is shown in **Table 16. Figure 11** shows the corresponding histogram. The probability values can be found using the binomial probability formula or using Pascal's triangle.

North Wind Picture Archive

The normal curve was first developed by **Abraham De Moivre** (1667–1754), but his work went unnoticed for many years. It was independently redeveloped by Pierre de Laplace (1749–1827) and Carl Friedrich Gauss (1777–1855). Gauss found so many uses for this curve that it is sometimes called the *Gaussian curve.*

Table 16 Probability Distribution

x	$P(x)$
0	0.03125
1	0.15625
2	0.31250
3	0.31250
4	0.15625
5	0.03125
Sum:	1.00000

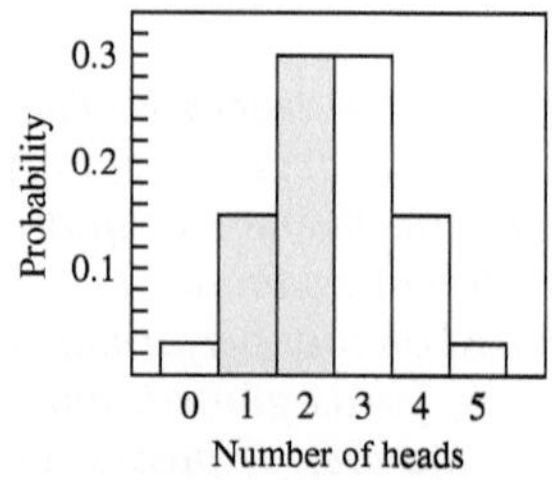

Figure 11

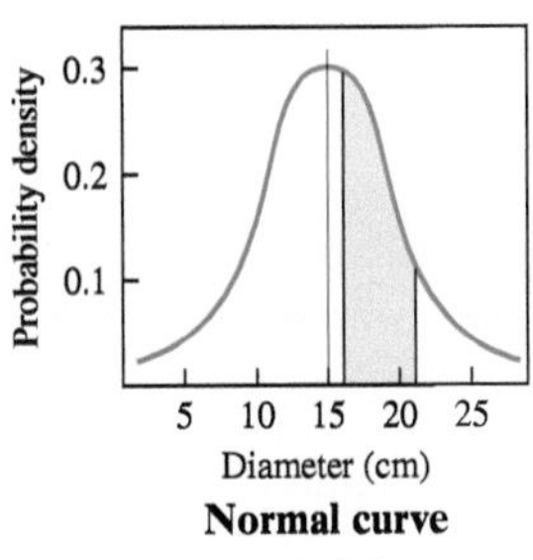

Normal curve

Figure 12

Since each rectangle in **Figure 11** is 1 unit wide, the *area* of the rectangle is also equal to the probability of the corresponding number of heads. The area, and thus the probability, for the event "1 head or 2 heads" is shaded in the figure. The graph consists of 6 distinct rectangles since "number of heads" is a *discrete* variable with 6 possible values. The sum of the 6 rectangular areas is exactly 1 square unit.

In contrast to the discrete "number of heads" distribution in **Table 16**, a probability distribution for camellia blossom diameters cannot be tabulated or graphed in quite the same way, since this variable is *continuous*. The graph would be smeared out into a "continuous" bell-shaped curve (rather than a set of rectangles) as shown in **Figure 12**. The vertical scale on the graph in this case shows what we call "probability density," the probability per unit along the horizontal axis.

Definition and Properties of a Normal Curve

The camellia blossom curve is highest at a diameter value of 15 cm, its center point, and drops off rapidly and equally toward a zero level in both directions. Such a symmetric, bell-shaped curve is called a **normal curve.** Any random variable whose graph has this characteristic shape is said to have a **normal distribution.**

The area under the curve along a certain interval is numerically equal to the probability that the random variable will have a value in the corresponding interval. The area of the shaded region in **Figure 12** is equal to the probability of a randomly chosen blossom having a diameter in the interval from the left extreme, say 16.4, to the right extreme, say 21.2. Normal curves are very important in the study of statistics because ***a great many continuous random variables have normal distributions, and many discrete variables are distributed approximately normally.***

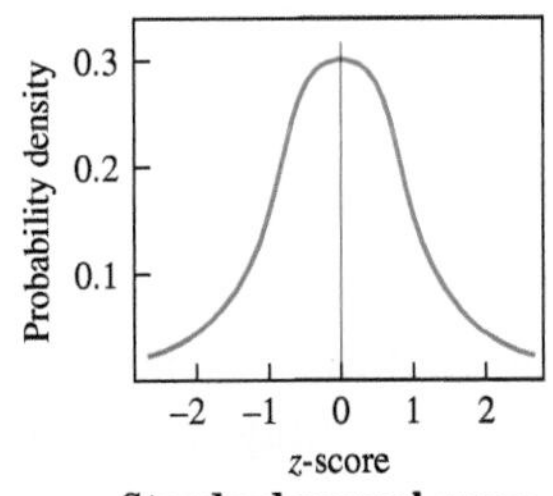

Standard normal curve

Figure 13

Each point on the horizontal scale of a normal curve lies some number of standard deviations from the mean (positive to the right, negative to the left). This number is the "standard score" for that point. It is the same as the z-score defined in **Section 4**. By relabeling the horizontal axis, as in **Figure 13**, we obtain the **standard normal curve**, which we can use to analyze *any* normal (or approximately normal) distribution. We relate the random variable value, x, to its z-score by

$$z = \frac{x - \bar{x}}{s}.$$

Figure 14 shows several of infinitely many possible normal curves. Each is completely characterized by its mean and standard deviation. Only one of these, the one marked S, is the *standard* normal curve. That one has mean 0 and standard deviation 1.

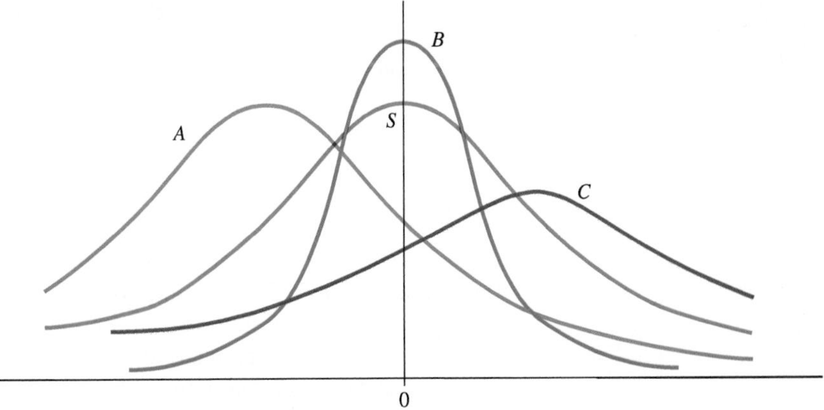

Normal curve S is standard, with mean = 0 and standard deviation = 1.
Normal curve A has mean < 0 and standard deviation = 1.
Normal curve B has mean = 0 and standard deviation < 1.
Normal curve C has mean > 0 and standard deviation > 1.

Figure 14

Close but Never Touching When a curve approaches closer and closer to a line, without ever actually meeting it (as a normal curve approaches the horizontal axis), the line is called an **asymptote**, and the curve approaches the line **asymptotically**.

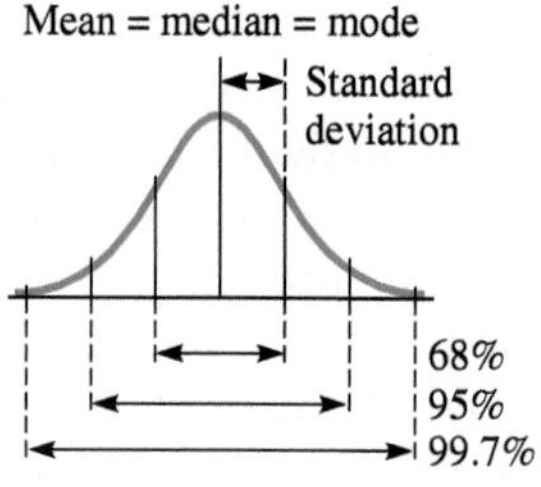

Figure 15

Several properties of normal curves are summarized below and are illustrated in **Figure 15**.

Properties of Normal Curves

The graph of a normal curve is bell-shaped and symmetric about a vertical line through its center.

The mean, median, and mode of a normal curve are all equal and occur at the center of the distribution.

Empirical Rule About 68% of all data values of a normal curve lie within 1 standard deviation of the mean (in both directions), about 95% within 2 standard deviations, and about 99.7% within 3 standard deviations.

The empirical rule indicates that a very small percentage of the items in a normal distribution will lie more than 3 standard deviations from the mean (approximately 0.3%, divided equally between the upper and lower tails of the distribution). As we move away from the center, the curve *never* actually touches the horizontal axis. No matter how far out we go, there is always a chance of an item occurring even farther out. Theoretically then, the range of a true normal distribution is infinite.

EXAMPLE 1 Applying the Empirical Rule

Suppose 300 chemistry students take a midterm exam and that the distribution of their scores can be treated as normal. Find the number of scores falling into each of the following intervals.

(a) Within 1 standard deviation of the mean

(b) Within 2 standard deviations of the mean

SOLUTION

(a) By the empirical rule, 68% of all scores lie within 1 standard deviation of the mean. Since there is a total of 300 scores, the number of scores within 1 standard deviation is as follows.

$$0.68(300) = 204 \quad 68\% = 0.68$$

(b) A total of 95% of all scores lie within 2 standard deviations of the mean.

$$0.95(300) = 285 \quad 95\% = 0.95$$

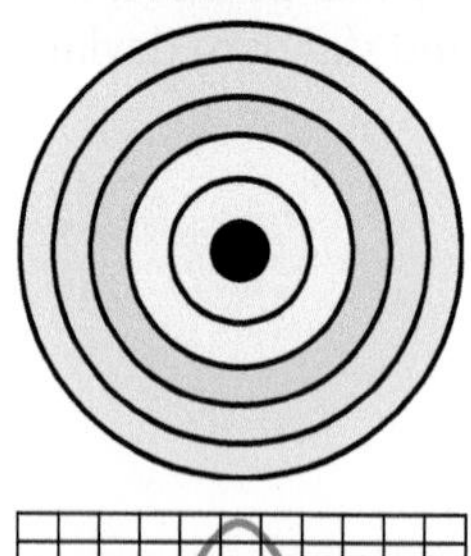

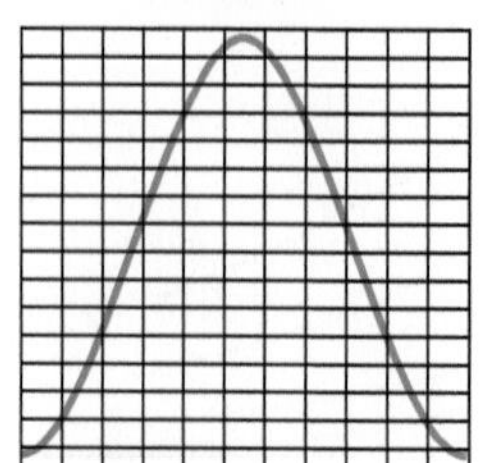

A normal distribution occurs in darts if the player, always aiming at the bull's-eye, tosses a fairly large number of times, and the aim on each toss is affected by independent random errors.

A Table of Standard Normal Curve Areas

Most questions we need to answer about normal distributions involve regions other than those within 1, 2, or 3 standard deviations of the mean. We might need the percentage of items within $1\frac{1}{2}$ or $2\frac{1}{5}$ standard deviations of the mean, or perhaps the area under the curve from 0.8 to 1.3 standard deviations above the mean.

In such cases, we need more than the empirical rule. The traditional approach is to refer to a table of area values, such as **Table 17**, which appears on the next page. Computer software packages designed for statistical uses usually will produce the required values on command and some advanced calculators also have this capability. Those tools are recommended. As an optional approach, we illustrate the use of **Table 17** here.

The column under *A* gives the proportion of the area under the entire curve that is between $z = 0$ and a positive value of z.

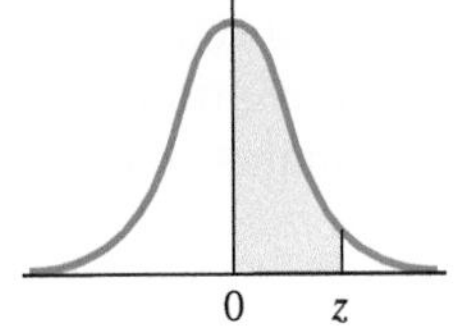

Because the curve is symmetric about the 0-value, the area between $z = 0$ and a *negative* value of z can be found by using the corresponding positive value of z.

Table 17 Areas Under the Standard Normal Curve

z	A	z	A	z	A	z	A	z	A	z	A
.00	.000	.56	.212	1.12	.369	1.68	.454	2.24	.487	2.80	.497
.01	.004	.57	.216	1.13	.371	1.69	.454	2.25	.488	2.81	.498
.02	.008	.58	.219	1.14	.373	1.70	.455	2.26	.488	2.82	.498
.03	.012	.59	.222	1.15	.375	1.71	.456	2.27	.488	2.83	.498
.04	.016	.60	.226	1.16	.377	1.72	.457	2.28	.489	2.84	.498
.05	.020	.61	.229	1.17	.379	1.73	.458	2.29	.489	2.85	.498
.06	.024	.62	.232	1.18	.381	1.74	.459	2.30	.489	2.86	.498
.07	.028	.63	.236	1.19	.383	1.75	.460	2.31	.490	2.87	.498
.08	.032	.64	.239	1.20	.385	1.76	.461	2.32	.490	2.88	.498
.09	.036	.65	.242	1.21	.387	1.77	.462	2.33	.490	2.89	.498
.10	.040	.66	.245	1.22	.389	1.78	.462	2.34	.490	2.90	.498
.11	.044	.67	.249	1.23	.391	1.79	.463	2.35	.491	2.91	.498
.12	.048	.68	.252	1.24	.393	1.80	.464	2.36	.491	2.92	.498
.13	.052	.69	.255	1.25	.394	1.81	.465	2.37	.491	2.93	.498
.14	.056	.70	.258	1.26	.396	1.82	.466	2.38	.491	2.94	.498
.15	.060	.71	.261	1.27	.398	1.83	.466	2.39	.492	2.95	.498
.16	.064	.72	.264	1.28	.400	1.84	.467	2.40	.492	2.96	.498
.17	.067	.73	.267	1.29	.401	1.85	.468	2.41	.492	2.97	.499
.18	.071	.74	.270	1.30	.403	1.86	.469	2.42	.492	2.98	.499
.19	.075	.75	.273	1.31	.405	1.87	.469	2.43	.492	2.99	.499
.20	.079	.76	.276	1.32	.407	1.88	.470	2.44	.493	3.00	.499
.21	.083	.77	.279	1.33	.408	1.89	.471	2.45	.493	3.01	.499
.22	.087	.78	.282	1.34	.410	1.90	.471	2.46	.493	3.02	.499
.23	.091	.79	.285	1.35	.411	1.91	.472	2.47	.493	3.03	.499
.24	.095	.80	.288	1.36	.413	1.92	.473	2.48	.493	3.04	.499
.25	.099	.81	.291	1.37	.415	1.93	.473	2.49	.494	3.05	.499
.26	.103	.82	.294	1.38	.416	1.94	.474	2.50	.494	3.06	.499
.27	.106	.83	.297	1.39	.418	1.95	.474	2.51	.494	3.07	.499
.28	.110	.84	.300	1.40	.419	1.96	.475	2.52	.494	3.08	.499
.29	.114	.85	.302	1.41	.421	1.97	.476	2.53	.494	3.09	.499
.30	.118	.86	.305	1.42	.422	1.98	.476	2.54	.494	3.10	.499
.31	.122	.87	.308	1.43	.424	1.99	.477	2.55	.495	3.11	.499
.32	.126	.88	.311	1.44	.425	2.00	.477	2.56	.495	3.12	.499
.33	.129	.89	.313	1.45	.426	2.01	.478	2.57	.495	3.13	.499
.34	.133	.90	.316	1.46	.428	2.02	.478	2.58	.495	3.14	.499
.35	.137	.91	.319	1.47	.429	2.03	.479	2.59	.495	3.15	.499
.36	.141	.92	.321	1.48	.431	2.04	.479	2.60	.495	3.16	.499
.37	.144	.93	.324	1.49	.432	2.05	.480	2.61	.495	3.17	.499
.38	.148	.94	.326	1.50	.433	2.06	.480	2.62	.496	3.18	.499
.39	.152	.95	.329	1.51	.434	2.07	.481	2.63	.496	3.19	.499
.40	.155	.96	.331	1.52	.436	2.08	.481	2.64	.496	3.20	.499
.41	.159	.97	.334	1.53	.437	2.09	.482	2.65	.496	3.21	.499
.42	.163	.98	.336	1.54	.438	2.10	.482	2.66	.496	3.22	.499
.43	.166	.99	.339	1.55	.439	2.11	.483	2.67	.496	3.23	.499
.44	.170	1.00	.341	1.56	.441	2.12	.483	2.68	.496	3.24	.499
.45	.174	1.01	.344	1.57	.442	2.13	.483	2.69	.496	3.25	.499
.46	.177	1.02	.346	1.58	.443	2.14	.484	2.70	.497	3.26	.499
.47	.181	1.03	.348	1.59	.444	2.15	.484	2.71	.497	3.27	.499
.48	.184	1.04	.351	1.60	.445	2.16	.485	2.72	.497	3.28	.499
.49	.188	1.05	.353	1.61	.446	2.17	.485	2.73	.497	3.29	.499
.50	.191	1.06	.355	1.62	.447	2.18	.485	2.74	.497	3.30	.500
.51	.195	1.07	.358	1.63	.448	2.19	.486	2.75	.497	3.31	.500
.52	.198	1.08	.360	1.64	.449	2.20	.486	2.76	.497	3.32	.500
.53	.202	1.09	.362	1.65	.451	2.21	.486	2.77	.497	3.33	.500
.54	.205	1.10	.364	1.66	.452	2.22	.487	2.78	.497	3.34	.500
.55	.209	1.11	.367	1.67	.453	2.23	.487	2.79	.497	3.35	.500

Interfoto/Alamy

Carl Friedrich Gauss (1777–1855) was one of the greatest mathematical thinkers of history. In his *Disquisitiones Arithmeticae,* published in 1798, he pulled together work by predecessors and enriched and blended it with his own into a unified whole. The book is regarded by many as the true beginning of the theory of numbers.

Of his many contributions to science, the statistical method of least squares is the most widely used today in astronomy, biology, geodesy, physics, and the social sciences. Gauss took special pride in his contributions to developing the method. Despite an aversion to teaching, he taught an annual course in the method for the last twenty years of his life.

It has been said that Gauss was the last person to have mastered all of the mathematics known in his day.

The table gives the fraction of all scores in a normal distribution that lie between the mean and z standard deviations from the mean. ***Because of the symmetry of the normal curve, the table can be used for values above the mean or below the mean.*** All of the items in the table can be thought of as corresponding to the area under the curve. The total area is arranged to be 1.000 square unit, with 0.500 square unit on each side of the mean. The table shows that at 3.30 standard deviations from the mean, essentially all of the area is accounted for. Whatever remains beyond is so small that it does not appear in the first three decimal places.

EXAMPLE 2 Applying the Normal Curve Table

Use **Table 17** to find the percent of all scores that lie between the mean and the following values.

(a) One standard deviation above the mean

(b) 2.45 standard deviations below the mean

SOLUTION

(a) Here $z = 1.00$ (the number of standard deviations, written as a decimal to the nearest hundredth). Refer to **Table 17**. Find 1.00 in the z column. The table entry is 0.341, so 34.1% of all values lie between the mean and one standard deviation above the mean.

Another way of looking at this is to say that the area in color in **Figure 16** represents 34.1% of the total area under the normal curve.

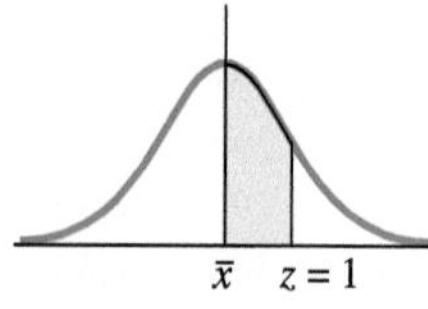

Figure 16

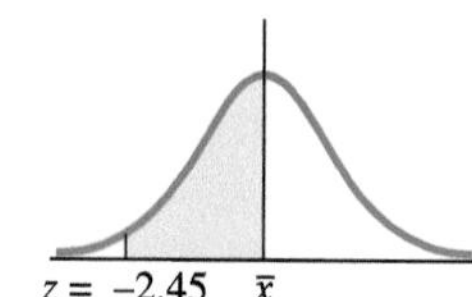

Figure 17

(b) Even though we go *below* the mean here (to the left), **Table 17** still works since the normal curve is symmetrical about its mean. Find 2.45 in the z column. A total of 0.493, or 49.3%, of all values lie between the mean and 2.45 standard deviations below the mean. This region is colored in **Figure 17**.

EXAMPLE 3 Finding Probabilities of Phone Call Durations

The time lengths of phone calls placed through a certain company are distributed normally with mean 6 minutes and standard deviation 2 minutes. If 1 call is randomly selected from phone company records, what is the probability that it will have lasted more than 10 minutes?

SOLUTION

Here 10 minutes is two standard deviations above the mean. The probability of such a call is equal to the area of the colored region in **Figure 18.**

From **Table 17**, the area between the mean and two standard deviations above is 0.477 ($z = 2.00$). The total area to the right of the mean is 0.500. Find the area from $z = 2.00$ to the right by subtracting.

$$0.500 - 0.477 = 0.023$$

The probability of a call exceeding 10 minutes is 0.023, or 2.3%.

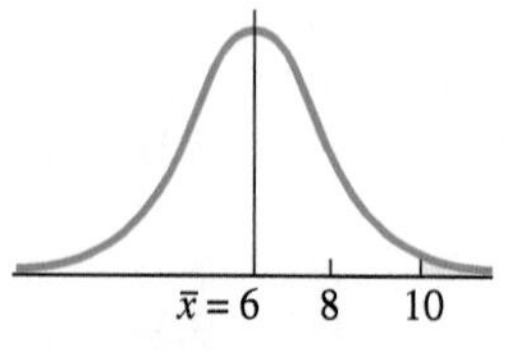

Figure 18

A Basic Consumer (T)issue It all started when a reporter on consumer issues for a Midwest TV station received a complaint that rolls of Brand X toilet paper manufactured by Company Y did not have the number of sheets claimed on the wrapper. Brand X is supposed to have 375 sheets, but three rolls of it were found by reporters to have 360, 361, and 363.

Shocked Company Y executives said that the **odds against** six rolls having fewer than 375 sheets each are 1 billion to 1. They counted sheets and found that several rolls of Brand X actually had 380 sheets each (machines count the sheets only in 10s). TV reporters made an independent count, and their results agreed with Company Y.

What happened the first time? Well, the reporters hadn't actually counted sheets, but had measured rolls and divided the length of a roll by the length of one sheet. Small variations in length can be expected, which add up over a roll, giving false results.

This true story perhaps points up the distinction in probability and statistics between **discrete values** and **continuous values.**

EXAMPLE 4 Finding Areas Under the Normal Curve

Find the total areas indicated in the regions in color in each of **Figures 19** and **20.**

SOLUTION

For **Figure 19**, find the area from 1.45 standard deviations below the mean to 2.71 standard deviations above the mean. From **Table 17**, $z = 1.45$ leads to an area of 0.426, while $z = 2.71$ leads to 0.497. The total area is the sum of these, or $0.426 + 0.497 = 0.923$.

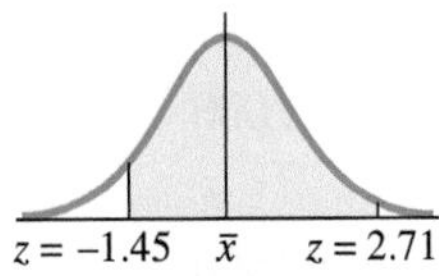

Figure 19

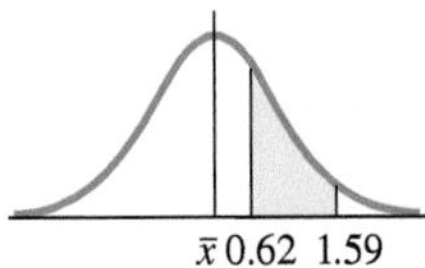

Figure 20

To find the indicated area in **Figure 20**, refer again to **Table 17**. From the table, $z = 0.62$ leads to an area of 0.232, while $z = 1.59$ gives 0.444. To get the area between these two values of z, subtract the areas.

$$0.444 - 0.232 = 0.212$$

Interpreting Normal Curve Areas

Examples 2–4 emphasize the *equivalence* of three quantities, as follows.

Meaning of Normal Curve Areas

In the standard normal curve, the following three quantities are equivalent.

1. **Percentage** (of total items that lie in an interval)
2. **Probability** (of a randomly chosen item lying in an interval)
3. **Area** (under the normal curve along an interval)

Which quantity we think of depends upon how a particular question is formulated. They are all evaluated by using A-values from **Table 17.**

In general, when we use **Table 17**, z is the z-score of a particular data item x. When one of these values is known and the other is required, as in **Examples 5 and 6,** we use the formula

$$z = \frac{x - \bar{x}}{s}.$$

EXAMPLE 5 Applying the Normal Curve to Driving Distances

In one area, the distribution of monthly miles driven by motorists has mean 1200 miles and standard deviation 150 miles. Assume that the number of miles is closely approximated by a normal curve, and find the percent of all motorists driving the following distances.

(a) Between 1200 and 1600 miles per month

(b) Between 1000 and 1500 miles per month

SOLUTION

(a) Start by finding how many standard deviations 1600 miles is above the mean. Use the formula for z.

$$z = \frac{1600 - 1200}{150} = \frac{400}{150} \approx 2.67$$

From **Table 17**, 0.496, or 49.6%, of all motorists drive between 1200 and 1600 miles per month.

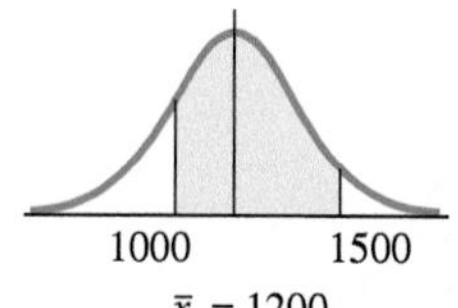

Figure 21

(b) As shown in **Figure 21**, values of z must be found for both 1000 and 1500.

$$\text{For 1000:} \quad z = \frac{1000 - 1200}{150} = \frac{-200}{150} \approx -1.33$$

$$\text{For 1500:} \quad z = \frac{1500 - 1200}{150} = \frac{300}{150} = 2.00$$

From **Table 17**, $z = -1.33$ leads to an area of 0.408, while $z = 2.00$ gives 0.477. This means a total of

$$0.408 + 0.477 = 0.885, \quad \text{or} \quad 88.5\%,$$

of all motorists drive between 1000 and 1500 miles per month. ▮▮▮

EXAMPLE 6 Identifying a Data Value Within a Normal Distribution

A particular normal distribution has mean $\bar{x} = 81.7$ and standard deviation $s = 5.21$. What data value from the distribution would correspond to $z = -1.35$?

SOLUTION

Solve for x.

$$z = \frac{x - \bar{x}}{s} \qquad z\text{-score formula}$$

$$-1.35 = \frac{x - 81.7}{5.21} \qquad \text{Substitute the given values for } z, \bar{x}, \text{ and } s.$$

$$-1.35(5.21) = \frac{x - 81.7}{5.21}(5.21) \qquad \text{Multiply each side by 5.21 to clear the fraction.}$$

$$-7.0335 = x - 81.7 \qquad \text{Simplify.}$$

$$74.6665 = x \qquad \text{Add 81.7.}$$

Rounding to the nearest tenth, the required data value is 74.7. ▮▮▮

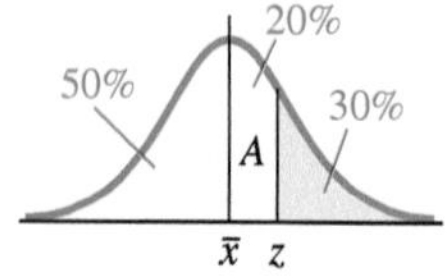

Figure 22

EXAMPLE 7 Finding z-Values for Given Areas Under the Normal Curve

Assuming a normal distribution, find the z-value meeting each condition.

(a) 30% of the total area is to the right of z.

(b) 80% of the total area is to the left of z.

SOLUTION

(a) Because 50% of the area lies to the right of the mean, there must be 20% between the mean and z. (See **Figure 22**.) In **Table 17**, $A = 0.200$ corresponds to $z = 0.52$ or 0.53, or we could average the two: $z = 0.525$.

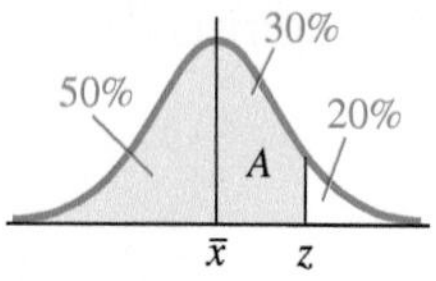

Figure 23

(b) This situation is shown in **Figure 23**. The 50% to the left of the mean plus 30% additional makes up the 80%. From **Table 17**, $A = 0.300$ implies $z = 0.84$. ▮▮▮

5 EXERCISES

Note: For problems requiring the calculation of z-scores or A-values, our answers are based on* Table 17*. By using a calculator or computer package, you will sometimes obtain a slightly more accurate answer.

Identify each variable quantity as discrete *or* continuous.

1. the number of heads in 50 tossed coins

2. the number of babies born in one day at a certain hospital

3. the average weight of babies born in a week

4. the heights of seedling pine trees at six months of age

5. the time as shown on a digital watch

6. the time as shown on a watch with a sweep hand

Measuring the Mass of Ore Samples *Suppose* 100 *geology students measure the mass of an ore sample. Due to human error and limitations in the reliability of the balance, not all the readings are equal. The results are found to closely approximate a normal curve, with mean* 86 g *and standard deviation* 1 g.

Use the symmetry of the normal curve and the empirical rule to estimate the number of students reporting readings in the following ranges.

7. more than 86 g

8. more than 85 g

9. between 85 and 87 g

10. between 84 and 87 g

Distribution of IQ Scores *On standard IQ tests, the mean is* 100, *with a standard deviation of* 15. *The results come very close to fitting a normal curve. Suppose an IQ test is given to a very large group of people. Find the percent of people whose IQ scores fall into each category.*

11. less than 100

12. greater than 115

13. between 70 and 130

14. more than 145

Find the percent of area under a normal curve between the mean and the given number of standard deviations from the mean. (Note that positive indicates above the mean, while negative indicates below the mean.)

15. 1.50

16. 0.92

17. −1.08

18. −2.25

Find the percent of the total area under a normal curve between the given values of z.

19. $z = 1.41$ and $z = 1.83$

20. $z = -1.74$ and $z = -1.14$

21. $z = -3.11$ and $z = 2.06$

22. $z = -1.98$ and $z = 1.02$

Find a value of z such that each condition is met.

23. 10% of the total area is to the right of z.

24. 4% of the total area is to the left of z.

25. 9% of the total area is to the left of z.

26. 23% of the total area is to the right of z.

Lifetimes of Lightbulbs *The Better lightbulb has an average life of* 600 hr, *with a standard deviation of* 50 hr. *The length of life of the bulb can be closely approximated by a normal curve. A warehouse manager buys and installs* 10,000 *such bulbs. Find the total number that can be expected to last each amount of time.*

27. at least 600 hr

28. between 600 and 675 hr

29. between 675 and 740 hr

30. between 490 and 720 hr

31. less than 740 hr

32. less than 510 hr

Weights of Chickens *The chickens at Benny and Ann Rice's farm have a mean weight of* 1850 g *with a standard deviation of* 150 g. *The weights of the chickens are closely approximated by a normal curve. Find the percent of all chickens having each weight.*

Sandeep Subb/iStockphoto

33. more than 1700 g

34. less than 1800 g

35. between 1750 and 1900 g

36. between 1600 and 2000 g

Filling Cereal Boxes *A certain dry cereal is packaged in* 24-oz *boxes. The machine that fills the boxes is set so that, on the average, a box contains* 24.5 oz. *The machine-filled boxes have contents weights that can be closely approximated by a normal curve. What percentage of the boxes will be underweight if the standard deviation is as follows?*

37. 0.5 oz

38. 0.4 oz

39. 0.3 oz

40. 0.2 oz

41. ***Recommended Daily Vitamin Allowances*** In nutrition, the recommended daily allowance of vitamins is a number set by the government to guide an individual's daily vitamin intake. Actually, vitamin needs vary drastically from person to person, but the needs are closely approximated by a normal curve. To calculate the recommended daily allowance, the government first finds the average need for vitamins among people in the population and the standard deviation. The **recommended daily allowance** is then defined as the mean plus 2.5 times the standard deviation. What fraction of the population will receive adequate amounts of vitamins under this plan?

Recommended Daily Vitamin Allowances *Find the recommended daily allowance for each vitamin if the mean need and standard deviation are as follows. (See **Exercise 41.**)*

42. mean need = 1800 units;
standard deviation = 140 units

43. mean need = 159 units;
standard deviation = 12 units

*Assume the following distributions are all normal, and use the areas under the normal curve given in **Table 17** to find the appropriate areas.*

44. ***Filling Cartons with Milk*** A machine that fills quart milk cartons is set up to average 32.2 oz per carton, with a standard deviation of 1.2 oz. What is the probability that a filled carton will contain less than 32 oz of milk?

David R. Frazier Photolibrary, Inc./Alamy

45. ***Finding Blood Clotting Times*** The mean clotting time of blood is 7.47 sec, with a standard deviation of 3.6 sec. What is the probability that an individual's blood-clotting time will be less than 7 sec or greater than 8 sec?

46. ***Sizes of Fish*** The average length of the fish caught in Lake Amotan is 12.3 in., with a standard deviation of 4.1 in. Find the probability that a fish caught there will be longer than 18 in.

47. ***Size Grading of Eggs*** To be graded extra large, an egg must weigh at least 2.2 oz. If the average weight for an egg is 1.5 oz, with a standard deviation of 0.4 oz, how many of five dozen randomly chosen eggs would you expect to be extra large?

Photos.com/Thinkstock

Distribution of Student Grades *Peter Davis teaches a course in marketing. He uses the following system for assigning grades to his students.*

Grade	Score in Class
A	Greater than $\bar{x} + 1.5s$
B	$\bar{x} + 0.5s$ to $\bar{x} + 1.5s$
C	$\bar{x} - 0.5s$ to $\bar{x} + 0.5s$
D	$\bar{x} - 1.5s$ to $\bar{x} - 0.5s$
F	Below $\bar{x} - 1.5s$

From the information in the table, what percent of the students receive the following grades?

48. A 49. B 50. C

51. Do you think this system would be more likely to be fair in a large freshman class in psychology or in a graduate seminar of five students? Why?

Normal Distribution of Student Grades *A teacher gives a test to a large group of students. The results are closely approximated by a normal curve. The mean is 75 with a standard deviation of 5. The teacher wishes to give As to the top 8% of the students and Fs to the bottom 8%. A grade of B is given to the next 15%, with Ds given similarly. All other students get Cs. Find the bottom cutoff (rounded to the nearest whole number) for the following grades. (Hint: Use **Table 17** to find z-scores from known A-values.)*

52. A 53. B 54. C 55. D

*A normal distribution has mean 76.8 and standard deviation 9.42. Follow the method of **Example 6** and find data values corresponding to the following values of z. Round to the nearest tenth.*

56. $z = 0.72$ 57. $z = 1.44$

58. $z = -2.39$ 59. $z = -3.87$

60. What percentage of the items lie within 1.25 standard deviations of the mean
(a) in any distribution (using the results of Chebyshev's theorem)?
(b) in a normal distribution (by **Table 17**)?

61. Explain the difference between the answers to parts (a) and (b) in **Exercise 60.**

EXTENSION Regression and Correlation

Linear Regression • Correlation

Table 18 Age vs. Income

Resident	Age	Annual Income
A	19	2150
B	23	2550
C	27	3250
D	31	3150
E	36	4250
F	40	4200
G	44	4350
H	49	5000
I	52	4950
J	54	5650

Linear Regression One very important branch of inferential statistics, called **regression analysis,** is used to compare quantities or variables, to discover relationships that exist between them, and to formulate those relationships in useful ways.

Suppose a sociologist gathers data on a few (say ten) of the residents of a small village in a remote region in order to get an idea of how annual income (in dollars) relates to age in that village. The data are shown in **Table 18**.

The first step in analyzing these data is to graph the results, as shown in the **scatter diagram** of **Figure 24**. (Graphing calculators will plot scatter diagrams.)

Once a scatter diagram has been produced, we can draw a curve that best fits the pattern exhibited by the sample data points. This curve can have any one of many characteristic shapes, depending on how the quantities involved are related. The best-fitting curve for the sample points is called an **estimated regression curve.** If, as in the present discussion, the points in the scatter diagram seem to lie approximately along a straight line, the relation is assumed to be linear, and the line that best fits the data points is called the **estimated regression line.**

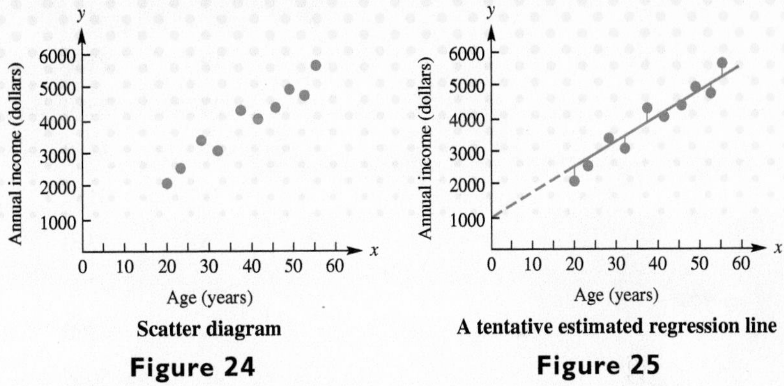

Scatter diagram

Figure 24

A tentative estimated regression line

Figure 25

If we let x denote age and y denote income in the data of **Table 18** and assume that the best-fitting curve is a line, then the equation of that line will take the form

$$y = ax + b,$$

where a is the slope of the line and b is the y-coordinate of the y-intercept (the y-value at which the line, if extended, would intersect the y-axis).

To completely identify the estimated regression line, we must find the values of the **regression coefficients** a and b, which requires some calculation. In **Figure 25**, a *tentative* line has been drawn through the scatter diagram.

For each x-value in the data set, the corresponding y-value usually differs from the value it would have if the data point were exactly on the line. These differences are shown in the figure by vertical segments. Choosing another line would make some of these differences greater and some lesser. The most common procedure is to choose the line where the sum of the squares of all these differences is minimized. This is called the **method of least squares,** and the resulting line is called the **least squares line.**

In the equation of the least squares line, the variable y' can be used to distinguish the *predicted* values (which would give points on the least squares line) from the *observed* values y (those occurring in the data set).

The least squares criterion mentioned above leads to specific values of a and b. We shall not give the details, which involve differential calculus, but the results are given here. (Σ—the Greek letter *sigma*—represents summation just as in earlier sections.)

Regression Coefficient Formulas

The **least squares line** $y' = ax + b$ that provides the best fit to the data points $(x_1, y_1), (x_2, y_2), \ldots, (x_n, y_n)$ has coefficient values as follows.

$$a = \frac{n(\Sigma xy) - (\Sigma x)(\Sigma y)}{n(\Sigma x^2) - (\Sigma x)^2} \qquad b = \frac{\Sigma y - a(\Sigma x)}{n}$$

EXAMPLE 1 Computing and Graphing a Least Squares Line

Find the equation of the least squares line for the age and income data given in **Table 18**. Graph the line.

SOLUTION

Start with the two columns on the left in **Table 19** (which just repeat the original data). Then find the products $x \cdot y$, and the squares x^2.

Table 19 Age and Income Calculations

x	y	$x \cdot y$	x^2
19	2150	40,850	361
23	2550	58,650	529
27	3250	87,750	729
31	3150	97,650	961
36	4250	153,000	1296
40	4200	168,000	1600
44	4350	191,400	1936
49	5000	245,000	2401
52	4950	257,400	2704
54	5650	305,100	2916
Sums: 375	39,500	1,604,800	15,433

Mary Evans Picture Library/Alamy

Francis Galton (1822–1911) learned to read at age three, was interested in mathematics and machines, but was an indifferent mathematics student at Trinity College, Cambridge. He became interested in researching methods of predicting weather. It was during this research that Galton developed early intuitive notions of **correlation** and **regression** and posed the problem of multiple regression.

Galton's key statistical work is *Natural Inheritance*. In it, he set forth his ideas on regression and correlation. He discovered the correlation coefficient while pondering Alphonse Bertillon's scheme for classifying criminals by physical characteristics. It was a major contribution to statistical method.

From the table, $\Sigma x = 375$, $\Sigma y = 39{,}500$, $\Sigma xy = 1{,}604{,}800$, and $\Sigma x^2 = 15{,}433$. There are 10 pairs of values, so $n = 10$. Now find a with the formula given above.

$$a = \frac{10(1{,}604{,}800) - 375(39{,}500)}{10(15{,}433) - (375)^2} = \frac{1{,}235{,}500}{13{,}705} \approx 90.15$$

Finally, use this value of a to find b.

$$b = \frac{39{,}500 - 90.15(375)}{10} \approx 569.4$$

The equation of the least squares line can now be written.

$$y' = 90x + 569 \quad \text{Coefficients are rounded.}$$

Letting $x = 20$ in this equation gives $y' = 2369$, and $x = 50$ implies $y' = 5069$. The two points (20, 2369) and (50, 5069) are used to graph the regression line in **Figure 26** on the next page. Notice that the intercept coordinates (0, 569) also fit the extended line.

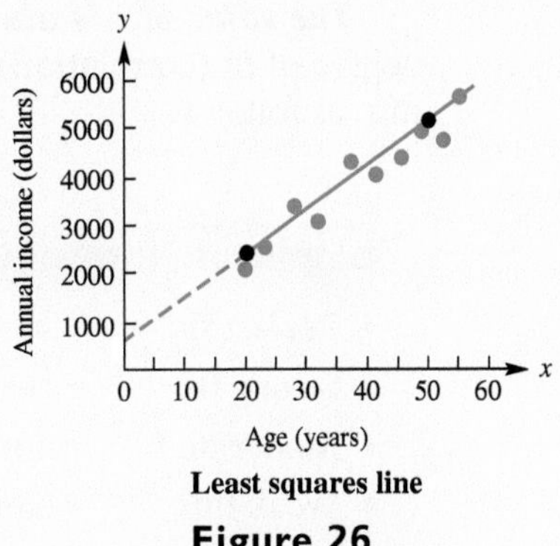

Least squares line

Figure 26

■■■

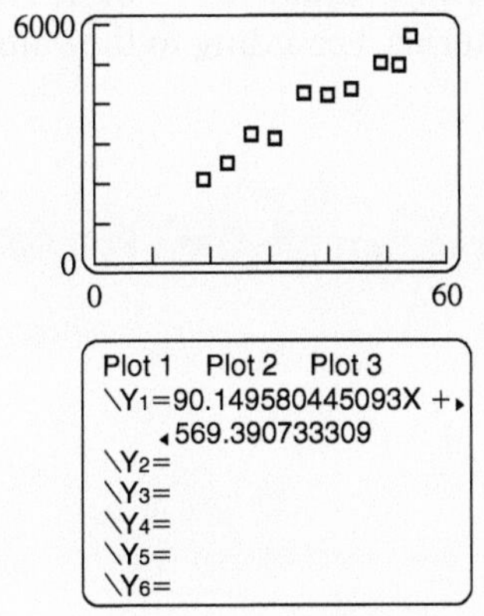

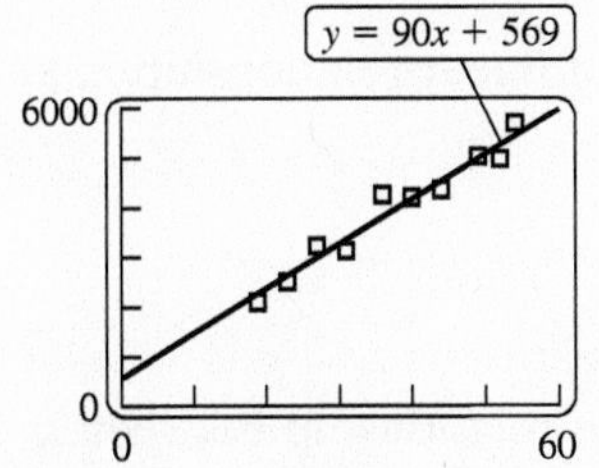

The information in **Figure 26** and the accompanying discussion is supported in these screens.

A computer or a scientific, statistical, or graphing calculator is recommended for finding regression coefficients. Tedious calculations, such as in **Example 1,** can be avoided and the regression line produced automatically.

EXAMPLE 2 Predicting from a Least Squares Line

Use the result of **Example 1** to predict the income of a village resident who is 35 years old.

SOLUTION

$$y' = 90x + 569 \quad \text{Equation from Example 1}$$
$$y' = 90(35) + 569 \quad \text{Let } x = 35.$$
$$y' = 3719$$

Based on the given data, a 35-year-old will make about \$3719 per year. ■■■

Correlation Once an equation for the line of best fit (the least squares line) has been found, it is reasonable to ask, "Just how good is this line for predictive purposes?" If the points already observed fit the line quite closely, then future pairs of scores can be expected to do so. If the points are widely scattered about even the "best-fitting" line, then predictions are not likely to be accurate.

In general, the closer the *sample* data points lie to the least squares line, the more likely it is that the entire *population* of (x,y) points really do form a line, that is, that x and y really are related linearly. Also, the better the fit, the more confidence we can have that our least squares line (based on the sample) is a good estimator of the true population line.

One common measure of the strength of the linear relationship in the sample is called the **sample correlation coefficient,** denoted r. It is calculated from the sample data according to the following formula.

Sample Correlation Coefficient Formula

In linear regression, the strength of the linear relationship is measured by the correlation coefficient $\boldsymbol{r}$, calculated as follows.

$$r = \frac{n(\Sigma xy) - (\Sigma x)(\Sigma y)}{\sqrt{n(\Sigma x^2) - (\Sigma x)^2} \cdot \sqrt{n(\Sigma y^2) - (\Sigma y)^2}}$$

The value of r is always between −1 and 1, or perhaps equal to −1 or 1. The degree of fit (correlation) can be described in general terms, according to the value of r, as follows.

Degree of Fit of an Estimated Regression Line to Sample Data Points

- Perfect fit: $r = 1$ or $r = -1$
- Strong fit: r close (but not equal) to 1 or -1
- Moderate fit: r not close to 0, and not close to 1 or -1
- Weak fit: r equal, or nearly equal, to 0

The sign (plus or minus) of r determines the type of linear relationship, if any, between the variables x and y.

Direct and Inverse Linear Relationships

- If $r > 0$, the regression line has positive slope. The relationship between x and y is ***direct***—as x increases, y also increases.
- If $r < 0$, the regression line has negative slope. The relationship between x and y is ***inverse***—as x increases, y decreases.
- If $r = 0$, no linear relationship between x and y is indicated.

EXAMPLE 3 Finding a Correlation Coefficient

Find r for the age and income data of **Table 19.**

SOLUTION

Almost all values needed to find r were computed in **Example 1.**

$$n = 10 \quad \Sigma x = 375 \quad \Sigma y = 39{,}500 \quad \Sigma xy = 1{,}604{,}800 \quad \Sigma x^2 = 15{,}433$$

```
LinReg
 y=ax+b
 a=90.14958045
 b=569.3907333
 r²=.9572823948
 r=.9784080922
```

The slope a and y-intercept b of the regression equation, along with r^2 and r, are given. Compare with **Examples 1 and 3.**

The only missing value is Σy^2. Squaring each y in the original data and adding the squares gives

$$\Sigma y^2 = 167{,}660{,}000.$$

Now use the formula to find that $r = 0.98$ (to two decimal places). This value of r, very close to 1, shows that age and income in this village are highly correlated. (The fit of the estimated regression line is strong.) The fact that r is positive indicates that the linear relationship is direct; as age increases, income also increases. ∎∎∎

EXAMPLE 4 Analyzing the Aging Trend in the U.S. Population

The World Almanac and Book of Facts 2010 reported the following U.S. Census Bureau data concerning the aging U.S. population over the last century.

Year	1910	1920	1930	1940	1950	1960	1970	1980	1990	2000	2010
Percent 65 and over	4.3	4.7	5.4	6.8	8.1	9.2	9.8	11.3	12.5	12.4	13.0

Let x represent time, in decades, from 1910, so $x = 0$ in 1910, $x = 1$ in 1920, $x = 2$ in 1930, and so on. Let y represent percent 65 and over in the population. Based on the data table, carry out the following.

(a) Plot a scatter diagram.

(b) Compute and graph the least squares regression line.

(c) Compute the correlation coefficient.

(d) Use the regression line to predict the percent 65 and over in 2050, and discuss the validity of the prediction.

SOLUTION

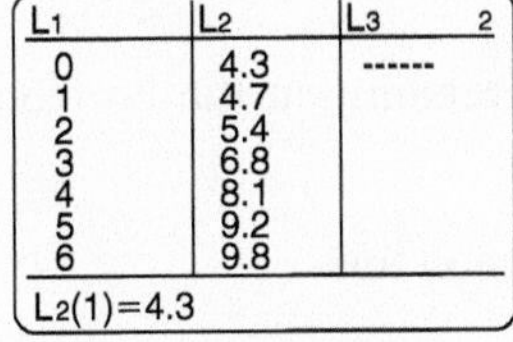

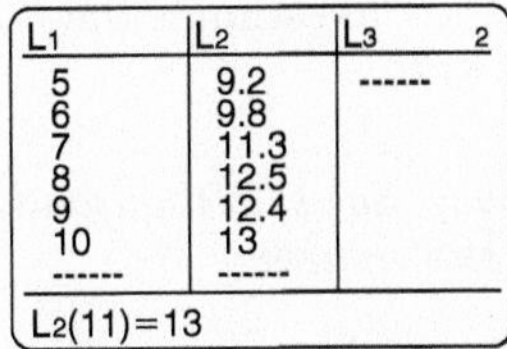

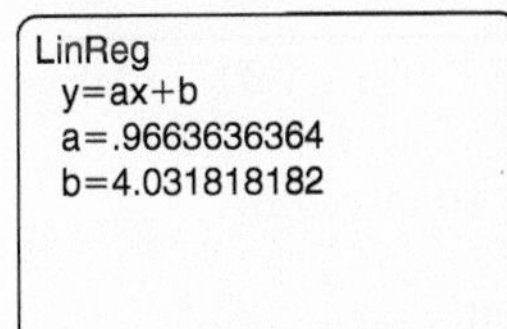

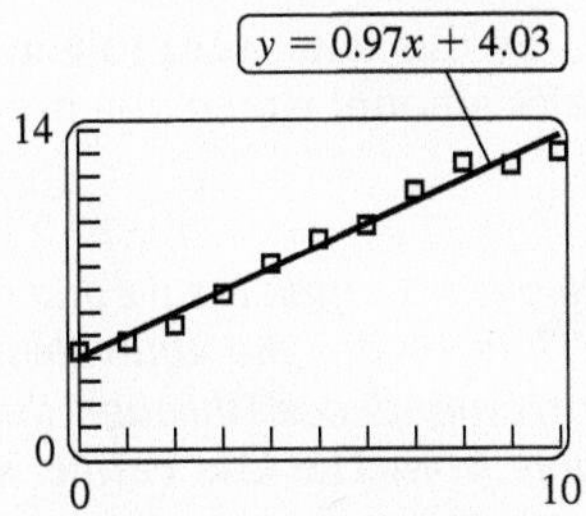

These screens support **Example 4(b).**

(a) The data points are plotted in **Figure 27**.

(b) We entered the x- and y-values into lists L1 and L2, respectively, in a calculator to obtain the equation of the least squares regression line.

$$y' = 0.97x + 4.03$$ Coefficients are rounded.

This line is shown in **Figure 27** as a dashed line.

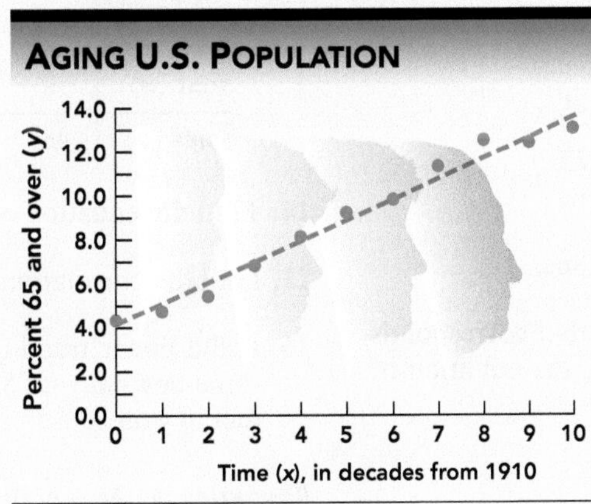

Figure 27

(c) $\Sigma x = 55, \quad \Sigma x^2 = 385, \quad n = 11, \quad \Sigma y = 97.5,$ $\Sigma y^2 = 968.97, \quad \Sigma(xy) = 593.8$ — All values are from the calculator, using two-variable statistics.

$$r = \frac{n(\Sigma xy) - (\Sigma x)(\Sigma y)}{\sqrt{n(\Sigma x^2) - (\Sigma x)^2} \cdot \sqrt{n(\Sigma y^2) - (\Sigma y)^2}}$$ Correlation coefficient formula

$$= \frac{11 \cdot 593.8 - 55 \cdot 97.5}{\sqrt{11 \cdot 385 - 55^2} \cdot \sqrt{11 \cdot 968.97 - 97.5^2}}$$

$$= 0.990211\ldots$$

$$r \approx 0.99$$

(d)

$$y' = 0.97x + 4.03$$ Estimated regression line

$$= 0.97 \cdot 14 + 4.03$$ The year 2050 corresponds to $x = 14$.

$$y \approx 17.6$$ 17.61 has been rounded here.

Although the correlation was strong ($r \approx 0.99$) for the data points we had, it is risky to extrapolate a regression line too far out. There may be factors (such as declining numbers of baby boomers in the population) that may slow the aging phenomenon. (Incidentally, the Census Bureau projects 20.2% in 2050.) ∎∎∎

EXTENSION EXERCISES

Correlating Fertilizer and Corn Ear Size *In a study to determine the linear relationship between the length (in decimeters) of an ear of corn (y) and the amount (in tons per acre) of fertilizer used (x), the following values were determined.*

$$n = 10 \qquad \Sigma xy = 75$$
$$\Sigma x = 30 \qquad \Sigma x^2 = 100$$
$$\Sigma y = 24 \qquad \Sigma y^2 = 80$$

1. Find an equation for the least squares line.

2. Find the correlation coefficient.

3. If 3 tons per acre of fertilizer are used, what length (in decimeters) would the regression equation predict for an ear of corn?

Correlating Celsius and Fahrenheit Temperatures *In an experiment to determine the linear relationship between temperatures on the Celsius scale (y) and on the Fahrenheit scale (x), a student got the following results.*

$$n = 5 \qquad \Sigma xy = 28{,}050$$
$$\Sigma x = 376 \qquad \Sigma x^2 = 62{,}522$$
$$\Sigma y = 120 \qquad \Sigma y^2 = 13{,}450$$

4. Find an equation for the least squares line.

5. Find the reading on the Celsius scale that corresponds to a reading of 120° Fahrenheit, using the equation of **Exercise 4.**

6. Find the correlation coefficient.

Correlating Heights and Weights of Adult Men *A sample of 10 adult men gave the following data on their heights and weights.*

Height (inches) (x)	62	62	63	65	66
Weight (pounds) (y)	120	140	130	150	142

Height (inches) (x)	67	68	68	70	72
Weight (pounds) (y)	130	135	175	149	168

7. Find the equation of the least squares line.

8. Using the results of **Exercise 7,** predict the weight of a man whose height is 60 inches.

9. What would be the predicted weight of a man whose height is 70 inches?

10. Compute the correlation coefficient.

Correlating Reading Ability and IQs *The table below gives reading ability scores and IQs for a group of 10 individuals.*

Reading (x)	83	76	75	85	74
IQ (y)	120	104	98	115	87

Reading (x)	90	75	78	95	80
IQ (y)	127	90	110	134	119

11. Plot a scatter diagram with reading on the horizontal axis.

12. Find the equation of a regression line.

13. Use your regression line equation to estimate the IQ of a person with a reading score of 65.

Correlating Yearly Sales of a Company *Sales, in thousands of dollars, of a certain company are shown here.*

Year (x)	0	1	2	3	4	5
Sales (y)	48	59	66	75	80	90

14. Find the equation of the least squares line.

15. Find the correlation coefficient.

16. If the linear trend displayed by this data were to continue beyond year 5, what sales amount would you predict in year 7?

Comparing the Ages of Dogs and Humans *It often is said that a dog's age can be multiplied by 7 to obtain the equivalent human age. A more accurate correspondence (through the first 14 years) is shown in this table from* The Old Farmer's Almanac, *2000 edition.*

Dog age (x)	$\frac{1}{2}$	1	2	3	4	5	6	7
Equivalent human age (y)	10	15	24	28	32	36	40	44

Dog age (x)	8	9	10	11	12	13	14
Equivalent human age (y)	48	52	56	60	64	68	70.5

17. Plot a scatter diagram for the given data.

18. Find the equation of the regression line, and graph the line on the scatter diagram of **Exercise 17.**

19. Describe where the data points show the most pronounced departure from the regression line, and explain why this might be so.

Stockbyte/Thinkstock

20. Compute the correlation coefficient.

Statistics on the Westward Population Movement *The data show the increase in the percentage of U.S. population in the West since about the time of the California Gold Rush.*

Census Year	Time, in Decades from 1850 (x)	Percentage in West (y)
1850	0	0.8%
1870	2	2.6
1890	4	5.0
1910	6	7.7
1930	8	10.0
1950	10	13.3
1970	12	17.1
1990	14	21.2

Source: The World Almanac and Book of Facts 2000.

21. Taking x and y as indicated in the table, find the equation of the regression line.

22. Compute the correlation coefficient.

23. Describe the degree of correlation (for example, as strong, moderate, or weak).

24. Would you expect the linear trend apparent in the table to persist into the mid 21st century? Why or why not?

Comparing State Populations with Governors' Salaries *The table shows the ten most populous states (as of 2008) and the salaries of their governors (as of September 2009).*

Rank	State	Population, in Millions (x)	Governor's Salary, in Thousands of Dollars (y)
1	California	37	174
2	Texas	24	150
3	New York	19	179
4	Florida	18	130
5	Illinois	13	177
6	Pennsylvania	12	175
7	Ohio	11	142
8	Michigan	10	177
9	Georgia	10	139
10	North Carolina	9	140

Source: The World Almanac and Book of Facts 2010.

25. Find the equation of the estimated regression line.

26. Compute the correlation coefficient.

27. Describe the degree of correlation (for example, as strong, moderate, or weak).

28. What governor's salary would this linear model predict for a state with a population of 15 million citizens?

COLLABORATIVE INVESTIGATION

Combining Sets of Data

Divide your class into two separate groups, one consisting of the women and the other consisting of the men. Each group is to select a recorder to write the group's results. As a group, carry out the following tasks. (You may want to devise a way to allow the members of the groups to provide personal data anonymously.)

1. Record the number of members (n) in your group.
2. Collect shoe sizes (x) and heights in inches (y) for all members of the group.
3. Compute the mean, median, and mode(s), if any, for each of the two sets of data.
4. Compute the standard deviation of each of the two sets of data.
5. Construct a box plot for each of the two sets of data.
6. Plot a scatter diagram for the x-y data collected.
7. Find the equation of the least squares regression line

$$y' = ax + b.$$

8. Evaluate the correlation coefficient (r).

9. Evaluate the strength of the linear relationship between shoe size and height for your group.

Now re-combine your two groups into one. Discuss and carry out the following tasks.

1. If possible, compute the mean of the heights for the combined group, using only the means for the two individual groups and the number of members in each of the two groups. If this is not possible, explain why and describe how you *could* find the combined mean. Obtain the combined mean.

2. Do the same as in item 1 above for the median of the heights for the combined group.

3. Do the same for the mode of the heights for the combined group.

4. Fill in the table below, pertaining to heights, and discuss any apparent relationships among the computed statistics.

	Number of Members	Mean	Median	Mode
Women				
Men				
Combined				

CHAPTER TEST

Cheaters Never Learn *The table here shows the results of an educational study of university physics students, comparing exam scores with students' rates of copying others' homework. The numbers in the table approximate letter grades on a 4-point scale (4.0 is an A, 3.0 is a B, and so on). Answer the questions in Exercises 1–4 in terms of copy rate.*

Copy Rate	Pretest	Exam 1	Exam 2	Exam 3	Final exam
<10%	2.70	2.75	2.90	2.80	2.95
10% to 30%	2.50	2.45	2.35	2.40	2.30
30% to 50%	2.45	2.43	2.30	2.10	2.00
>50%	2.40	2.05	1.70	1.80	1.60

Source: Table created using data from research reported in Physics Review-Special Topics-Physics Education *by David J. Palazzo, Young-Jin Lee, Rasil Warnakulasooriya, and David E. Pritchard of the Massachusetts Institute of Technology (MIT) physics faculty.*

1. Which students generally improved their exam performance over the course of the semester?

2. Which students did better on exam 3 than or exam 2?

3. Which students had lower scores consistently from one exam to the next throughout the semester?

4. Do you think that copying homework is generally a *cause* of lower exam scores? Explain.

5. ***Crude Oil Production*** The table in the right column above shows total 2008 production of crude oil (in millions of barrels) by the five top-producing states.

State	Total
Texas	398
Alaska	250
California	215
Louisiana	73
Oklahoma	64

Source: Energy Information Administration.

Use this information to determine each of the following.

(a) the mean production per state

(b) the range

(c) the standard deviation

(d) the coefficient of variation

(e) If 26 additional lesser producing states averaged (mean) 14 million barrels in 2008, what was the mean production for all 31 states?

Champion Trees *The table on the next page lists the 9 largest national champion trees, based on the formula*

$$T = G + H + 0.25C,$$

where T = *total points,*

G = *girth (circumference of trunk 4.5 feet above the ground),*

H = *height,*

and C = *average crown spread.*

Tree Type	G (in.)	H (ft)	C (ft)	T	Location
Giant sequoia	1020	274	107	1321	Sequoia National Park, CA
Coast redwood	950	321	75	1290	Jedediah Smith Redwoods State Park, CA
Coast redwood	895	307	83	1223	Jedediah Smith Redwoods State Park, CA
Coast redwood	867	311	101	1203	Prairie Creek Redwoods State Park, CA
Western red cedar	761	159	45	931	Olympic National Park, WA
Sitka spruce	668	191	96	883	Olympic National Park, WA
Douglas-fir	512	301	65	829	Jedediah Smith Redwoods State Park, CA
Douglas-fir	505	281	71	804	Olympia National Forest, WA
Port-Orford cedar	522	242	35	773	Siskiyou National Forest, OR

Source: The World Almanac and Book of Facts 2010.

Use this information for Exercises 6 and 7.

6. For the nine trees listed, find the following.

(a) the median height

(b) the first quartile in girth

(c) the eighth decile in total points

USGS National Wetlands Research Center

7. The tenth ranking tree in the country is a Common Bald Cypress on Cat Island, LA, with $G = 647$ inches, $H = 96$ feet, and $C = 74$ feet. For this tree, answer the following questions.

(a) Find its total points.

(b) Where would it have ranked based on girth alone?

(c) How much taller would it have needed to be to displace the ninth ranked tree?

(d) Assuming roughly a circular cross-section at 4.5 feet above the ground, approximate the diameter of the trunk (to the nearest foot) at that height.

Stimulus Bill *The table shows seven major categories (in alphabetical order) of the 2009 congressional stimulus bill (total $787 billion).*

Expenditure Category	Budgeted Amount ($ billions)
1. Education and Job Training	128.2
2. Energy	70.3
3. Environment	15.6
4. Health	152.0
5. Housing	20.5
6. Infrastructure	32.1
7. Transportation	48.2

Source: Congressional Budget Office.

8. Construct a bar graph for these data.

9. What percentage was assigned to health?

10. If $20 billion was allocated to health care–related information technology, what percentage of the total package went to *other* health categories?

11. What percentage was allocated to the three greatest categories combined?

Client Contacts of a Publisher's Representative *Tami Dreyfus, a publishing company representative, recorded the following numbers of client contacts for twenty-two days in March. Use the given data for Exercises 12–14.*

12	8	15	11	20	18	14	22	13	26	17
19	16	25	19	10	7	18	24	15	30	24

12. Construct grouped frequency and relative frequency distributions. Use five uniform classes of width 5 where the first class has a lower limit of 6. (Round relative frequencies to two decimal places.)

13. From your frequency distribution of **Exercise 12,** construct **(a)** a histogram and **(b)** a frequency polygon. Use appropriate scales and labels.

14. For the data above, how many uniform classes would be required if the first class had limits 7–9?

In Exercises 15–18, find the indicated measures for the following frequency distribution.

Value	8	10	12	14	16	18
Frequency	3	8	10	8	5	1

15. the mean

16. the median

17. the mode

18. the range

19. ***Exam Scores in a Physics Class*** The following data are exam scores achieved by the students in a physics class. Arrange the data into a stem-and-leaf display with leaves ranked.

79	43	65	84	77	70	52	61	80	66
68	48	55	78	71	38	45	64	67	73
77	50	67	91	84	33	49	61	79	72

Use the stem-and-leaf display shown here for Exercises 20–25.

Stem	Leaves
2	3 3 4
2	6 7 8 9 9
3	0 1 1 2 3 3 3 4
3	5 6 7 8 8 9
4	1 2 2 4
4	5 7 9
5	2 4
5	8
6	0

Compute the measures required in Exercises 20–24.

20. the median

21. the mode(s), if any

22. the range

23. the third decile

24. the eighty-fifth percentile

25. Construct a box plot for the given data, showing values for the five important quantities on the numerical scale.

26. ***Test Scores in a Training Institute*** A certain training institute gives a standardized test to large numbers of applicants nationwide. The resulting scores form a normal distribution with mean 80 and standard deviation 5. Find the percent of all applicants with scores as follows. (Use the empirical rule.)

(a) between 70 and 90

(b) greater than 95 or less than 65

(c) less than 75

(d) between 85 and 90

Heights of Spruce Trees *In a certain young forest, the heights of the spruce trees are normally distributed with mean 5.5 meters and standard deviation 2.1 meters. If a single tree is selected randomly, find the probability (to the nearest thousandth) that its height will fall in each of the following intervals.*

27. less than 6.5 meters

28. between 6.2 and 9.4 meters

Season Statistics in Major League Baseball *The tables below show the 2009 statistics on games won for all three divisions of both major baseball leagues. In each case,*

n = *number of teams in the division,*

$\overline{x}$ = *average (mean) number of games won,*

and s = *standard deviation of number of games won.*

American League

East Division	Central Division	West Division
$n = 5$	$n = 5$	$n = 4$
$\overline{x} = 84.2$	$\overline{x} = 76.4$	$\overline{x} = 86.0$
$s = 15.5$	$s = 10.9$	$s = 9.0$

National League

East Division	Central Division	West Division
$n = 5$	$n = 6$	$n = 5$
$\overline{x} = 79.0$	$\overline{x} = 78.0$	$\overline{x} = 84.0$
$s = 14.1$	$s = 9.7$	$s = 10.9$

Refer to the preceding tables for Exercises 29–31.

29. Overall, who had the greatest winning average, the East teams, the Central teams, or the West teams?

30. Overall, where were the teams the least "consistent" in number of games won, East, Central, or West?

31. Find (to the nearest tenth) the average number of games won for all West Division teams.

32. The Boston Red Sox, in the East Division of the American League, and the Los Angeles Dodgers, in the West Division of the National League, each won 95 games. Use z-scores to determine which of these two teams did relatively better within its own division of 5 teams.

Charlie Riede/AP Images

ANSWERS TO SELECTED EXERCISES

1 Exercises

1. (a)

x	f	$\frac{f}{n}$
0	10	$\frac{10}{30} \approx 33\%$
1	7	$\frac{7}{30} \approx 23\%$
2	6	$\frac{6}{30} = 20\%$
3	4	$\frac{4}{30} \approx 13\%$
4	2	$\frac{2}{30} \approx 7\%$
5	1	$\frac{1}{30} \approx 3\%$

(b)

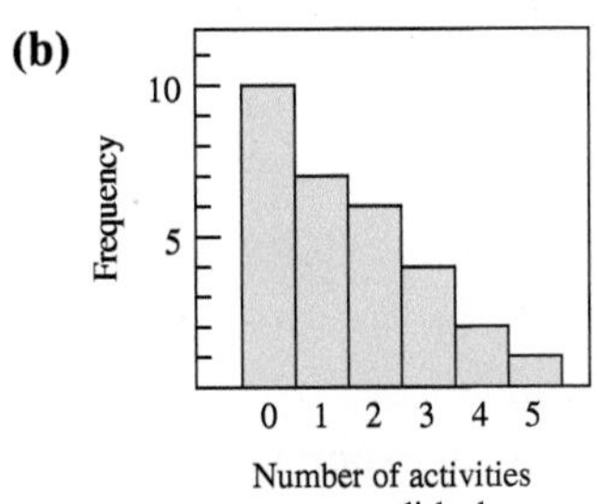

(c)

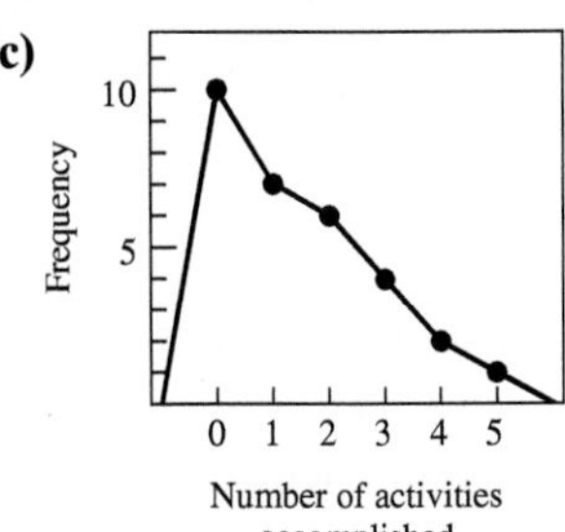

3. (a)

Class Limits	Tally	Frequency f	Relative Frequency $\frac{f}{n}$
45–49	|||	3	$\frac{3}{54} \approx 5.6\%$
50–54	卌 卌 ||||	14	$\frac{14}{54} \approx 25.9\%$
55–59	卌 卌 卌 |	16	$\frac{16}{54} \approx 29.6\%$
60–64	卌 卌 卌 ||	17	$\frac{17}{54} \approx 31.5\%$
65–69	||||	4	$\frac{4}{54} \approx 7.4\%$
	Total:	$n = 54$	

(b)

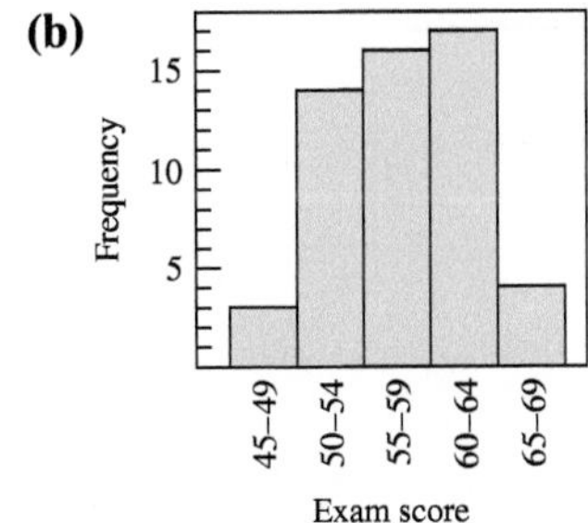

(c)

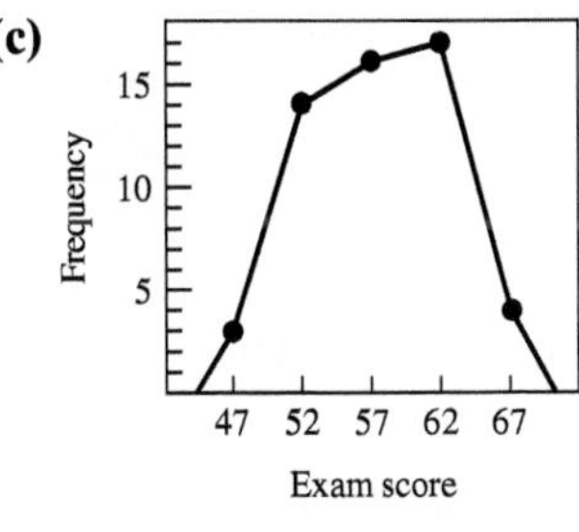

5. (a)

Class Limits	Tally	Frequency f	Relative Frequency $\frac{f}{n}$
70–74	||	2	$\frac{2}{30} \approx 6.7\%$
75–79	|	1	$\frac{1}{30} \approx 3.3\%$
80–84	|||	3	$\frac{3}{30} = 10.0\%$
85–89	||	2	$\frac{2}{30} \approx 6.7\%$
90–94	卌	5	$\frac{5}{30} \approx 16.7\%$
95–99	卌	5	$\frac{5}{30} \approx 16.7\%$
100–104	卌 |	6	$\frac{6}{30} = 20.0\%$
105–109	||||	4	$\frac{4}{30} \approx 13.3\%$
110–114	||	2	$\frac{2}{30} \approx 6.7\%$
	Total:	$n = 30$	

(b)

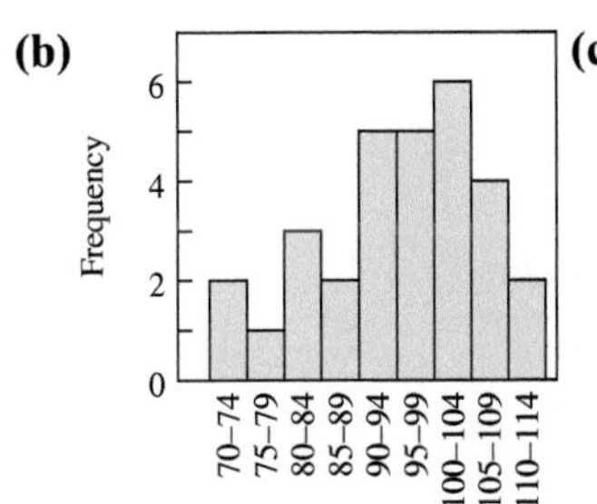

(c)

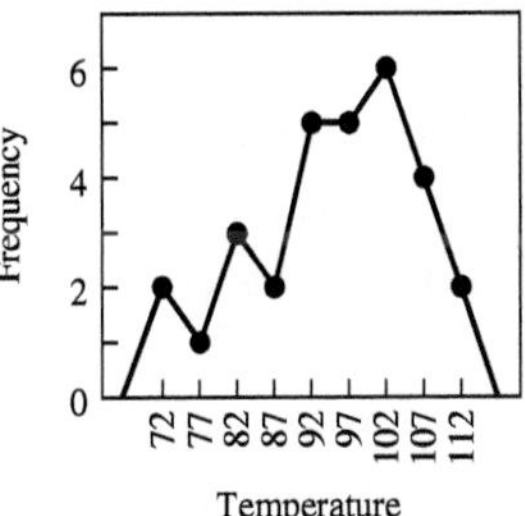

7.

0	7 9 8
1	1 1 2 8 9 4 3 1 0 5 0 5 5
2	7 0 9 6 6 2 2 5 2 3 4 4
3	8 1

9.

0	8 5 4 9 6 9 4 8
1	6 0 1 8 8 2 4 0 2 8 6 3
2	6 1 2 5 1 3
3	0 4 6
4	4

11. 2001 **13.** 2005, 2006, 2007, and 2011

15.

Surplus (+) or Deficit (–)

Billions of Dollars: 400, 0, –400, –800, –1,200, –1,600, –2,000

Year: 2001 2002 2003 2004 2005 2006 2007 2008 2009 2010 2011

17. 3.8% in 2008 **19.** Answers will vary.

21. Medicare & Medicaid; 83°

23. 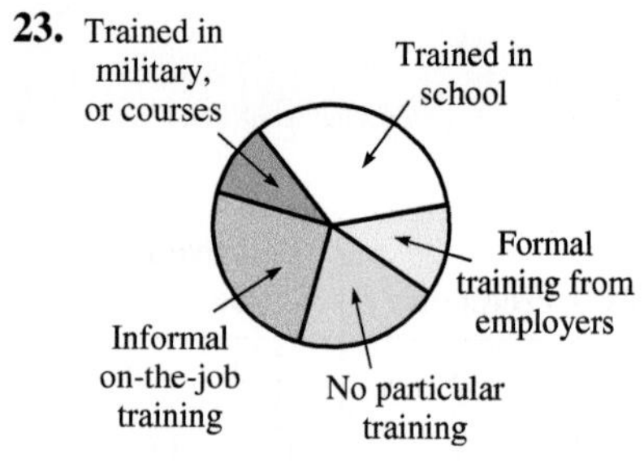

25. about 79 years **27.** **(a)** about 6 years **(b)** Answers will vary. **29.** Answers will vary. **31.** Answers will vary. **33.** Answers will vary.

35. **(a)**

Letter	Probability
A	0.208
E	0.338
I	0.169
O	0.208
U	0.078

(b)

37. Answers will vary. **39.** **(a)** 0.225 **(b)** 0.275 **(c)** 0.425 **(d)** 0.175

41. **(a)**

Sport	Probability
Sailing	0.225
Hang gliding	0.125
Snowboarding	0.175
Bicycling	0.075
Canoeing	0.300
Rafting	0.100

(b) empirical **(c)** Answers will vary.

2 Exercises

1. **(a)** 15.2 **(b)** 12 **(c)** none **3.** **(a)** 216.2 **(b)** 221 **(c)** 196 **5.** **(a)** 5.2 **(b)** 5.35 **(c)** 4.5 and 6.2 **7.** **(a)** 0.8 **(b)** 0.795 **(c)** none **9.** **(a)** 129 **(b)** 128 **(c)** 125 and 128 **11.** **(a)** 10.7 million **(b)** 10.65 million **(c)** 10.6 million **13.** **(a)** 73.9 **(b)** 17.5 **(c)** 0 **15.** mean = 47.4; median and mode remain the same **17.** \$59.7 billion **19.** 5.27 seconds **21.** 2.42 seconds **23.** the mean **25.** mean = 77; median = 80; mode = 79 **27.** 92 **29.** **(a)** 597.4 **(b)** 600 **(c)** 615 **31.** 2.41 **33.** 648 million **35.** China: 372; India: 1008; United States: 87; Indonesia: 324; Brazil: 61 **37.** 328.2 million **39.** **(a)** 8.25 **(b)** 8 **41.** **(a)** 66.25 **(b)** 64.5 **43.** 6 **45.** **(a)** 19.4 **(b)** 15.5 **(c)** 11 **47.** **(a)** 74.8 **(b)** 77.5 **(c)** 78 **49.** Answers will vary. **51.** **(a)** mean = 13.7; median = 16; mode = 18 **(b)** median **53.** **(a)** 4 **(b)** 4.25 **55.** **(a)** 6 **(b)** 9.33 **57.** 80 **59.** no **61.** Answers will vary.

3 Exercises

1. the sample standard deviation **3.** **(a)** 13 **(b)** 4.24 **5.** **(a)** 19 **(b)** 6.27 **7.** **(a)** 40 **(b)** 11.51 **9.** **(a)** 1.14 **(b)** 0.37 **11.** **(a)** 12 **(b)** 3.61 **13.** $\frac{3}{4}$ **15.** $\frac{21}{25}$ **17.** 88.9% **19.** 64.0% **21.** $\frac{3}{4}$ **23.** $\frac{15}{16}$ **25.** $\frac{1}{4}$ **27.** $\frac{4}{49}$ **29.** \$202.50 **31.** six **33.** There are at least nine. **35.** **(a)** $s_A = 2.35; s_B = 2.58$ **(b)** $V_A = 46.9; V_B = 36.9$ **(c)** sample B **(d)** sample A **37.** **(a)** $\bar{x}_A = 68.8; \bar{x}_B = 66.6$ **(b)** $s_A = 4.21; s_B = 5.27$ **(c)** brand A, since $\bar{x}_A > \bar{x}_B$ **(d)** brand A, since $s_A < s_B$ **39.** Brand A ($s_B = 3539 > 2116$) **41.** 18.71; 4.35 **43.** 8.71; 4.35 **45.** 56.14; 13.04 **47.** Answers will vary. **49.** −3.0 **51.** 4.2 **53.** 7.55 and 23.45 **55.** no **57.** Answers will vary.

4 Exercises

1. 58 **3.** 62 **5.** Janet (since $z = 0.48 > 0.19$) **7.** Yvette (since $z = -1.44 > -1.78$) **9.** −0.2 **11.** 1.0 **13.** Saudi Arabia **15.** United Kingdom **17.** Canada in exports (Canada's exports z-score was 2.4, China's imports z-score was 1.7, and $2.4 > 1.7$.) **19.** **(a)** The median is \$54.5 billion. **(b)** The range is 261 − 12 = 249. **(c)** The middle half of the items extend from \$29 billion to \$70 billion. **21.** Answers will vary. **23.** Answers will vary. **25.** Answers will vary. **27.** the overall distribution **29.** Both are skewed to the right, imports about twice as much as exports. **31.** **(a)** no **(b)** Answers will vary. **33.** Answers will vary. **35.** Answers will vary. **37.** $Q_1 = 97.6, Q_2 = 100.2, Q_3 = 104.4$ **39.** $P_{65} = 103.2$ **41.** 101.0

43. 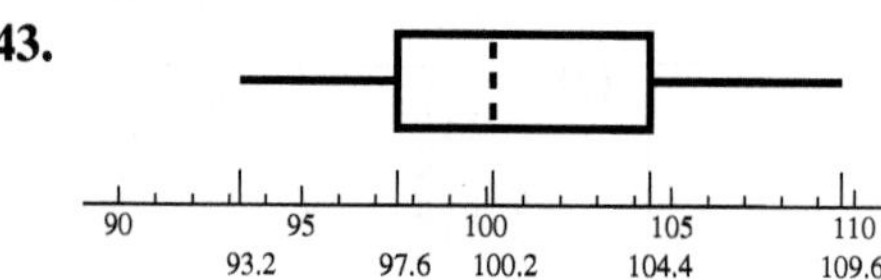

45. 93.3 **47.** 10

5 Exercises

1. discrete **3.** continuous **5.** discrete **7.** 50 **9.** 68 **11.** 50% **13.** 95% **15.** 43.3% **17.** 36.0% **19.** 4.5% **21.** 97.9% **23.** 1.28 **25.** −1.34 **27.** 5000 **29.** 640 **31.** 9970 **33.** 84.1% **35.** 37.8% **37.** 15.9% **39.** 4.7% **41.** 0.994, or 99.4% **43.** 189 units **45.** 0.888 **47.** about 2 eggs **49.** 24.2% **51.** Answers will vary. **53.** 79 **55.** 68 **57.** 90.4 **59.** 40.3 **61.** Answers will vary.

Extension Exercises

1. $y' = 0.3x + 1.5$ **3.** 2.4 decimeters **5.** 48.9°
7. $y' = 3.35x - 78.4$ **9.** 156 lb

11.

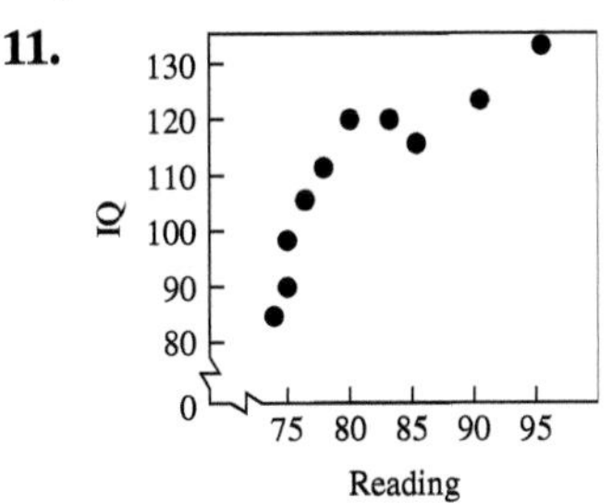

13. 79 **15.** $r = 0.996$

17.

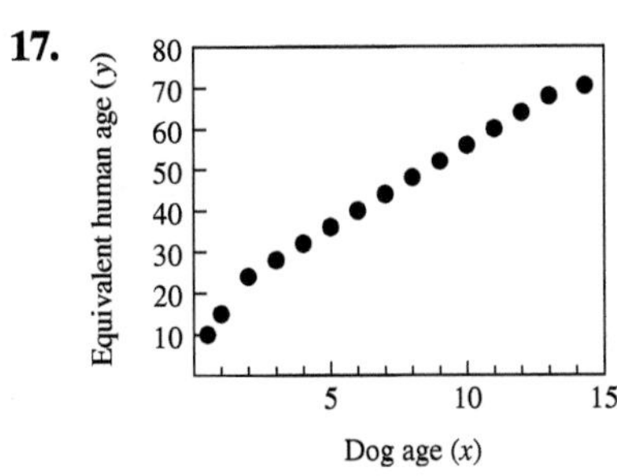

19. Answers will vary. **21.** $y' = 1.44x - 0.39$
23. The linear correlation is strong.
25. $y' = 0.5219x + 149.8$
27. The linear correlation is weak to moderate.

Chapter Test

1. those who copied less than 10% **2.** those with copy rates from 10% to 30% or greater than 50%
3. those with copy rate from 30% to 50%
4. Answers will vary. **5. (a)** 200 million barrels **(b)** 334 million barrels **(c)** 138 million barrels **(d)** 69 **(e)** 44 million barrels
6. (a) 281 feet **(b)** 517 inches **(c)** 1290
7. (a) 762 **(b)** 7th **(c)** 12 feet **(d)** 17 feet

8.

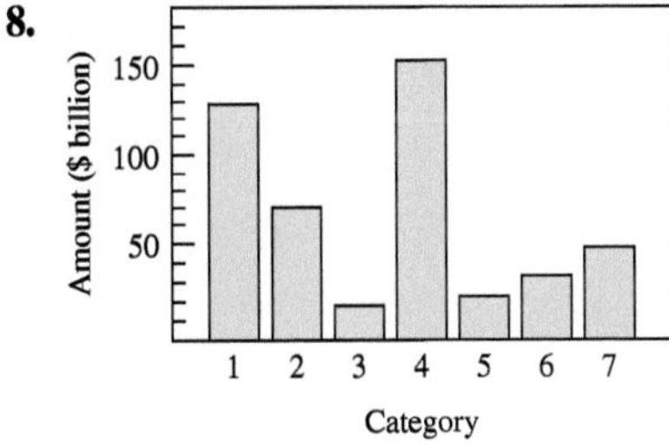

9. 19.3% **10.** 16.8% **11.** 44.5%

12.

Class Limits	Frequency f	Relative Frequency $\frac{f}{n}$
6–10	3	$\frac{3}{22} \approx 0.14$
11–15	6	$\frac{6}{22} \approx 0.27$
16–20	7	$\frac{7}{22} \approx 0.32$
21–25	4	$\frac{4}{22} \approx 0.18$
26–30	2	$\frac{2}{22} \approx 0.09$

13. (a)

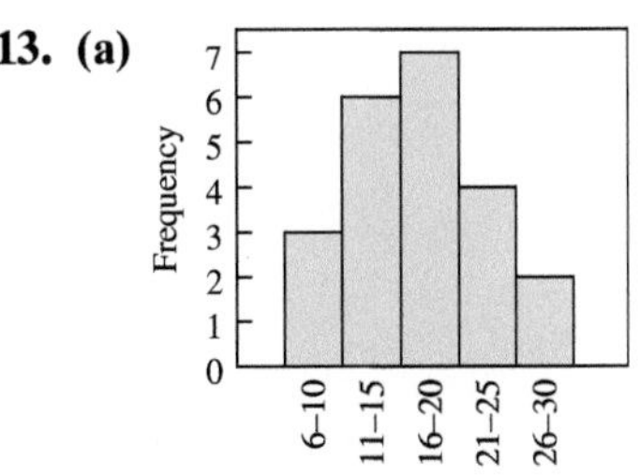

(b)

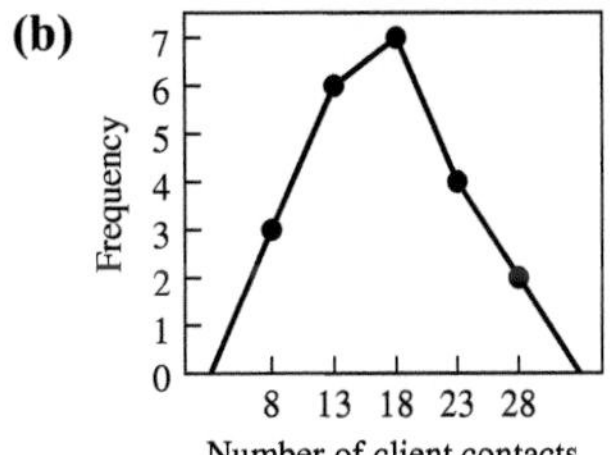

14. 8 **15.** 12.4 **16.** 12 **17.** 12 **18.** 10

19.

Stem	Leaves
3	3 8
4	3 5 8 9
5	0 2 5
6	1 1 4 5 6 7 7 8
7	0 1 2 3 7 7 8 9 9
8	0 4 4
9	1

20. 35 **21.** 33 **22.** 37 **23.** 31 **24.** 49

25.

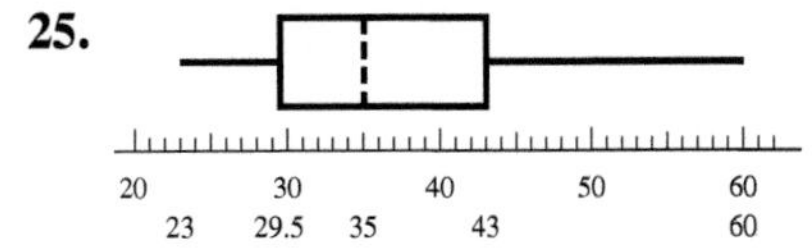

26. (a) about 95% **(b)** about 0.3% **(c)** about 16% **(d)** about 13.5% **27.** 0.684 **28.** 0.340 **29.** West
30. East **31.** 84.9 **32.** Dodgers (since $z = 1.01 > 0.70$)

Statistics

1 Exercises

1. (a) Remember that f represents the frequency of each data value, that $\frac{f}{n}$ is a comparison of each frequency to the frequency to the overall number of data values.

x	f	$\frac{f}{n}$
0	10	$\frac{10}{30} \approx 33\%$
1	7	$\frac{7}{30} \approx 23\%$
2	6	$\frac{6}{30} = 20\%$
3	4	$\frac{4}{30} \approx 13\%$
4	2	$\frac{2}{30} \approx 7\%$
5	1	$\frac{1}{30} \approx 3\%$

(b)

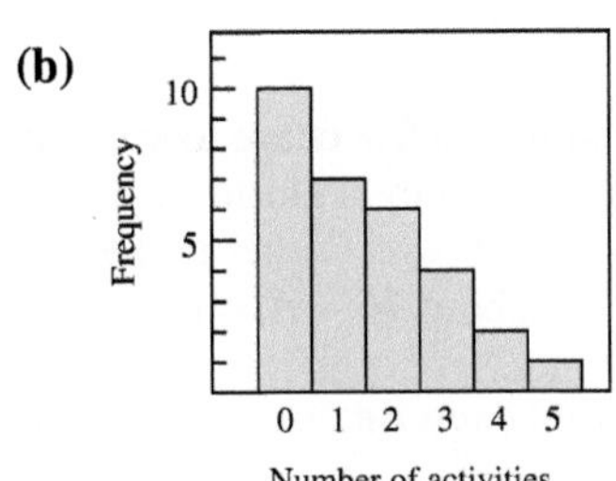

(c)

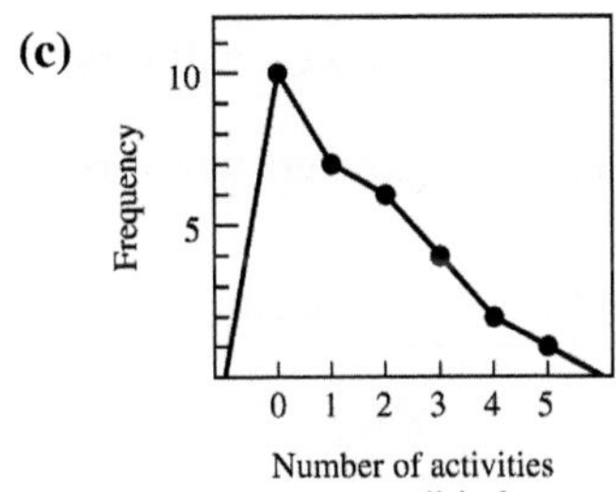

3. (a)

Class Limits	Tally	Frequency f	Relative Frequency $\frac{f}{n}$
45–49	|||	3	$\frac{3}{54} \approx 5.6\%$
50–54	𝍸 𝍸 ||||	14	$\frac{14}{54} \approx 25.9\%$
55–59	𝍸 𝍸 𝍸 |	16	$\frac{16}{54} \approx 29.6\%$
60–64	𝍸 𝍸 𝍸 ||	17	$\frac{17}{54} \approx 31.5\%$
65–69	||||	4	$\frac{4}{54} \approx 7.4\%$

Total: $n = 54$

(b)

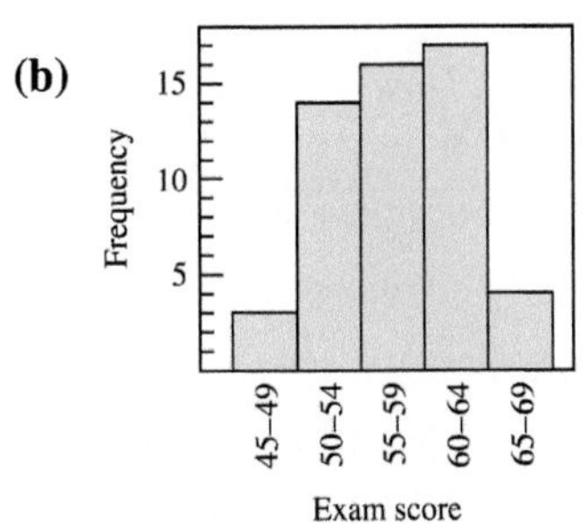

(c)

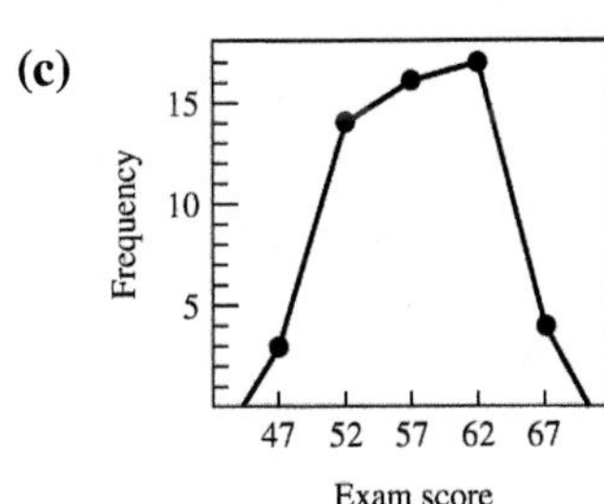

5. (a)

Class Limits	Tally	Frequency f	Relative Frequency $\frac{f}{n}$
70–74	||	2	$\frac{2}{30} \approx 6.7\%$
75–79	|	1	$\frac{1}{30} \approx 3.3\%$
80–84	|||	3	$\frac{3}{30} = 10.0\%$
85–89	||	2	$\frac{2}{30} \approx 6.7\%$
90–94	𝍸	5	$\frac{5}{30} \approx 16.7\%$
95–99	𝍸	5	$\frac{5}{30} \approx 16.7\%$
100–104	𝍸 |	6	$\frac{6}{30} = 20.0\%$
105–109	||||	4	$\frac{4}{30} \approx 13.3\%$
110–114	||	2	$\frac{2}{30} \approx 6.7\%$

Total: $n = 30$

(b)

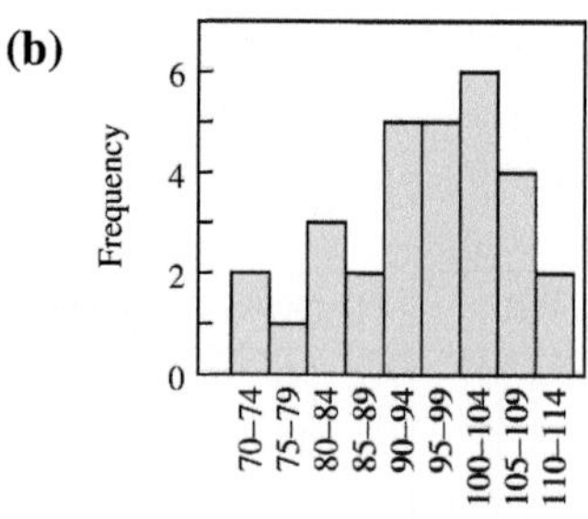

(c)

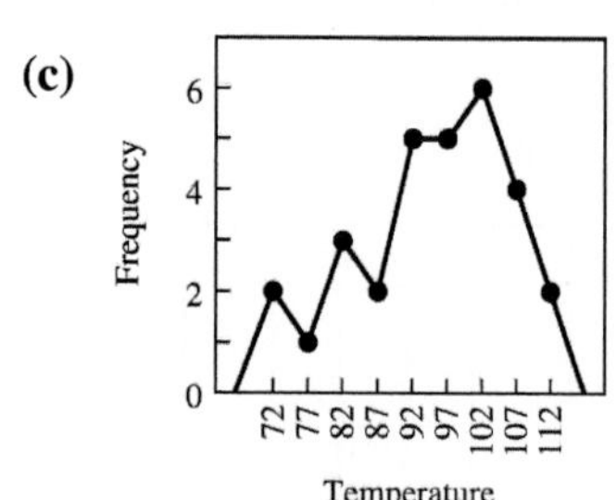

7.

Stem	Leaves
0	7 9 8
1	1 1 2 8 9 4 3 1 0 5 0 5 5
2	7 0 9 6 6 2 2 5 2 3 4 4
3	8 1

9.

Stem	Leaves
0	8 5 4 9 6 9 4 8
1	6 0 1 8 8 2 4 0 2 8 6 3
2	6 1 2 5 1 3
3	0 4 6
4	4

11. From the graph, receipts exceeded outlays in 2001.

13. From the graph, receipts appear to have climbed faster than outlays in 2005, 2006, 2007, and 2011.

15.

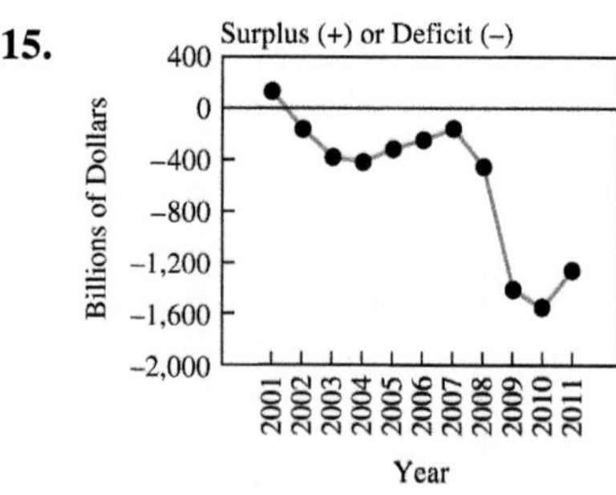

17. From the graph for consumer price index, the highest index occurred in 2008 and was about 3.8%.

19. Writing exercise; answers will vary.

21. The greatest single expense category is represented by the largest portion of the circle graph, and that is Medicare & Medicaid spending. The portion of the graph for this category represents 23% of the spending, and thus also 23% of the area of the circle. To find the central angle of the sector, find 23% of 360°.
$(0.23)(360) \approx 83°$

23. To calculate the number of degrees in each sector of the circle, multiply each percentage in decimal form times 360°. Here are a few examples:
$0.33(360) \approx 119°$
$0.25(360) = 90°$
$0.12(360) \approx 43°$

Trained in military, or courses
Trained in school
Formal training from employers
Informal on-the-job training
No particular training

25. Examine the graph to see that she would be about 79.

27. **(a)** Examine the 6% curve to see that Claire's money will run out at age 76. If she reaches age 70, her money would last for about $76 - 70 = 6$ years.

(b) Writing exercise; answers will vary.

29. Writing exercise; answers will vary.

31. Writing exercise; answers will vary.

33. Writing exercise; answers will vary.

35. **(a)**

Letter	Probability
A	$\frac{0.08}{0.385} \approx 0.208$
E	$\frac{0.13}{0.385} \approx 0.338$
I	$\frac{0.065}{0.385} \approx 0.169$
O	$\frac{0.08}{0.385} \approx 0.208$
U	$\frac{0.03}{0.385} \approx 0.078$

(b)

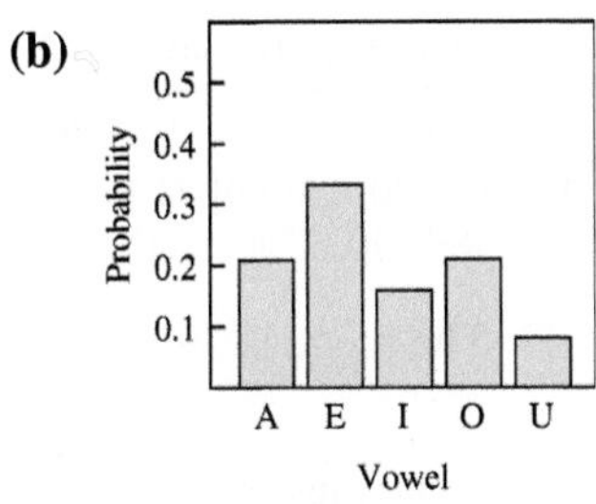

37. Writing exercise; answers will vary.

39. **(a)** Read the table in Exercise 38 to see that the probability is 0.225 that a given student studied 30–39 hours.

(b) The student would fall into either the 40–49 hour range or the 50–59 hour range. Add the probabilities: 0.175 + 0.100 = 0.275.

(c) Fewer than 30 hours means either 20–29 hours or 10–19 hours. Add the probabilities: 0.275 + 0.150 = 0.425.

(d) At least 50 hours means 50 or more; the categories included are 50–59, 60–69, and 70–79. Add the probabilities: 0.100 + 0.050 + 0.025 = 0.175.

41. **(a)**

Class Limits	Probability
Sailing	$\frac{9}{40} = 0.225$
Hang gliding	$\frac{5}{40} = 0.125$
Snowboarding	$\frac{7}{40} = 0.175$
Bicycling	$\frac{3}{40} = 0.075$
Canoeing	$\frac{12}{40} = 0.300$
Rafting	$\frac{4}{40} = 0.100$

(b) Empirical

(c) Writing exercise; answers will vary.

2 Exercises

1. **(a)** $\bar{x} = \frac{7+9+12+14+34}{5} = \frac{76}{5} = 15.2$

(b) The data is given in order from smallest to largest; the median is 12.

(c) There is no mode.

3. **(a)** $\bar{x} = \frac{218+230+196+224+196+233}{6}$
$= \frac{1297}{6}$
≈ 216.2

(b) Arrange the values from smallest to largest: 196, 196, 218, 224, 230, 233. Find the mean of the two middle numbers: $\frac{218+224}{2} = \frac{442}{2} = 221.$

(c) The mode is 196.

5. **(a)** $\bar{x} = \frac{3.1+4.5+6.2+7.1+4.5+3.8+6.2+6.3}{8}$
$= \frac{41.7}{8}$
≈ 5.2

(b) Arrange the values from smallest to largest or vice versa: 3.1, 3.8, 4.5, 4.5, 6.2, 6.2, 6.3, 7.1.
Find the mean of the two middle numbers: $\frac{4.5+6.2}{2} = 5.35.$

(c) The set of values is bimodal: 4.5 and 6.2.

7. **(a)** $\bar{x} = \frac{.78+.93+.66+.94+.87+.62+.74+.81}{8}$
$= \frac{6.35}{8}$
≈ 0.8

(b) Arrange the values from smallest to largest or vice versa: 0.62, 0.66, 0.74, 0.78, 0.81, 0.87, 0.93, 0.94.
Find the mean of the two middle numbers: $\frac{0.78+0.81}{2} = 0.795.$

(c) There is no mode.

9. **(a)** The sum of the data is 1032.
$\bar{x} = \frac{1032}{8} = 129$

(b) Arrange the values from smallest to largest or vice versa: 125, 125, 127, 128, 128, 131, 132, 136. The two middle numbers are both 128.

The median is $\frac{128+128}{2} = 128.$

(c) There are two modes: 125 and 128.

11. (a) The sum of the number of departures (in millions) is 106.7.

$\bar{x} = \frac{106.7}{10} \approx 10.7$ million

(b) Arrange the data from smallest to largest. The two middle numbers are 10.6 and 10.7. The median is $\frac{10.6+10.7}{2} = 10.65$ million.

(c) The mode is 10.6 million.

13. (a) The sum of the number of fatalities is 739.

$\bar{x} = \frac{739}{10} = 73.9$

(b) Arrange the data from smallest to largest. The two middle numbers are 13 and 22. The median is $\frac{13+22}{2} = 17.5.$

(c) The mode is 0.

15. The mean using the new data is $\bar{x} = \frac{474}{10} = 47.4.$ The median and mode remain the same.

17. The sum of the spending is \$298.3 billion. The mean is $\bar{x} = \frac{298.3}{5} \approx \$59.7$ billion.

19. The sum of the data is 36.92. Then $\bar{x} = \frac{36.92}{7} = 5.27$ seconds.

21. The sum for the new list is 16.94. Then $\bar{x} = \frac{16.94}{7} = 2.42$ seconds.

23. The mean was affected more.

25. $\bar{x} = \frac{79+81+44+89+79+90}{6} = \frac{462}{6} = 77$

Arrange in order from smallest to largest; 44, 79, 79, 81, 89, 90. The median is $\frac{79+81}{2} = 80.$ The mode is 79.

27. Let x = the score he must make. Replace the score of 44 with x.

$$\frac{x+79+79+81+89+90}{6} = 85$$

$$\frac{6}{1} \cdot \frac{x+79+79+81+89+90}{6} = 85 \cdot 6$$

$$x+418 = 510$$

$$x = 92$$

29. (a)

Value	Frequency	Value · Frequency
615	17	10,455
590	7	4130
605	9	5445
579	14	8106
586	6	3516
600	5	3000
Totals	58	34,652

Then $\bar{x} = \frac{34,652}{58} \approx 597.4.$

(b) From part (a), there are 58 items. The formula for the position of the median is $\frac{\sum f+1}{2} = \frac{58+1}{2} = 29.5.$

This means that the median is halfway between the 29th and 30th item. A chart showing cumulative frequency shows the value. Note that the values must be arranged in order.

Value	Frequency	Cumulative Frequency
579	14	14
586	6	20
590	7	27
600	5	32
605	9	41
615	17	58

The value 600 is the median.

(c) Examine the frequency column to see that the mode is 615.

31.

Units	Grade	Units · Grade Value
4	C	$4 \cdot 2 = 8$
7	B	$7 \cdot 3 = 21$
3	A	$3 \cdot 4 = 12$
3	F	$3 \cdot 0 = 0$
17		41

Then $\overline{x} = \frac{41}{17} \approx 2.41$, to the nearest hundredth.

33. The sum of the populations (in millions) is 3242. Then $\overline{x} = \frac{3242}{5} \approx 648$ million.

35. China: $\frac{1{,}339{,}000{,}000 \text{ people}}{3{,}601{,}000 \text{ sq mi}}$
≈ 372 persons per square mile

India: $\frac{1{,}157{,}000{,}000 \text{ people}}{1{,}148{,}000 \text{ sq mi}}$
≈ 1008 persons per square mile

United States: $\frac{307{,}000{,}000 \text{ people}}{3{,}537{,}000 \text{ sq mi}}$
≈ 87 persons per square mile

Indonesia: $\frac{240{,}000{,}000 \text{ people}}{741{,}000 \text{ sq mi}}$
≈ 324 persons per square mile

Brazil: $\frac{199{,}000{,}000 \text{ people}}{3{,}265{,}000 \text{ sq mi}}$
≈ 61 persons per square mile

37. The sum of the number of PCs in use in 2008 (in millions) is 1969.1. Then $\overline{x} = \frac{1969.1}{6} \approx 328.2$ million.

39. (a) The mean number of crew members per plane is $\overline{x} = \frac{11+9+6+7}{4} = \frac{33}{4} = 8.25$.

(b) The median number of crew members per plane is $\frac{7+9}{2} = 8$.

41. (a)

Flight	Total Persons per Plane
American #111	$11 + 76 + 5 = 92$
United #175	$9 + 51 + 5 = 65$
American #77	$6 + 53 + 5 = 64$
United #93	$7 + 33 + 4 = 44$

The mean number of persons per plane is $\overline{x} = \frac{92+65+64+44}{4} = \frac{265}{4} = 66.25$.

(b) The median number of persons per plane is $\frac{64+65}{2} = 64.5$.

43. The median number of silver medals is $\frac{6+6}{2} = 6$.

45. (a) The sum of the "Total" column is 194.
$\overline{x} = \frac{194}{10} = 19.4$

(b) The median is $\frac{15+16}{2} = 15.5$.

(c) The mode is 11.

47. (a) $x = \frac{47+51+53+56+\cdots+96}{34}$
$= \frac{2544}{34}$
≈ 74.8

(b) The scores are listed from smallest to the largest. Because there is an even number of scores, the median is the mean of the two middle numbers, the 17th and 18th scores: $\frac{77+78}{2} = 77.5$.

49. Writing exercise; answers will vary.

51. **(a)**

Value	Frequency	Value · Frequency
0	1	0
1	1	1
3	1	3
14	2	28
15	1	15
16	2	32
17	2	34
18	3	54
19	1	19
20	1	20
Totals	15	206

$\overline{x} = \frac{206}{15} = 13.7$

Position of the median is $\frac{15+1}{2} = 8.$

The position is the 8th piece of data.

Value	Frequency	Cumulative Frequency
0	1	1
1	1	2
3	1	3
14	2	5
15	1	6
16	2	8
17	2	10
18	3	13
19	1	14
20	1	15

Examine the table to see that the median is located in the row for the value of 16. The mode is 18 with a frequency of 3.

(b) The median, 16, is most representative of the data.

53. 2, 3, 5, 7; the median is $\frac{3+5}{2} = 4.$

(a) There are 4 numbers listed.

(b) $\overline{x} = \frac{2+3+5+7}{4} = \frac{17}{4} = 4.25$

55. 1, 3, 6, 10, 15, 21; the median is $\frac{6+10}{2} = 8.$

(a) There are 6 numbers listed.

(b) $\overline{x} = \frac{1+3+6+10+15+21}{6} = \frac{56}{6} \approx 9.33$

57. Arrange the numbers from smallest to largest. At this point it is uncertain where x will lie. However, if a single number must be the mean, median, and mode, then one of the given numbers must be that number. Because the median is the middle number and five values are given, the median must be 70 or 80. Try each of these as a mean to see which one works.

$$\frac{60+70+80+110+x}{5} = 70$$
$$\frac{5}{1} \cdot \frac{320+x}{5} = 70 \cdot 5$$
$$320 + x = 350$$
$$x = 30$$

This value does not work.

$$\frac{60+70+80+110+x}{5} = 80$$
$$\frac{5}{1} \cdot \frac{320+x}{5} = 80 \cdot 5$$
$$320 + x = 400$$
$$x = 80$$

This value works. The set of numbers is {60, 70, 80, 80, 110}. The value 80 is the mean, median, and mode.

59. No

61. Writing exercise; answers will vary.

3 Exercises

1. The sample standard deviation will be larger because the denominator is $n - 1$ instead of n.

3. **(a)** The range is $15 - 2 = 13$.

(b) To find the standard deviation:

1. First find the mean, $\bar{x} = \frac{56}{7} = 8.$

2 and 3. Find each deviation from the mean $(x-\bar{x})$ and square each deviation $(x-\bar{x})^2$.

Data	Deviations	Squared Deviations
2	$2-8=-6$	$(-6)^2 = 36$
5	$5-8=-3$	$(-3)^2 = 9$
6	$6-8=-2$	$(-2)^2 = 4$
8	$8-8=0$	$(0)^2 = 0$
9	$9-8=1$	$(1)^2 = 1$
11	$11-8=3$	$(3)^2 = 9$
15	$15-8=7$	$(7)^2 = 49$
Total		108

4. Sum the squared deviations. The sum is 108.
5. Divide by $n-1$.
$\frac{108}{7-1} = 18$
6. Take the square root.
$\sqrt{18} \approx 4.24$

5. **(a)** The range is 41 – 22 = 19.

(b) To find the standard deviation:

1. First find the mean, $\bar{x} = \frac{210}{7} \approx 30.$

2 and 3. Find each deviation from the mean $(x-\bar{x})$ and square each deviation $(x-\bar{x})^2$.

Data	Deviations	Squared Deviations
27	$27-30=-3$	$(-3)^2 = 9$
34	$34-30=4$	$(4)^2 = 16$
22	$22-30=-8$	$(-8)^2 = 64$
41	$41-30=11$	$(11)^2 = 121$
30	$30-30=0$	$(0)^2 = 0$
25	$25-30=-5$	$(-5)^2 = 25$
31	$31-30=1$	$(1)^2 = 1$
Total		236

4. Sum the squared deviations. The sum is 236.
5. Divide by $n-1$.
$\frac{236}{7-1} \approx 39.3$
6. Take the square root.
$\sqrt{39.3} \approx 6.27$

Some of the details are omitted in the following exercises. See Exercises 3–6 for details of computing standard deviation. A spreadsheet is a very useful tool in obtaining the intermediate calculations.

7. **(a)** The range is 348 – 308 = 40.

(b) To find the standard deviation:
1. First find the mean.
$\bar{x} = \frac{3233}{10} = 323.3$
2 and 3. Find each deviation from the mean $(x-\bar{x})$ and square each deviation $(x-\bar{x})^2$.
4. Sum the squared deviations. The sum is 1192.1.
5. Divide by $n-1$.
$\frac{1192.1}{10-1} \approx 132.456$
6. Take the square root.
$\sqrt{132.456} \approx 11.51$

9. **(a)** The range is 85.62 – 84.48 = 1.14.

(b) To find the standard deviation:
1. First find the mean.

$\bar{x} = \frac{763.62}{9} \approx 84.85$

2 and 3. Find each deviation from the mean $(x - \bar{x})$ and square each deviation $(x - \bar{x})^2$.

4. Sum the squared deviations. The sum is 1.0915.

5. Divide by $n - 1$.

$\frac{1.0915}{9-1} \approx 0.13644$

6. Take the square root.

$\sqrt{0.13644} \approx 0.37$

11. (a) The range is 13 − 1 = 12.

(b) To find the standard deviation:
1. First find the mean.

Value	Frequency	Value · Frequency
13	3	39
10	4	40
7	7	49
4	5	20
1	2	2
Totals	21	150

Then $\bar{x} = \frac{150}{21} \approx 7.143.$

2 and 3. Find each deviation from the mean $(x - \bar{x})$ and square each deviation $(x - \bar{x})^2$. These steps are shown in the table.

Value	Deviations	Squared Deviations	$\text{Freq} \cdot (x - \bar{x})^2$
13	5.857	34.304	3(34.304)
10	2.857	8.162	4(8.162)
7	−0.143	0.020	7(0.020)
4	−3.143	9.878	5(9.878)
1	−6.143	37.736	2(37.736)
Total			260.562

4. The fourth column shows the frequency of each value multiplied by the squared deviation. After multiplying each of these, find the sum: 260.562.

5. Divide by $n - 1$. Remember that the total number of values is 21.

$\frac{260.562}{21-1} = 13.0281$

6. Take the square root.

$\sqrt{13.0281} \approx 3.61$

13. According to Chebyshev's theorem, the fraction of scores that lie within 2 standard deviations of the mean is at least

$1 - \frac{1}{2^2} = 1 - \frac{1}{4} = \frac{3}{4}.$

15. According to Chebyshev's theorem, the fraction off scores that lie within $\frac{5}{2}$ standard deviations of the mean is at least

$1 - \frac{1}{\left(\frac{5}{2}\right)^2} = 1 - \frac{1}{\frac{25}{4}} = 1 - \frac{4}{25} = \frac{21}{25}.$

17. According to Chebyshev's theorem, the fraction of scores that lie within 3 standard deviations of the mean is at least

$1 - \frac{1}{(3)^2} = 1 - \frac{1}{9} = \frac{8}{9}.$ Divide 8 by 9 and change the decimal $0.\overline{8}$ to 88.9%.

19. According to Chebyshev's theorem, the fraction of scores that lie within $\frac{5}{3}$ standard deviations of the mean is at least

$1 - \frac{1}{\left(\frac{5}{3}\right)^2} = 1 - \frac{1}{\frac{25}{9}} = 1 - \frac{9}{25} = \frac{16}{25}.$

Divide 16 by 25 and change the decimal 0.64 to 64%.

21. Since 64 is 2 standard deviations below the mean (80 − 2 · 8 = 64) and 96 is 2 standard deviations above the mean (80 + 2 · 8 = 96), find the minimum fraction of values that lie within 2 standard deviations of the mean. See Exercise 13 for the answer $\frac{3}{4}$.

23. Since 48 is 4 standard deviations below the mean (80 − 4 · 8 = 48) and 112 is 4 standard deviations above the mean (80 + 4 · 8 = 112), find the minimum fraction of values that lie within 4 standard deviations of the mean. See Exercise 14 for the answer $\frac{15}{16}$.

25. This is equivalent to finding the largest fraction of values that lie outside 2 standard deviations from the mean. There are at least $1-\frac{1}{2^2}=1-\frac{1}{4}=\frac{3}{4}$ of the values within 2 standard deviations of the mean. Thus, the largest fraction of values that lie outside this range would be: $1-\frac{3}{4}=\frac{1}{4}$.

27. To find how many standard deviations below the mean 52 is, use $\frac{52-80}{8}=-3.5$. Also, the value 108 is 3.5 standard deviations above the mean. Then we must find the largest fraction of values that lie outside 3.5 or $\frac{7}{2}$ standard deviations from the mean. There are at least $1-\frac{1}{\left(\frac{7}{2}\right)^2}=1-\frac{1}{\left(\frac{49}{4}\right)}=1-\frac{4}{49}=\frac{45}{49}$ of the values within 3.5 standard deviations of the mean. Thus, the largest fraction of values that lie outside this range of values would be $1-\frac{45}{49}=\frac{4}{49}$.

29. The sum of the values is \$2430. Then $x=\frac{2430}{12}=\$202.50$.

31. The standard deviation is \$80.38. Then \$202.50 − 80.38 = \$122.12, and \$202.50 + 80.38 = \$282.88. There are six bonus amounts that fall within these two boundaries: \$175, \$185, \$190, \$205, \$210, and \$215.

33. $1-\frac{1}{2^2}=1-\frac{1}{4}=\frac{3}{4}$

Then $\frac{3}{4}$ of the data is $\frac{3}{4}\cdot 12=9$. There should be at least 9 amounts.

35. **(a)** Using the six steps to find the standard deviation of the samples:
Sample *A*
1. Find the mean.

Value, x	Frequency, f	$x\cdot f$
3	2	6
4	1	4
7	1	7
8	1	8
Totals	5	25

Then $\bar{x}_A=\frac{25}{5}=5$.

2 and 3. find each deviation from the mean $(x-\bar{x})$ and square each deviation, $(x-\bar{x})^2$. These steps are shown in the table.

x	$x-\bar{x}$	$(x-\bar{x})^2$	$f\cdot(x-\bar{x})^2$
3	−2	4	8
4	−1	1	1
7	2	4	4
8	3	9	9
Totals			22

4. The fourth column shows the frequency of each value multiplied by the squared deviation. After multiplying each of these, find the sum: 22.
5. Divide by $n-1$. Remember that the total number of values is 5.
   $\frac{22}{5-1}=5.5$
6. Take the square root.
   $S_A=\sqrt{5.5}\approx 2.35$

Sample *B*
1. Find the value.

Value, x	Frequency, f	$x\cdot f$
3	1	3
5	1	5
6	1	6
7	1	7
8	1	8
10	2	20
Totals	7	49

Then, $\overline{x}_B = \dfrac{49}{7} = 7.$

2 and 3. Find each deviation from the mean $(x - \overline{x})$ and square each deviation, $(x - \overline{x})^2$. These steps are shown in the table.

x	$x-\overline{x}$	$(x-\overline{x})^2$	$f\cdot(x-\overline{x})^2$
3	–4	16	16
5	–2	4	4
6	–1	1	1
7	0	0	0
8	1	1	1
10	3	9	18
Total			40

4. The fourth column shows the frequency of each value multiplied by the squared deviation. After multiplying each of these, find the sum: 40.
5. Divide by $n - 1$. Remember that the total number of values is 7.
$\dfrac{40}{7-1} = 6.67$
6. Take the square root.
$S_B = \sqrt{6.67} \approx 2.58$

(b) To find the sample coefficients of variation:

$V_A = \dfrac{S_A}{\overline{x}} \cdot 100 \approx \dfrac{2.35}{5} \cdot 100 \approx 46.9$

Note: Answers may vary in accuracy. Above answer made use of most accurate value of S_A which was carried over in calculator from the initial calculated value of S.

$V_B = \dfrac{S_B}{\overline{x}} \cdot 100 \approx \dfrac{2.58}{7} \cdot 100 \approx 36.9$

(c) Sample B has the higher dispersion as indicated by the larger standard deviation.

(d) Sample A has the higher relative dispersion as indicated by the larger coefficient of variation.

37. (a) Calculate sample means:
Sample A

	Value, x	Frequency, f
	64	1
	65	1
	70	1
	71	1
	74	1
Totals	344	5

Thus, $\overline{x}_A = \dfrac{344}{5} = 68.8.$

Sample B

	Value, x	Frequency, f
	60	1
	62	1
	69	1
	70	1
	72	1
Totals	333	5

Thus, $\overline{x}_B = \dfrac{333}{5} = 66.6.$

(b) Calculate sample standard deviations:
Sample A

x	$x-\overline{x}$	$(x-\overline{x})^2$
64	–4.8	23.04
65	–3.8	14.44
70	1.2	1.44
71	2.2	4.84
74	5.2	27.04
Total		70.8

$\dfrac{70.8}{5-1} = 17.1$

$S_A = \sqrt{17.7} \approx 4.21$

Sample B

x	$x-\overline{x}$	$(x-\overline{x})^2$
60	−6.6	43.56
62	−4.6	21.16
69	2.4	5.76
70	3.4	11.56
72	5.4	29.16
Total		111.2

$$\frac{111.2}{5-1}=27.8$$

$$S_B=\sqrt{27.8}\approx 5.27$$

(c) Brand A should last longer, since $\overline{x}_A > \overline{x}_B$.

(d) Brand A should have the more consistent lifetime, since $S_A < S_B$.

39. To answer this question, the standard deviation values must be compared. The standard deviation for Brand A is given as $S_A = 2116$ miles. To calculate the standard deviation for Brand B modules, follow the procedure given in the text or use a calculator or spreadsheet. The value of the standard deviation is $S_B = 3539$ miles. Brand A is more consistent because the value of the standard deviation is smaller.

41. $\overline{x}=\dfrac{13+14+17+19+21+22+25}{7}$

$=\dfrac{131}{7}$

≈ 18.71

To find the standard deviation:

1. The mean is 18.71.

2 and 3. Find each deviation from the mean $(x-\overline{x})$ and square each deviation $(x-\overline{x})^2$. These steps shown in the table.

Data	Deviations	Squared Deviations
13	13 − 18.71 = −5.71	$(-5.71)^2=32.6041$
14	14 − 18.71 = −4.71	$(-4.71)^2=22.1841$
17	17 − 18.71 = −1.71	$(-1.71)^2=2.9241$
19	19 − 18.71 = 0.29	$(0.29)^2=0.0841$
21	21 − 18.71 = 2.29	$(2.29)^2=5.2441$
22	22 − 18.71 = 3.29	$(3.29)^2=10.8241$
25	25 − 18.71 = 6.29	$(6.29)^2=39.5641$
Total		113.4287

4. Sum the squared deviations. The sum is 113.4287.

5. Divide by $n-1$.

$$\frac{113.4287}{7-1}\approx 18.90478$$

6. Take the square root. $\sqrt{18.90478}\approx 4.35$

43. $\bar{x} = \dfrac{3+4+7+9+11+12+15}{7}$

$= \dfrac{61}{7}$

≈ 8.71

To find the standard deviation:
1. The mean is 8.71.
2 and 3. Find each deviation from the mean $(x-\bar{x})$ and square each deviation $(x-\bar{x})^2$. These steps are shown in the table.

Data	Deviations	Squared Deviations
3	$3-8.71$ $=-5.71$	$(-5.71)^2 = 32.6041$
4	$4-8.71$ $=-4.71$	$(-4.71)^2 = 22.1841$
7	$7-8.71$ $=-1.71$	$(-1.71)^2 = 2.9241$
9	$9-8.71$ $=0.29$	$(0.29)^2 = 0.0841$
11	$11-8.71$ $=2.29$	$(2.29)^2 = 5.2441$
12	$12-8.71$ $=3.29$	$(3.29)^2 = 10.8241$
15	$15-8.71$ $=6.29$	$(6.29)^2 = 39.5641$
Total		113.4287

4. Sum the squared deviations. The sum is 113.4287.
5. Divide by $n-1$.
$\dfrac{113.4287}{7-1} \approx 18.90478$
6. Take the square root. $\sqrt{18.90478} \approx 4.35$

45. $\bar{x} = \dfrac{39+42+51+57+63+66+75}{7}$

$= \dfrac{393}{7}$

≈ 56.14

To find the standard deviation:
1. The mean is 56.14.
2 and 3. Find each deviation from the mean $(x-\bar{x})$ and square each deviation $(x-\bar{x})^2$. These steps are shown in the table.

Data	Deviations	Squared Deviations
39	$39-56.14$ $=-17.14$	$(-17.14)^2 = 293.7796$
42	$42-56.14$ $=-14.14$	$(-14.14)^2 = 199.9396$
51	$51-56.14$ $=-5.14$	$(-5.14)^2 = 26.4196$
57	$57-56.14$ $=0.86$	$(0.86)^2 = 0.7396$
63	$63-56.14$ $=6.86$	$(6.86)^2 = 47.0596$
66	$66-56.14$ $=9.86$	$(9.86)^2 = 97.2196$
75	$75-56.14$ $=18.86$	$(18.86)^2 = 355.6996$
Total		1020.8572

4. Sum the squared deviations. The sum is 1020.8572.
5. Divide by $n-1$.
$\dfrac{1020.8572}{7-1} \approx 170.14287$
6. Take the square root.
$\sqrt{170.14287} \approx 13.04$

47. Writing exercise; answers will vary.

49. Control cities:

$x = \dfrac{+1+(-8)+(-5)+0}{4} = \dfrac{-12}{4} = -3.0$

51. To find the standard deviation for the control cities:

Steps 1, 2, and 3. Find each deviation from the mean for the control cities, $(x-\bar{x})$ and square each deviation, $(x-\bar{x})^2$. These steps are shown in the table.

Data	Deviations	Squared Deviations
+1	$1-(-3.0)$ $=4.0$	$(4.0)^2=16$
−8	$-8-(-3.0)$ $=-5.0$	$(-5.0)^2=25$
−5	$-5-(-3.0)$ $=-2.0$	$(-2.0)^2=4$
0	$0-(-3.0)$ $=3.0$	$(3.0)^2=9$
Total		54

4. Sum the squared deviations. The sum is 54.

5. Divide by $n-1$.
$\frac{54}{4-1}\approx 18$

6. Take the square root. $\sqrt{18}\approx 4.2$

53. $15.5-7.95=7.55$; $15.5+7.95=23.45$

55. No, because the individual data items cannot be identified.

57. Writing exercise; answers will vary.

4 Exercises

For each of Exercises 1–4, make use of z-scores.

1. Find 15% of 40 items: $0.15(40)=6$. Select the 7th item in the data set, which is 58.

3. The third decile is the same as 30%. Find 30% of 40 items: $0.30(40)=12$. Select the 13th item in the data set, which is 62.

5. The z-score for Neil: $x=\frac{5-4.6}{2.1}=0.19$

The z-score for Janet: $z=\frac{6-4.9}{2.3}=0.48$

Janet's score is greater than Chris's score, so her score is better.

7. The z-score for Nicole's Brand A tires:
$z=\frac{37{,}000-45{,}000}{4500}\approx -1.78$

The z-score for Yvette's Brand B tires:
$z=\frac{35{,}000-38{,}000}{2080}\approx -1.44$

Yvette's score is greater than Nicole's score, so that score is better.

9. Find the mean by dividing the sum of values in the Population column (1918 million) by 10, the number of trading countries.
$\bar{x}=\frac{1918}{10}=191.8$

Find s by using the six-step process described in Section 3 or by entering the data into a calculator or spreadsheet that contains the function to calculate s. The standard deviation is approximately 405.

Use the formula $z=\frac{x-\bar{x}}{s}$, where x is Japan's population.
$z=\frac{127-191.8}{405}\approx -0.2$

11. The sum of the Exports column is 745 (billion U.S.$).
$\bar{x}=\frac{745}{10}=74.5$

Find s by using the six-step process described in Section 3 or by entering the data into a calculator or spreadsheet that contains the function to calculate s. The standard deviation is approximately 77. Use the formula $z=\frac{x-\bar{x}}{s}$, where x is exports to Mexico.
$z=\frac{151-74.5}{77}\approx 1.0$

13. The fifteenth percentile in population is found by taking 15% of the 10 scores or $(0.15)(10)=1.5$. Take the fifteenth percentile to be the second item up, Saudi Arabia, when the countries are arranged from smallest (bottom) to largest population (top).

15. The fourth decile in imports is found by taking 40% of the 10 scores or $(0.40)(10)=4$. After arranging the import values from lowest to largest, take the fifth score up, United Kingdom, to be the fourth decile.

17. Compare the corresponding z-scores to determine which country was relatively higher. From Exercise 10, China's imports z-score is 1.7. Calculating Canada's exports z-score (by calculator) we arrive at 2.4. Canada's exports z-score is relatively higher since $2.4>1.7$.

19. **(a)** The median is \$54.5 billion.

(b) The range is 261 − 12 = 249.

(c) The middle half of the items extend from \$29 billion to \$70 billion.

21. Writing exercise; answers will vary.

23. Writing exercise; answers will vary.

25. Writing exercise; answers will vary.

27. The "skewness coefficient" is a measure of the overall distribution.

29. Both are skewed to the right, imports about twice as much as exports.

31. **(a)** No; this would only be true if Q_1 and Q_3 are symmetric about Q_2.

(b) Writing exercise; answers will vary.

33. Writing exercise; answers will vary.

35. Writing exercise; answers will vary.

37. The second, Q_2, which is the same value as the median average, can be found by calculating the mean average of the fifth and sixth (two middle) scores: $\frac{99.9+100.5}{2} = 100.2$.
The first quartile is the same value as the median of all scores below the Q_2. Since there are five scores below Q_2, choose the middle or third score for $Q_1 \cdot Q_1$ is thus 97.6.
The third quartile is the median of all values above Q_2. Since there are five scores, we choose the middle, or third score, which is 104.4 for Q_3.

39. The sixty-fifth percentile, P_{65}, is found by taking 65% of the 10 scores of (0.65)(10) = 6.5. Take the seventh score up, 103.2, to be P_{65}.

41. The midquartile $= \frac{Q_1 + Q_3}{2}$

$$= \frac{97.6 + 104.4}{2}$$

$$= 101.0$$

43.

90 95 100 105 110

93.2 97.6 100.2 104.4 109.6

45. If Eli Manning had completed one more pass in 2009, then
$A = 509$
$C = 318$
$T = 27$
$Y = 4021$
$I = 14$
and Rating = 93.3.

47. Solve the rating formula for I if
$A = 497$
$C = 336$
$T = 49$
$Y = 4557$
and Rating = 121.1.

$$121.1 = \frac{\left(250 \cdot \frac{336}{497}\right) + \left(1000 \cdot \frac{49}{497}\right) + \left(12.5 \cdot \frac{4557}{497}\right) + 6.25 - \left(1250 \cdot \frac{I}{497}\right)}{3}$$

$$363.3 \approx 169.0 + 98.6 + 114.6 + 6.25 - 2.5I$$
$$363.3 = 388.45 - 2.5I$$
$$-25.15 = -2.5I$$
$$10 \approx I$$

Peyton Manning was intercepted 10 times.

5 Exercises

1. Discrete because the variable can take on only fixed number values such as 1, 2, 3, etc., up to and including 50.

3. Continuous because the variable is not limited to fixed values. It is measurable rather than countable.

5. Discrete because the variable is limited to fixed values.

7. This represents all values to the right of the mean, which is 50% of the total number of values or 50% of 100 students: 0.50(100) = 50 students.

9. These values are 1 standard deviation above and 1 standard deviation below the mean, respectively; (86 ± 1). By the empirical rule, 68% of all scores lie within 1 standard deviation of the mean. Then 0.68(100) = 68.

11. Less than 100 represents all values below the mean. This is 50% of the area under the curve or 50% of all the data.

13. The score 70 lies 2 standard deviations below the mean, and 130 lies 2 standard deviations above the mean. According to the empirical rule, 95% of the data lies within 2 standard deviations of the mean.

15. To find the percent of area between the mean and 1.5 standard deviations, use Table 10 to locate a z-score of 1.5. Read the value of A in the next column.
This is the area from the mean to the corresponding value of z. The area is 0.433, which is 43.3%.

17. Because of the symmetry of the normal curve, the area between the mean and a z value of -1.08 is the same as that from the mean to a z value of $+1.08$. Use Table 10 to locate a z-score of 1.08. Read the value of A in the next column. this is the area from the mean to the corresponding value of z. The area is 0.360, which is 36.0%.

19. It is helpful to sketch the area under the normal curve.

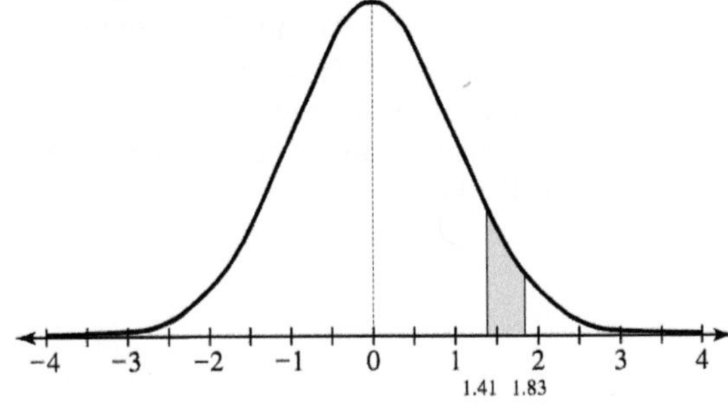

To find the area between $z = 1.41$ and

$z = 1.83$, use the z-table to find the area between the mean and $z = 1.83$. The area is 0.466. Find the area between the mean and $z = 1.41$, which is 0.421. Subtracting, $0.466 - 0.421 = 0.045$, which is 4.5%.

21. It is helpful to sketch the area under the normal curve.

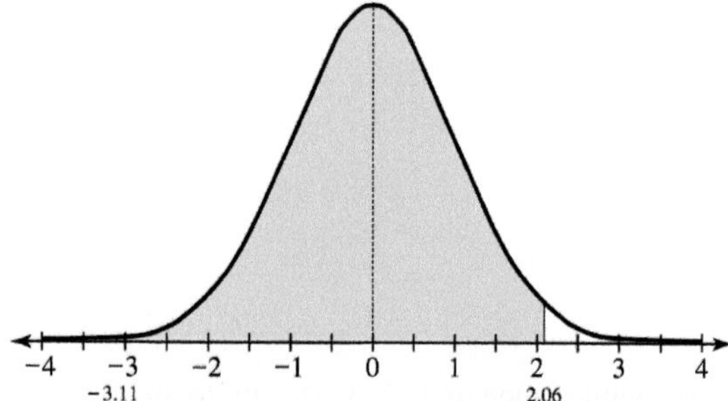

Add the areas under the curve from the mean to $z = -3.11$ to that from the mean to $z = 2.06$. The first area is the same as that from the mean to $z = +3.11$, which is 0.499. The area from the mean to $z = 2.06$ is 0.480. Find the total area: $0.499 + 0.480 = 0.979$ or 97.9%.

23. If 10% of the total area is to the right of the z-score, there is 50% − 10% = 40% of the area between the mean and the value of z. From the z-table, find 0.40 in the A column. This area under the curve of 40% or 0.40 yields a z-score of 1.28.

25. If 9% of the total area is to the left of z, the z-score is below the mean, so the answer will be negative. (A sketch helps to see this.) Subtract 9% from 50% to find the amount of area between the mean and the value of z: 50% − 9% = 41%. Now find 0.41 in the A column to locate the appropriate value for z: 1.34. The z-score is −1.34.

27. Since the mean is 600 hr, we can expect half of the bulbs or 5000 bulbs to last at least 600 hr.

29. Find the z-score for 675:

$$z = \frac{675 - 600}{50} = 1.5.$$

Find the z-score for 740:

$$z = \frac{740 - 600}{50} = 2.8.$$

It is helpful to sketch the area under the normal curve.

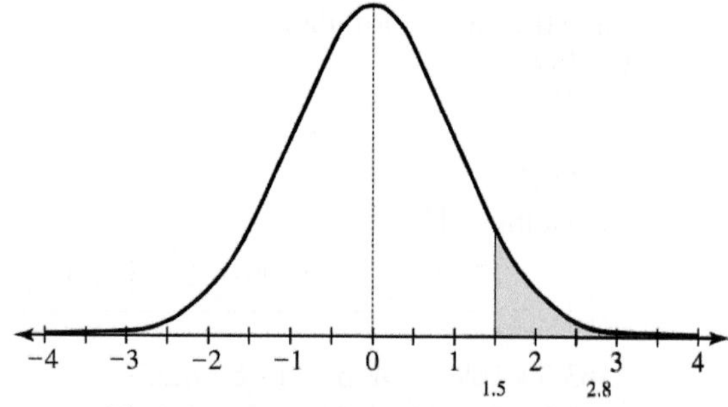

Find the amount of area under the normal curve between 1.5 and 2.8 by finding the corresponding values for A and then subtracting the smaller from the larger: $0.497 - 0.433 = 0.064$
Finally, find 6.4% of 10,000:
$0.064(10000) = 640$

31. Find the z-score for 740:

$$z = \frac{740 - 600}{50} = 2.8.$$

It is helpful to sketch the area under the normal curve.

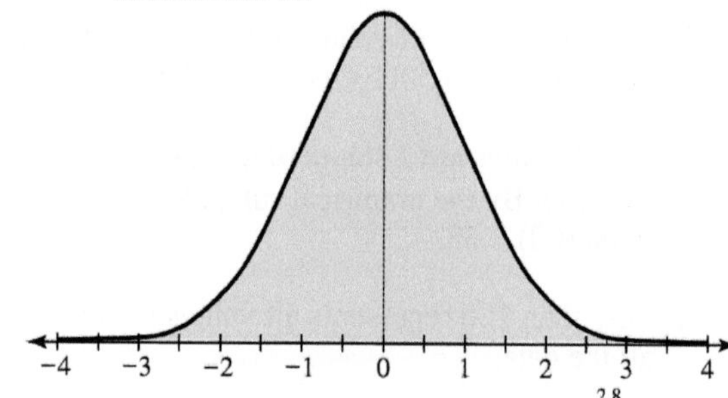

Find the amount of area under the normal curve between the mean and 2.8 by finding the corresponding value for A: 0.497. Add this area value to 0.5: $0.497 + 0.5 = 0.997$.
Finally, find 99.7% of 10,000:
$0.997(10000) = 9970$.

33. Because the mean is 1850 and the standard deviation is 150, the value 1700 corresponds to $z = -1$. Use the empirical rule to evaluate the corresponding area under the curve. The area between $z = -1$ and the mean is half of 68% or 34 %. The area to the right of the mean is 50%. The total area to the right of $z = -1$ is $34 + 50 = 84\%$.
If the z-table is used, the answer is 84.1%, because the area value in the table for $z = 1$ is 0.341.

35. Find the z-score for 1750:

$$z = \frac{1750 - 1850}{150} \approx -0.67.$$

Find the z-score for 1900:

$$z = \frac{1900 - 1850}{150} = 0.33.$$

It is helpful to sketch the area under the normal curve.

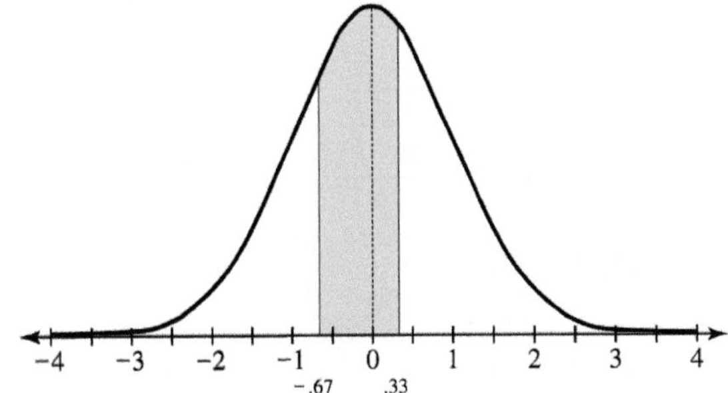

Find the amount of area under the normal curve between −0.67 and 0.33 by finding the corresponding values from area and then adding the values: 0.249 + 0.129 = 0.378. This is 37.8%.

37. The z-score corresponding to 24 oz when $s = 0.5$ is found by $z = \frac{24 - 24.5}{0.5} = -1$. The fraction of boxes that are underweight is equivalent to the area under the curve to the left of −1. It is helpful to sketch the area under the normal curve.

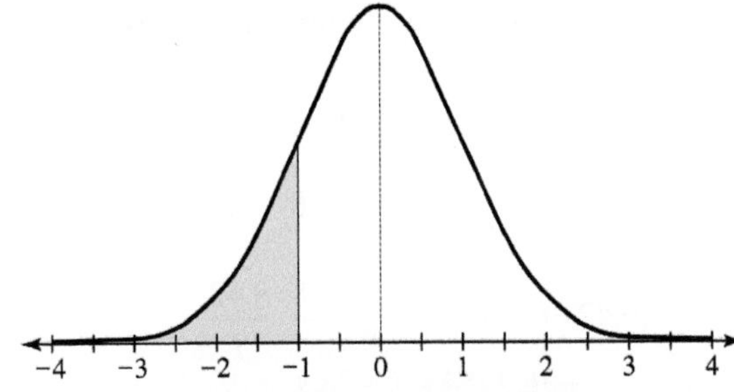

From the z-table, the area under the curve between the mean and +1 is 0.341. Subtract 0.341 from 0.5 to obtain the area under the curve to the right of +1: 0.5 − 0.341 = 0.159. Because of symmetry, this is also the amount of area under the curve to the left of −1. The answer is 0.159 or 15.9%.

39. The z-score corresponding to 24 oz when $s = 0.3$ is found by $z = \frac{24 - 24.5}{0.3} \approx -1.67$.

The fraction of boxes that are underweight is equivalent to the area under the curve to the left of −1.67.

It is helpful to sketch the area under the normal curve.

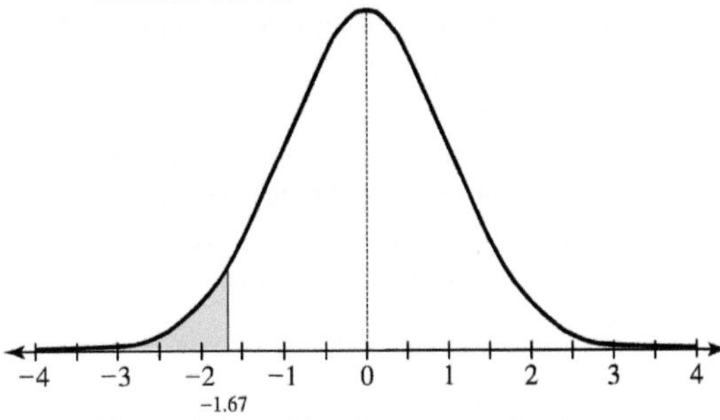

From the z-table, the area under the curve between the mean and +1.67 is 0.453. Subtract 0.453 from 0.5 to obtain the area under the curve to the right of +1.67: 0.5 − 0.453 = 0.047. Because of symmetry, this is also the amount of area under the curve to the left of −1.67. The answer is 0.047 or 4.7%.

41. The mean plus 2.5 times the standard deviation, $\bar{x} + 2.5s$, corresponds to $z = 2.5$ no matter what the values of $\bar{x}$ and s are:

$$\begin{aligned} z &= \frac{\text{value} - \text{mean}}{\text{standard deviation}} \\ &= \frac{(\bar{x} + 2.5s) - \bar{x}}{s} \\ &= \frac{2.5s}{s} \\ &= 2.5. \end{aligned}$$

The fraction of the population between the mean and $z = 2.5$ is 0.494, by the z-table. The fraction below the mean is 0.5. The sum of these is 0.5 + 0.494 = 0.994 or 99.4%.

43. The RDA is the value corresponding to $z = 2.5$. Use the z-score formula to find x:

$$\begin{aligned} z &= \frac{x - \bar{x}}{s} \\ 2.5 &= \frac{x - 159}{12} \\ (12) \cdot 2.5 &= \frac{x - 159}{12} \cdot \frac{12}{1} \\ 30 &= x - 159 \\ 189 &= x \end{aligned}$$

The RDA is 189 units.

45. Find the z-score for 7: $z = \frac{7 - 7.47}{3.6} \approx -0.13$.

Find the z-score for 8: $z = \frac{8 - 7.47}{3.6} \approx 0.15$.

The area under the curve to the left of −0.13 and the area under the curve to the right of 0.15 must be added to answer the question.

Use the z-table to obtain 0.052 for the area between the mean and +0.13. The area to the right of 0.13 is then $0.5 - 0.052 = 0.448$. Because of symmetry, this is the amount of area to the left of −0.13.
Use the z-table to obtain 0.060 for the area between the mean and 0.15. The area to the right of 0.15 is then $0.5 - 0.060 = 0.440$. The sum of these two areas is $0.448 + 0.440 = 0.888$.

47. Find the z-score for 2.2:
$$z = \frac{2.2 - 1.5}{0.4} = 1.75.$$
Find the area under the normal curve between the mean and 1.75, which is 0.460. Subtract 0.460 from 0.5 to obtain the area under the curve to the right of $z = 1.75$: $0.5 - 0.460 = 0.040$ or 4.0%. Find 4.0% of five dozen: $(0.04)(5 \cdot 12) = 2.4$. The answer is about 2 eggs.

49. Find the area as a percent between $\bar{x} + \left(\frac{1}{2}\right)s$ and $\bar{x} + \left(\frac{3}{2}\right)s$. This is the area between $z = \frac{1}{2}$ or 0.5 and $z = \frac{3}{2}$ or 1.5.
The area under the curve from the mean to $z = 0.5$ is 0.191; the area under the curve from the mean to $z = 1.5$ is 0.433. Subtract: $0.433 - 0.191 = 0.242$ or 24.2%.

51. Writing exercise; answers will vary.

53. To find the bottom cutoff grade, $0.15 + 0.08 = 0.23$ must be the amount of area under the normal curve to the right of the grade. That means that the amount of area between the mean and this cutoff grade is $0.5 - 0.23 = 0.27$. Locate this area value in the A column; it corresponds to a z-score of 0.74. Then use the z-score formula to find x:
$$z = \frac{x - \bar{x}}{s}$$
$$0.74 = \frac{x - 75}{5}$$
$$(5) \cdot (0.74) = \frac{x - 75}{5} \cdot \frac{5}{1}$$
$$3.7 = x - 75$$
$$78.7 = x$$
Rounded to the nearest whole number, the cutoff score should be 79.

55. To find the bottom cutoff grade, 0.08 must be the amount of area under the normal curve to the left of the grade. That means that the amount of area between the mean and this cutoff grade is $0.5 - 0.08 = 0.42$. Locate this area value in the A column; it corresponds to a z-score of 1.40 or 1.41. Use 1.405. The negative z-score, however, must be used because the grade is below the mean.
$$z = \frac{x - \bar{x}}{s}$$
$$-1.405 = \frac{x - 75}{5}$$
$$(5) \cdot (-1.405) = \frac{x - 75}{5} \cdot \frac{5}{1}$$
$$-7.025 = x - 75$$
$$68 \approx x$$
The cutoff grade should be 68.

57. Replace $\bar{x}$, s and z in the z-score formula and solve for x:
$$z = \frac{x - \bar{x}}{s}$$
$$1.44 = \frac{x - 76.8}{9.42}$$
$$(9.42) \cdot (1.44) = \frac{x - 76.8}{9.42} \cdot \frac{9.42}{1}$$
$$13.5648 = x - 76.8$$
$$90.4 \approx x$$

59. Replace $\bar{x}$, s and z in the z-score formula and solve for x:
$$z = \frac{x - \bar{x}}{s}$$
$$-3.87 = \frac{x - 76.8}{9.42}$$
$$(9.42) \cdot (-3.87) = \frac{x - 76.8}{9.42} \cdot \frac{9.42}{1}$$
$$-36.4554 = x - 76.8$$
$$40.3 \approx x$$

61. Writing exercise; answers will vary.

EXTENSION: REGRESSION AND CORRELATION

1. The equation of the least squares line is $y' = ax + b$ where a and b are found as follows:

$$a = \frac{n(\Sigma xy) - (\Sigma x)(\Sigma y)}{n(\Sigma x^2) - (\Sigma x)^2}$$
$$= \frac{10(75) - (30)(24)}{10(100) - (30)^2}$$
$$= \frac{750 - 720}{1000 - 900}$$
$$= \frac{30}{100}$$
$= 0.3$, and
$$b = \frac{\Sigma y - a(\Sigma x)}{n}$$
$$= \frac{24 - 0.3(30)}{10}$$
$$= \frac{24 - 9}{10}$$
$= 1.5$.

Then the equation for the least squares line is $y' = 0.3x + 1.5$.

3. The regression equation is $y' = 0.3x + 1.5$. Find y' when $x = 3$ tons.
$y = 0.3(3) + 1.5 = 0.9 + 1.5 = 2.4$ decimeters

5. The regression equation is $y' = 0.556x - 17.8$. Find y' when $x = 120°$.
$$y' = 0.556(120) - 17.8$$
$$= 66.76 - 17.8$$
$$= 48.92°$$

7. The table shows how to calculate all the sums that are needed in the formula for the least squares line.

x	y	x^2	y^2	xy
62	120	3844	14400	7440
62	140	3844	19600	8680
63	130	3969	16900	8190
65	150	4225	22500	9750
66	142	4356	20164	9372
67	130	4489	16900	8710
68	135	4624	18225	9180
68	175	4624	30625	11900
70	149	4900	22201	10430
72	168	51840	28224	12096
$\Sigma x = 663$	$\Sigma y = 1439$	$\Sigma x^2 = 44059$	$\Sigma y^2 = 209739$	$\Sigma xy = 95748$

The equation of the least squares line is $y' = ax + b$ where a and b are found as follows.

$$a = \frac{n(\Sigma xy) - (\Sigma x)(\Sigma y)}{n(\Sigma x^2) - (\Sigma x)^2}$$
$$= \frac{10(95748) - (663)(1439)}{10(44059) - (663)^2}$$
$$= \frac{957480 - 954057}{440590 - 439569}$$
$$= \frac{3423}{1021}$$
$$\approx 3.35, \text{ and}$$
$$b = \frac{\Sigma y - a(\Sigma x)}{n}$$
$$= \frac{1439 - 3.35(663)}{10}$$
$$= \frac{1439 - 2221.05}{10}$$
$$= -78.2$$

The value for b calculated here differs slightly from the one in the text because of rounding error.
It is highly recommended that a scientific calculator or spreadsheet be used, because then rounding is only done at the very end of all the calculations. There the value of a was rounded before using it in the calculation for b. Then the equation for the least squares line is $y' = 3.35x - 78.2$.

The value for b in the text is -78.4.

9. The regression equation is $y' = 3.35x - 78.4$. Find y' when $x = 70$ in.

$$y' = 3.35(70) - 78.4$$
$$= 234.5 - 78.4$$
$$\approx 156 \text{ pounds}$$

11.

13. The regression equation is $y' = 2x - 51$. Find y' when $x = 65$.

$y' = 2(65) - 51 = 130 - 51 = 79$

15. Use a scientific calculator or a spreadsheet to calculate the various sums needed in the formula, or see Exercise 7 for the detailed process. Actually, a calculator or spreadsheet can calculate the value of r.

$\Sigma x = 15$; $\Sigma y = 418$; $\Sigma x^2 = 55$; $\Sigma y^2 = 30266$; $\Sigma xy = 1186$; and $n = 6$.

Substitute the sums into the formula for the coefficient of correlation.

$$r = \frac{n(\Sigma xy) - (\Sigma x)(\Sigma y)}{\sqrt{n(\Sigma x^2) - (\Sigma x)^2} \cdot \sqrt{n(\Sigma y^2) - (\Sigma y)^2}}$$
$$= \frac{6(1186) - (15)(418)}{\sqrt{6(55) - (15)^2} \cdot \sqrt{6(30266) - (418)^2}}$$
$$= \frac{7116 - 6270}{\sqrt{330 - 225} \cdot \sqrt{181596 - 174724}}$$
$$= \frac{846}{\sqrt{105} \cdot \sqrt{6872}}$$
$$\approx \frac{846}{10.25 \cdot 82.90}$$
$$\approx 0.996$$

17.

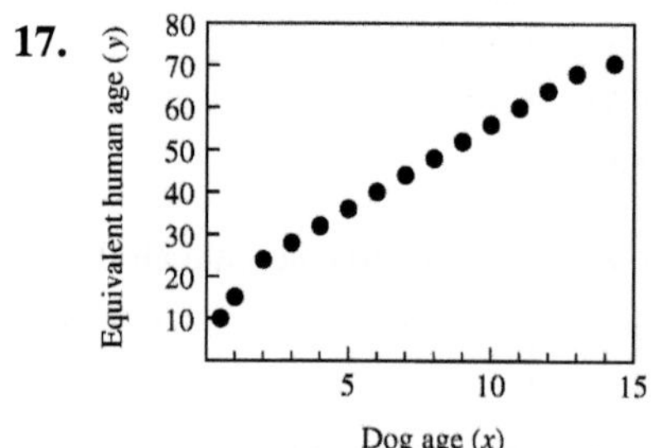

19. Writing exercise; answers will vary.

21. Use a scientific calculator or a spreadsheet to calculate the various sums needed in the formula. Actually, a calculator or spreadsheet can calculate the appropriate values for a and b needed for the regression line equation. See Exercise 7 for the details of calculating the following sums.

$\Sigma x = 56$; $\Sigma y = 77.7$; $\Sigma x_2 = 560$;

$\Sigma y^2 = 1110.43$; $\Sigma xy = 786.4$ and with $n = 8$.

The equation of the least squares line is $y' = ax + b$ where

$$a = \frac{n(\Sigma xy) - (\Sigma x)(\Sigma y)}{n(\Sigma x^2) - (\Sigma x)^2}$$
$$= \frac{8(786.4) - (56)(77.7)}{8(560) - (56)^2}$$
$$= \frac{6291.2 - 4351.2}{4480 - 3136}$$
$$= \frac{1940}{1344}$$
≈ 1.44, and
$$b = \frac{\Sigma y - a(\Sigma x)}{n}$$
$$= \frac{77.7 - 1.44(56)}{8}$$
$$= \frac{77.7 - 80.64}{8}$$
≈ -0.37

Again, it is recommended that a scientific calculator or spreadsheet be used to calculate these values in order to avoid rounding error. (The value of a has been rounded here.) The value for b that is calculated in the text is -0.39. Then the equation for the least squares line $y' = 1.44x - 0.39$.

23. The linear correlation of 0.99 is strong.

25. Use a scientific calculator or a spreadsheet to calculate the various sums needed in the formulas. Actually, a calculator or spreadsheet can calculate the appropriate values for a and b needed for the regression line equation. See Exercise 7 for the details of calculating the following sums.
$\Sigma x = 163$; $\Sigma y = 1583$

$\Sigma x^2 = 3345$; $\Sigma y^2 = 254,085$

$\Sigma xy = 26,162$ and $n = 10$

The equation of the least squares line is $y' = ax + b$ where
$$a = \frac{n(\Sigma xy) - (\Sigma x)(\Sigma y)}{n(\Sigma x^2) - (\Sigma x)^2}$$
$$= \frac{10(26,162) - (163)(1583)}{10(3345) - (163)^2}$$
≈ 0.5219

and
$$b = \frac{\Sigma y - a(\Sigma x)}{n}$$
$$= \frac{1583 - 0.5219(163)}{10}$$
≈ 149.8

Then the equation for the regression line is $y' = 0.5219x + 149.8$.

27. The linear correlation is weak to moderate.

Chapter Test

1. Examine the scores in the table. Students who copied less than 10% generally improved their exam performance over the course of the semester.

2. Students with copy rates from 10% to 30% or greater than 50% did better on exam 3 than exam 2.

3. Students with copy rates from 30% to 50% consistently had lower scores from one exam to the next throughout the semester.

4. Writing exercise; answers will vary.

5. **(a)** $\overline{x} = \frac{398 + 250 + 215 + 73 + 64}{5}$
$= \frac{1000}{5}$
$= 200$ million barrels

(b) The range is 398 – 64 = 334 million barrels.

(c) Calculate the deviations from the mean $(x - \overline{x})$ and the squared deviations $(x - \overline{x})^2$.

x	$x - \overline{x}$	$(x - \overline{x})^2$
398	198	39,204
250	50	2500
215	15	225
73	–127	16,129
64	–136	18,496
Total		76,554

$$\frac{\text{Total}}{n-1} = \frac{76,554}{5-1} = 19,138.5$$
$s = \sqrt{19,138.5} \approx 138$ million barrels

(d) $V = \frac{s}{\overline{x}} \cdot 100 = \frac{138}{200} \cdot 100 = 69$

(e) $\overline{x} = \frac{398 + 250 + 215 + 73 + 64 + 14 \cdot 26}{5 + 26}$
$= \frac{1364}{31}$
$= 44$ million barrels

6. (a) Arrange the data for height in order from smallest to largest. The middle value is 281 feet.

(b) Arrange the data for girth in order from smallest to largest. The median is 761 inches. The first quartile is the median of the values below 761 inches or

$$\frac{512+522}{2} = 517 \text{ inches.}$$

(c) The eighth decile is found by taking 80% of the 9 data entries, or (0.80)(9) = 7.2. Take the 8th score up, 1290, to be the eighth decile.

7. (a) $T = G + H + 0.25C$

$$\begin{aligned} T &= 647 + 96 + 0.25(74) \\ &= 743 + 18.5 \\ &\approx 762 \end{aligned}$$

(b) Based on girth alone, the Common Bald Cypress would have ranked 7th.

(c) The ninth ranked tree had 773 total points. If the Common Bald Cypress had been 12 feet taller, it would have had 762 + 12 = 774 total points and would have displaced the ninth ranked tree.

(d) With a circumference (girth) of 647 inches, the diameter would have been about $\frac{647}{\pi} \approx 205.9$ inches, or about 17 feet.

8.

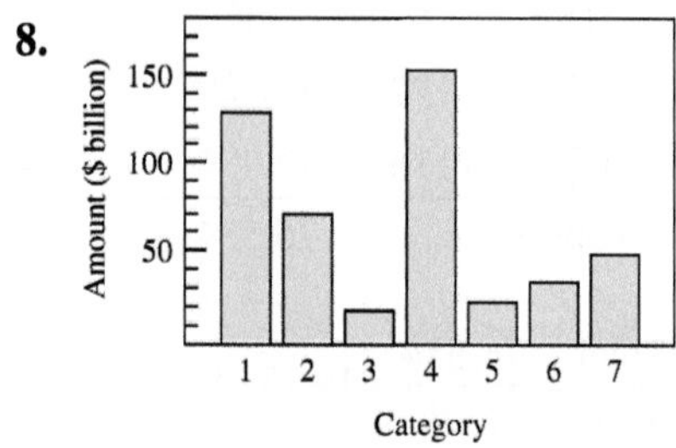

9. Of the $787 billion in the whole stimulus bill, $152.0 billion was assigned to health, or about $\frac{152.0}{787} \approx 0.193$ or 19.3%.

10. $152.0 billion − $20 billion = $132.0 billion went to other health categories, or about $\frac{132.0}{787} \approx 0.168$ or 16.8%.

11. The three greatest categories combined were 128.2 + 152.0 + 70.3 = $350.5 billion of the stimulus bill, or $\frac{350.5}{787} \approx 0.445$ or 44.5%.

12. A tally column is not shown here, but it is useful when creating a frequency distribution by hand.

Class Limits	Frequency f	Relative frequency $\frac{f}{n}$
6–10	3	$\frac{3}{22} \approx 0.14$
11-15	6	$\frac{6}{22} \approx 0.27$
16–20	7	$\frac{7}{22} \approx 0.32$
21–25	4	$\frac{4}{22} \approx 0.18$
26–30	2	$\frac{2}{22} \approx 0.09$

13. (a)

(b)

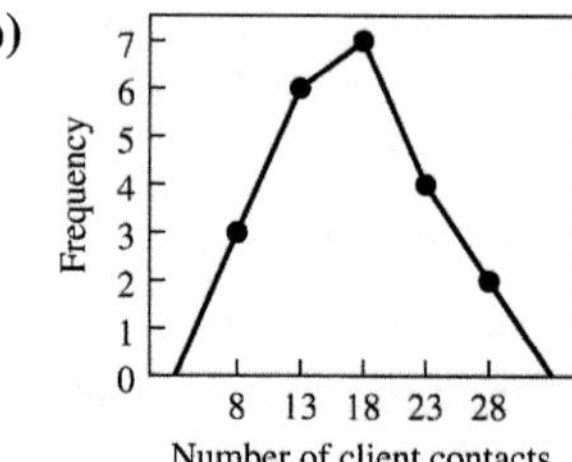

14. If the first class had limits of 7–9, this would be a width of 3. The smallest value is 8, and the largest value is 30. All the data must be included within the classes that are constructed. The classes would be:

7–9
10–12
13–15
16–18
19–21
22–24
25–27
28–30.

this is a total of 8 classes.

15.

Value	Frequency	Value · Frequency
8	3	24
10	8	80
12	10	120
14	8	112
16	5	80
18	1	18
Totals	35	434

Then $\bar{x} = \dfrac{434}{35} = 12.4.$

16. There are 35 items. The formula for the position of the median is

$$\frac{\Sigma f + 1}{2} = \frac{35+1}{2} = 18.$$

This means that the median is 18th item when the values are arranged from smallest to largest. A chart showing cumulative frequency shows that the value is in the row for a cumulative frequency of 21.

Value	Frequency	Cumulative Frequency
8	3	3
10	8	11
12	10	21
14	8	29
16	5	34
18	1	35

The value 12 is the median.

17. Examine the frequency column to see that the mode is 12, with a frequency of 10.

18. The range of the data is 18 – 8 = 10.

19. The leaves are arranged in rank order (from smallest to largest).

3	3 8
4	3 5 8 9
5	0 2 5
6	1 1 4 5 6 7 7 8
7	0 1 2 3 7 7 8 9 9
8	0 4 4
9	1

20. There are 33 items. The formula for the position of the median is

$$\frac{\Sigma f + 1}{2} = \frac{33+1}{2} = 17.$$

This means that the median is the 17th item when the values are arranged from smallest to largest. Count the values in the stem-and-leaf display in the text to see that the 17th value is 35.

21. The mode is 33; it occurs 3 times.

22. The range of the data is 60 – 23 = 37.

23. The third decile is the same as the 30th percentile. First, 0.30(33) = 9.9. Then the 10th value is the location of the third decile. This value is 31.

24. The eighty-fifth percentile is located by first taking 85% of the 33 data items: 0.85(33) = 28.05. Then the 29th value is located at the 85th percentile. This value is 49.

25. The values shown in the box plot are: Minimum value, 23; Maximum value, 60; Q_1, 29.5; Q_2, 35; and Q_3, 43.

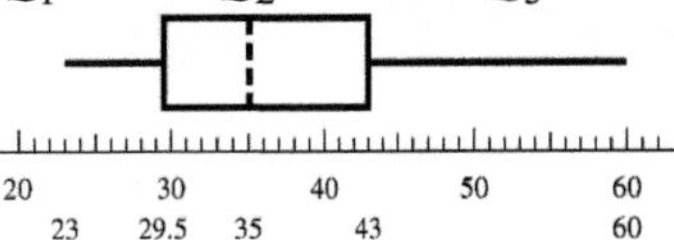

26. **(a)** The scores 70 and 90 are each two standard deviations away from the mean, because the mean is 80 and the value of one standard deviation is 5. According to the empirical rule, approximately 95% of the data lie within two standard deviations of the mean.

(b) The score of 95 is three standard deviations above the mean; the score of 65 is three standard deviations below the mean. According to the empirical rule, approximately 99.7% of the data lie within this interval. Therefore, 100 – 99.7 = 0.3% lie outside this interval.

(c) The score of 75 is one standard deviation below the mean. Using the empirical rule, if 68% of the scores lie within one standard deviation of the mean, then 34% of the scores lie between 75 and 80. Subtract 34% from 50% to find the percentage of scores that are less than 75: 50 – 34 = 16%.

(d) The score of 85 is one standard deviation above the mean; the score of 90 is two standard deviations above the mean. From Exercise 21 we know that about 34% of the scores lie between 80 and 85. Also from the empirical rule, approximately 95% of the scores lie within two standard deviations. Half of 95% is 47.5%. Subtract 34% from 47.5% to find the percentage of scores between 85 and 90: 47.5 − 34 = 13.5%.

27. First find the z-score for 6.5:

$$z = \frac{6.5 - 5.5}{2.1} \approx 0.48.$$

It is always helpful to sketch the area under the normal curve that is being sought. Then find the amount of area between the mean and $z = 0.48$. The amount is 0.184. This area must be added to 0.5, the amount of area under the normal curve below the mean:

0.184 + 0.5 = 0.684

28. First find the z-scores for 6.2 and 9.4:

$$z = \frac{6.2 - 5.5}{2.1} \approx 0.33$$

$$z = \frac{9.4 - 5.5}{2.1} \approx 1.86$$

It is always helpful to sketch the area under the normal curve that is being sought.

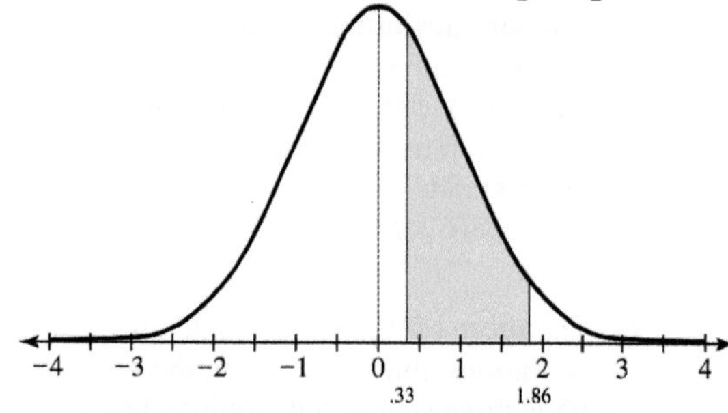

We are trying to find the amount of area under the curve between a z-score of 0.33 and a z-score of 1.86. Find the amount of area between the mean and $z = 1.86$. The amount is 0.469. Find the amount of area between the mean and $z = 0.33$; it is 0.129. the smaller value must be subtracted from the larger.

0.469 − 0.129 = 0.340

29. Find the means of the three groups.

Eastern teams: $\frac{84.2 + 79.0}{2} = 81.6$

Central teams: $\frac{5(76.4) + 6(78.0)}{11} \approx 77.3$

Western teams: $\frac{4(86.0) + 5(84.0)}{9} \approx 84.9$

The teams in the West had the greatest winning average. (Note that we must use a weighting factor, frequency, in the mean calculations for the Central and Western teams since there are a different number of teams in each of these leagues.)

30. Find the means of the standard deviations.

Eastern teams: $\frac{15.5 + 14.1}{2} = 14.8$

Central teams: $\frac{5(10.9) + 6(9.7)}{11} \approx 10.25$

Western teams: $\frac{4(9.0) + 5(10.9)}{9} \approx 10.06$

The Eastern teams were the least "consistent" because their standard deviation (variation) is the largest. (Note that again we must use a weighting factor, frequency, in the average calculations for the Central and Western teams since there are a different number of teams in each of these leagues.)

31. The average number of games won for all West Division teams is 84.9. See the Western Division teams winning average in Exercise 29.

32. Boston Red Sox:

$$z = \frac{x - \overline{x}}{s} = \frac{95 - 84.2}{15.5} = \frac{10.8}{15.5} = 0.70$$

Los Angeles Dodgers:

$$z = \frac{x - \overline{x}}{s} = \frac{95 - 84.0}{10.9} = \frac{11.0}{10.9} = 1.01$$

Thus, the Dodgers did relatively better, since $z = 1.01 > 0.70$.

Index

Page references followed by "f" indicate illustrated figures or photographs; followed by "t" indicates a table.